A TEXT-BOOK OF METALLURGY

A TEXT-BOOK OF METALLURGY

BY

A. R. BAILEY, M.Sc., A.I.M.
LECTURER IN METALLURGY
CONSTANTINE TECHNICAL COLLEGE, MIDDLESBROUGH

MACMILLAN AND CO., LIMITED
ST. MARTIN'S STREET, LONDON
1954

MACMILLAN AND COMPANY LIMITED
London Bombay Calcutta Madras Melbourne

THE MACMILLAN COMPANY OF CANADA LIMITED
Toronto

ST MARTIN'S PRESS INC
New York

This book is copyright in all countries which are signatories to the Berne Convention

PRINTED IN GREAT BRITAIN

PREFACE

THE aim of this book is to provide a modern and thorough introduction to physical and process metallurgy for students of metallurgy at Universities and Technical Colleges. It is hoped that it will meet the very real need that exists for a student's book on general metallurgy. Moreover, although presenting an overall picture, the book takes a number of subjects to quite advanced levels. At the end of each chapter a fairly comprehensive list of additional reading is given, so that the book can provide the basis for most of the student's reading.

The first six chapters deal with the nature, structure and properties of metals and alloys, and the methods used for the examination of metallic structures. The treatment includes an introduction to modern atomic theories, the solidification of metals, and a comprehensive account of phase equilibria in binary alloys, together with fairly detailed treatment of the deformation processes in metals and their behaviour under stress in service. The chapter on the physical examination of metallic structures is of necessity a summary of methods and includes most recent developments.

This is followed by consideration of the theoretical and practical aspects of metal production, namely, of ores and their preparation, and of extraction and refining techniques. In each case the reasons for the use of the techniques are discussed and, wherever possible, a physical-chemical background has been developed. The section concludes with a chapter outlining the production of the common base non-ferrous metals, and another dealing with iron and steel manufacture ; brief mention of metallurgical refractories and fuels is also made in these chapters.

The next chapter covers the manufacture of ingots and compares the different procedures for producing castings. The metallurgy of solidification under practical conditions, such as grain arrangement, shrinkage and gas effects, and segregation is also discussed. In the subsequent chapter, the various mechanical working processes are described and compared, as well as electroforming and powder metallurgy. Jointing practice, heat-treatment and the application of protective coatings are also outlined. The treatment of process metallurgy in the book is on a general basis, and where appropriate modern developments are described. Lastly, there are chapters on the testing of metals, both by mechanical and non-destructive methods, and on metallurgical pyrometry.

At the end of the book there is a large collection of past examination questions, which have been mainly classified according to the chapter to which they are most relevant. The questions have been selected from degree examination papers of various Universities and from those of the Institution of Metallurgists, City and Guilds of London Institute, and several bodies setting examinations of ordinary National Certificate level. Grateful acknowledgement is made to those bodies which have allowed questions to be reproduced.

With regard to the illustrations, the author wishes to thank Mr. J. Oliver, B.Sc., A.I.Mech.E., for making a large number of the drawings. Thanks must go also to the numerous individuals and organisations who have supplied information or allowed their illustrations to be used or copied; individual acknowledgement is made in each case to the origin of tabulated data and illustrations. Unless otherwise stated, the photographs and drawings of microstructures have been prepared by the author. Finally, in this connection, mention should be made of the great care which has been exercised by Mr. L. E. Carroll, of Messrs. Macmillan, in the preparation of the blocks.

The author acknowledges, as well, the considerable help received from the Joint Library of the Iron and Steel Institute and Institute of Metals, and in particular from Mr. R. Elsdon and Mr. Alan E. Chattin, past and present Librarians, respectively. He has also had much helpful discussion with present colleagues at the Constantine Technical College and with past colleagues at the British Non-Ferrous Metals Research Association and Battersea Polytechnic.

Finally, the author wishes to pay tribute to the continual and patient guidance which he has received at every stage in the preparation of the book from Mr. A. J. V. Gale; and last but not least, to the forbearance, encouragement and help of his wife.

A. R. BAILEY

CONTENTS

Commonly used Greek Letters

α	alpha	κ	kappa
β	beta	λ	lambda
γ	gamma	μ	mu
Δ, δ	delta	ν	nu
		π	pi
ϵ	epsilon	ρ	rho
ζ	zeta	σ	sigma
η	eta	τ	tau
θ	theta	ϕ	phi
ι	iota	ω	omega

CHAPTER 1

CRYSTALLOGRAPHY OF PURE METALS

In metallurgy, metallic elements are known usually as *pure metals* ; the emphasis is on their elemental nature and the absence of intentional alloying, rather than on the specific degree of purity. However, many commercial metals are available today in large quantities with less than about 0·1 per cent impurities and often less than 0·01 per cent.

Crystal structures of solid pure metals. It will be appreciated that true solids are crystalline, in that their atoms are arranged in regular patterns. In the case of metals the crystallinity is not usually manifested by external regularity of form. For the immediate purpose, it will be convenient to regard the individual atoms as tiny spheres with diameters of the order of 10^{-8} cm. Atomic patterns or crystal structures may be represented by three-dimensional figures, such as cubes and hexagonal prisms. These figures indicate the positions of the centres of the atoms and show conveniently the unit of the pattern. It must be understood that the atoms vibrate about these positions ; the amplitude increases with rise in temperature ; at room temperature it is of the order of a tenth the atomic diameter.

The atoms in most metals are clustered together as closely, or nearly as closely, as possible. The majority of pure metals have one of three relatively simple crystal structures. On the foregoing basis these are represented and known as the face-centred cubic (F.C.C.), the hexagonal close-packed (C.P.H. or H.C.P.), and the body-centred cubic (B.C.C.) structures (Fig. 1). These are also referred to as space-lattices, although this is not a strictly correct term in the case of the hexagonal structure, for in a space-lattice every position has identical surroundings. Although accurately and conventionally representing the patterns, there is a tendency for the method to exaggerate differences between structures. Thus the face-centred cubic and the hexagonal close-packed structures are in fact very similar, being alternative ways of closest packing. Each layer in these structures has the same pattern ; the difference arises in their position over one another.

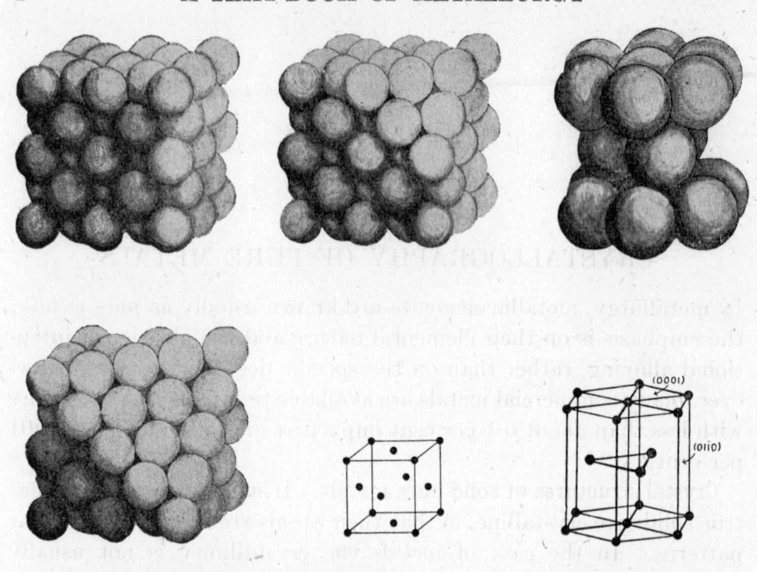

(*a*) Face-centred cubic structure

(*b*) Hexagonal close-packed structure

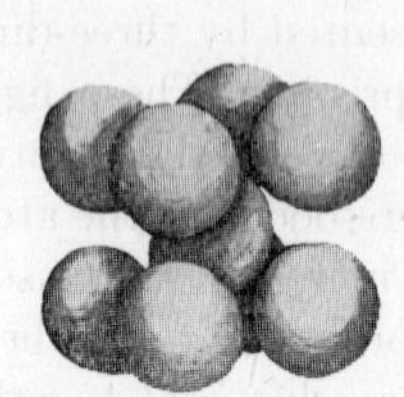

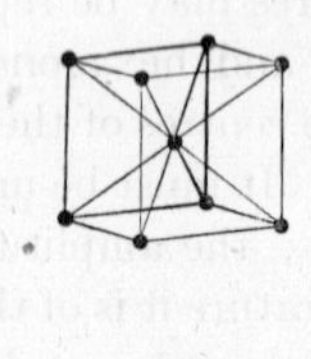

(*c*) Body-centred cubic structure

FIG. 1. Crystal structures of pure metals. From *The Structure of Metals and Alloys*, by W. Hume-Rothery. Inst. Metals.

TABLE 1. CRYSTAL STRUCTURES OF SOME PURE METALS

Face-centred cubic ; nickel (ordinary form), gold, silver, copper, lead, aluminium, calcium.[1]

Close-packed hexagonal ; magnesium, beryllium, zinc,[2] cadmium,[2] cobalt.[1]

Body-centred cubic ; molybdenum, tungsten,[1] iron (below about 900° C.), chromium (ordinary form), sodium, potassium, barium, lithium.

[1] Allotropic, low-temperature form.
[2] Not truly close-packed.

Polymorphism or allotropy in metals. A number of elements have more than one possible crystal structure; these are said to be **polymorphic.** In the case of the common pure metals exhibiting this characteristic, the different structures are stable over different ranges of temperature. Thus iron is body-centred cubic at room temperature and up to about 900° C. At this transition temperature it changes to face-centred cubic, which is stable from about 900° to 1400° C.; above the latter temperature it reverts to body-centred cubic. The actual number of forms varies for the different metals, and each may be different (unlike iron). Further, a different structure may be stable at low temperature compared with that at room temperature, as occurs with tin.

As well as thermal changes, definite changes in volume occur at the transformation temperatures, according to the crystal structures involved. Thus on heating pure iron there is a contraction at about 900° C., when the structure changes from body-centred cubic to the denser face-centred cubic arrangement, and vice versa at 1400° C. (Fig. 2); in practice there is a lag in the transformations both on heating and cooling. The disintegration of tin into a powder at low temperatures, referred to as "tin-pest", is due to the pronounced expansion accompanying the transformation of the normal white tin to the less dense low-temperature modification known as grey tin; the specific gravities are 7·3 and 5·75, respectively. The theoretical transformation temperature is reported to be 13·2° C., but in practice there is considerable lag or undercooling, and the presence of the normal impurities inhibits the change; thus the phenomenon does not generally cause difficulties in practice. Homer and Watkins state that "the addition of about 0·1 per cent bismuth to tin and solders should be sufficient to guard against the change when prolonged exposure to low temperatures is expected."

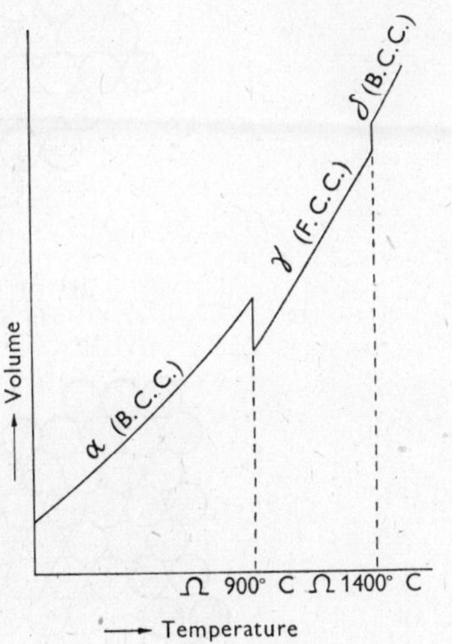

Fig. 2. Volume changes in pure iron.

Among other allotropic metals are calcium, cobalt, manganese and tungsten. Nickel and chronium are normally face-centred and body-centred cubic, respectively, but close-packed hexagonal modifications have been prepared electrolytically.

Single crystal and polycrystalline metal. In the simplest case, the atomic pattern is continuous throughout the whole mass of the metal. When this occurs the metal is said to be a **single crystal**; such a state is uncommon. Usually the pattern is discontinuous and changes its inclination from place to place (Fig. 3). The inclination of an atomic arrangement is generally referred to as its **orientation.**

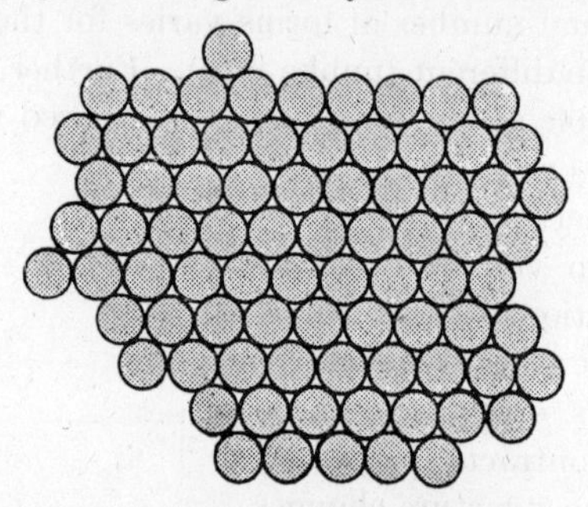

(a) Arrangement of atoms in a single crystal

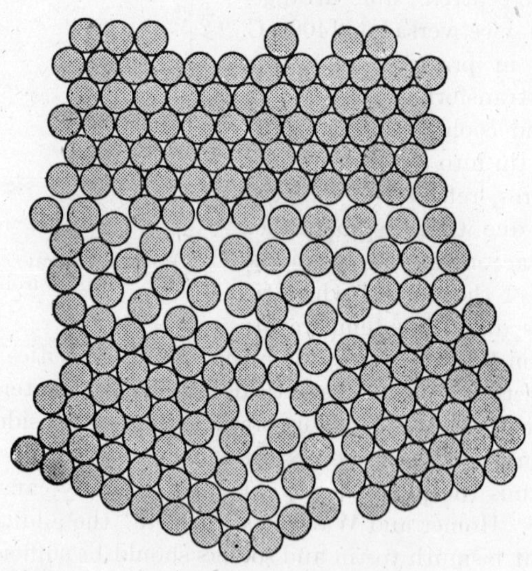

(b) Arrangement of atoms in a polycrystalline metal

FIG. 3. Sketch illustrating difference between (*a*) single crystal and (*b*) polycrystalline metal; note the junction of three crystals and the distorted boundary between them.

Thus pure metal normally consists of a number of zones of different orientation, although the actual pattern in each zone is the same. The orientation may be random as in Fig. 3*b*, or there may be preferred orientation which is described in Chapter 5. The zones are called **crystals** or **grains** and the metal is said to be **polycrystalline.** The change from one orientation to another occurs over relatively small distances, and it is apparent that in these transition regions the pattern is distorted. The regions are known as the grain or crystal boundaries. There are indications that these boundaries have a slightly lower melting point than the grain bodies. Metal in the single-crystal state is usually softer and weaker than when polycrystalline ; hence generally its only use is for experimental purposes.

Crystallisation of pure metals. The commonest form of crystallisation in metals is from the molten state. In liquid metals the atoms, although milling about, are very close together, presenting almost a blurred picture of the solid form. It is probable that in various zones, especially when the temperature is only slightly above the melting point, the atoms do take up a regular pattern, but these zones will be short-lived.

A solid metal melts on heating when the supply of thermal energy is sufficient to overcome the forces of attraction holding the atoms in a regular arrangement. The converse holds when the metal is cooled from the liquid state. In this way it can be seen that the melting point is an indication of the strength of bonding between the atoms, which in fact

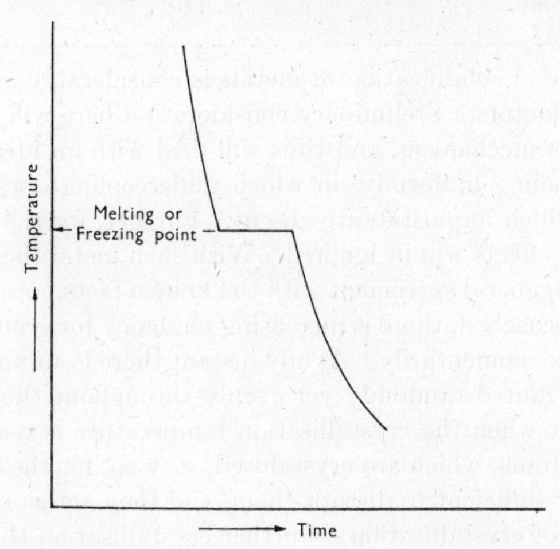

FIG. 4. Cooling curve of pure metal.

is very variable from metal to metal. The actual energy required at the melting point is represented by the latent heat. Provided there is no undercooling, a pure metal crystallises, solidifies, or freezes from the liquid state at a constant temperature. A simple cooling curve of temperature against time shows a marked arrest at the freezing temperature (Fig. 4). The arrest is due to the latent heat of freezing evolved by the liquid $\rightleftarrows$ solid change, which compensates for the heat being lost to the surroundings, and is sufficient to keep the temperature of the metal constant while solidification proceeds (Table 2). On melting, the heating curve shows the same form, heat being required at the same temperature to break up the regular essentially rigid structure of the solid.

TABLE 2. MELTING POINTS AND LATENT HEATS OF PURE METALS

Metal	Melting point (° C.)	Latent heat of fusion (cal./gm.)
Aluminium	660	95
Copper	1083	50
Gold	1063	16
Iron	1539	65
Lead	327	6
Magnesium	650	89
Nickel	1453	74
Platinum	1773·5	27
Silver	960·8	25
Tin	232	14·5
Zinc	419	24

The mode of solidification of metals is considerably affected by a number of factors. Preliminary consideration here will concentrate on the basic mechanism, and thus will deal with an ideal still mass of metal cooling uniformly, in which undercooling does not occur, and from which impurities are absent. Further, for the time being, contraction effects will be ignored. With such metal the following is a picture in general agreement with the known facts. As the melting point is approached, there is increasing tendency for groups of atoms to crystallise momentarily. At any instant there is a number of such points distributed randomly yet evenly throughout the metal. At the moment when the crystallisation temperature is reached, these groups of atoms, which are crystallised, stay so, for the heat energy is no longer sufficient to disrupt them, and they act as the nuclei or beginnings of crystallisation. Further crystallisation then proceeds from these centres, as it is easier for uncrystallised atoms to attach themselves to the nuclei already present rather than to form new nuclei or aggregates.

First, while there is no interference between growth from different centres, skeleton shapes or crystals are formed. From each nucleus there is preferential growth in certain directions, resulting in tree- or fern-like forms, which are known as **dendrites** or **dendritic crystals**. It is generally accepted that in the metals having some cubic form of crystal structure there are three directions of growth at right angles to one another (Fig. 5). Thus, initially, dendrites with six arms are produced. Later, secondary arms branch off parallel to the main ones. This continues with tertiary and quaternary branching, depending especially on the distance apart of the nuclei.

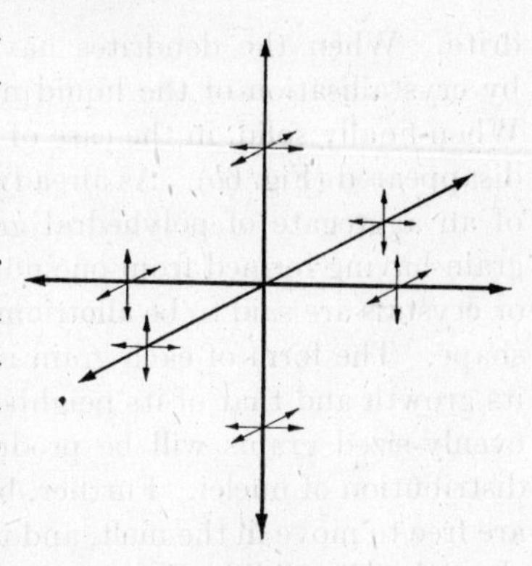

FIG. 5. Crystallisation axes in cubic metals.

It should be noted that, even in the cubic metals, there may be some deviation from the above process ; a number of factors must contribute. In some hexagonal metals there is evidence of dendrites with four main directions of growth.

The cross-sectional shape of the dendrite arms varies from rounded to angular ; surface tension is an important factor affecting the contours. Considerable thickening of the arms may proceed with directional growth, or the bulk may occur later when the extension of the branches is prevented by interference with others.

Unless the dendrites are distorted on contact with each other, or bent by currents in the liquid metal during growth, the orientation should be continuous throughout each den-

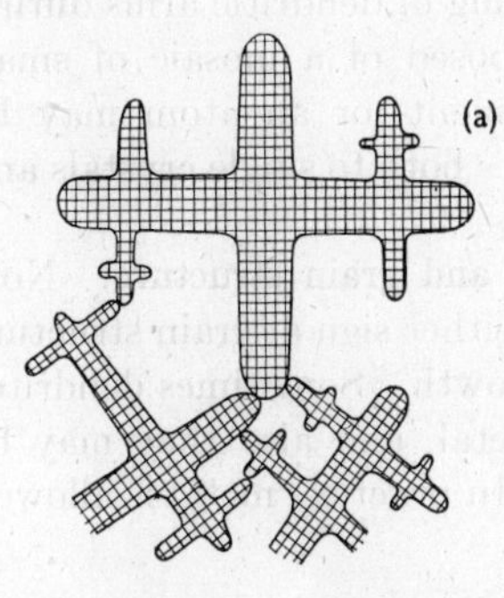

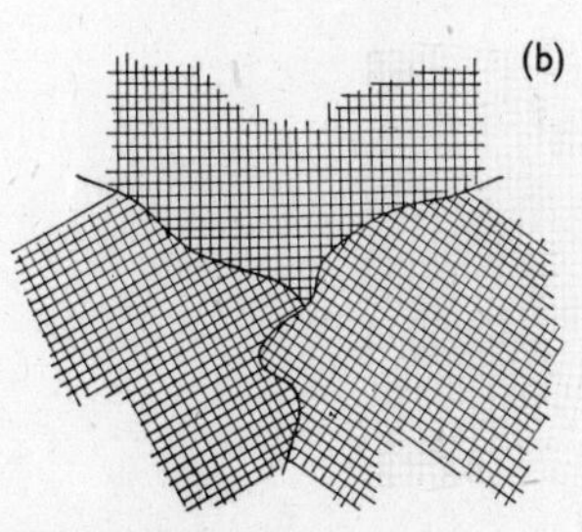

FIG. 6. Crystallisation of polycrystalline metal, showing how each grain forms from a dendrite. The shading indicates the orientation of the atomic pattern.

drite. When the dendrites have met, solidification is completed by crystallisation of the liquid metal remaining between the arms. When finally solid, in the case of pure metals the dendritic form has disappeared (Fig. 6*b*). As already described, the solid metal consists of an aggregate of polyhedral grains of different orientation, each grain having formed from one nucleus via one dendrite. The grains or crystals are said to be **allotriomorphic**, that is, without any regular shape. The form of each grain is determined as a balance between its growth and that of its neighbours. Provided cooling is uniform, evenly-sized grains will be produced due to the random yet even distribution of nuclei. Further, before different dendrites meet they are free to move in the melt, and this will aid even distribution. It is clear that if solidification can be made to proceed from one nucleus via one dendrite, a single crystal will be produced. Actually this is the basis of one method of preparation for experimental purposes.

Ideal crystals: imperfections in crystals. In an ideal crystal, the atomic arrangement is perfectly regular and continuous throughout. In practice, there are usually some irregularities; for example, a lineage structure (Fig. 7) may exist due to bending of dendritic arms during solidification, the crystal may be composed of a mosaic of small blocks which are slightly out of alignment, or an atom may be missing from various points. This applies both to single crystals and individual ones of a polycrystalline mass.

Natural evidence of dendritic growth and grain structure. Normally, in solidified pure metal there is neither sign of grain structure nor evidence of the dendritic mode of growth. Sometimes dendrites are seen on the free surface of cast metal, and also they may be seen on the inside of "bled" castings. In practice, metal is allowed

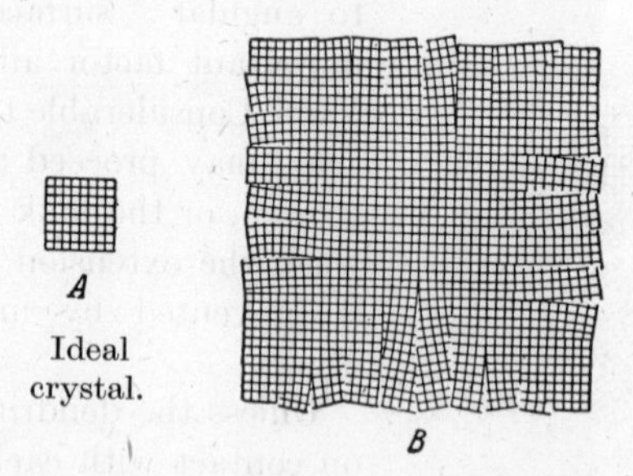

FIG. 7. Diagram showing lineage structure introduced by dendritic crystallisation. From the *Structure of Metals and Alloys*, by W. Hume-Rothery. Inst. Metals.

FIG. 8. Dendrites showing on the surface of cast antimony. From *Metallography*, by C. H. Desch. Longmans, Green.

to solidify in a metallic or refractory mould, and it generally reproduces the internal surface detail of this container. But the top or free surface solidifying in contact with the air is not so restricted, and dendrites growing along the top may show themselves (Fig. 8). Their appearance is likely to be masked by dirt and severe oxidation, and it will also be affected by the surface tension of the liquid metal.

With regard to " bled " castings, when metals are solidifying in moulds, solidification proceeds from the outside inwards, as the heat is lost in this way. Consequently there will be intermediate stages when the casting consists of a solid shell with a molten interior. If this is now " bled ", that is, the molten metal emptied out, it may be possible to see in the interior the dendrites which were advancing at the solid/liquid interface. Dendrites may sometimes be seen in the contraction " pipes " of castings.

Grain markings are in some instances visible on the free and other

Fig. 9. Grains visible (without preparation) on the free surface of cast zinc. Photographed (*a*) with oblique illumination, (*b*) with direct illumination ×4.

surfaces of castings (Figs. 9 and 10) ; reasons are discussed on p. 145.

Recent evidence indicates that dendritic crystallisation may not always occur in pure metals. Thus the interior surface of a bled casting of zinc shows only grain faces visible, appearing somewhat like those shown in Fig. 9. It is too early to make any generalisation.

Fig. 10. Grains showing up naturally on the surface of cast copper which has solidified in contact with an iron mould. ×1·5.

Frequently with cast metal, natural indications of the mode and form of crystallisation, when present, are large enough to be distinguished clearly by eye, or with the aid of a simple lens.

PREPARATION OF METALS TO REVEAL THEIR GRAINS

In a sample of solid pure metal free from impurities and gas or shrinkage cavities, unless the dendritic pattern is revealed on the surface, it will not be possible to show it up in any other way. This is because the dendritic form is obliterated when dendrites meet and thicken up to form grains. However, it is possible by special preparations to reveal the grains. As already pointed out, in some cases the grains naturally show up without preparation, but this is comparatively uncommon. In any event the markings are easily destroyed by handling, and then do not naturally reappear. Further, it is only the faces of the grains at the surface which are seen.

One method of preparation might be to decompose the metal into its constituent grains. This would depend on finding suitable means of decomposition without distortion. From a service point of view, such possibilities are fortunately limited, and few examples can be given. But Lacombe describes the separation of the crystals in high-purity aluminium (in the recrystallised condition) after immersion in 10 per cent hydrochloric acid for 25–30 days. Brass, containing about 52 per cent copper, 48 per cent zinc, which like a pure metal is composed of one type of grains, may be disintegrated (Fig. 11) by a slight blow after coating with mercury. (A good method of doing this is to immerse the brass in dilute mercurous nitrate solution. After disintegration, the grains are coated with mercury, which can be removed by heating to volatilise it. The grains are then cooled rapidly in water to minimise oxidation.)

Examination of fractured surfaces also gives useful indication of the grains.

The method generally used, and usually the most informative, is

FIG. 11. Brass decomposed into its constituent grains. ×2.

to cause the grains to show up on a surface which may then be examined by eye or microscopically by reflected light. For the present, the structure seen in this way will be referred to as the **microstructure** whether or not a microscope is used to examine it. The microstructure is also commonly known as the crystal or grain structure. Crystal structure is not a suitable term because it is specifically used to denote the actual arrangement of the atoms in crystals.

In many cases, even with large-grained metal, surface imperfections would mask the structure, although the grains might be differentiated. It thus becomes necessary usually to improve the surface in question by polishing. The quality of the polish depends especially on the grain-size. After polishing, the surface requires etching so as to differentiate the grains exposed in it. Etching involves treatment of the surface with acid or some other solvent. The reagent attacks the grain sections in such a way that they reflect varying amounts of light, and thus show up in contrast (Fig. 12). At the same time, the grain boundaries are preferentially attacked to a slight extent, and fine grooves are formed in these regions; slight difference in level between the grains may also be produced. The effect at the boundaries is particularly noticeable with microscopic examination, when the boundaries usually appear as black lines (Fig. 13). Generally, when the grains are large and the structure is examined by eye, differences in brightness predominate (Fig. 12), although usually the boundary grooves are present. The appearance of an etched surface, including the contrast between the grains, is dependent on such factors as the illumination, the

FIG. 12. Polished and etched surface of cast lead. ×1·5.

FIG. 13. Polished and etched section of cast copper. ×50.
Note that the apparently tiny grains in the field are due to the plane of section slicing through the tips of certain grains.

metal in question, the relative orientation of the grains, and the etching reagent.

External surfaces of the metal may be examined after polishing and etching, but a more representative idea is obtained by sectioning suitably and preparing the cut face. Even so, it must be remembered that in some respects the direct two-dimensional picture produced is restricted, for the only grains showing up are those cut by the section. A plane section of a polyhedral grain is a polygon, and the section of an aggregate of such grains consists of a number of connected polygons (as in Figs. 12 and 13) ; and one actually speaks in a loose manner of polygonal grains or crystals, that is, with respect to the section.

Considerable experience is necessary to obtain full possible information of the conditions in the body of the metal from a prepared plane section. With metal that is known to be even in structure, one section may be sufficient. But, where the structure may be uneven, as in cast metal, several sections are necessary from different parts, and so chosen from a knowledge of the mode of formation as to be most revealing. Polishing and etching techniques are discussed in more detail in Chapter 6.

The dendritic mode of growth and grain outlines may be indicated at polished surfaces in cast pure metals by the presence of insoluble impurities which have segregated to interdendritic or intergranular positions. Gas or shrinkage cavities formed in the same places may act in a similar way. Further, when the metal contains soluble impurities, etching may produce a cored or skeleton structure also revealing the dendritic formation of the grains.

Other examples of dendritic crystallisation. Most alloys solidify, at least in part, in a dendritic manner. However, this mode of crystallisation is not limited to metals, or to crystallisation from the molten state. Thus dendritic growth occurs in a number of minerals and mineral systems. Dendritic markings may be observed in ice and snow ; and ammonium chloride crystallises in dendritic form from aqueous solution.

Metal dendrites may also be produced from aqueous solutions by electrolysis or displacement by another metal, and by electrolysis of fused salts, particularly when incoherent deposits are made. When coherent electrolytic deposits are formed, they are generally polycrystalline aggregates ; if deposited on a metal base, they may continue its structure. Nickel and chromium have face- and body-centred cubic crystal structures, respectively, as normally prepared. But, under certain conditions of electrolysis, close-packed hexagonal forms have been produced.

Metal crystals deposited directly from the vapour (of the pure metal or a compound) may take a dendritic shape ; or, as in sublimed magnesium, more regular shapes with plane faces may be developed. As in electrolytic deposition, growth is apparently normal to the depositing surface, forming relatively long (columnar) crystals.

Supercooling or undercooling in pure metals. Frequently a metal will cool below its freezing temperature without crystallising. This is especially so with fast rates of cooling and in the absence of agitation or of solid impurities which can act as nuclei. The phenomenon is known as undercooling or supercooling and occurs also with alloys, and similar "delay" is experienced with solid changes. When solidification does start, the latent heat evolved may be sufficient to raise the temperature again to the true freezing point, at which solidification continues (Fig. 14*b*) ; if the rate of cooling is very rapid, it may not reach this temperature (Fig. 14*c* and *d*). The phenomenon of undercooling indicates that a lower temperature is required to form stable nuclei than for their subsequent growth.

When molten metal undercools, it first enters the *metastable region*, in which it can exist as a liquid almost indefinitely. On the addition of a small crystal of the metal, however, the metastable

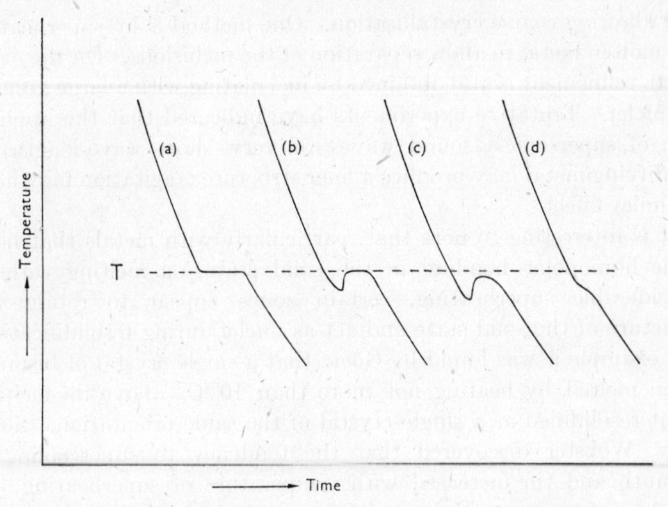

FIG. 14. Cooling curves showing undercooling : (*a*) ideal ; (*b*), (*c*) and (*d*) show undercooling. *T* indicates true freezing point.

metal will crystallise using this as nucleus to form one grain, or more if several nuclei are added. Crystals of certain foreign materials may serve the same purpose if they have a similar structure to the metal. Single crystals are prepared by utilising this effect. Addition of crystallisation nuclei is termed *inoculation*.

If there is no inoculation, with further cooling the metal, still without solidifying, enters the *labile region*, when crystallisation can be initiated by agitation. In the absence of any external influences the metal may persist for some time as liquid in this region, especially in the upper temperature range, but eventually it will crystallise spontaneously from a number of centres. At any stage in the labile region, spontaneous crystallisation will immediately occur from many centres if the liquid metal is inoculated with one small solid particle. When crystallisation proceeds in the labile region, many nuclei are formed due to the high degree of instability, and hence a fine grain-size is produced. Thus any factor which induces supercooling into this region tends to refine the grain-size; one of the most effective is the rate of cooling. Generally, the faster the rate of cooling the finer is the grain-size ; this applies to alloys as well as pure metals.

In practice, undercooling with consequent fine grain-size is also induced by treatments aimed at removing inherent inclusion of foreign matter, which might act as nuclei preventing undercooling and allowing coarse crystallisation. One method is by superheating the molten metal to allow separation of the inclusions. On the other hand, refinement is also obtained by inoculating with a large number of nuclei. Tentative experiments have indicated that the application of supersonics (sound waves of very short wave-length) to solidifying metal may produce a finer structure ; agitation may have a similar effect.

It is interesting to note that, particularly with metals that have some homopolar bonding in the solid state, on melting without considerable superheating, certain zones appear to retain the structure of the solid state and act as nuclei during resolidification. For example it was found by Goetz that a single crystal of bismuth when melted by heating not more than 10° C., above its melting point resolidified as a single crystal of the same orientation. Similarly, Webster discovered that the tendency to supercooling in bismuth and tin increased with temperature of superheating. A number of cases are known where molecules of compounds and elements apparently persist in the liquid state.

Other phenomena associated with the solidification of metals, together with a number of practical aspects, are dealt with in Chapter 11.

ADDITIONAL READING

1. *The Structure of Metals and Alloys,* by W. Hume-Rothery. Institute of Metals Monograph and Report Series No. 1. (Institute of Metals, 1947).

2. *Structure of Metals,* by C. S. Barrett. (2nd Ed. McGraw-Hill, 1952).

3. *Metals,* by (Sir) H. Carpenter and J. M. Robertson. Vol. I. (Oxford Univ. Press, 1939).

4. *Metallography,* by C. H. Desch. Sixth Ed. (Longmans Green, 1944).

5. *The Solidification of Metals and Alloys,* Symposium. Amer. Inst. Min. Met. Eng., 1951.

CHAPTER 2

ATOMIC STRUCTURE AND COHESION BETWEEN ATOMS

Structure of the atom. It is accepted that an atom has an open structure. It consists of a relatively small central part, the nucleus, containing most of the mass; around the nucleus move at great speed one or more components known as electrons. Electrons are fundamental components, whereas atomic nuclei are made up of more than one component. Details of nuclear structure are not of great direct importance in metallurgy at present, and will not be considered here. Electrons and nuclei will be treated as discrete particles. Atoms have an effective diameter of the order of 10^{-8} cm. whereas the diameters of nuclei are of the order of 10^{-12} to 10^{-13} cm. The occupied volume of an atom is approximately 10^{-12} to 10^{-15} of the effective volume.

The cohesion between electrons and nucleus in an atom is one of electrical attraction, as it is between atoms in molecules and crystals. The nucleus bears a net positive charge which is exactly balanced by the sum of the negative charges of the electrons, so that the normal atom as a whole is electrically neutral. The differences between the elements lie in the number of electrons contained in their atoms, and the value of their nuclear mass and positive charge. If the number of electrons surrounding the nucleus of a free and complete atom is Z, and the value of the negative charge on one electron e, then the positive charge on the nucleus is numerically equal to Ze. Z is known as the **atomic number** of the element.

It is possible to tabulate the elements in order of increasing number of extra-nuclear electrons and in general of increasing atomic mass (see table, p. 497). Hydrogen has the lightest and simplest atom, which has one electron. Helium is next with two, lithium following with three, and so on, gold for example having seventy-nine electrons.

With atoms containing more than one electron, the question arises as to the electronic distribution. The electrons may be considered as moving in sets around the nucleus. The sets are limited in the number of electrons they can incorporate, for example two or eight. Proceeding through the elements (page 497), it will be seen that as the number of electrons increases, so more sets are formed. Each subsequent set moves in a path of larger diameter than the previous one. New sets are not formed until the preceding one has been filled. Sometimes a set is temporarily filled or stable, and in the elements following a new set is formed ; then later extra electrons start joining the previous set. This can be seen in proceeding from scandium (21) to nickel (28), for example ; the elements of such a range are referred to as **transition elements.**

The number of electrons in the outer set, that is, the **valency electrons,** is most important in deciding the nature and strength of combination and cohesion between atoms. Elements with the same number of valency electrons have similar properties ; this is qualified by the Periodic Classification (Table 3). Most of the metals have one or two valency electrons, although some have more. A characteristic of the electron grouping of transition elements is that they have variable valency. For this reason in the Periodic Classification they form a section on their own, although they have a number of points of similarity with other elements ; they have a definitely metallic nature.

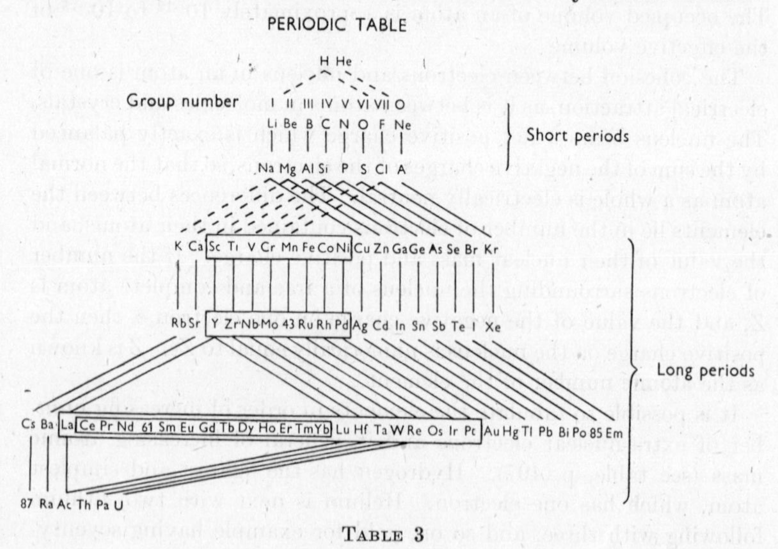

TABLE 3

The connecting lines in the Table indicate similarity in chemical properties. The three complete ranges of transition metals are enclosed ; the subdivision in the third contains the rare earth elements.

TYPES OF ATOMIC BONDING

There are four primary types of bonding between atoms in crystals, namely, homopolar, ionic, metallic, and van der Waals, of which the first three are the most important. There are typical instances of crystals where each of the four predominates, but in a number of cases coherence is due to more than one type of bonding. Thus, as a simple example, chlorine molecules are formed by homopolar linkage, and the molecules are held together in solid chlorine by van der Waals forces. It should be noted that even where one form of linkage is responsible for general coherence, other forms may obtain to varying extent, although in the main they may be masked by the stronger predominating forces; van der Waals forces are always present. In actual fact, when all the combinations of atoms are considered, it is apparent that there is a gradual transition from one extreme type of bonding to another.

Atoms with unfilled outer electrónic sets are unstable compared with those with filled sets. They tend to acquire stability of grouping by giving up their valency electrons to other atoms, or by filling their valency sets with electrons gained from, or shared with, other atoms. Atoms with a small number of valency electrons have a tendency to lose them; elements, such as the true metals, have atoms of this kind and are said to be **electropositive**. Reciprocally, elements, the atoms of which have nearly filled valency sets and tend to gain electrons, are known as **electronegative**. With regard to the Periodic Table, it is found that the electronegative properties in any period increase with increase in group number, and in any group with decrease in atomic number.

The three main types of bonding between atoms result from the above tendencies. The ionic linkage occurs by appropriate loss and gain of electrons between atoms of different elements, and the homopolar form when there is sharing of electrons between the atoms of one or more elements. Metallic bonding may be regarded as a special form of homopolar bonding. Atoms which have filled outer sets are relatively stable, and show little tendency to combine amongst themselves or with other atoms. This is the case with the inert gases, helium, neon, argon, etc. Such atoms crystallise at low temperatures, when they are held together by a weak force of attraction, namely, van der Waals linkage. This force may also bind stable molecules together and, as pointed out above, is present in all crystals though generally masked.

A useful guide to the strength of any type of bonding is the

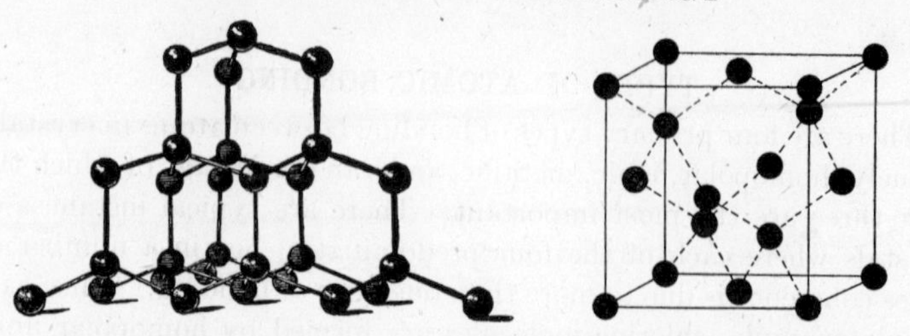

FIG. 15. Alternative ways of representing the crystal structure of diamond. From *Textbook of Inorganic Chemistry*, by J. R. Partington. Macmillan.

melting point of the solid formed. However, when two forms of bonding are important, this fact must be given consideration. Van der Waals bonding is in general considerably weaker than the other three types.

Homopolar or covalent bond. This occurs between the like atoms of an element, or in compound formation between the atoms of different elements. Homopolar bonding can only predominate in all directions in the crystal for elements having four valency electrons in their atoms. The classical example is carbon in the form of diamond. The arrangement taken up is such that each carbon atom is surrounded by four others with each of which it shares two pooled electrons (Fig. 15), so that it has in effect eight valency electrons which fill its outer group. The carbon atoms are then held together by their mutual attraction for the shared electrons. The actual crystal structure is known as tetrahedral, because the four close neighbours of any atom are arranged at the corners of a tetrahedron. Silicon, germanium, and grey tin (a low temperature form) are tetra (4)-valent,[1] and are bound together in the solid state in essentially the same way, and crystallise with the same structure as diamond; although in these elements the metallic type of bonding increases in importance, in the order given.

Compounds may be formed between tetravalent elements by homopolar bonding, for example, silicon carbide (SiC). Further, similar compounds may be formed between elements of different valencies provided the number of valency electrons per atom averages four; for example, zinc with two, and sulphur with six

[1] In connection with valency it should be noted that with normal chemical nomenclature a monovalent element may have in its atom one valency electron, or on the other hand, seven, requiring one electron to fill the valency set. Similarly, divalent indicates that the atoms have two or six valency electrons and trivalent three or five.

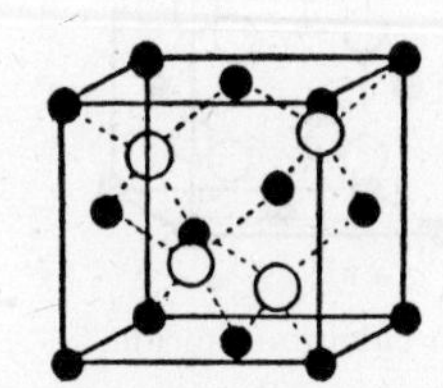

FIG. 16. The zinc-blende structure of ZnS.

Figs. 16, 17 and 18 are from *The Structure of Metals and Alloys*, by W. Hume-Rothery. Inst. Metals.

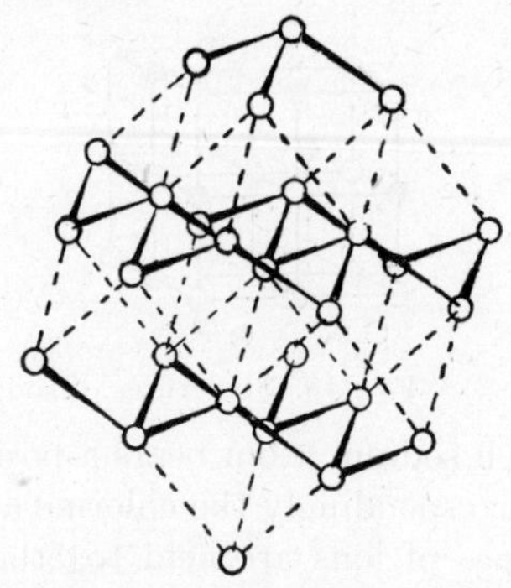

FIG. 17. Crystal structure of antimony showing the double layers of atoms.

valency electrons form zinc sulphide, (ZnS); and aluminium (3) and antimony (5) form AlSb. The crystal structures commonly occurring in such homopolar compounds are essentially similar to that of diamond; for example, that of zinc sulphide in the form of zinc blende (Fig. 16). In many homopolar compounds there are traces of metallic bonding, and hence signs of metallic properties; thus SiC and ZnS have some electrical conductivity—they are actually semi-conductors.

Homopolar bonding is not possible in the crystals of elements whose atoms contain less than four valency electrons, but it may be partly responsible for the coherence in elements when the atoms contain five, six, or seven valency electrons. For example, antimony, bismuth, selenium, and tellurium form virtually indefinite molecules in two directions (Fig. 17), and in a normal crystal the molecules are bound together by metallic forces; the case of chlorine has already been mentioned.

As a general rule, when homopolar bonding occurs in elements, each atom in the crystal is surrounded by $8 - N$ close neighbours, where N is the number of the group in which the element is placed in the Periodic Table, which is equal to the number of valency electrons possessed by the atoms of the element.

Ionic, electrovalent, or heteropolar bond. This occurs between the atoms of different elements. Stable electronic grouping is achieved by the loss and gain of electrons. Sodium chloride is the classical example of an ionic compound. Each sodium atom has one valency electron, and each chlorine atom seven. The sodium atoms each attain stability by giving up their one electron to a chlorine atom, thus filling the chlorine valency set. As a result of losing one electron

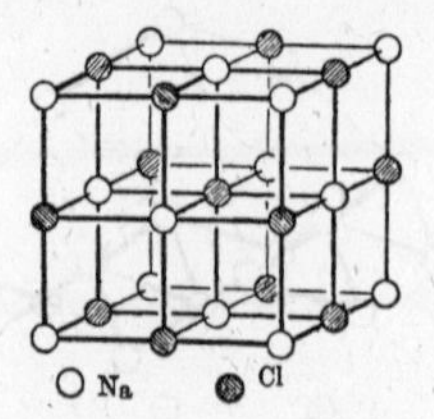

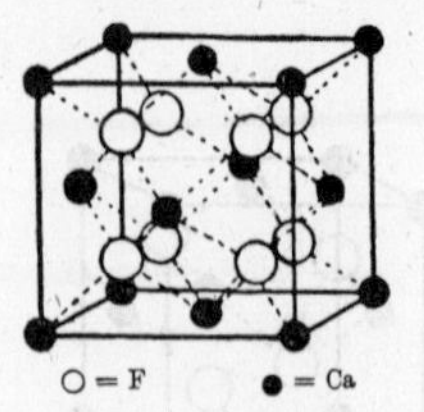

FIG. 18. Structures of sodium chloride and calcium fluoride.

each sodium atom bears a positive charge, becoming a positive ion. Correspondingly the chlorine atoms become negative ions. The two types of ions are held together in the sodium chloride crystal by direct electrostatic attraction of like for unlike charges (Fig. 18). An alternative arrangement with higher co-ordination may be obtained when the atoms are closer in size, as in caesium chloride (CsCl), which has a body-centred cubic structure with each ion surrounded by eight of the other ions. The sodium chloride bond involves one electron. Correspondingly magnesium oxide (MgO) is formed with the same structure involving exchange of two electrons and the bond is stronger ; hence magnesium oxide has a higher melting point than sodium chloride. Further, different proportions of atoms may be involved, and, for example, the calcium fluoride (CaF_2) (Fig. 18) or considerably more complicated structures may be obtained.

Metallic bond. This applies in most pure metals and alloys, but attention will be confined here to the former. The metallic atoms, as it were, pool their valency electrons, and thus become positive ions (with stable, filled, outer electron sets). The ions are held together by their attraction for the common valency electrons. The valency electrons may be regarded as forming a " cloud ", " gas " or " atmosphere ", and are free to move throughout the metal, although under normal conditions they are prevented from leaving it.

CRYSTAL STRUCTURES AND PROPERTIES RESULTING FROM THE DIFFERENT BONDS

When other factors do not prevail, the atoms in crystals arrange themselves as closely together as possible (although preserving their open structure), that is, in the position of *lowest* potential energy ; as an approximate comparison, lead shot will take up a regular close-packed arrangement if shaken to settle them down. This is what happens in metals, for there are no electrical or directed electronic considerations to be obeyed, bonding being multi-directional.

Thus the face-centred cubic and hexagonal close-packed structures, which are alternative ways of close-packing, are common in metals. Regular close-packing is denser than the irregular or statistical close-packing existing in liquid metals. The body-centred cubic structure also occurring in metals is fairly close-packed, although not so close as the other two structures. The metallic structures have high co-ordination, that is, a relatively large number of equidistant neighbours, namely, twelve in the face-centred cubic and hexagonal close-packed structures, and eight in the body-centred cubic.

In homopolar crystals, it has been seen that the bonding is directional, and relatively open and complex structures are formed to satisfy the electronic demands ; for example, the diamond structure has a co-ordination number of four.

With ionic crystals the factors to be balanced are the tendency to close-packing, electron exchange and the requirements of electrical neutrality ; thus comparatively more open and complex structures are often obtained than with metals.

Ionic bonds are generally fairly strong. There is more variation with the homopolar linkage, and considerable variation with the metallic bond ; compare, for example, the melting points of tungsten and magnesium. Permanent deformation in crystals occurs by the movement of one layer over another, and depends on the crystal structure and bonding between the atoms. Metals are usually plastic, due to their simple atomic arrangements and multi-directional bonding. On the other hand, ionic and homopolar crystals are often hard and brittle.

Metals are good conductors of heat and electricity, whereas ionic and homopolar crystals are generally insulators, or semi-conductors.

Metallic bonding predominates in a large group of elements, which crystallise with one of the simple hexagonal close-packed, face-centred and body-centred cubic structures, and display the typical metallic properties of good plasticity and conductivity, and possess a metallic lustre. As Pauling has pointed out, a transition between the predomination of homopolar and metallic bonding is illustrated by the elements carbon (diamond), silicon, germanium, tin and lead in group IV*b*. Diamond is homopolar, and an insulator, whereas metallic bonding occurs in lead, which crystallises with the face-centred cubic structure. It is considered in the latter case that the atoms only become ionised to the extent of two electrons, the other two valency electrons staying attached to the ions. Silicon is slightly conducting, and the conductivity increases as we proceed towards lead, as the proportion of metallic bonding increases. Antimony, bismuth, selenium and tellurium illustrate clearly the existence of homopolar and metallic bonding. These elements have some conductivity and metallic lustre, but tend to be brittle. In many cases the intermediate types of elements are semi-conductors. Similar transition of bonding types occurs between combinations of different atoms. This aspect is discussed in the case of metals in Chapter 3.

ZONE OR BAND THEORY

The foregoing treatment has been based essentially on the Bohr conception of the atom (1913). In this theory the electrons were imagined as moving in definite circular or elliptical orbits around the nucleus. In many cases each set of electrons discussed earlier would be distributed in several orbits, depending on the number. The electrons in the same orbit in the atoms of any particular element were considered to have the same energy, and to be able to rotate in their orbit without loss of energy : only certain values were possible.

The energy of electrons results from their kinetic energy (due to movement), and potential energy (due to attraction for the nucleus, which varies with distance from nucleus and value of nuclear charge). The total energy and the potential energy increase with distance from the nucleus, whereas the kinetic energy decreases. The work of Moseley (1913) showed that the energy values were not the same for corresponding orbits in different atoms, but increased with atomic number.

It is proposed in this section to give a glimpse of some developments in atomic theory and attitude since the Bohr theory, and their application to electrical conductivity. A turning point in atomic theory was the acceptance of Heisenberg's Uncertainty Principle (1927), which shows that with sizes of the order of electrons it is impossible to specify the nature of electrons, whether they are particles or not, or determine their exact position at any time. The Bohr concept of rigid orbits was discarded and the whereabouts of electrons is now discussed in terms of " probability " ; attention is given to the energies of the electrons, for which the same definite values are taken as in the Bohr theory. It has been shown experimentally (Davisson and Germer, 1927) that electrons may behave in a wave-like manner ; it had been previously suggested that this was likely, for example, by de Broglie in 1924. On this basis has evolved the " wave mechanics " method of calculating the energies of elec-

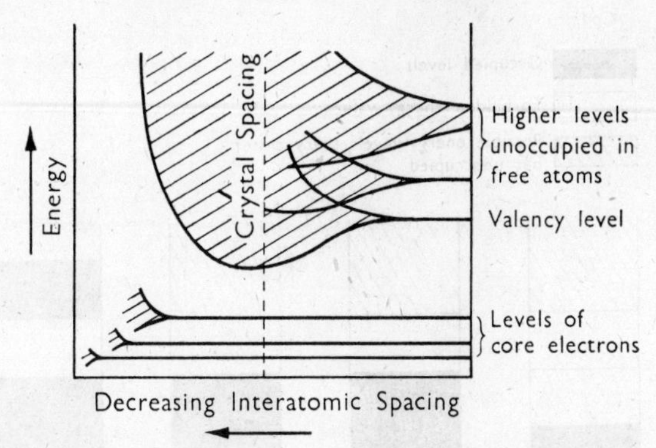

FIG. 19. Broadening of atomic energy levels in the solid state. From *Theoretical Structural Metallurgy*, by A. H. Cottrell. Arnold.

trons and describing their behaviour in probability terms, associated with names such as de Broglie and Schrödinger. It is not implied that electrons are waves ; their nature is left indefinite.

The energy values or levels of the electrons are definite and separate in free uncombined atoms, although some may be close together; intermediate values are not possible. Not more than two electrons may have the same energy value (Pauli Principle). The energy levels may be discussed, whether or not they are actually occupied.

In solid metals the valency electrons are pooled, and the positive ions take up a regular close-packed arrangement. In one sense the ions remain as separate entities, and the ionic electrons in each case have virtually the same energy values as in the free atoms. The valency electrons occupy a band or zone of extremely close, nevertheless distinct, energy values ; their levels in the free state are said to broaden into a band in the solid (Fig. 19). The higher energy levels normally unoccupied in the free atoms also broaden. If bands overlap they are said to have hybridised.

Each valency level in the free atom may contain one or two electrons. In the solid, each of these levels broadens into a band of N levels, where N is the number of atoms (in the case of simple metallic structures). Thus the larger the crystal the greater the number of levels, although the width of the band stays constant. Each level in the band can contain two electrons ; hence if there is one valency electron per atom, as in a number of metals, the band will be half filled. If the atoms have two valency electrons the band will be filled ; with three valency electrons the second band will be half filled. Whether or not the valency bands overlap depends on the

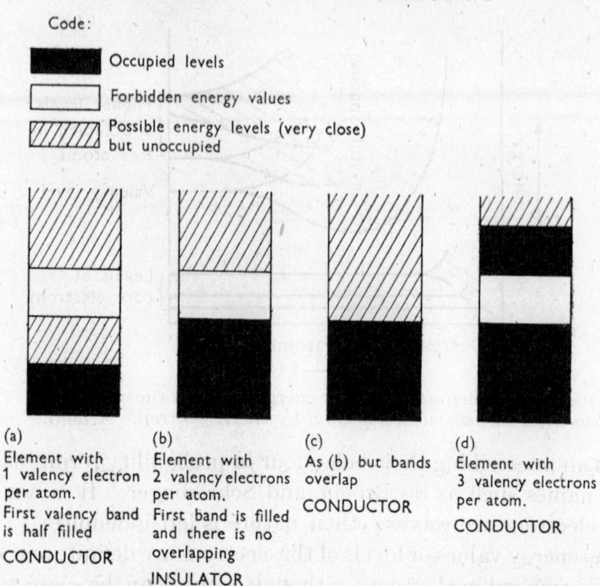

FIG. 20. Simple valency band or zone diagrams, representing various possibilities.

ions and their arrangement. If it were not for the ions the valency band would be continuous. The valency energy bands or zones may be represented diagrammatically as in Fig. 20, which shows the possibilities described above. None of these diagrams shows the distribution of the levels in the energy bands. This distribution is shown by $N(E)$ curves, which represent the number of energy states per unit volume of the crystal for each increment of energy (Fig. 21). The termination of the occupied levels in partly filled zones is sharp only at absolute zero ; at higher temperatures it is gradual because the heat increases the energy of some of the electrons.

The formation of valency bands has been shown by long wavelength X-ray emission spectra from the solids. It should be realised that the energy diagrams have no *real* existence in any way in the crystals.

The valency electrons in homopolar and ionic crystals occupy energy bands essentially similar to those described above, but the bands in these cases are filled and do not overlap.

Electrical conduction with respect to band theory. In a perfectly regular arrangement of stationary ions of the same kind the valency electrons can move freely through the structure, although there is no general drift in any particular direction. With application of an electric field, there is a tendency for the energies of some of the valency electons to be increased, and for them to move or drift in the direction of the field ; this constitutes electrical conduction (although in certain cases conductivity may also result from ionic movement). During conduction the electron drift may be very slow, such as a few inches per hour. Conduction can only occur if the valency electron can accept extra energy, that is, be excited into higher levels. Excitation results with normal fields only if there is an energy level not much higher than the highest occupied one into which electrons may pass. Solid elements may therefore be broadly

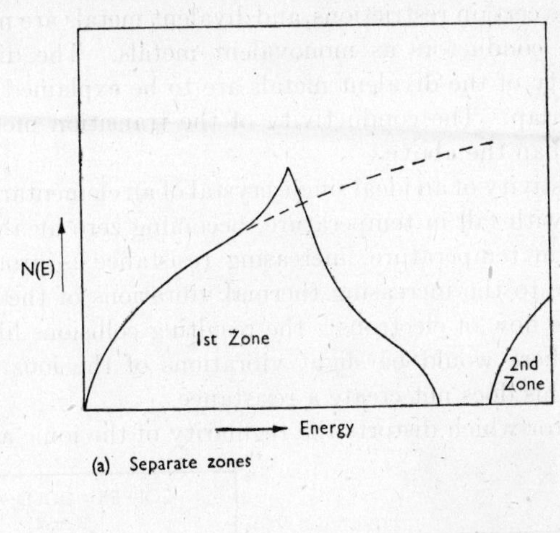

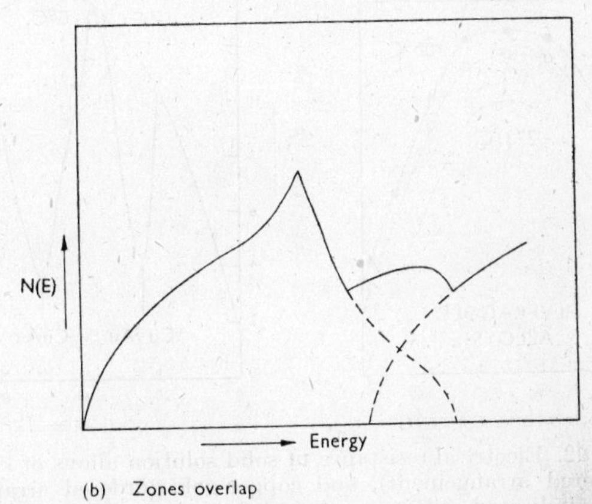

Fig. 21. Examples of $N(E)$ curves. The dotted curve in (a) shows the form that would be taken if it were not for the effect of the ions.

divided into **insulators** and **conductors**, depending on whether or not there is a forbidden energy zone starting immediately above the value of the electrons with the highest energy (Fig. 20). It should be noted that valency electrons with lower energies may only take part in conduction when others above have been progressively excited, leaving vacant levels. In some cases a number of the valency electrons may be prevented from taking part by the conditions of overlap, or for example, in the case shown in Fig. 20*d*.

Metals with one or three valency electrons are conductors because they have unfilled valency bands. The conduction in metals with two valency electrons is due to the overlapping of bands. The overlap imposes certain restrictions, and divalent metals are not generally such good conductors as monovalent metals. The differences in conductivity of the divalent metals are to be explained in the form of the overlap. The conductivity of the transition metals is more involved than the above.

The resistivity of an ideal single crystal of an elementary conductor decreases with fall in temperature, becoming zero at absolute zero. With rise in temperature, increasing resistance is brought about. This is due to the increasing thermal vibrations of the ions, which impede the flow of electrons ; the resulting collisions liberate heat. Actually there would be slight vibrations of the ions at absolute zero, but this does not create a resistance.

Any factor which distorts the regularity of the ionic arrangement

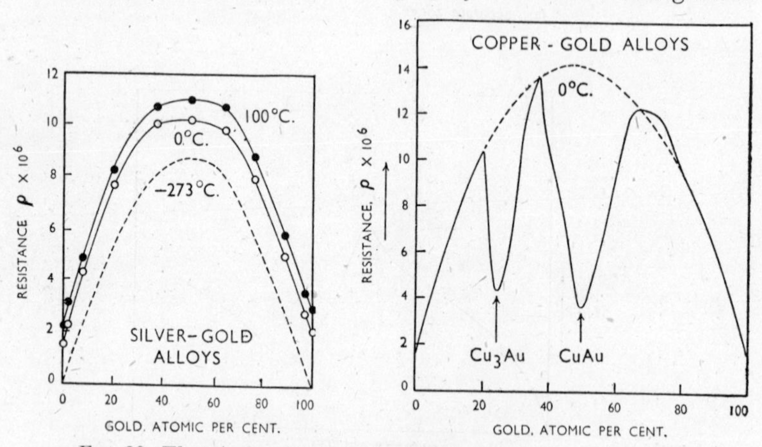

FIG. 22. Electrical resistance of solid solution alloys of silver-gold (disordered arrangement), and copper-gold (ordered arrangements occur as indicated, with consequent lowering of resistance). From *An Introduction to the Electron Theory of Metals*, by G. V. Raynor. Inst. Metals.

increases the resistivity. The conductivity of elementary metals is thus reduced by soluble impurities or alloying elements which are incorporated in the lattice of the metal, causing some distortion, even if the impurities are themselves good conductors; an ordered arrangement of the two kinds of atoms, however, has a lower resistance than a disordered one (Fig. 22). Insoluble impurities and alloying elements have much less effect, provided that continuous films of non-conducting material do not form around the grains. When non-conducting constituents are present as disconnected globules, their main effect is merely to reduce the volume of metal available for conduction. Distortion of the crystal structure of a metal or alloy by cold work also slightly reduces the electrical conductivity; for example, that of hard drawn copper is about 2·5 per cent less than that of the undeformed metal. It will be appreciated that conductivity will to some extent be reduced by the presence of grain boundary zones.

In ionic compounds and homopolar elements and compounds the bands are filled and do not overlap; hence the crystals are insulators, or in a number of cases semi-conductors. Further, with ionic crystals there is virtually no interchange of electrons between ions. In the case of covalent bonding, where there is sharing of valency electrons, although the probability is greatest that these electrons are to be found at the position indicated by a rigid concept of sharing, it is now considered that the electrons are in continual movement through the crystal. However, the movement does not give conducting power, because there are no vacant energy levels near.

Semi-conductors. There is an intermediate class of substances known as semi-conductors; some examples are selenium, tellurium, cuprous and cupric oxides, zinc oxide, lead sulphide, zinc sulphide and silver iodide. These would be insulators at absolute zero, but become conducting as the temperature rises, their resistance decreasing with rise in temperature. These semi-conductors are characterised by filled energy bands; but only a narrow forbidden range exists between the uppermost filled band and the next empty permissible band. It is possible then for thermal energy to excite electrons across the forbidden zone into the next empty zone, where the excited electrons are available for conduction. The presence of impurities is also important in helping to bridge this gap.

It must be realized that the foregoing has given the scantiest non-mathematical idea of modern theory, and much has been glossed over; but some indication, at least, of modern conceptions is imperative to the student of metallurgy today. A completely co-ordinated theory of the solid state is far from reached, but a good beginning has been made.

ADDITIONAL READING

1. *The Structure of Metals and Alloys,* by W. Hume-Rothery. Monograph and Report Series, No. 1. (Institute of Metals. 1947).

2. *Structure of Metals,* by C. S. Barrett. (2nd Edit., McGraw-Hill. 1952).

3. *The Physics of Metals,* by F. Seitz. (McGraw-Hill, 1943).

4. *Theoretical Structural Metallurgy,* by A. H. Cottrell. (Arnold, 1948).

5. *Crystal Chemistry,* by R. C. Evans. (Cambridge Univ. Press, 1946).

6. *An Introduction to X-ray Metallography,* by A. Taylor. (Chapman and Hall, 1945).

7. *An Introduction to the Electron Theory of Metals,* by G. V. Raynor. Monograph and Report Series, No. 4. (Institute of Metals, 1947).

8. *Electrons, Atoms, Metals and Alloys,* by W. Hume-Rothery. (Louis Cassier, 1948). (In the form of dialogue).

9. *Atomic Theory for Students of Metallurgy,* by W. Hume-Rothery. Monograph and Report Series, No. 3. (Institute of Metals, 1946). (This is an advanced text).

CHAPTER 3

BINARY ALLOYING

METALS are generally used in the form of **alloys**, unless some particular characteristic of pure metals is a paramount requirement, such as high electrical conductivity. An alloy is a combination of two or more metallic elements, or in certain cases an important component may be a metalloid or even a non-metal, provided the product displays metallic properties. A binary alloy contains two components, a ternary alloy three, a quaternary four, and so on. An alloy system constitutes all the possible combinations between the components.

Binary alloys form the natural starting point for the study of alloying; essentially all the basic principles are involved. Most commercial alloys (Table 7, page 90) contain more than two component elements; but it is often convenient to interpret them on a binary basis, although this must be done with care.

Alloys are generally made in the molten state, and then allowed to solidify and cool down to room temperature. Some alloys go into service in this condition, but in many cases working and heat-treatment follow. The effect of these treatments is considered in subsequent chapters. Alloys may be made in other ways, such as by powder-metallurgy technique or by electro-deposition, but these methods will not be discussed here.

LIQUID ALLOYS

In the molten state there are two possibilities:

(1) Commonly the two metals are *miscible*, blending to form one liquid solution.

(2) Sometimes the metals are *immiscible* and the molten alloy consists of two liquids. It is doubtful whether absolute liquid immiscibility ever occurs—at least a few atoms dissolve. The copper-lead, aluminium-lead, zinc-lead, aluminium-cadmium, aluminium-sodium, copper-thallium and copper-selenium systems afford examples of partial liquid miscibility with intermediate compositions

consisting of two solutions. In such systems complete liquid miscibility may be obtained at higher temperatures.

The factors governing behaviour in liquid alloys have not been studied to the same extent as with solid alloys. However, as pointed out by Raynor and Hume-Rothery, it would appear that, as with solid solubility, liquid solubility depends in a number of cases to some degree on the "atomic size-factor". In addition, the surface tensions of the molten metals may have some bearing. Also, a tendency for the two metals to combine to form stable compounds which do not dissociate until the melting point is well exceeded may cause partial miscibility (Hume-Rothery).

CONDITIONS IN SOLID ALLOYS

Liquid immiscibility is often followed by immiscibility in the solid state. However, with the more general case of systems in which complete liquid miscibility is obtained, there is a considerable range of possibilities in the solid state. In alloys of this kind there are at

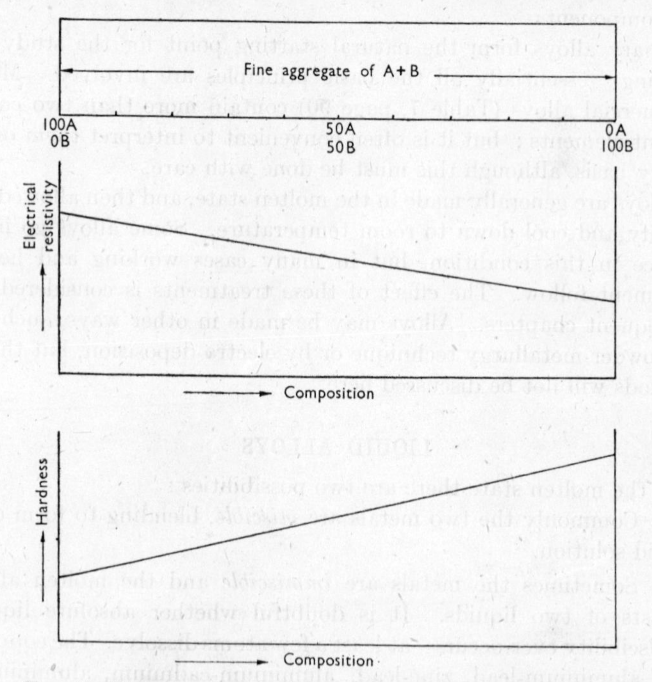

Fig. 23. Diagram representing complete solid immiscibility in an alloy system, and showing variation in physical properties (*A* and *B* are any two pure metals which behave in this way).

room temperature two extreme possibilities, namely solid immiscibility, and solid miscibility.

(1) **Complete Solid Immiscibility.** As with the corresponding case in the liquid state, there will also be very slight mutual solubility.

The tin-zinc system may be taken as an example ; when solid, the alloys are found to be composed of an intimate and coherent, fine aggregate of crystals of pure tin and pure zinc (Fig. 23) ; the proportions and arrangement of the two kinds of crystals vary with composition. The bismuth-cadmium system affords another example.

The structures of alloys are revealed in the same way as those of pure metals by polishing and etching. It is usually necessary to examine alloys microscopically to determine their full structure. The actual structures obtained in the various types of systems are illustrated in the next chapter.

(2) **Complete Solid Miscibility.** When the two metals are completely miscible in the solid state, every alloy in the system is composed of one type of grain similar to a pure metal, and known as a " solid solution " (Fig. 24). It is impossible from the microstructure to distinguish one alloy (when stable) from another or from a pure metal, although there will in some cases be a colour difference. In certain conditions the grains are uneven in composition, that is, *heterogeneous*, giving a structure which is characteristic of a solid solution.

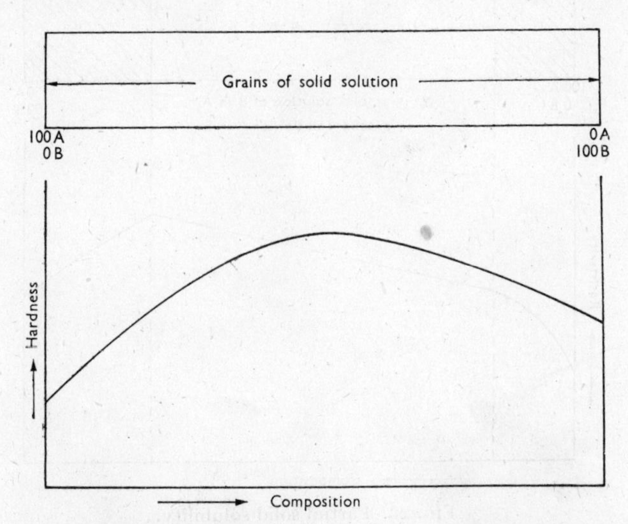

Fig. 24. Complete solid miscibility between two metals. For variation in electrical resistivity, see Fig. 22, p. 28.

Examples of complete solid solubility are the copper-nickel, gold-silver, tungsten-molybdenum, and magnesium-cadmium alloy systems. The best conception of the nature of a solid solution is obtained from the crystal structure, which aspect is discussed later in this chapter. Solid solutions have similar properties to pure metals, but they are generally stiffer and not such good conductors.

(3) **Partial Solid Solubility** (no intermediate constituents). This is a fairly common occurrence in solid alloys; it is intermediate between the two extremes just considered. Up to a certain percentage of one metal is dissolved in the other, and vice versa. Intermediate compositions, that is, between the two limits of solid solubility, are composed of an aggregate of the two solid solutions (Fig. 25). The actual structures obtained in the intermediate alloys are similar in a number of cases to those occurring with conditions of complete solid immiscibility, except that the aggregate is of two solid solutions and not of pure metals. Examples are the copper-silver, and lead-tin alloys.

(4) **Systems in which one or more intermediate constituents is formed.** In a large number of alloy systems at certain specific intermediate compositions, or more often over certain intermediate ranges of composition, constituents may be formed which differ to varying extents from solid solutions. For the present they will be

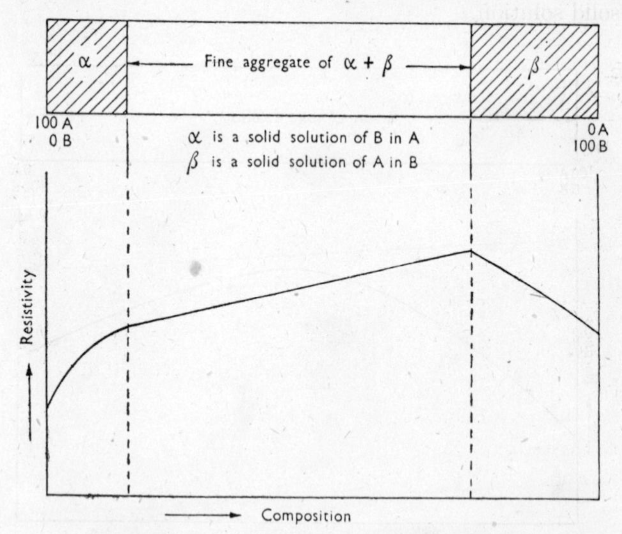

Fig. 25. Partial solid solubility.

Note: the hardness curve for this and subsequent examples follows the same general form as the resistivity curve

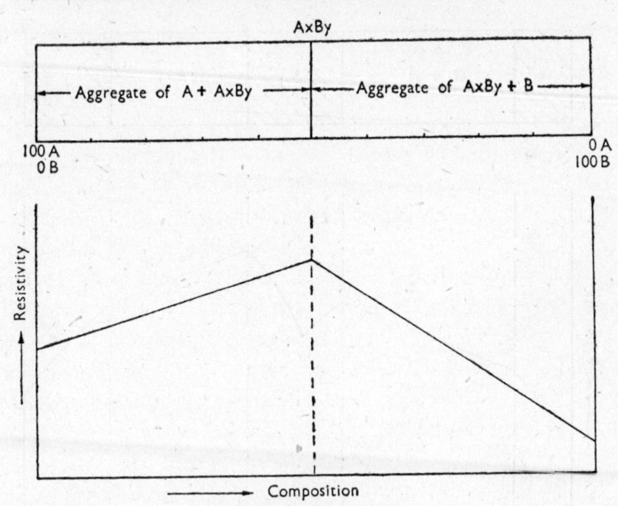

(*a*) An intermediate constituent is formed at a specific composition, but there is no primary solid solubility.

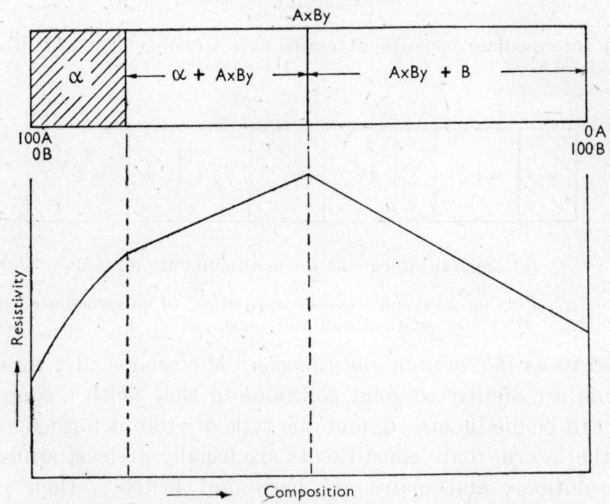

(*b*) As (*a*), but there is some primary solubility of metal *B* in metal *A*.

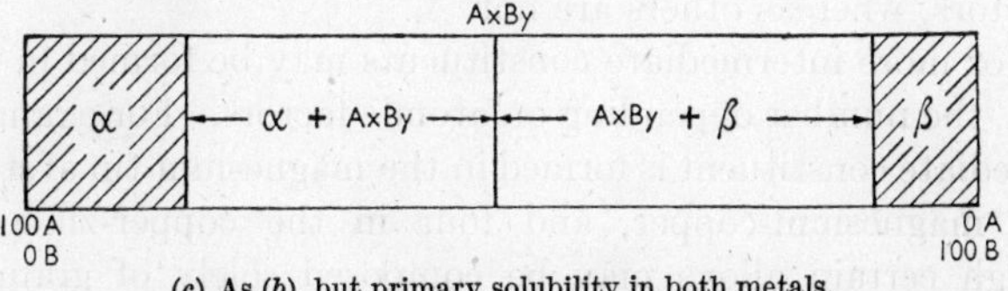

(*c*) As (*b*), but primary solubility in both metals.

26. Diagrams showing formation of one intermediate constituent in a system.

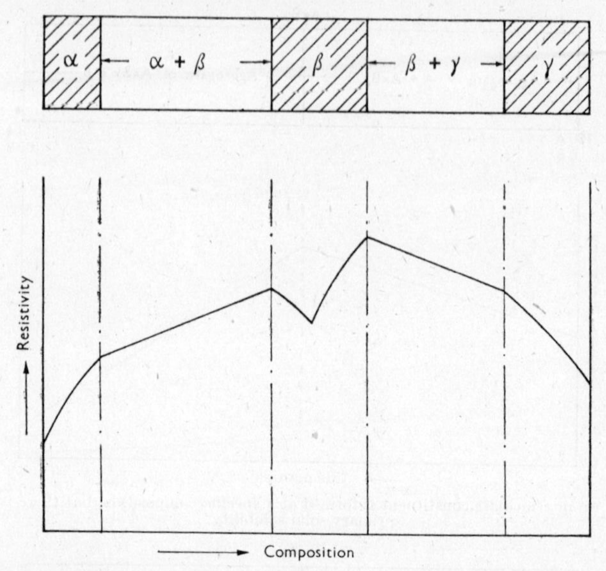

(*a*) Intermediate constituent exists over a range of composition.

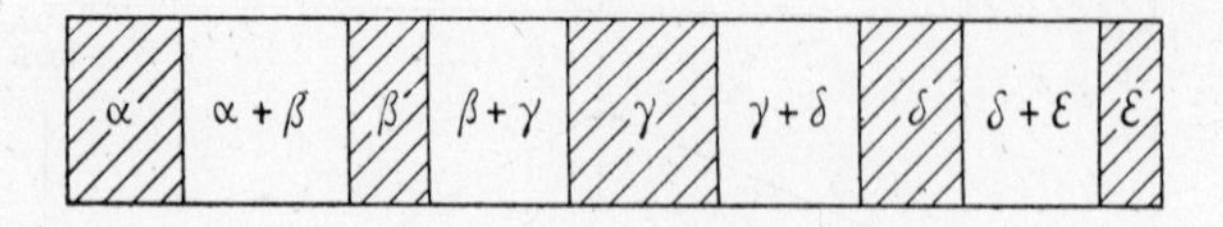

(*b*) Several intermediate constituents are formed.

FIG. 27. Further examples of the formation of intermediate constituents in alloy systems.

referred to as *intermediate constituents*. Microscopically, these constituents are similar to solid solutions in that neither component metal can be distinguished, and one type of grain is formed. However, the intermediate constituents are usually at least stiffer than solid solutions, and many are hard and brittle; their crystal structures differ from those of the basis metals; and some may be conductors, whereas others are not.

One or more intermediate constituents may be formed in any one system, the number depending on atomic factors. For example, one intermediate constituent is formed in the magnesium-tin system, two in the magnesium-copper, and four in the copper-zinc system. Although certain alloys may be composed solely of grains of an intermediate constituent, with regard to the whole system some form of solid immiscibility always exists due to the limited if not greatly restricted range of existence of the constituents; and due also to the fact that because of their different crystal structures the constituents are immiscible with the component metals or solid solutions based on them. It is clear that different intermediate constituents in the same system are immiscible with each other. Certain alloys are therefore composed of aggregates of pure metal or solid solution and intermediate constituent, or of two intermediate constituents, depending on the number formed (Figs. 26 and 27).

It was pointed out at the beginning of this chapter that a principal component of an alloy need not necessarily be a metal, the most common example being carbon in steel and cast-iron. Such systems are also covered by the foregoing classification of liquid and solid conditions, at least in the useful range.

PRIMARY SOLID SOLUTIONS

In the more usual form of solid solution, the atoms of both metals are arranged on the same crystal structure (Figs. 28 *a* and *b*), which is actually that of the basis metal, although the dimensions may be altered and the structure distorted to a certain extent so as to accommodate the atoms of the second metal if these are not the same size as those of the basis metal. However, there is a limit to the accommodation possible. When solid solubility occurs in this way, it is known as **substitutional.** There is a second kind of solubility, when **interstitial** solid solutions are formed, with the second kind of atoms arranged in the spaces or interstices between the others (Fig. 28*c*).

In both the above cases of solid solubility, the essential atomic pattern of the basis metal is retained, and strictly the solutions should be referred to as "primary solid solutions." An alternative name is "terminal solid solution"; this is particularly apt when there is partial solubility with or without intermediate constituents being formed. It should be pointed out that generally when solid solutions are referred to without other qualification, the primary type is implied.

Primary substitutional solid solutions. The *solute* (dissolved) *atoms* take their places on the lattice of the *solvent* (basis) *metal.* In other words, the solute atoms are substituted for the solvent ones. In the case of complete solid solubility, which occurs when the metals have closely similar atomic natures, the two solutions, as it were, merge completely. In such a case the term **solvent** will be applied to whichever metal predominates. The two solutions do

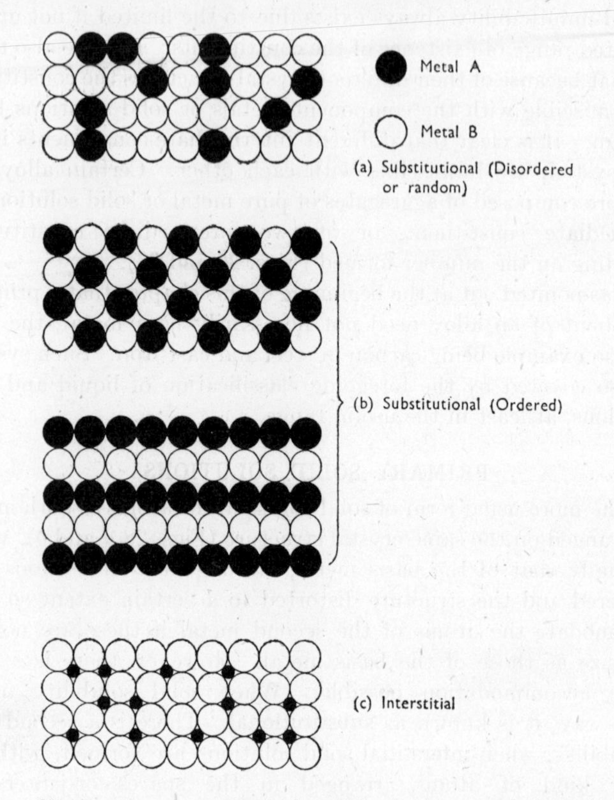

FIG. 28. Atomic arrangements in solid solutions (two dimensional representation).

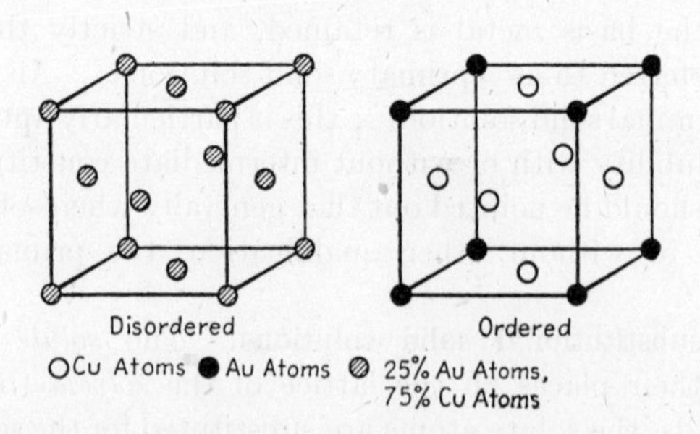

FIG. 29. Ordering in copper-gold alloy (Cu_3Au).

Note: the lattice drawing of the ordered structure does not include enough atoms to show the correct proportion of copper and gold atoms, although consideration of an aggregate will show that this is achieved then. Figs. 29 and 31*a* are from *Structure of Metals*, by C. S. Barrett. McGraw-Hill.

not merge in the case of partial solid solubility, because their crystal structures are different either in actual pattern, or to an appreciable amount in dimensions ; this condition arises when the component metals differ in such ways as their elemental forms.

The two kinds of atoms in substitutional solutions in the stable condition are distributed fairly uniformly. But, in certain cases at simple atomic proportions, definite " ordered " structures are obtained (Figs. 28*b* and 29) ; such structures are also known as **superlattices.** At other compositions in the system, the structures may become as ordered as they possibly can. Ordered structures usually exist at room and moderately elevated temperatures ; at higher temperatures the atoms take up the average random distribution of the disordered state. There is a difference in properties between the ordered and disordered states. The electrical conductivity is higher in the ordered structure (Fig. 22, p. 28), and the specific heat is affected (Fig. 30*b*). Although mechanical properties are altered by ordering, it is not possible to make a brief generalisation. In some cases, by fast cooling, disordered structures may be retained at room temperature in alloys normally of an ordered structure.

Factors governing substitutional solubility. These were first stated as rules, principally by Hume-Rothery, although some are now capable of further interpretation. The rules are based on a thorough study of many results of alloying as determined experimentally. It cannot be said that they are universal, or that they necessarily are the only factors involved ; but they do give a sound general indication of the position, which may be summed up by saying that the closer the two metals are in atomic nature the more there is likely to be extensive solubility. The factors involved are as follow.

(1) For considerable solid solubility to be likely, the atomic diameters of the two metals should not differ by more than about 14 per cent of that of the solvent ; up to this value constitutes a favourable " size-factor ". The atomic diameter in each case is taken as the shortest distance apart of the centres of atoms in the elemental crystal as determined by X-rays. The effective diameter, however, does vary according to the combination. Although the likelihood of solubility falls off as the size limit is reached, there is not a rigid distinction, and borderline cases may go either way.

(2) Further, the crystal structures of the two metals in their elemental form should be the same. It is apparent that these conditions must be obeyed for complete solubility, otherwise the two solutions would not merge.

(3) Solid solubility is restricted by the formation of intermediate constituents. These are likely to form especially when the valencies of the two metals are different.

(4) In connection with differences in valency another factor arises, pointed out by Bernal, and called the *relative valency effect* by Hume-Rothery. Addition of atoms with a greater number of valency electrons to a structure of atoms with fewer valency electrons increases the " electron concentration ", which is the ratio of the total number of valency electrons in the alloy to the total number of atoms. It appears that such increase is limited. Reciprocally, the extent to which the electron concentration may be decreased appears to be very restricted. The electron concentration effect applies especially when one of the metals concerned has one valency electron per atom.

The foregoing factors must be considered together when assessing the likely solubility of two metals ; if they are not all favourable there may be some solubility, and even if they are distinctly unfavourable there may be slight solubility. In the case of copper and silver, factors are favourable, except that the size-factor is a borderline case, and there is partial solid solubility (maximum weight percentages are 8 silver and 8·8 copper, atomic percentages are 4·9 and 14·1, respectively). In the copper-zinc system the size-factor is favourable, but the metals have different crystal structures and different valencies ; however, copper dissolves a considerable amount of zinc, namely 39 weight per cent maximum (38·4 atomic per cent), but zinc only dissolves 2·7 per cent copper maximum (2·6 atomic per cent) (solution here involves reduction of electron concentration) ; several intermediate constituents are formed also in this system. The copper-magnesium system is a rather extreme case ; the size-factor is unfavourable, crystal structures and valencies are different, and there is a tendency to form intermediate constituents (two are formed), yet copper dissolves a certain amount of magnesium, namely 2·6 weight per cent maximum (6·5 atomic per cent), although the amount of reverse solubility is negligible. The copper-aluminium system illustrates the restrictive effects of valency difference ; the size-factor is favourable and the crystal structures similar, yet the maximum solubility of aluminium in copper is 9·4 weight per cent (about 20 atomic per cent) and that of copper in aluminium is 5·7 weight per cent (2·5 atomic per cent) ; intermediate constituents are formed. Solubility is very restricted in the magnesium-lead system due to the formation of an intermediate constituent, the size-factor being favourable. In the case of the copper-lead and aluminium-lead systems, very unfavourable size-factors appear to predominate, and there is liquid immiscibility as well as virtually complete solid insolubility. The maximum limits of solid solubility given above apply to elevated temperatures; at room temperature the figures are usually less and often markedly so.

There is noticeable similarity of atomic nature between those metals which form complete solid solubility (Table 4). Generally the two elements are in the same group in the Periodic Table; although this is not always the case, as when transition elements are involved, for example with the copper-nickel and gold-platinum systems.

TABLE 4. BINARY SYSTEMS IN WHICH THERE IS COMPLETE SOLID SOLUBILITY
(at least on solidification)

Ordering and other changes occur in some of the alloys on cooling to room temperature.

Face-centred cubic	*Body-centred cubic*	*Others*
copper-gold	iron-chromium	arsenic-antimony
copper-nickel	molybdenum-tungsten	antimony-bismuth
copper-platinum	potassium-rubidium	selenium-tellurium
gold-platinum	potassium-caesium	germanium-silicon
gold-silver	rubidium-caesium	
nickel-palladium	*Hexagonal close-packed*	
nickel-platinum	magnesium-cadmium	
platinum-palladium		
calcium-strontium		

Primary Interstitial Solid Solutions. These are formed between a number of transition elements such as iron, tungsten, nickel and cobalt, and metalloids or non-metals with considerably smaller atoms, as carbon, nitrogen, hydrogen and boron. Thus the occurrence of such solutions is limited, and it is apparent that there is no question of complete interstitial solubility. The commonest example is carbon in face-centred cubic iron (8·5 atomic per cent maximum, 2·0 per cent by weight), and to a much less extent in body-centred cubic iron (about 0·04 per cent maximum by weight). According to Hägg, for interstitial alloying of any kind, the difference in atomic diameter between solute and solvent should be greater than about 41 per cent of the solvent diameter (size ratio 0·59). An explanation due to Seitz for the different interstitial solubility of carbon in the two forms of iron is that the size-factor is border-line (0·63), and, although body-centred cubic iron is a more open structure, there are spaces in the face-centred cubic structure larger than any in the body-centred cubic form. Corresponding solubility occurs with nitrogen in iron, where the size-factor is 0·56.

Characteristics of Solid Solutions. Solid solutions exist over various ranges of composition, although interstitial ones are always limited in extent. When their crystal structures and atomic bonding are of the metallic type, which is the usual case, solid solutions are plastic, although generally stiffer than pure metals. Solid solutions are conductors, although not so good as the pure metals on which they are based (Fig. 22, p. 28). Further, solid solutions invariably solidify in a dendritic manner over a range of temperature, which is often intermediate between the melting points of the component metals; in practice, the solutions often solidify with heterogeneous grains.

INTERMEDIATE CONSTITUENTS

Intermediate constituents (also known as "intermediate phases", "intermetallic compounds" or merely as "compounds") as a complete class reveal an almost continuous change of structure, bonding and properties from those of solid solutions to those of normal chemical compounds.

A general characteristic of intermediate constituents is that the crystal structure differs from that of either of the component metals, if not in actual pattern, at least in dimensions. The bonding and structure adopted in an intermediate constituent will be those which produce the most stable combination, having the lowest potential energy for the composition concerned.

There are three well-known types of intermediate constituents, namely valency, electron and interstitial compounds.

Valency compounds. Valency compounds obey the normal chemical rules of valency and are bonded together essentially by ionic or homopolar forces, or a combination of these. Thus MgSe and BaTe are ionic, and have the sodium chloride structure; Mg_2Sn and Mg_2Pb are also ionic, with the calcium fluoride structure. AlSb and ZnTe are homopolar, and have the ZnS (zinc blende) structure.

Valency compounds tend to be formed when the valencies of the two component elements are suitable for loss and gain or sharing of electrons. The electrochemical factor is important; the more electropositive the element with few valency electrons, and the more electronegative the other, the greater is the tendency for a compound to form and the greater is its stability when formed.

Valency compounds are formed with atomic size differences considerably beyond the substitutional solid solution limit.

Valency compounds are usually hard and brittle, and are not generally proper conductors; they are often semi-conductors, although Mg_2Pb is recently reported as being metallic in conducting power. The compounds exist at specific compositions or over restricted ranges, and their melting points are usually at constant temperatures; the actual values are relatively high, and as with Mg_2Sn (melting point about 780° C.) may be higher than that of either of the component metals. Valency compounds may crystallise into shapes with plane faces, although in some cases dendritic growth is possible. The crystals are homogenous, and by virtue of the bonding there is a regular distribution of the two kinds of atoms.

Electron compounds. It was found (largely by Hume-Rothery and Westgren) that the existence of a considerable number of compounds between metals not markedly different in electrochemical nature corresponded to certain electron concentrations. The concentrations are represented by whole number ratios, although there is often considerable latitude in composition; in some cases the ratio is not actually included in the range. On the basis of valency electron to atom ratios of 3 : 2, 7 : 4 and 21 : 13, a large number of compounds has been recognised (Table 5 and Fig. 30); the term *electron compound* was suggested by Bernal.

TABLE 5. EXAMPLES OF ELECTRON COMPOUNDS

Valency electron to atom ratio of 3 : 2 (β-phases).

Body-centred cubic structure

CuBe, CuZn, AgMg,
AgZn, AuZn, AuCd,
Cu_3Al, Cu_3Ga, Cu_5Sn,
CoAl, NiAl, FeAl

Complex cubic (" β-*Manganese* ") *structure*

Ag_3Al, Au_3Al,
Cu_5Si, $CoZn_3$

Hexagonal close-packed structure

Cu_5Ge, Ag_7Sb

Valency electron to atom ratio of 21 : 13 (γ-phases)

Complex cubic (" γ-*Brass* ") *structure*

Cu_5Zn_8, Fe_5Zn_{21}, Au_5Zn_8, Cu_5Cd_8,
Ni_5Zn_{21}, Ag_5Cd_8, Cu_9Al_4, Rh_5Zn_{21},
Cu_9Ga_4, Pd_5Zn_{21}, Cu_9In_4, Pt_5Zn_{21},
$Cu_{31}Si_8$, Ni_5Cd_{21}, $Cu_{31}Sn_8$, Ag_5Zn_8

Valency electron to atom ratio 7 : 4 (ϵ-phases)

Hexagonal close-packed structure

$CuZn_3$, $AgCd_3$, $CuCd_3$, Ag_3Sn,
Cu_3Sn, Ag_5Al_3, Cu_3Ge, Au_5Al_3,
Cu_3Si, $AuZn_3$, $AgZn_3$, $AuCd_3$, Au_3Sn.

Note: The valency of transition metals is taken as zero in calculating the ratios.

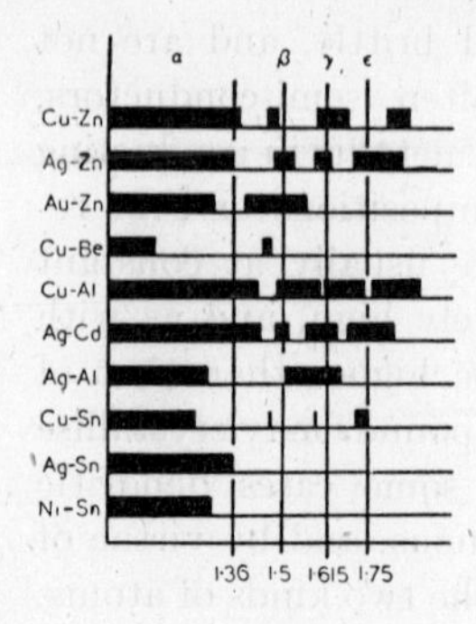

FIG. 30. Solid solubility limits and range of existence of electron compounds in terms of electron concentration compared with Hume-Rothery's ratios. From *An Introduction to X-ray Metallography*, by A. Taylor. Chapman & Hall.

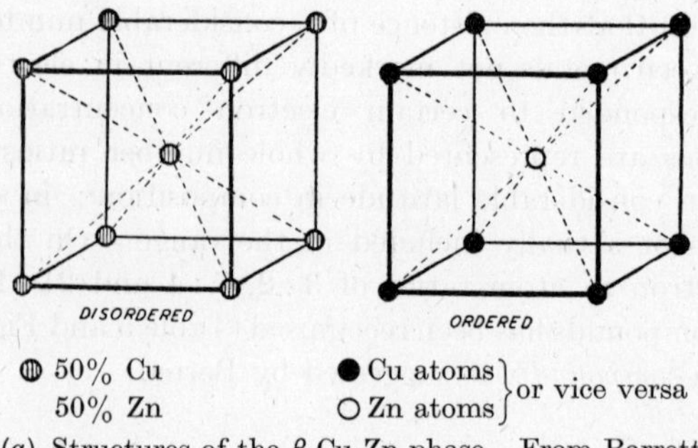

(*a*) Structures of the β Cu-Zn phase. From Barrett.

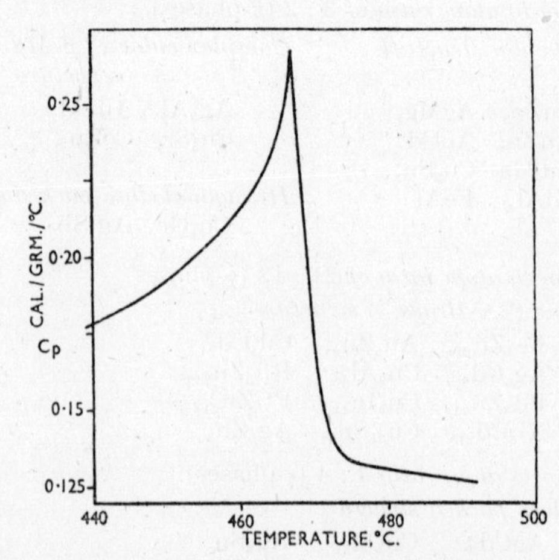

(*b*) Variation in specific heat with temperature of β Cu-Zn (49·7 weight per cent Zn). From C. Sykes and H. Wilkinson, *J. Inst. Metals*, 1937, **61**, 231.

FIG. 31. Ordering in the beta copper-zinc phase.

Generally, electron compounds occur in systems where the size factor is favourable, although there is more latitude than for primary solid solutions. The bonding in electron compounds is essentially metallic as in solid solutions. In fact, electron compounds are similar structurally to primary solid solutions, except that their actual crystal structures are different in pattern usually, but sometimes only in dimensions, from those of the basis metals. For this reason electron compounds are sometimes known as "secondary solid solutions".

Ordering may occur in electron compounds as in primary solid solutions (Fig. 31).

The zone theory (page 24) has been applied by H. Jones to the formation of electron compounds, and the restriction of primary solubility. Thus in the case of the copper-zinc system (which is similar at room temperature to that represented in Fig. 27*b*), copper will dissolve the higher valency zinc while retaining the face-centred cubic structure until the electron concentration increases from 1 to about 1·4. The valency band of the copper is half-filled; the addition of zinc (valency 2) fills it further; the band is not altered, since the crystal structure remains the same. The concentration of 1·4 corresponds to a critical point in the band, beyond which addition of further electrons causes a marked increase in the energy of the highest-energy electrons and in the energy of the structure, which then becomes unstable. It can be shown that the body-centred cubic structure is more stable when the electron concentration is around 1·5, for its valency band is different and is not filled to the critical point by the concentration of 1·5. Alloys whose composition is such that the electron concentration is about 1·5 form one type of grain with a body-centred cubic arrangement of the atoms, that is, they consist of the 3/2 electron compound. An electron concentration of 1·4 represents the limit of primary solid solubility.

In the intermediate region the change-over of structure occurs, and intermediate compositions consist of an aggregate of the solid solution and the electron compound. This treatment explains one aspect of the relative valency effect on solubility (page 40). Similar treatment can be applied to the formation of the γ- and ϵ-constituents. Corresponding behaviour is found in other cases, although the value of the limiting electron concentration for primary solubility and the extent of the electron compounds are modified, in particular, by a borderline or unfavourable atomic size-factor.

Electron compounds are generally conductors and exist over a range of composition. The compounds with complex structures, for example, Cu_5Zn_8 and Cu_9Al_4, are brittle. Some of the body-centred cubic structures are known to be plastic, especially at elevated temperatures ; for example, CuZn and Cu_3Al. It is possible also that some of the hexagonal close-packed compounds behave likewise. With regard to melting points and mode of solidification, electron compounds are similar to solid solutions.

Other compounds. There are certain compounds similar to electron compounds, although they do not follow the standard ratios. Thus in the silver-lithium system, compounds centred about AgLi and Ag_3Li_{10} are formed with the body-centred cubic and γ-structures, respectively, although the valencies of both silver and lithium are unity.

There is a number of compounds with bonding partly metallic and partly of valency nature. Many of these crystallise with the nickel-arsenide structure, which consists of alternate layers of metal and metalloid atoms. The metal atoms are in a simple hexagonal pattern, while the metalloid atoms have the close-packed hexagonal arrangement. A fair range of composition is possible. Typical examples are CuSn, AuSn, FeSn, PtSn, PtPb, NiBi, FeTe.

An interesting case arises with the magnesium-zinc system. The substitution size-factor is unfavourable, and primary solid solubility is very restricted. The valencies are the same, and so are the individual crystal structures, apart from some dimensional difference ; yet several compounds are formed in which the bonding is apparently metallic. It is suggested that the size effect is predominating here with regard to compound formation. Cadmium also has the same valency as magnesium and similar crystal structure ; but the size-factor is favourable, and in the magnesium-cadmium system there is complete solid solubility, although ordering occurs.

The formation of the compounds Cu_2Mg, Au_2Pb, Au_2Bi and ZrW_2 is thought also to be largely governed by relative atomic size, as with the magnesium-zinc system ; again the bonding is apparently metallic.

Interstitial compounds. Apart from the compounds just discussed in which atomic size is a factor, there is a class of compounds characterised by pronounced differences in atomic diameters of the components, namely, the interstitial compounds. These are formed between the same class of elements as form interstitial solid solutions, and the same limiting size-factor obtains. Compounds may be formed with transition metals in which there is little or no primary solubility. Bonding appears to be metallic in a number of cases. The metal atoms in interstitial compounds, for which the size-factor is favourable, usually take up a simple crystal structure, although different from that of the metal in its elementary form (Table 6); there is some latitude in composition. But, those, such as iron carbide, Fe_3C (Fig. 32), in which the size conditions are borderline, form complex structures at fairly fixed compositions; the arrangement of the two kinds of atoms is regular.

The interstitial compounds have high melting points (usually higher than the metal itself) and are very hard and brittle. They are usually conductors. The carbides are of great importance in steels and cemented carbide tools; nitrides are formed in a process for surface-hardening steel.

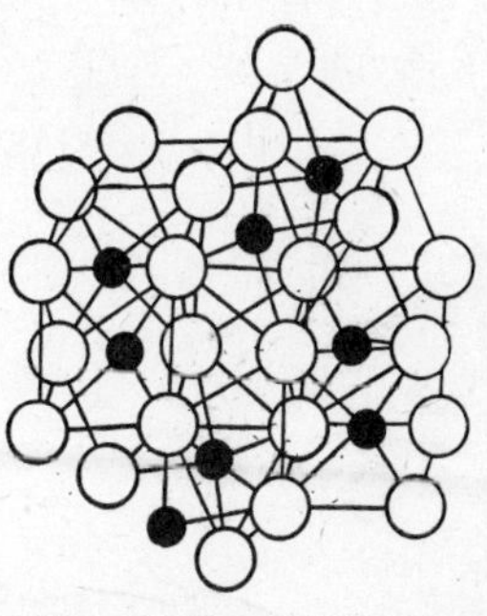

FIG. 32. Crystal structure of cementite (Fe_3C). From *Physics of Metals*, by F. Seitz. McGraw-Hill.

Interstitial compounds are also formed between the small elements and metals other than transition ones, especially the more electro-positive, for example, CaC_2) and BaC_2). Bonding is of valency nature and non-metallic properties are obtained.

TABLE 6. EXAMPLES OF INTERSTITIAL COMPOUNDS (Seitz)

Diameter ratio	
	Hexagonal close-packed
0·32	Ta_2H
0·53	Ta_2C
0·55	Mn_2N
0·55	W_2C
0·56	Cr_2N
0·56	Mo_2C
0·56	Fe_2N
0·58	V_2C
	Body-centred cubic
0·32	TaH
	Simple hexagonal
0·52	MoN
0·58	WC
	Face-centred cubic
0·53	TaC
0·55	Mn_4N
0·56	CrN
0·56	Fe_4N
0·58	VC
0·59	W_2N

All the metals in the above table are body-centred cubic in their ordinary, elementary form at room temperature, except manganese which has a complex structure.

ADDITIONAL READING

The same texts as in Chapter 2 are recommended, and especially No. 1. In addition, note the general references at the end of Chapter 5.

CHAPTER 4

CONSTITUTIONAL DIAGRAMS OF BINARY ALLOYING

It has been seen that a number of constituents may be formed in a complete alloy system. Further, alloys solidify in a variety of ways, giving rise to different configurations of the constituents. In addition, certain constituents may undergo changes in the solid state as the temperature falls after solidification. For example, a solid solution may be stable only at elevated temperatures, and may break down on cooling to form two new constituents. Many systems on which important commercial alloys are based are comparatively complex in these ways.

Hence it is necessary to have some conventional and convenient way of representing clearly and accurately the conditions in both the liquid and solid alloys of a system, the way in which solidification proceeds, and the existence of any solid reactions or changes. The simple diagrams used in Chapter 3 are only suitable for indicating room-temperature conditions. For fuller description of alloy constitution, graphs known as **phase** or **constitutional diagrams**, with temperature plotted vertically against percentage composition, are used. The composition may be expressed in atomic or weight percentage ; in practice, the latter is generally used. Although it is possible to make certain theoretical observations and even predictions, the diagrams are determined experimentally, and thus are subject to modifications as techniques, instrumental accuracies and the purity of metals improve.

The basic method of determination is by thermal analysis, that is, by taking cooling curves on a representative series of alloys in the system. When a cooling alloy changes state, whether to crystallise from the liquid, or to undergo some solid change, heat is evolved (or vice versa on heating). The heat manifests itself as an arrest on the cooling curve, and thus all changes should be indicated. The arrest points may be " boosted " by different methods (Fig. 33). In practice, the thermal analysis must be supplemented by other

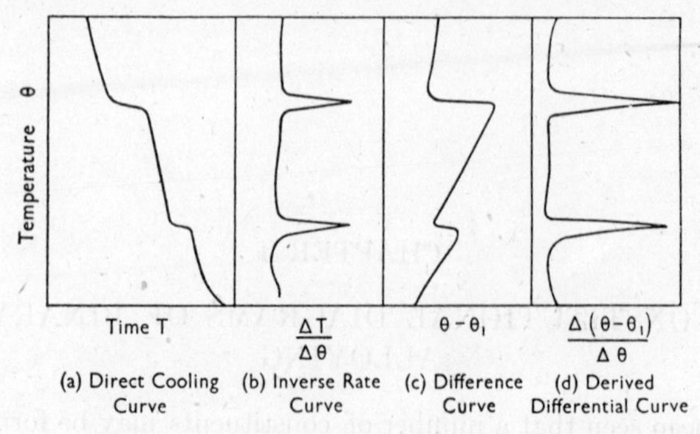

FIG. 33. Types of cooling curves (after Desch). In the difference curves the temperature (θ) of the metal under examination is compared with that (θ_1) of a sample undergoing no change in the range being investigated.

techniques, notably microscopic study and X-ray examination, especially for conditions in the solid state; but, for the present, it will be taken that the complete diagram may be determined by thermal means.

The actual constitutional diagram is constructed from the results of the cooling curves by plotting arrest temperatures against composition, and then joining corresponding points. The completed diagram is composed of a number of zones indexed by temperature and composition (*see* subsequent figs.); each zone contains one or two phases. The vapour phase is usually ignored. In binary systems there may be one or two liquid phases, commonly one; that is, there are conditions of complete liquid miscibility. In the solid state in binary systems, there may be a considerable number of different phases formed at various proportions of the component elements; any specific (stable) alloy will not contain more than two solid phases. Pure metals, solid solutions, and the various intermediate constituents comprise the solid phases. In general, the difference between the solid phases is in their crystal structures, either with respect to pattern or dimensions.

In this book, phase and constituent are used synonomously. The phases are generally indexed by the letters of the Greek alphabet. In one case, the iron-carbon system, the original efforts at giving each phase a proper name are retained, and names such as "ferrite", "austenite", and "cementite" are employed.

A phase or constitutional diagram is made to portray equilibrium conditions; hence an alternative name is **equilibrium diagram.** The stable conditions of equilibrium obtain at any temperature when the phases present are homogeneous, and there is no change with time in their composition. Except at any invariant points when three phases may be present, there should not be any change with time in the relative proportion of the phases present at equilibrium, that is, when there are two. The diagrams are based on an ideal rate of cooling so that equilibrium prevails at any temperature, that is, at equilibrium rate. Similar diagrams are of course used in many other instances to represent equilibrium conditions. Other examples which are of metallurgical interest are those showing the relationship between the constituents of slags, refractories, and salt-bath mixtures. In the same way the connection between liquid alloys and their vapours may be represented, and useful guidance as to the possibility and extent of separation by fractional distillation is obtained from such diagrams.

Interpretation of constitutional diagrams. Constitutional diagrams are the metallurgist's " blueprints ". It is essential, therefore, that the student should learn to read and understand them. Considerable experience and study of standard types of systems are necessary. For any specific result of alloying, or reaction, a characteristic form of constitutional diagram is obtained. Complex diagrams, in which a number of constituents are formed, and in which a number of reactions proceed, may be analysed part by part from knowledge of the basic forms.

In practice, alloys are rarely cooled at equilibrium rate, and considerable divergences from the conditions indicated by the equilibrium diagrams are frequently caused. Thus it is necessary also to examine closely such departures, so that the diagrams may be of practical service.

The essential basic types of diagrams necessary for the interpretation of binary systems in which there is *complete liquid miscibility* will now be described. The matter will be under two headings, namely (*a*) basic modes of solidification ; and (*b*) changes in the solid state. In the general cases, the boundary lines in the diagrams are often drawn straight, although usually in specific cases (and theoretically) they are curved. The treatment should be amplified by practical micro-examination of typical alloys of each standard type.

(*a*) BASIC MODES OF SOLIDIFICATION

The following discussion of solidification will follow the same classification as used in Chapter 3.

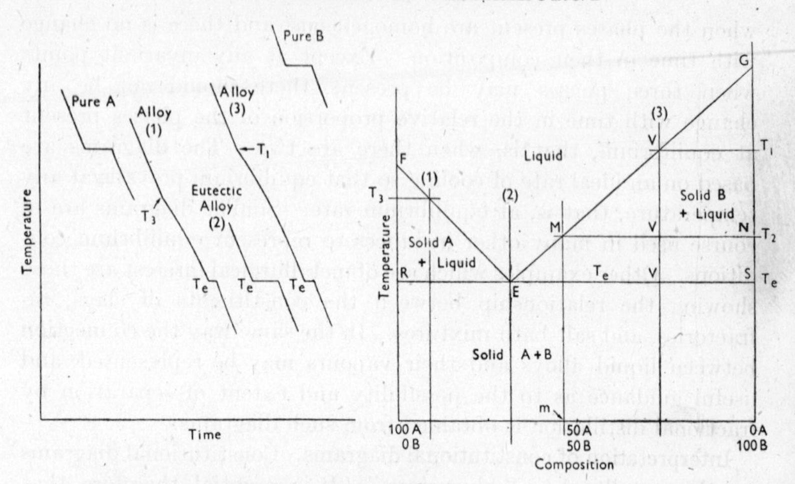

FIG. 34. Constitutional diagram for conditions of complete liquid miscibility and complete solid immiscibility (examples: tin-zinc and bismuth-cadmium), with typical cooling curves shown on the left. *FEG* is known as the liquidus and *RES* as the solidus.

(1) **Complete solid immiscibility.** One form of diagram is obtained (Fig. 34). No major changes occur in the solid state in such systems, although polymorphic transformations, for example, may occur in one or other of the pure metal constituents. *RES* is a horizontal, the value of which varies according to the particular system concerned, likewise the slopes and configurations of *FE* and *GE*.

To explain this type of system it is necessary to describe the cooling and solidification of three compositions. *Alloy* 2 is a specific composition varying for each system; it is known as the **eutectic alloy**, and solidifies at a constant temperature, the eutectic temperature, which is lower than that of either of the component pure metals. At the eutectic temperature the two pure metals crystallise together to give a characteristically fine aggregate (Fig. 35); usually neither shows the dendritic form.

Alloy 3 is typical of compositions between *E* and *S*: solidification begins at temperature T_1, when dendrites of pure *B* start growing. These dendrites are of random orientation, and continue growing while the temperature falls to T_e, that is, the eutectic temperature. With the crystallisation of the pure *B*, the composition of the remaining liquid is proportionately increased in *A*. The actual composition of the liquid changes along *VE* with fall in temperature. *At any intermediate temperature* T_2, *the composition of the liquid is m, and the proportion by weight of liquid to solid B is in the ratio*

$VN : VM$; the foregoing expresses the form of *two rules*, which can be applied with discrimination to the interpretation of constitutional diagrams for equilibrium conditions. The rules can be shown to follow from the nature of the diagrams; their application will be further illustrated in subsequent examples.

When the eutectic temperature is reached, the alloy consists of dendrites of B and liquid of eutectic composition in the proportion, $B : \text{liquid} = VE : VS$. While the temperature stays constant, the remaining liquid solidifies with the eutectic arrangement of A and B between the dendrites of B (Fig. 35). The shape of the dendrites varies according to the elements concerned (and also the rate of cooling). It should be noted that all alloys in the system finish solidifying at the same temperature; hence the horizontal line in the diagram. The only differences in behaviour between the various alloys in the range E to S are the temperature at which solidification commences, and the proportions of dendrites of B to the eutectic mixture.

Alloy 1 (typical of compositions between R and E) solidifies similarly to alloy 3 except that dendrites of A are formed.

In alloys composed of an aggregate of two constituents, as occur in the present case, it is advisable to distinguish between the use of

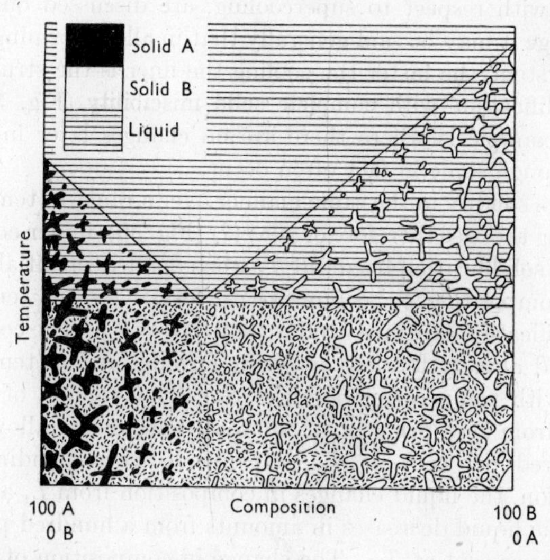

FIG. 35. Sketch showing microstructures in simple eutectic system. Note: the photographs in Fig. 42 and 43, although of alloys involving solid solutions, are typical of eutectic systems and should be compared with this sketch.

the terms " grain " and " crystal ". The solidification of a eutectic alloy starts from a number of centres, and when complete the structure consists of grains of eutectic. If the structure is examined in such a way that the separate constituents are not resolved, as by eye or at a low power, all that will be seen will be an aggregate of grains similar to a pure metal. Examination under a higher power will reveal the internal arrangement of the two types of crystals in the grains. When the structure consists of dendrites plus a small amount of eutectic, each grain usually contains one dendrite surrounded by a certain amount of associated eutectic. The usual indication of the grain boundary in such cases is a coarsening of the eutectic structure, although sometimes a boundary groove may result from etching. When substantial amounts of eutectic are present, some grains may be composed only of eutectic, whereas others contain a dendrite as well. In certain instances the structure may show a dendrite running through a number of grains of eutectic.

In the case of two-phase alloys, therefore, it is suggested that " grain " be used for the polyhedral shapes, and " crystal " for the ultimate micro-particles. In pure metals and single-phase alloys, the terms " grain " and " crystal " are interchangeable.

The patterns found in eutectics, and the effect of fast cooling, especially with respect to supercooling, are discussed on page 67. At this stage it may be said generally that in alloys forming a simple eutectic system, the faster the cooling the finer is the structure.

(2) **Solidification with complete solid miscibility** (Fig. 36). The simplest example is where there are no changes later in the solid state, although some in fact often occur.

All alloys solidify in the same manner over a range of temperature. Considering the case therefore of *alloy* (2) (Fig. 36), under equilibrium conditions solidification begins at T_1 when dendrites, initially of solid solution composition S_1, commence to form. As the temperature falls, solidification continues and is complete at T_3. The composition of the solid already formed, and that forming at any temperature, changes with temperature along S_1S_3. The volume of the solid increases from zero per cent of the total bulk of the alloy at T_1 to one hundred per cent at T_3. Meanwhile, corresponding to this solidification, the liquid changes in composition from L_1 at T_1 to L_3 at T_3. The liquid decreases in amounts from a hundred per cent at T_1 to zero per cent at T_3. The change in composition of the liquid is due to the solidification from it, and the absorption of A by the existing solid so as to change its composition in accordance with S_1S_3. Thus at T_3 the alloy is solid, and consists of homogeneous

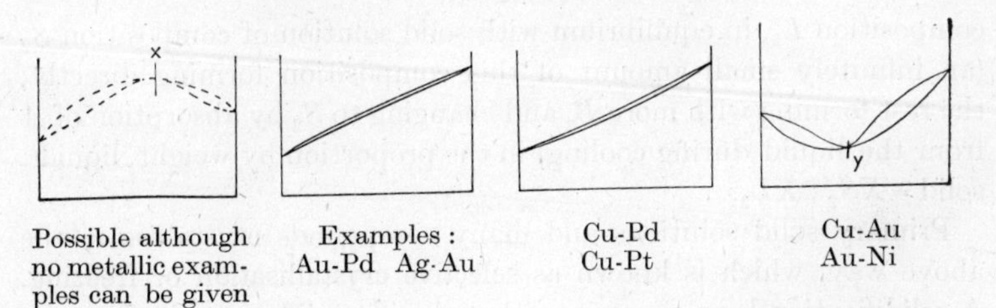

Alternative forms (compositions x and y crystallise at constant temperature).

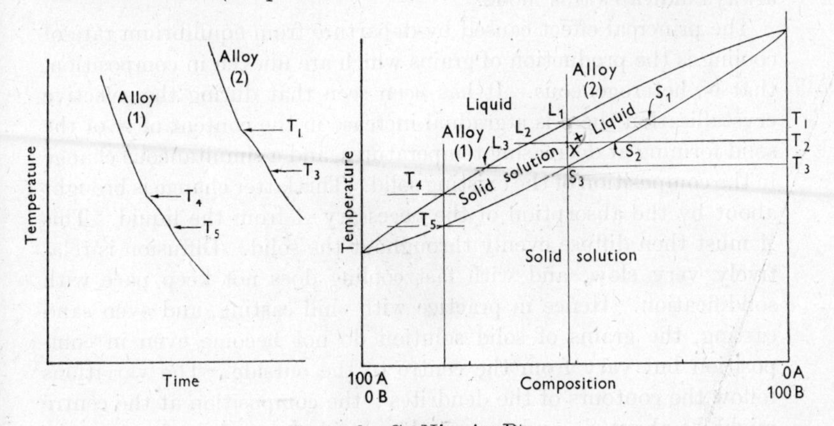

Examples Cu-Ni; Au-Pt.

FIG. 36. Cooling curves and constitutional diagrams for conditions of complete liquid and solid miscibility.

grains of solid solution, which ideally show no trace of their dendritic mode of growth, nor of the compositional changes with temperature (Figs. 37, 38*c*, 40*b*). At any intermediate temperature between T_1 and T_3, say T_2, the alloy consists of liquid solution of

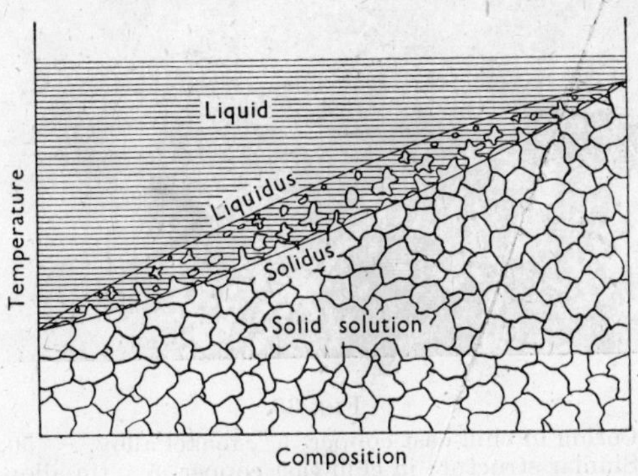

FIG. 37. Sketch illustrating microstructures in solid solution alloys.

composition L_2, in equilibrium with solid solution of composition S_2 (an infinitely small amount of this composition forming directly, the rest forming with more B, and changing to S_2 by absorption of A from the liquid during cooling) in the proportion by weight, liquid : solid $= XS_2 : XL_2$.

Primary solid solutions and many compounds crystallise in the above way, which is known as **selective crystallisation** or **freezing.** A solidification loop or range with a sloping solidus on the diagram always indicates this mode.

The principal effect caused by departure from equilibrium rate of cooling is the production of grains which are uneven in composition, that is, heterogeneous. It has been seen that during the selective crystallisation there is a gradual increase in the content of A of the solid forming at decreasing temperatures, and a simultaneous change in the composition of the existing solid. This latter change is brought about by the absorption of the necessary A from the liquid. This A must then diffuse evenly throughout the solid. Diffusion is relatively very slow, and with fast cooling does not keep pace with solidification. Hence in practice with chill casting, and even sand casting, the grains of solid solution do not become even in composition but vary from the centre to the outside. The variations follow the contours of the dendrites ; the composition at the centre might be about S_1, and that at the outside beyond L_3, for not only will liquid exist at T_3, but it will also contain more A than L_3. On polishing and etching the alloy, the various compositions are

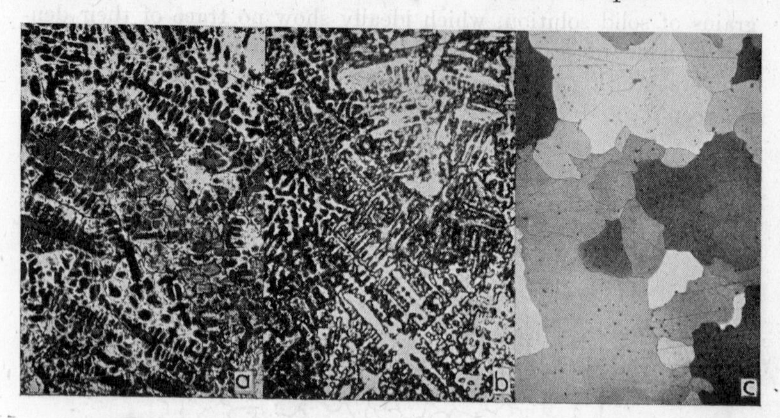

FIG. 38.
(*a*) Coring in chill-cast copper- 5% nickel alloy. × 50.
(*b*) Similar structure in chill-cast copper- 5% tin alloy. × 50.
(*c*) As (*b*), but annealed at 800° C. for 4 hours. × 50.

attacked differently, and the dendritic manner of growth revealed. The grains are said to be **cored** (Figs. 38–40), and such a structure is typical of a solid solution in the cast state in practice.

A cored structure is mildly unstable, but is usually retained indefinitely at room temperature, because little or no diffusion occurs at this temperature, and cooling to room temperature is rapid after solidification. However, at elevated temperatures in the solid state, when appreciable diffusion can occur, coring eventually disappears without change in the boundary configuration of the grains (Fig. 38*c* and 40*b*). Hot-working, or cold-working and annealing, remove coring, although a new set of grains is formed by these treatments.

It is apparent that infinitely fast cooling as well as slow cooling should produce no coring. Instantaneous solidification would give a supercooled liquid, or crystalline solid with infinitely small grains, with fairly even distribution of the two kinds of atoms. The maximum amount of coring would appear to be obtained in either sand or chill casting, depending on the metals concerned. The appearance varies, according to the rate of cooling and the metals in question, from sharp stages to gradual changes. Sometimes the contours revealed are more cellular than dendritic. A wide freezing range indicates considerable tendency to coring. As the solidifica-

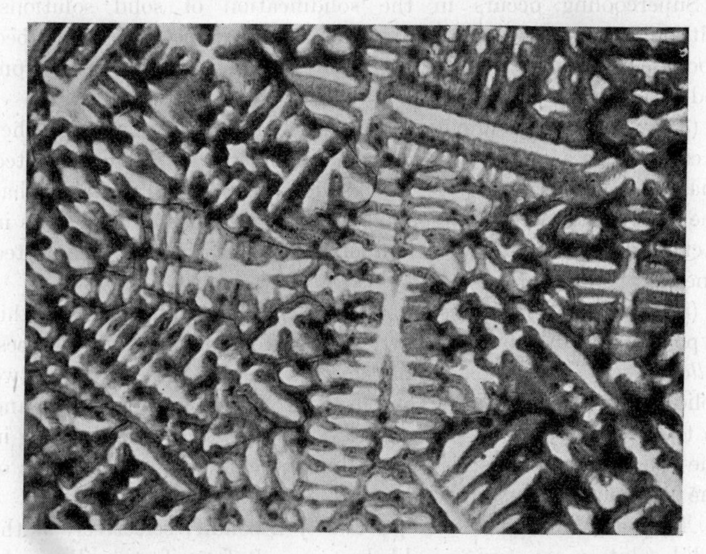

FIG. 39. Coring in 70/30 copper-zinc alloy, chill-cast. ×75. (It should be noted that the examples given in Figs. 38 (*b*), (*c*), 39 and 40 are terminal solid solutions.)

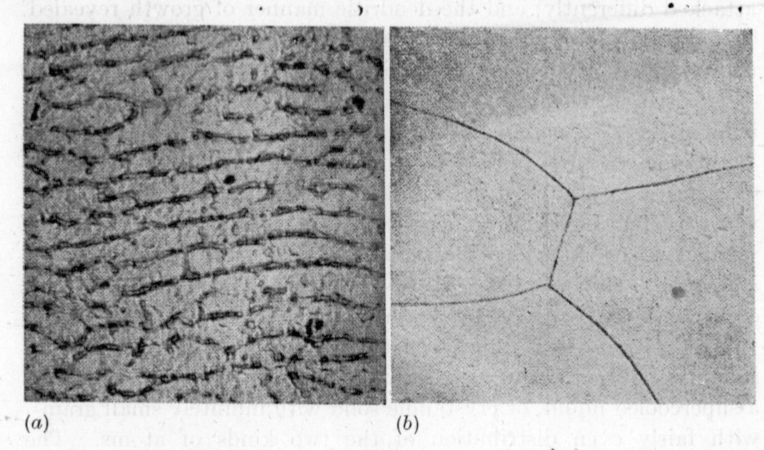
(a) (b)

FIG. 40.
(a) Coring in chill-cast solid solution of antimony in tin. × 250.
(b) Similar phase after annealing. × 50.
From D. Hanson and W. T. Pell-Walpole, *J. Inst. Metals*, 1936, **58**, 304.

tion loop approaches the horizontal, coring is likely to become pronounced, even though the loop may be narrow.

Supercooling occurs in the solidification of solid solutions. Although it modifies the temperatures and compositions described above, no marked structural alterations are to be noted, apart from reduction in the grain size.

(3) **Partial solid solubility** (no intermediate constituents). Either a eutectic or a peritectic reaction is involved. It should be noted that, in the following discussion of solidification, it will be taken that the respective maximum solid solubilities are constant, whereas in fact they usually vary with temperature as indicated by the dotted lines in the diagrams.

(i) *A eutectic occurs* (Figs. 41, 42 and 43). The interpretation of this type of diagram should be fairly apparent from the previous types. *Alloy E* solidifies at a constant temperature as a eutectic of the two solid solutions, α and β, of compositions X and Y respectively, and in the proportion $\alpha : \beta = EY : EX$. It is not usual to find coring in the solid-solution crystals comprising the eutectic; the fineness of the structure increases with the rate of cooling.

Alloys in the range O to X per cent of B solidify selectively as the solid solution α; coring is likely to result from fast cooling. In addition, in those compositions approaching X, fast cooling may cause the introduction of some eutectic into the structure. As a result of the fast cooling, coring occurs, and the liquid is thus enriched in B to the extent of the eutectic composition, so that some eutectic does form. Long reheating in the solid state after solidification will cause the disappearance of the eutectic.

Alloys between Y and 100 *per cent B* solidify in a similar manner to form the solid solution β. It should be noted that the dendrites first forming in the case of α alloys are richer in A than the average composition of the alloy, whereas with β alloys the material initially crystallising is rich in B. This difference also applies in cases of complete solubility when there is a minimum (vice versa for a maximum) on the curve (Fig. 36).

Alloys between X and E solidify as dendrites of α surrounded by

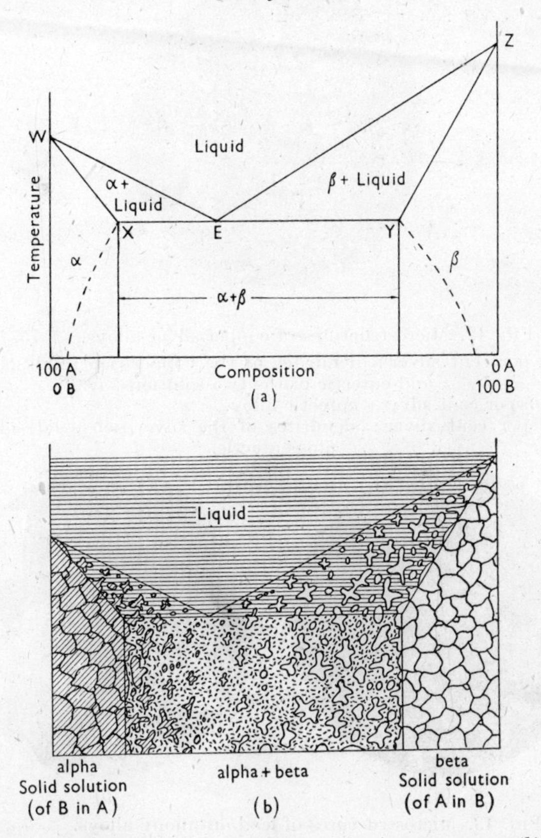

FIG. 41. Constitutional diagram (*a*) and microstructures (*b*) for a system in which there is complete liquid solubility and partial solid solubility. Examples are the Cu-Ag, Pb-Sn and Pb-Sb systems. The liquidus is *WEZ* and the solidus, *WXEYZ*.

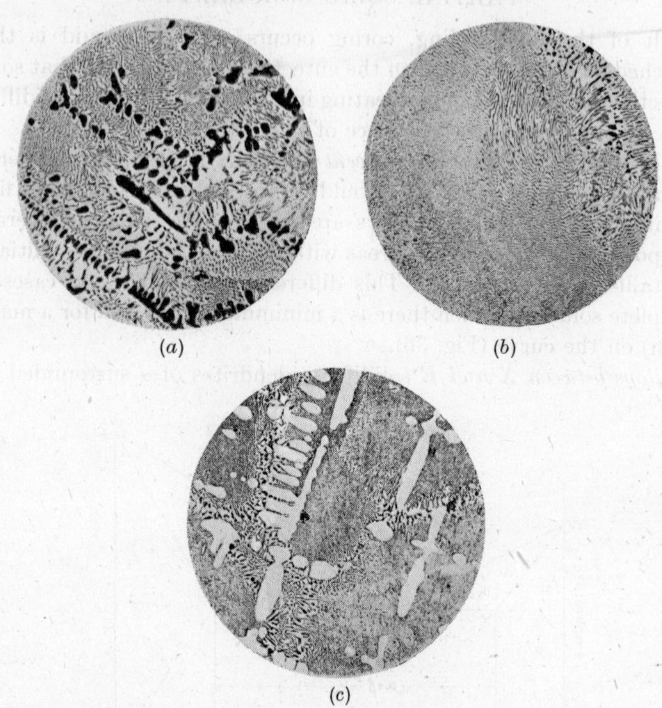

FIG. 42. Microstructures of copper-silver alloys. ×75.
(*a*) 60 per cent silver: dendrites of the copper-rich solid solution and eutectic of the two solutions.
(*b*) 71·5 per cent silver: eutectic alloy.
(*c*) 76 per cent silver: dendrites of the silver-rich solid solution plus eutectic.

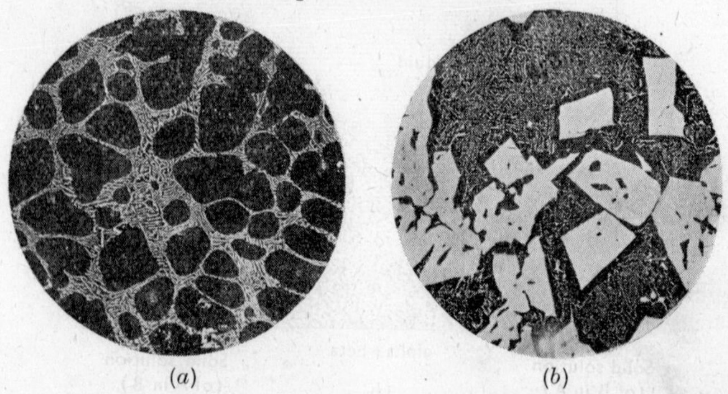

FIG. 43. Microstructures of lead-antimony alloys. ×75.
By courtesy of C. R. Groves.
(*a*) Contains 5 per cent antimony and shows lead-rich dendrites plus eutectic.
(*b*) Contains 25 per cent antimony, the structure being primary antimony-base crystals together with eutectic.

the eutectic of $\alpha + \beta$. Both the primary α and eutectic α are of composition X, and the eutectic β of composition Y. The α dendrites grow selectively until the liquid reaches eutectic composition. Fast cooling will cause coring in the dendrites, and as a result of the enrichment of the liquid composition with B, a larger proportion of eutectic than indicated by equilibrium conditions is likely to be formed. *Alloys between E and Y* crystallise in a corresponding manner.

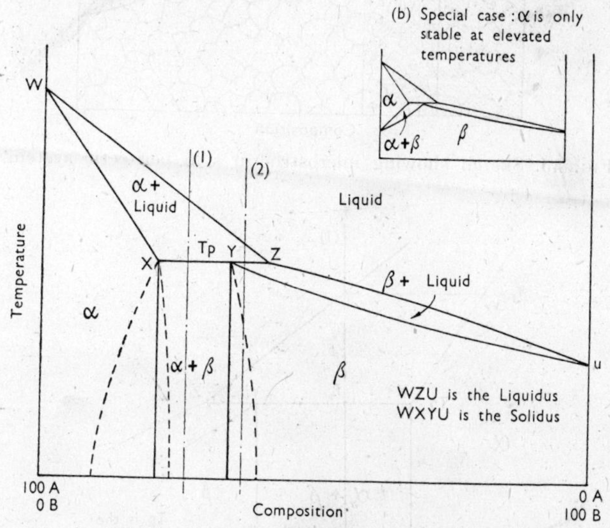

FIG. 44. Constitutional diagram representing complete liquid solubility and partial solid solubility (peritectic type).

(ii) *A peritectic occurs* (Figs. 44 and 45). Another kind of reaction is involved, which occurs at the same temperature in all alloys between X and Z; hence the horizontal line at Tp, the **peritectic temperature.** The reaction will be best understood from a description of the cooling and solidification of typical alloys involving the peritectic. For this purpose, alloys (1) and (2) may be followed. *Alloys containing between* 0 *and X per cent B* solidify selectively as the solid solution α, and *between Z and* 100 *per cent B* as solid solution β. Fast cooling will cause coring, and may cause the introduction of some β into the α-alloys, which approach X per cent B.

In *alloy* (1) which is typical of compositions between X and Y, (Fig. 46) solidification commences at T_1 and dendrites of α, initially of composition W, begin forming. Selective crystallisation of α continues down to T_p, the peritectic temperature; when the alloy

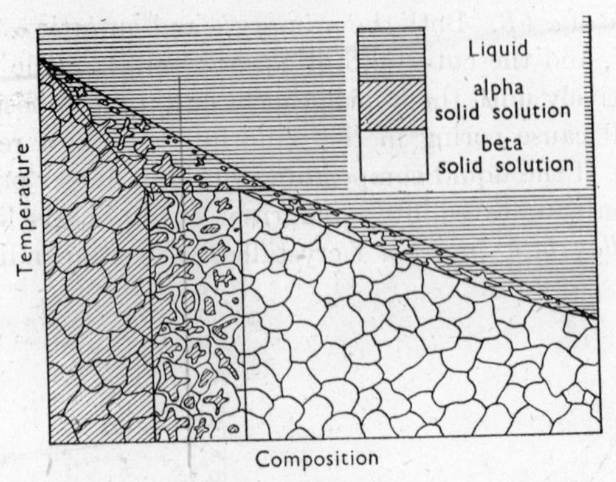

FIG. 45. Sketch showing microstructures in peritectic system.

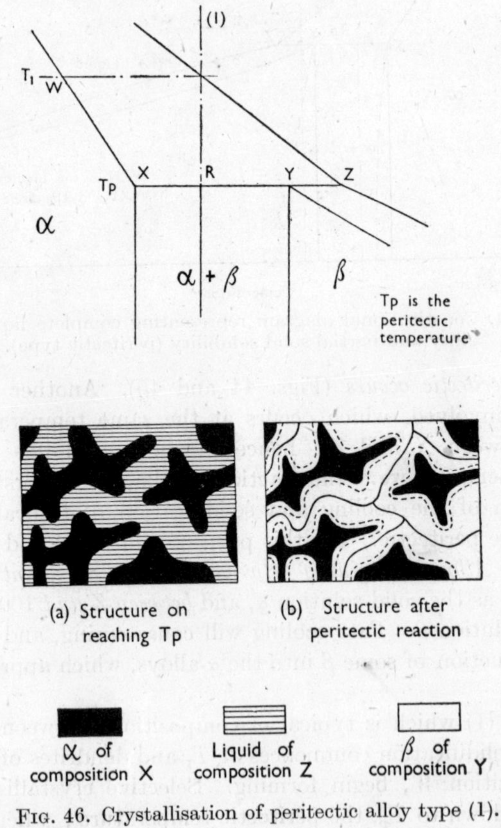

FIG. 46. Crystallisation of peritectic alloy type (1).

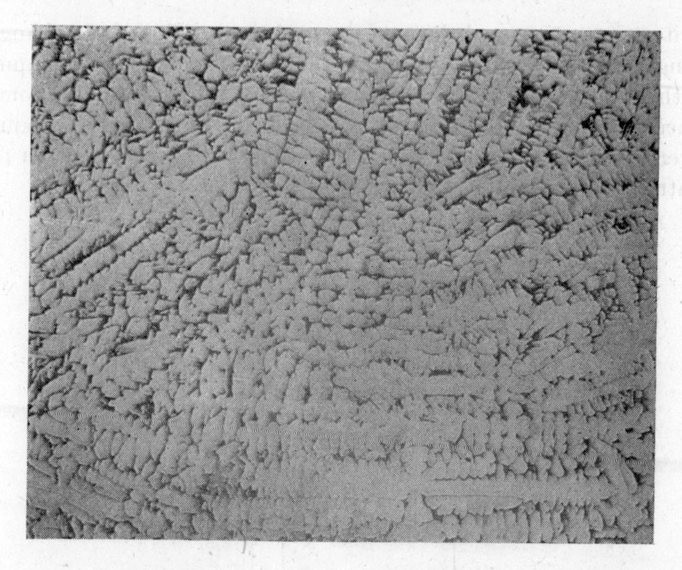

FIG. 47. Structure of an $\alpha - \beta$ brass (Cu65/Zn35); dendrites of α (light) with β (dark) produced by a peritectic reaction. $\times 50$.

reaches this temperature it is composed of solid α-dendrites of composition X and liquid of composition Z in the proportion α : liquid $= RZ : RX$. Then at T_p the peritectic reaction takes place, and all the remaining liquid reacts with some of the α-dendrites to form β of composition Y. The final structure consists of dendrites of α with a partial or complete network of the β; the proportion is $\alpha : \beta = RY : RX$ (Fig. 47). The main effects of fast cooling are to produce coring in the α and an intermediate zone between the α and β, for apart from the solid/liquid interface the reaction depends on solid diffusion, as well as there being rearrangement often of the atoms in changing from the α- to the β-pattern. The proportion of β will be increased by fast cooling.

The first stage in the solidification of *alloy* (2) (Fig. 48) is the same as in alloy (1): solidification begins at T_2 and when the peritectic is reached, the alloy consists similarly of dendrites of α, of composition X, and liquid of composition Z, but in the proportions α : liquid $= SZ : SX$. In this case, at the peritectic temperature, all the α reacts with some of the liquid to form β of composition Y; the proportion of β to remaining liquid is $SZ : SY$. After the peritectic reaction has occurred, the temperature falls and from T_p to T_3 the rest of the liquid solidifies directly, although selectively, as β, on that already formed. The composition of the β formed by the peritectic reaction, and that afterwards between T_p and T_3, changes along YU by absorption and diffusion inwards of B from the liquid, so that under equilibrium conditions at T_3 the structure is homogeneous grains of β of composition S. Fast cooling tends to produce heterogeneous grains and may cause some α to be retained in the centre of the grains.

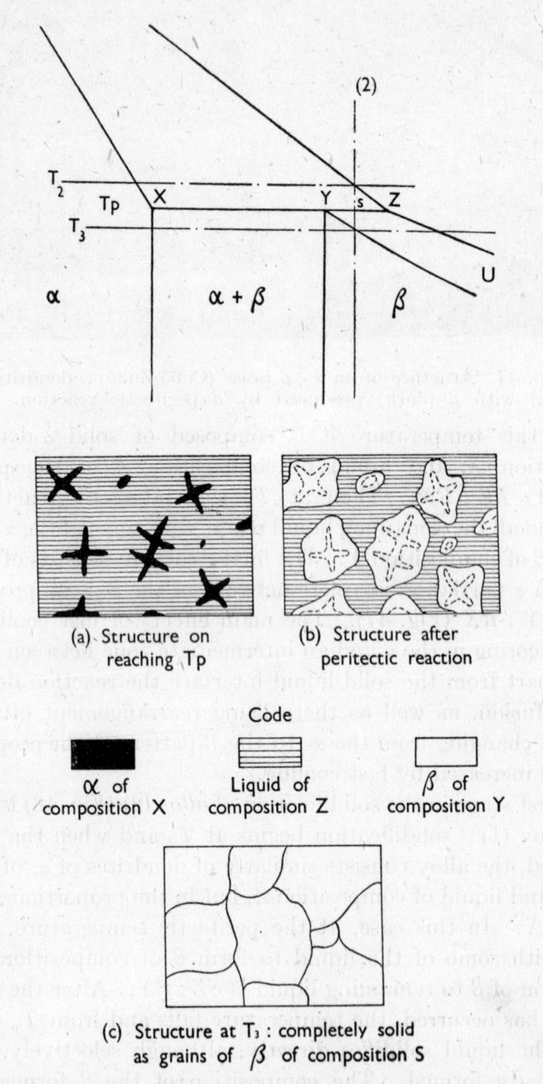

FIG. 48. Crystallisation of peritectic alloy type (2).

The silver-platinum system has an equilibrium diagram of the foregoing type, although changes occur eventually in the solid state ; the same remarks apply to the indium-thallium system. The iron-nickel and iron-manganese diagrams have the form shown in Fig. 44*b*, which yields a range of complete solid solubility, although in the two examples at lower temperatures in the solid state a change occurs again giving two phases.

There are numerous examples of peritectics in more complex diagrams, the peritectic involving a solid solution and a compound or two compounds.

(4) **Systems in which intermediate constituents are formed.** These involve eutectics and peritectics ; some general examples are given below. Apart from indicating changes in solid solubility, the examples do not involve solid changes as these have not yet been discussed. The same effects as already described are produced in these systems by fast cooling.

The simplest example is the case where one compound of restricted composition occurs and there is no primary solid solubility, a eutectic being formed between each pure metal and the compound at E_1 and E_2, respectively (Fig. 49). *Alloys between* 0 *and* E_1 *per cen* B solidify as dendrites of A plus eutectic of A and compound, and *between* E_2 *and* 100 *per cent* B as dendrites of B and eutectic of B and compound. In those alloys which crystallise as primary compound plus eutectic, the primary compound may be present in the

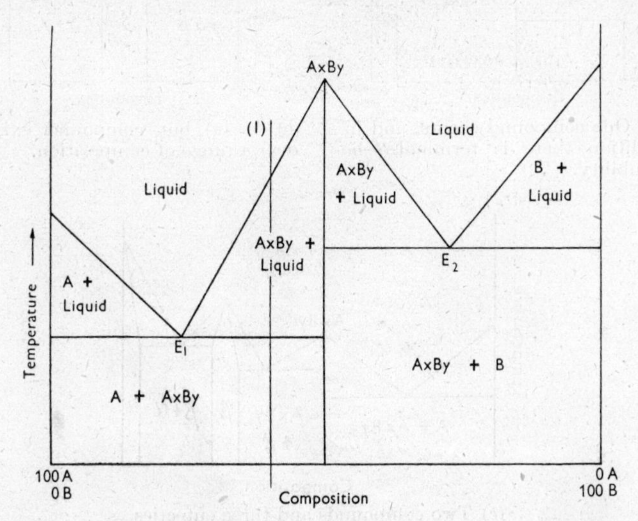

FIG. 49. Equilibrium diagram for system containing a compound.

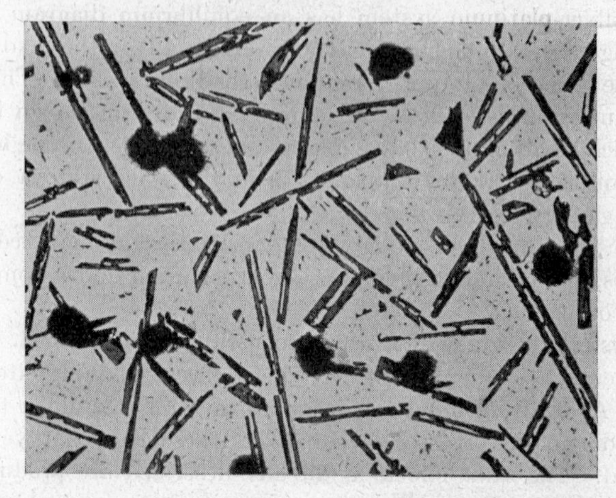

FIG. 50. Primary AlSb in a background of not clearly formed eutectic of AlSb and antimony. ×100. Alloy contains 90 per cent antimony and is of type (1) Fig. 49. The rounded black areas are porosity.

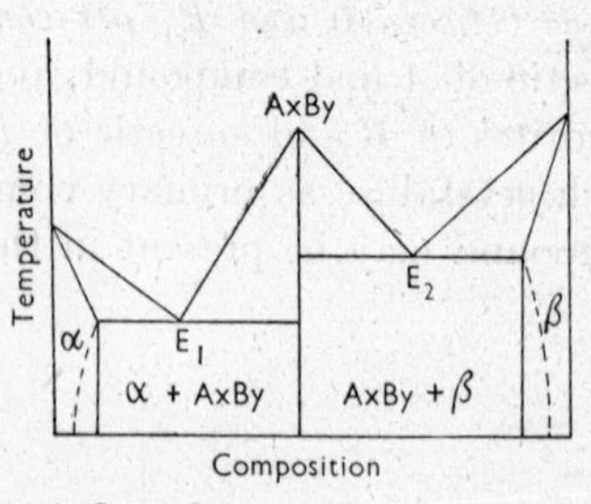

(*a*) One compound occurs, and in addition there is terminal solic solubility.

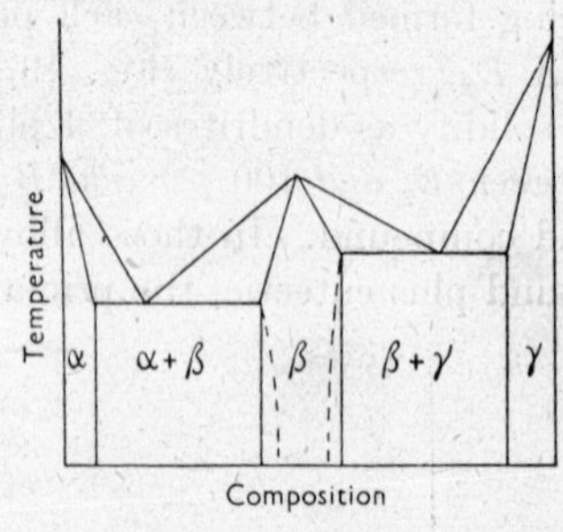

(*b*) As (*a*) but compound exists over a range of composition.

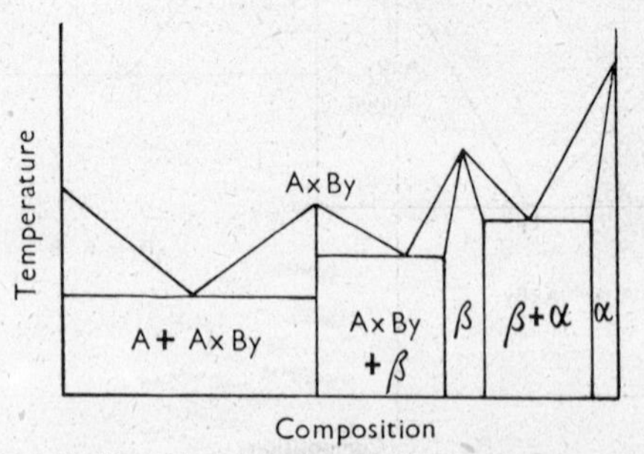

(*c*) Two compounds and three eutectics

FIG. 51. Further examples of equilibrium diagrams involving compounds.

dendritic form, or may assume a more regular shape with plane faces (Fig. 50).

There is little complication introduced by the occurrence of terminal solid solubility in such a system (Fig. 51*a*), or when, in addition, the compound exists over a range of composition (Fig. 51*b*). It will be seen in the latter case that, apart from the composition corresponding to the maximum on the liquidus, the compound solidifies selectively. The magnesium-tin, magnesium-lead, magnesium-silicon, magnesium-calcium, cadmium-antimony, barium-lead and aluminium-antimony systems are examples of one or other of the above modifications. In a similar manner, there may occur two compounds and three eutectics (Fig. 51*c*), examples being the copper-magnesium, silver-lithium and beryllium-nickel systems.

The occurrence of peritectic reactions is illustrated in Fig. 52. These diagrams can be interpreted by the method already described. However, for guidance the solidification of alloy x (Fig. 52*a*) and alloy y (Fig. 52*b*) will be described. *Alloy x* starts to solidify at T_1 by the growth of crystals of γ solid solution. At T_p the alloy consists of liquid of composition X and γ of composition P: the peritectic reaction occurs, yielding β (composition Z) and reducing the amount of liquid. As the temperature falls to T_e more β crystallises

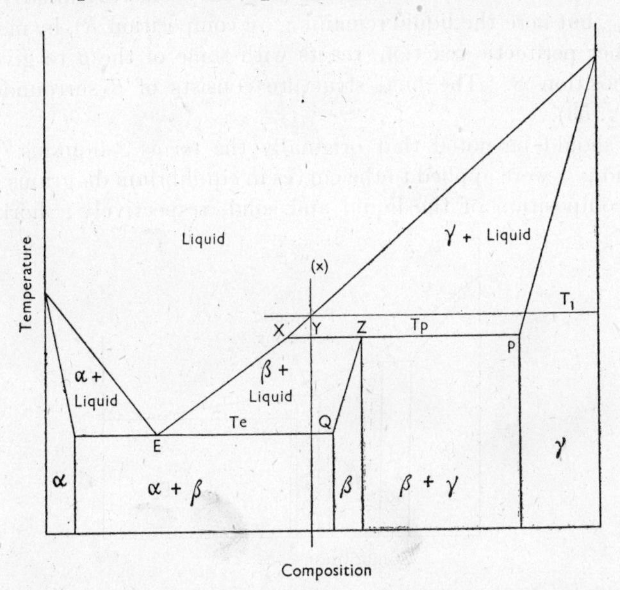

FIG. 52. Systems involving compounds and peritectic reactions.
(*a*) Example: Bi-Pb

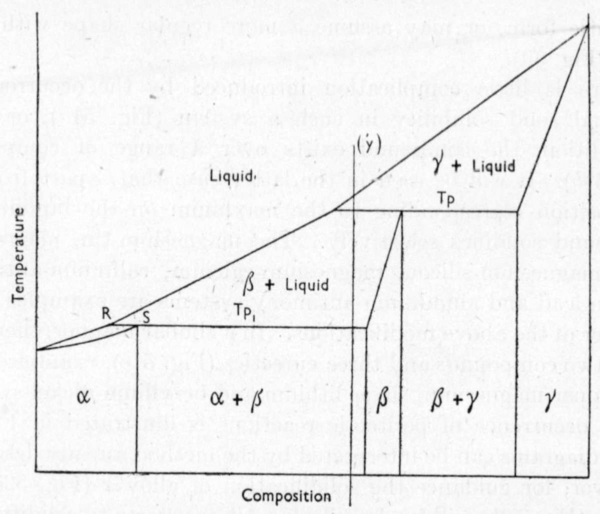

FIG. 52. Systems involving compounds and peritectic reactions.
(*b*) Examples : Sn-Sb ; In-Pb.

and at the same time all the β changes in composition along ZQ and the liquid along XE ; at T_e the remainder of the liquid crystallises as eutectic of α and β. *Alloy y* (Fig. 52*b*) behaves similarly down to T_{p_1}, but here the liquid remaining (of composition R), by means of another peritectic reaction, reacts with some of the β to give α of composition S. The final structure consists of β surrounded by α (Fig. 53).

It should be noted that originally the terms " liquidus " and " solidus " were applied to the curves in equilibrium diagrams giving the composition of the liquid and solid, respectively ; horizontal

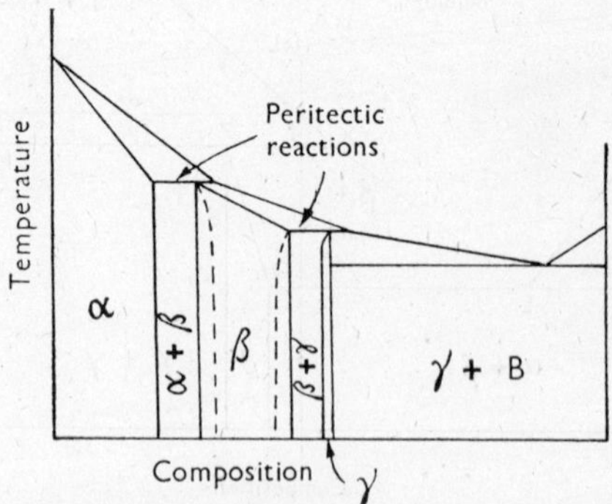

FIG. 52. Systems involving compounds and peritectic reactions.
(*c*) Example : Sn-Ag.

FIG. 53. Tin-antimony alloy showing compound crystals (white) in a background of solid solution. ×200. The Sn-Sb system is of the type shown in Fig. 52*b*, but the present composition lies just to the right of *S*. From D. Hanson and W. T. Pell-Walpole, *J. Inst. Metals*, 1936, **58**, 304.

lines then being tie lines. However, metallurgists now generally use the terms in connection with the beginning and end of solidification, or conversely of melting.

BINARY EUTECTICS AND THEIR STRUCTURES

Binary eutectics solidify at constant temperatures, and yield characteristic microstructures consisting of an intimate mechanical mixture of the two composite phases, the structure being relatively fine. The actual eutectic freezing point is lower than that of either of the constituents. The proportion of the phases in the eutectic varies, depending on the specific eutectic composition. In some cases the eutectic composition approaches extremely close to that of one of the constituents, with the eutectic temperature not much below the melting point of the adjacent constituent; the eutectic then consists largely of one phase.

It has been seen that an alloy system may contain one or more eutectics, and that they may be formed between pure metals, solid solutions, and intermediate constituents or some combination. An interesting case is that of the eutectic in the iron-carbon system at 4·3 per cent carbon (Fig. 231, 232*a* and 233, p. 316), which crystallises as a mixture of solid solution and compound; later, the solid solution decomposes, forming a eutectoid structure within the eutectic. A similar eutectic is found in the copper-aluminium system at 8·5 per cent aluminium (Fig. 383, p. 502).

In eutectic structures one phase usually appears as matrix with the other imbedded in it. The matrix of each eutectic grain has a continuous orientation, and it may be taken that if the imbedded phase is in separate crystals in one grain, these have at least some similarity of orientation, and that there is a relationship between the orientation of the two phases. No rigid classification of eutectic structures is possible, for they are affected by the conditions of solidification, such as the presence of nuclei or primary crystals of one of the constituents, the rate of cooling, the viscosity of the molten alloy, surface tension and the crystal structure of the components. It is quite common for there to be a fairly irregular structure although a number of more regular patterns are obtained (Fig. 54); a properly laminated structure is uncommon. The patterns obtained suggest that there must be different ways of crystallisation of the two constituents, such as, alternate, and simultaneous.

Eutectics are prone to undercooling, when finer structures result. The aluminium-silicon eutectic is also considerably refined by the addition of small amounts of sodium to the melt (leaving of the order of 0·015 per cent sodium in the metal). The treatment is known as **modification**, and the mechanical properties are greatly improved by the refinement of structure. The actual behaviour of the sodium is not known, but it has been suggested that existing solid nuclei are rendered ineffective by a molten coating produced by the sodium, thus

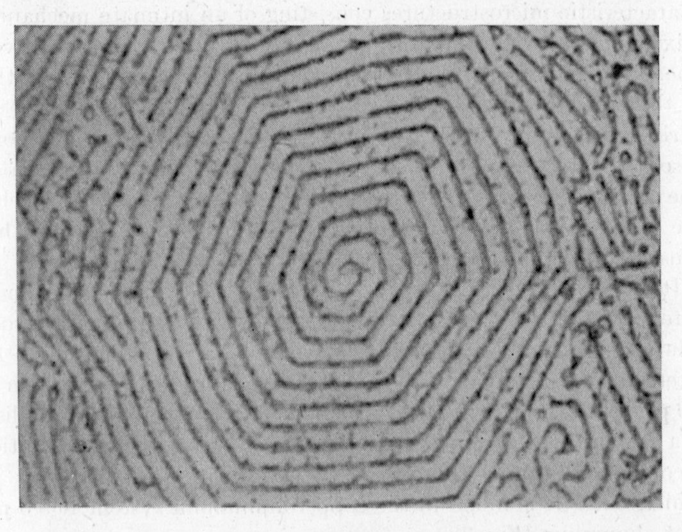

FIG. 54 (*a*). Zn–(Mg_2Zn_{11}?) eutectic. ×2500.
By courtesy of the British Non-Ferrous Metals Research Association.

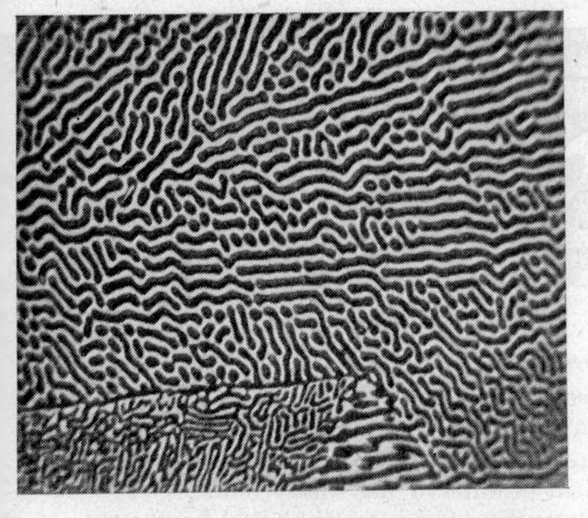

(*b*). Mg-Mg_2Cu eutectic. ×250. From W. R. D. Jones, *J. Inst. Metals*, 1931, **46**, 310.

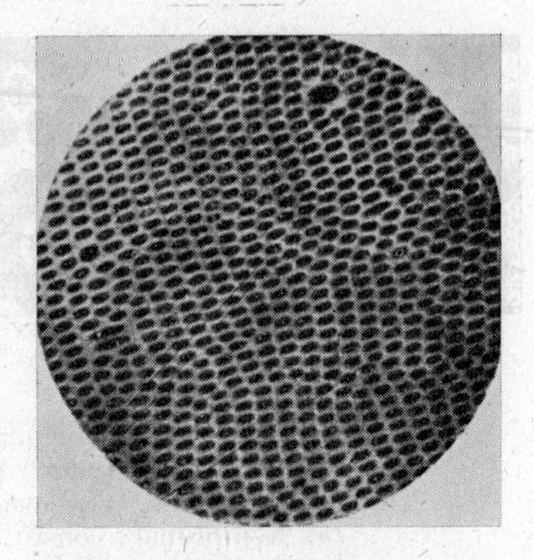

(*c*) Cu-Cu_2Sb eutectic. ×30.

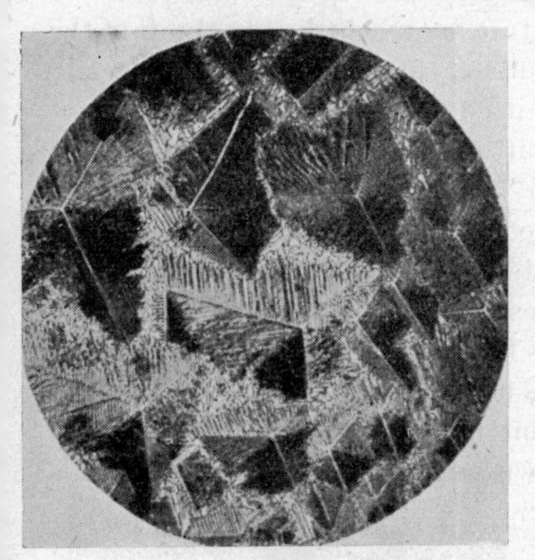

(*d*) Ag_3Sb-Sb eutectic. ×100.

(*e*) Pb-Sn eutectic. ×50.

Figs. *c*, *d* and *e* are from A. M. Portevin, *J. Inst. Metals*, 1923, **39**, 256.

FIG. 54. Eutectic structures.

permitting undercooling with consequent fine crystallisation. Among other theories, one proposed by Thall and Chalmers is based on interfacial tensions during solidification. The iron-graphite eutectic in grey cast iron is refined in a comparable manner; and also by superheating, which apparently allows separation of existing inclusions that might produce coarse crystallisation.

The supercooling of one constituent of the eutectic often leads to some degeneration of the structure. The effects are especially to be noticed in alloys, apart from the specific eutectic composition. During the first stages of solidification, dendrites or primary shapes

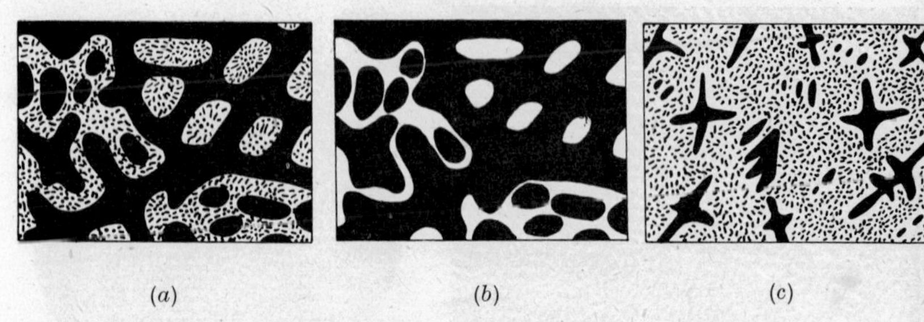

FIG. 55. Sketches showing effect of undercooling on microstructures of alloys in a eutectic series.
(a) Structure to be expected from equilibrium diagram.
(b) Non-primary constituent of eutectic has undercooled.
(c) As (b), but when larger amounts of eutectic should be present.

of the excess constituent (say B) form in the liquid ; and, when the eutectic composition and temperature are reached, only the B of the eutectic crystallises, being inoculated by the dendrites already present. This eutectic B attaches itself to the dendrites and does not form separate crystals. As a result, the liquid becomes supercooled with respect to the other eutectic constituent, say A. Eventually this A must crystallise spontaneously. If the alloy in question should only contain small amounts of eutectic, it is common for all the eutectic B to join the dendrites, and the supercooled A solidifies as a network around the dendrites (Fig. 55*b*). When larger amounts of eutectic are present, the result is usually a network of A separating the overlarge dendrites of B from the eutectic (Fig. 55*c*). In the latter case, the A forms on its own until the liquid composition is

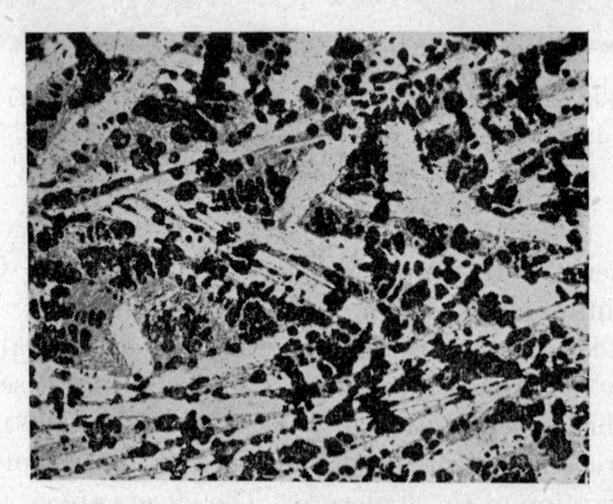

FIG. 56. White cast iron, showing two constituents in primary form (dark and white), together with eutectic. ×100. For normal structures, see Figs. 232*a* and 233, p. 317).

restored to the eutectic, when both the remaining A and B crystallise intimately. In extreme cases the spontaneously crystallising supercooled A may grow separate dendrites, and thus produce a structure not indicated at all by the constitutional diagram, consisting of dendrites of both constituents together with some eutectic; this structure may also be produced in the actual eutectic alloy. Further, the phenomenon may give rise to a coarse structure in the eutectic if none of the liquid crystallises in the characteristic eutectic manner. The author has observed two constituents in the primary form together with some eutectic in lead-antimony alloys and in white cast-iron (Fig. 56).

(*b*) CHANGES IN SOLID ALLOYS

These changes of structure are reversible; but unless the rate of change of temperature is very gradual, there is likely to be noticeable lag. Further, with rapid cooling, changes may not go to completion and equilibrium, and some metastable condition may be retained indefinitely at room temperature.

Diffusion is involved in a number of instances and its mechanism will therefore be briefly described before proceeding to details of the changes. **Solid diffusion** is the movement of atoms (metallic or non-metallic) through a crystal or polycrystal; in the case of metallic alloys it occurs in solid solutions and compounds: foreign atoms may diffuse in a pure metal provided they are soluble in it. Gases must dissociate into the atomic state before they can diffuse, and thus compound gases cannot diffuse as such. In many cases appreciable diffusion only occurs at elevated temperatures; the rate increases with increase of temperature.

From the two forms of alloying arise the two modes of diffusion, namely, **interstitial** and **substitutional diffusion.** In interstitial diffusion the smaller atoms move through the spaces between the others. The most likely mechanism of substitutional diffusion is that there are vacant atomic sites in the lattice, and these are utilised by the diffusing atoms (Fig. 57*a*), rather than squeezing through. In a sense the vacant sites can be said to diffuse also. The empty positions are thought to be inherent defects in the crystal structure, or they may be generated initially at the surface of the metal (Fig. 57 *b* and *c*).

It will be appreciated that rise of temperature, increasing the atomic vibrations and thus their tendency to change position, produces an increased rate of diffusion.

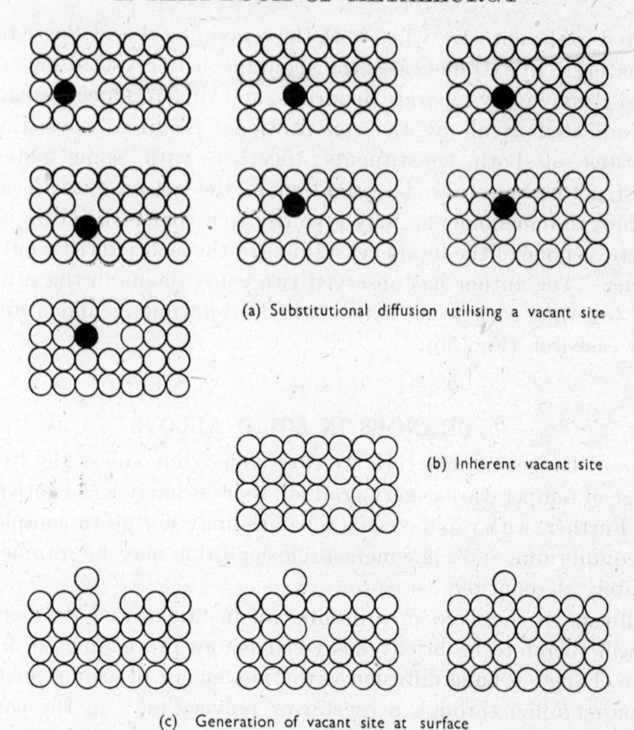

FIG. 57. Sketch illustrating mechanism of substitutional diffusion.

Change in magnetic properties. Strongly magnetic metals and alloys become essentially non-magnetic at some elevated temperature known as the **Curie point** and represented by a dotted line in equilibrium diagrams (Fig. 231, p. 316, Fig. 387, p. 506 and Figs. 393 and 394, p. 511).

Order-disorder changes. In primary and secondary solid solutions such changes are not considered as phase changes, and are also represented by dotted lines (Fig. 58 and Fig. 392 p. 510). Actually, when an ordered structure is heated there is a gradual decrease in the order; but a marked drop occurs at a specific temperature, and it is this point which is shown on equilibrium diagrams.

Changes in solid solubility. As already indicated, in terminal solid solutions the maximum solid solubility generally varies with temperature and it is necessary to consider the mechanism of these changes. In a similar manner with compounds existing over a range of composition, the limits vary with temperature.

The examples shown in Fig. 59 are the most convenient to treat

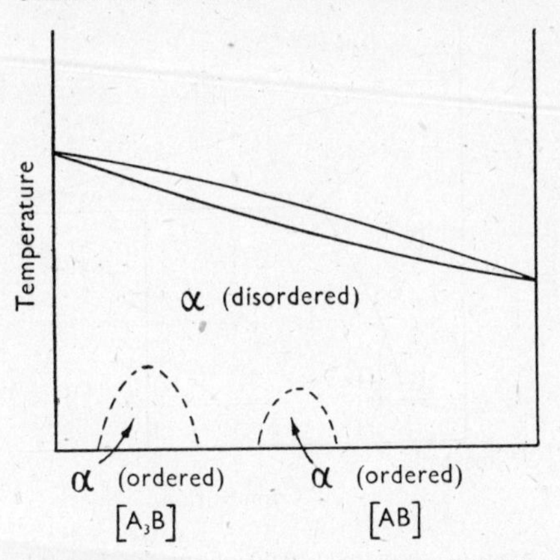

FIG. 58. Occurrence of ordering in a solid solution.

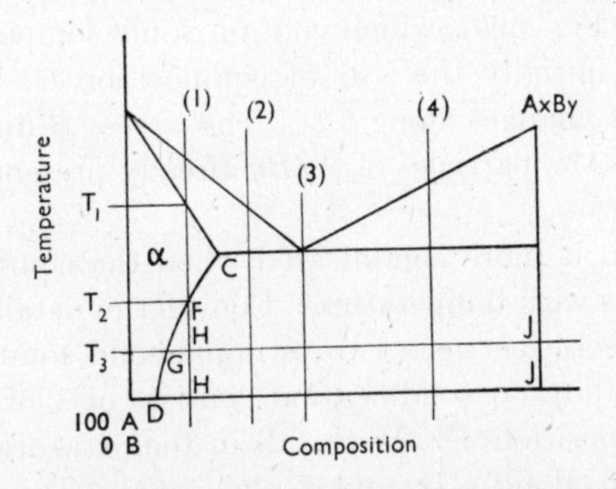

FIG. 59 (*a*). System showing variation in solid solubility limit.

first. *Alloy* (1) in both cases solidifies selectively as the solid solution α, and exists solely as homogeneous grains of this between T_1 and T_2. Below T_2 the A cannot continue to hold all the B in solution ; therefore, at T_2 ejection of B commences and continues down to room temperature ; B diffuses out of solution and concentrates at the grain boundaries of the α and along certain planes inside the crystals, where it arranges itself with atoms of A in the structure of the compound $AxBy$: the B is said to *precipitate* as $AxBy$. As the precipitation of $AxBy$ proceeds, the composition of the α changes along FD, so that at T_3, for example, the alloy consists of α of composition G and $AxBy$ in the proportion $HJ : HG$. The final structure at room temperature is α of composition D and $AxBy$ in the proportion $HJ : HD$. It should be stressed that although a duplex structure results from the change in alloy (1) (Fig. 59*a*), no eutectic structure is formed. In *alloys* (2), (3) and (4) (Fig. 59*a*),

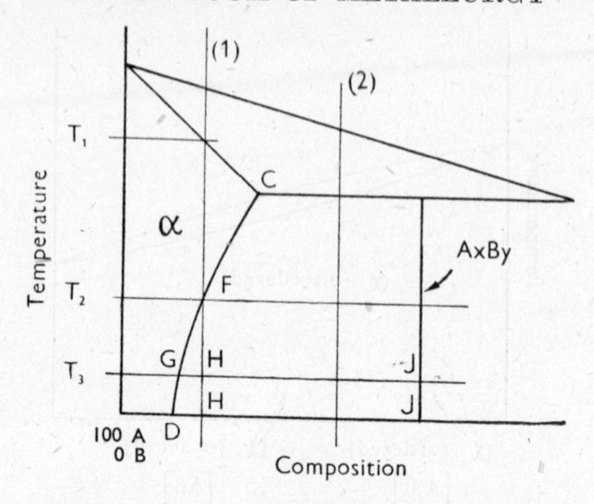

FIG. 59 (*b*). System showing variation in solid solubility limit

and *alloy* (2) (Fig. 59*b*), which contain some sompound directly on solidification, initially the α is of composition C, but with fall in temperature it changes along CD. The excess B diffuses out of the α and enlarges the particles of $AxBy$ already present, or forms fresh particles.

The position is more complicated when the composition of both phases changes with temperature. Consider in detail the type where there is a eutectic between two terminal solid solutions (Fig. 60*a*). The eutectic alloy on solidification consists of α of composition C, and β of composition F. With fall in temperature, the α changes in composition along CD, and β along FG. This takes place by countercurrent diffusion, the excess B diffusing from the α to the β and vice versa. Similar changes occur in *alloys* (1) and (2). The

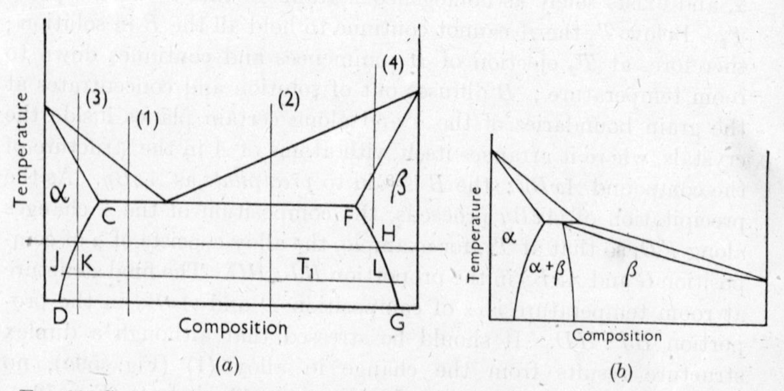

FIG. 60. Systems in which solid solubility limits change in adjacent phases.

change in proportion of the phases in these cases depends on the specific form of the diagram and the alloy under consideration. *Alloy* (3) corresponds to alloy (1) (Fig. 59) and changes from a single to a two-phase state. However, in the present case the composition of the β precipitate, initially H, also changes with fall in temperature along HG. At T_1, for example, the alloy is composed of α, of composition J, and precipitated β, of composition L, in the proportion $\alpha/\beta = KL/KJ$. The cooling of *alloy* (4) proceeds in a like manner.

Similar treatment to the foregoing may be applied to the interpretation of composition changes in compounds (Fig. 61*a* and *b*). Sometimes the limits of composition of a phase may increase with fall in temperature, resulting in a two-phase alloy becoming single phase, as alloy x (Fig. 61*b*); or, further, when there is an increase followed by a decrease in solubility, an alloy may solidify with two phases, change to single phase and then become duplex again, for example, alloy x (Fig. 61*c* and *d*).

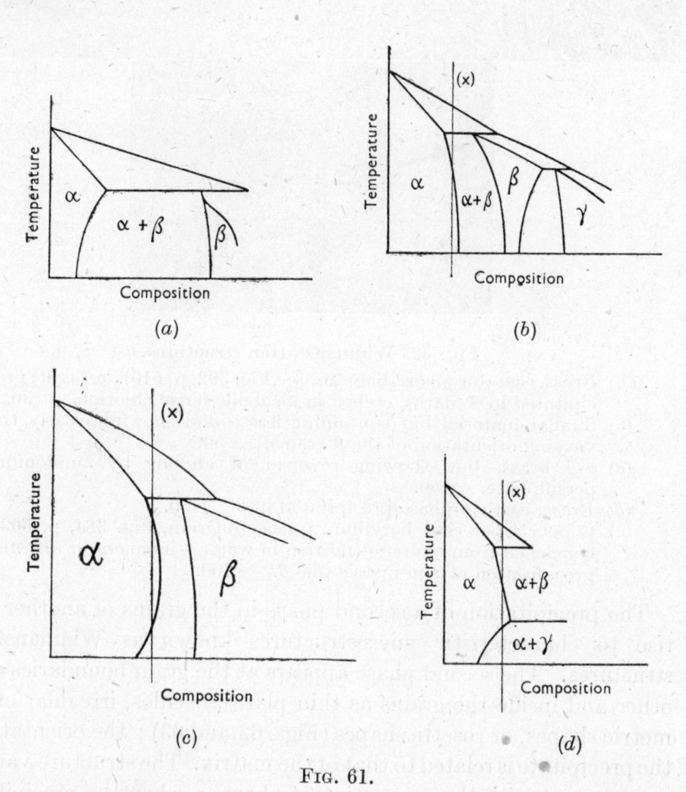

FIG. 61.

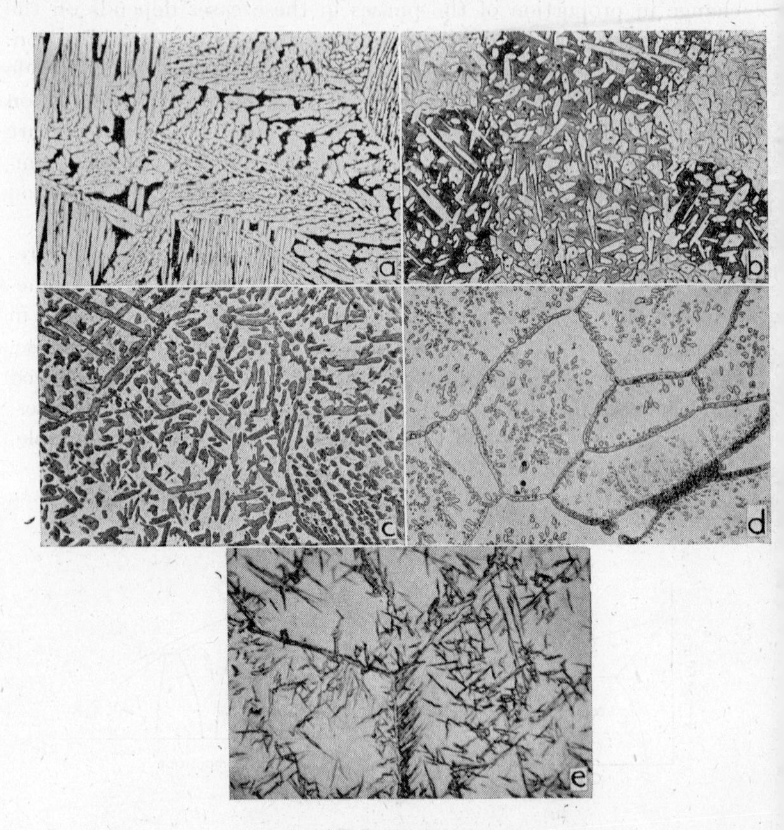

FIG. 62. Widmanstätten structures.

(*a*) Brass, cast (for phase diagram, see Fig. 392, p. 510). α (light) precipitated in β (dark), etched in alcoholic ferric chloride. $\times 30$.
(*b*) Similar material but containing less α and showing clearly the varying orientation of the β grains. $\times 50$.
(*c*) α-β brass, but showing reversal of etching by ammonium persulphate. $\times 50$.
(*d*) Brass, cast: γ-phase precipitated in β. $\times 50$.
(*e*) Copper-4 per cent beryllium (phase diagram, Fig. 384, p. 503). Quenched from molten condition in water: incipient or arrested precipitation of α in metastable β. $\times 700$.

The precipitation of a second phase in the grains of another gives rise to characteristic microstructures known as **Widmanstätten structures.** The second phase appears at the grain boundaries of the other and inside the grains as thin plates, needles, irregular or geometric shapes, or rosette shapes (Figs. 62 and 63); the orientation of the precipitate is related to that of the matrix. The structure varies to some extent with the proportion of phases; when the precipitating phase preponderates, the pattern produced is scarcely typical of that commonly represented as Widmanstätten, and in these cases the term is not always applied.

The above discussion has so far referred to equilibrium rates of cooling. The effect of fast cooling in cases where solubility decreases with fall in temperature is to reduce the amount of rejection that occurs, thus producing supersaturation, and to refine the size of any precipitate that does form (Fig. 62*e*). If a supersaturated phase is retained to room temperature by fast cooling, some precipitation or rejection on a submicroscopic scale may occur at room temperature or at some slightly elevated temperatures, although the structure is still metastable. This form of precipitation results in considerable hardening of the alloy, and the phenomenon is the basis of the industrial form of heat treatment known as " precipitation- ", " dispersion- ", or " age-hardening ", notable examples of its application being copper-beryllium and certain aluminium alloys. The commercial compositions are not binary, but the basis phase is a primary solid solution and the excess solute is rejected under equilibrium conditions as one or more hard compounds. In practice, treatment usually involves a definite " solution treatment " followed by fast cooling, and then " ageing " at room temperature, or " precipitation ", " tempering " or " artificially ageing " at moderately elevated temperatures. Continued heating of an " aged " phase will produce a

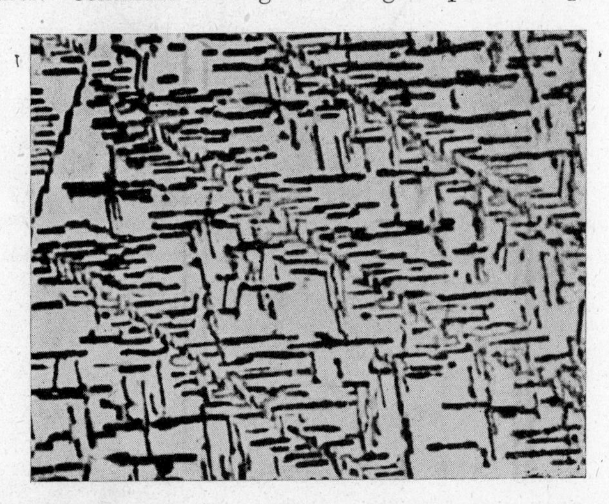

FIG. 63. Aluminium-4 per cent copper alloy, showing precipitation of compound after quenching the solid solution and reheating to about 200° C. ×100. (For phase diagram, see Fig. 381, p. 500). From G. Chaudron, *J. Inst. Metals*, 1949, 76, 6.

stable approximately equilibrium structure, with loss of the improvement in properties.

When there is an increase in solubility with fall in temperature, in alloys affected particularly, for example, alloys x (Figs. 61*b–d*), fast cooling tends to retain the high-temperature duplex structure. Thus chill casting retains the structure of dendritic α with interdendritic β in a 65/35 copper-zinc alloy (Figs. 47 p. 63 and 392 p. 510).

Eutectoid reactions. These involve the decomposition of a solid solution or compound at a constant temperature during cooling. The products of the decomposition are usually a solid solution and a compound or two compounds, none of which is the original phase (Fig. 64). It will be seen that the form of that part of the constitutional diagram representing the reaction is similar to that for a eutectic reaction. *Alloy* (1) is the eutectoid alloy: it solidifies as grains of β, but at T_e the β breaks down to a mixture of α and γ. By diffusion, A concentrates in certain zones and B in others until the compositions are X and Y, the α and γ patterns, respectively, being taken up; the proportion of $\alpha : \gamma$ is $EY : EX$. Some eutectoid is produced in all alloys between X and Y. *Alloy* (2) may be taken as typical of compositions between X and E. Above T_1 this alloy also consists of grains of β; but at T_1, α commences to precipitate in a Widmanstätten manner at the boundaries of, and inside, the

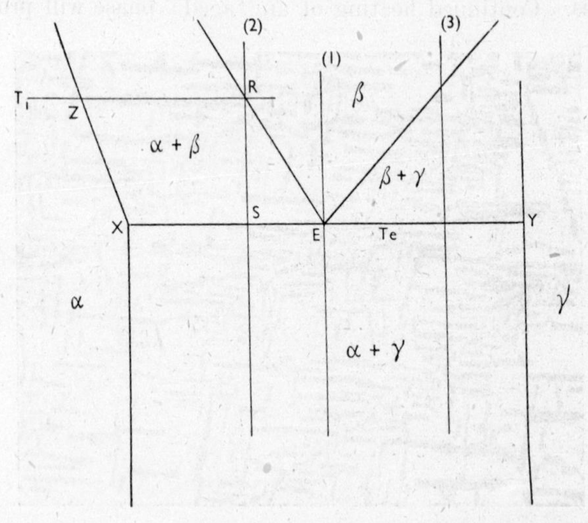

FIG. 64. Portion of equilibrium diagram (for two metals, A and B) representing a eutectoid reaction. T_e is the eutectoid temperature; as with the eutectic, the reaction is reversible at this temperature and can be represented as $\beta \rightleftharpoons \alpha + \delta$.

grains of the β. Initially the α is of composition Z, but as the temperature falls and it continues to form, its composition changes along ZX, while correspondingly the β changes in composition along RE. When the eutectoid temperature is reached, the alloy consists of α, of composition X, and β, of composition E, in the proportion of $\alpha : \beta = SE : SX$. While the temperature stays constant, the remaining β forms the eutectoid mixture. *Alloy* (3) behaves in a corresponding manner to (2), forming excess γ plus eutectoid. In the diagram under consideration, composition of the α and γ does not change with fall in temperature below T_e, but changes do occur and are interpreted as described in the previous section (p. 76).

The effect of fast cooling is to increase the undercooling and the fineness of the resultant structure. In alloys of types (2) and (3), there will be a reduction in the amount of excess α or γ, respectively, and hence an increase in the amount of eutectoid, and a corresponding change in its composition. Eventually, with an increased rate of cooling the eutectoid reaction and the proper precipitation of the excess constituent may be suppressed and a metastable structure produced, which may be very hard indeed. The rate of cooling necessary to cause these modifications varies from system to system. The real criterion is the temperature range in which decomposition occurs, and this is decided by the rate of transformation at sub-eutectoid temperatures coupled with the rate of cooling. A useful method of portraying the necessary information for an alloy is by **isothermal transformation,** or **transformation-temperature-time (T.T.T.) diagrams,** in which temperature is plotted against time (log) for different proportions of decomposition.

The two best-known examples of eutectoid reactions are in the iron-carbon system (Fig. 65), eutectoid composition about 0·80 per cent carbon, where a primary solid solution decomposes to another solution and a compound; and in the copper-aluminium system (Fig. 66) at 11·8 per cent aluminium, in which an electron compound undergoes decomposition to a solid solution and another compound. In both cases, in practice, alloys containing eutectoid are hardened by heat-treatment. The heat-treatment involves first fast cooling from the single-phase region (after heating into this) to yield a metastable structure. This hardening is followed by reheating (" tempering ") at moderate temperatures to allow further breakdown with consequent toughening, the final properties being regulated by the tempering temperature.

Refining the structure of any alloy gives improved mechanical properties; but the above case and that of precipitation hardening

FIG. 65. Eutectoid structure in steel; laminations of iron and iron carbide (dark). ×820. From *Metals*, by (Sir) H. Carpenter and J. M. Robertson. Oxford Univ. Press.

The equilibrium diagram is given in Fig. 231, p. 316.

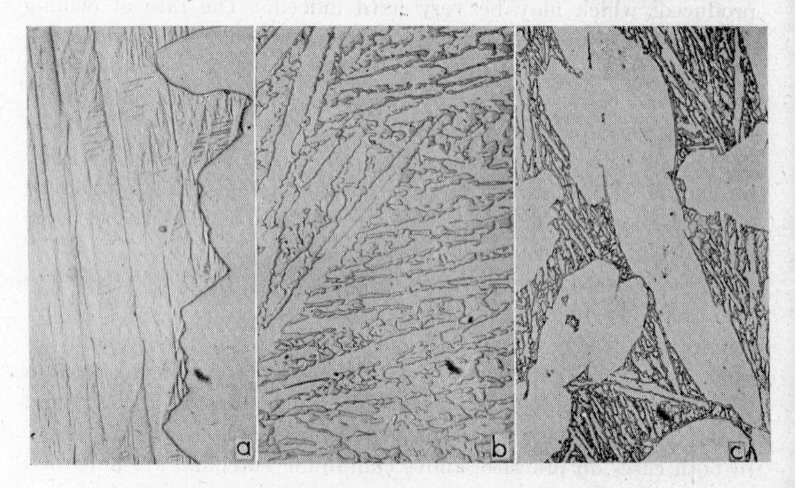

FIG. 66. Eutectoid structures in copper-aluminium system. (For phase diagram, see Fig. 383, p. 502).

(*a*) The proper breakdown has been prevented by fast cooling, and a metastable structure has resulted (the plain area on the right is excess of the α-phase). ×500.

(*b*) Coarse $(\alpha + \gamma^2)$ eutectoid structure obtained by furnace cooling. ×500. A laminated structure similar to that in Fig. 65 may also be obtained in this eutectoid.

(*c*) 10 per cent aluminium alloy, furnace cooled. The structure shows the excess α coarsely precipitated, together with the eutectoid. ×200.

give considerable scope both in properties and in the fact that application is to solid metal, which can be shaped first.

Another form of occurrence of a eutectoid is shown in simplified form in Fig. 67; an actual example is found in the copper-tin system (Fig. 391, page 409). The initial solidification of alloy x corresponds to alloy (1) in Fig. 44: β is formed by the peritectic reaction between the dendrites of α. On cooling, however, the composition of the β is adjusted by diffusion to that of the eutectoid point, when decomposition takes place (Fig. 68).

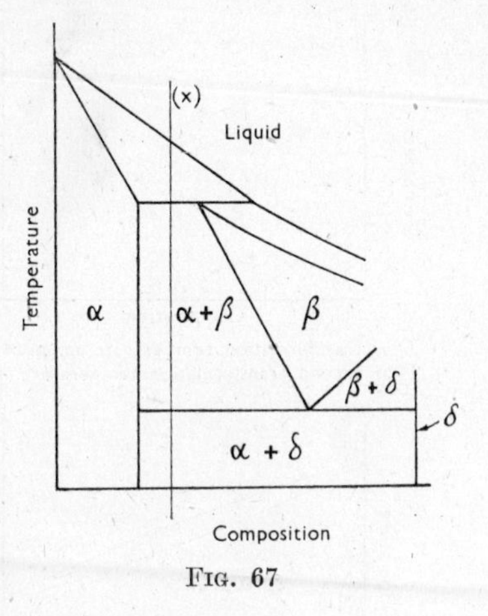

FIG. 67

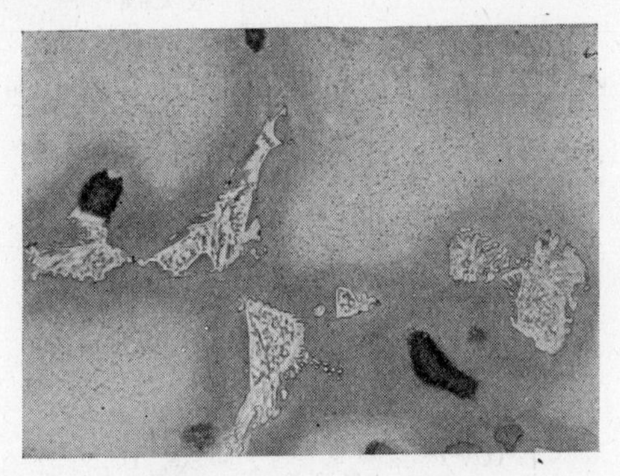

FIG. 68. Interdendritic areas of eutectoid in copper-tin alloy of type x (Fig. 67). Coring can also be seen in the solid solution. ×400.

Change in atomic pattern. Phase changes involving alteration in atomic pattern and corresponding to *polymorphic* transformations in the basis metal occur in certain solid alloys. The changes usually take place over a range of temperature (Fig. 69); they are found, for example, in many iron-rich alloys.

Effect of changes in lattice dimensions. In addition to the eutectic and peritectic types of partial miscibility in the solid state, a miscibility gap is produced by a curious change in the solid state (Fig. 70), examples being the gold-nickel and gold-platinum systems. The two varieties of solutions differ in lattice dimensions, but not in

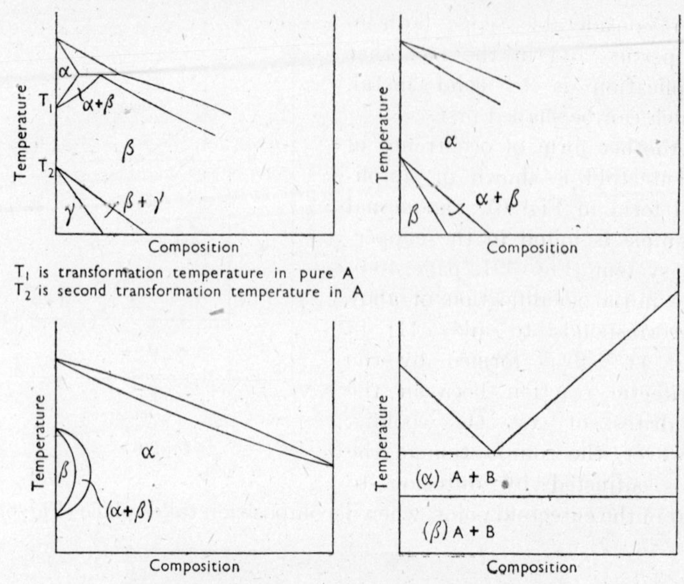

FIG. 69. Examples of phase changes in solid alloys due to polymorphism in a component metal.

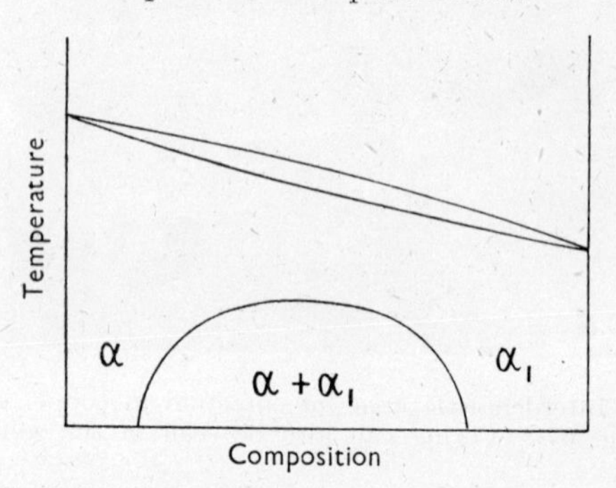

FIG. 70. Miscibility gap produced in a solid solution by change in lattice dimensions.

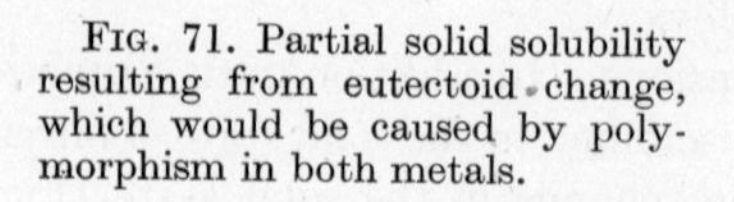
FIG. 71. Partial solid solubility resulting from eutectoid change, which would be caused by polymorphism in both metals.

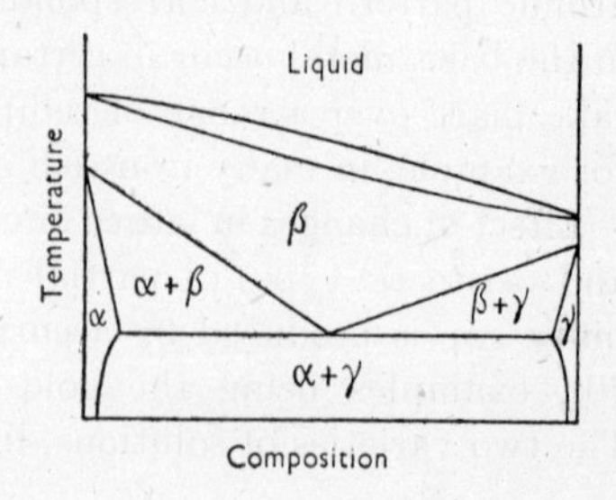

pattern ; the phases merge at elevated temperatures. Such a miscibility gap may occur in a terminal solid solution.

A fourth case of partial miscibility might be produced by a eutectoid reaction (Fig. 71), but no specific examples can be quoted.

Another curious reaction, this time proceeding isothermally, is shown in Fig. 72 ; it occurs in the aluminium-zinc system, for example. Corresponding to the miscibility gap effect, two modifications of α are formed with different lattice dimensions, but in this case at a constant temperature, T_m ; the α' changes to the α variety, the change in composition being effected by the simultaneous formation of the correct proportion of β of composition G. It should be stressed that, while the change is proceeding, the two compositions of the α are C and E, respectively, and under equilibrium conditions there are no intermediate compositions possible.

Thus *alloy* (1) is composed of grains of α' between the solidus and T_m, but here the temperature stays constant while a proportion of β forms and the α' changes to α. When this is complete, the temperature falls and more β precipitates from the α, so that the composition of the latter can follow CF; at the same time the composition of the β is adjusted to follow GH. *Alloy* (2), initially single phase, splits up into α and α' between T_1 and T_m : at T_m it consists of the two varieties in the proportion $\alpha : \alpha' = DE : DC$. Again the temperature stays constant at T_m until all the α' is converted to

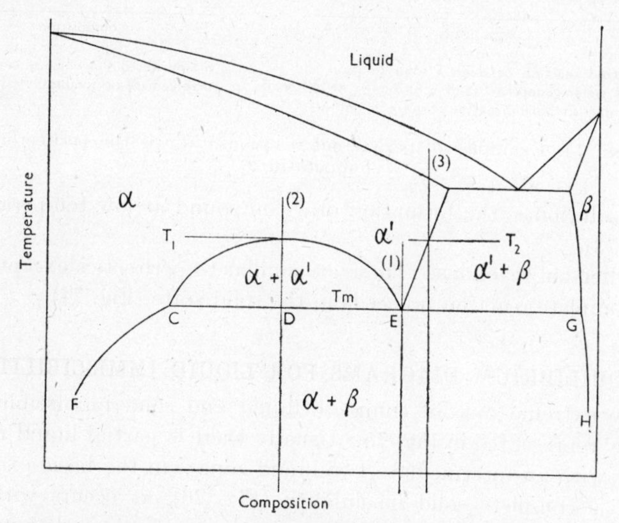

FIG. 72. Diagram showing isothermal reaction due to change in lattice dimensions.

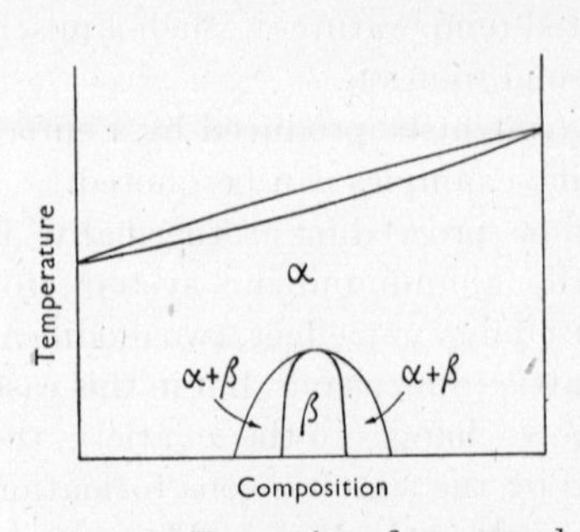

FIG. 73. Formation of compound at low temperatures. Examples are found in the chromium-iron and copper-palladium systems.

α with the co-formation of β. *Alloy* (3) is similar to alloy (1), except that precipitation of β (between T_2 and T_m) precedes the isothermal change. Because of the similarity to the monotectic reaction occurring in systems in which there is partial liquid immiscibility (*see* later), the author suggests the name *monotectoid* to describe the present change.

Low-temperature change. A stage further than ordering in a

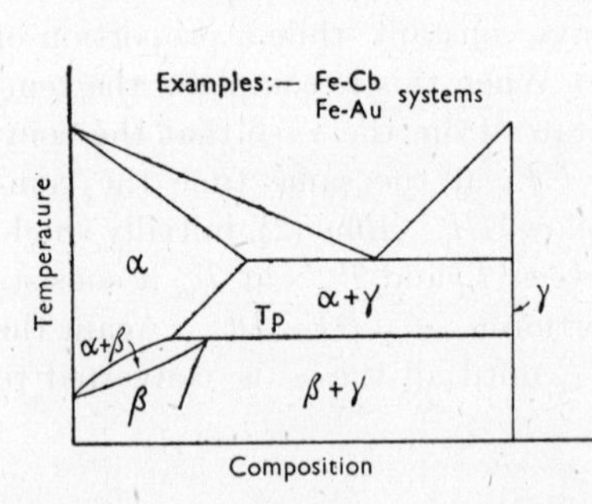

(i) Peritectoid reaction between a solid solution and a compound yielding another solid solution. (the α to β change is due to polymorphism of pure metal A)

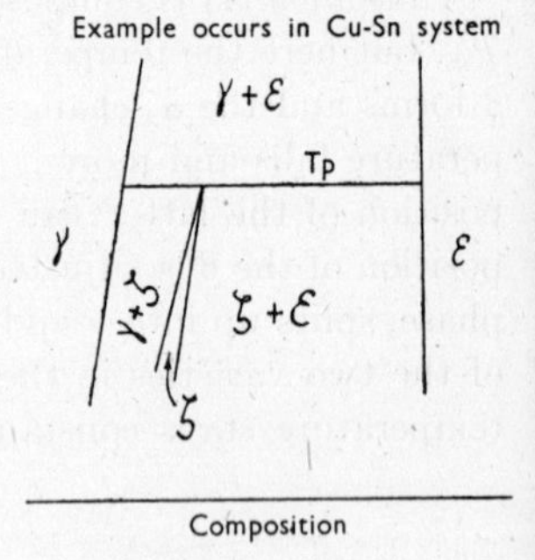

(ii) Peritectoid in which all constituents involved are compounds

FIG. 74. Examples of peritectoid reactions. *Tp* is the peritectoid temperature.

solid solution is the formation of a compound at low temperatures (Fig. 73).

Peritectoid reactions. These are similar to peritectics except that the complete reaction proceeds in the solid state (Fig. 74).

EQUILIBRIUM DIAGRAMS FOR LIQUID IMMISCIBILITY

The extreme case of complete liquid and solid immiscibility is simply represented in Fig. 75. Usually there is partial liquid miscibility with an intermediate two-liquid zone ; in the basic example there is complete solid insolubility (Fig. 76), as occurs with the aluminium-lead, aluminium-bismuth, copper-lead and zinc-lead systems. However, there are cases in which terminal solid solutions

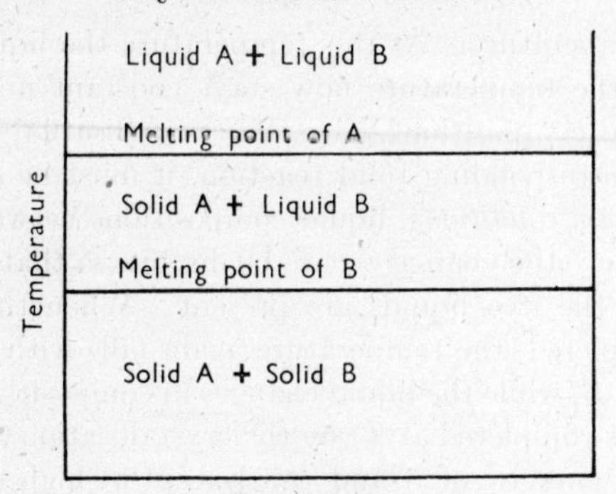

FIG. 75. Extreme case of complete liquid and solid immiscibility.

and compounds are formed. In some systems it is known that the two-liquid zone disappears at higher temperatures.

The basic diagram (Fig. 76) introduces another reaction, namely a **monotectic change** ; as pointed out above, a similar reaction occurs in the solid state. *Alloy* (1) commences to solidify at T_1, when pure B crystallises, continuing as the temperature falls to T_m, the

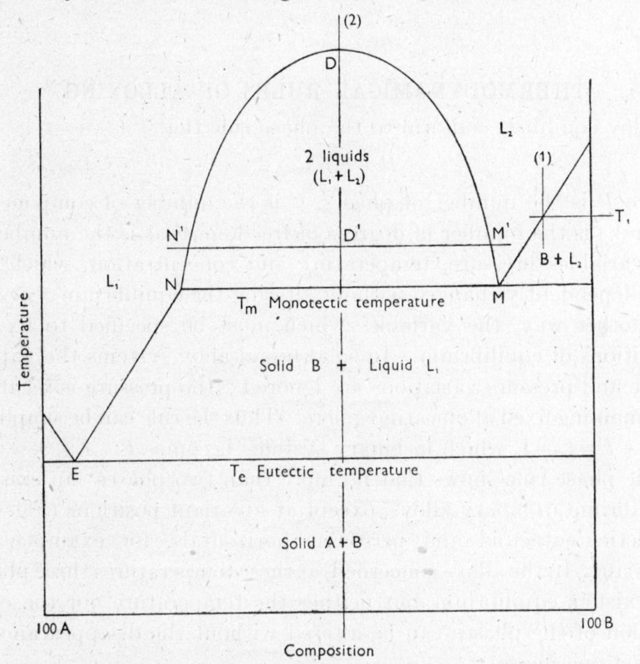

FIG. 76. Diagram representing partial liquid miscibility and complete solid immiscibility.

monotectic temperature. At this temperature the liquid is of composition M; the temperature now stays constant until the liquid has changed to composition N by the crystallisation of further B. As with the corresponding solid reaction, it must be stressed that, *under equilibrium conditions*, liquid compositions between N and M are not possible: the change occurs bit by bit, so that at any intermediate stage the two liquids are present. When the monotectic change is completed, the temperature again falls with the crystallisation of more B, while the liquid changes in composition along NE. Solidification is completed at T_e by the crystallisation of the remaining liquid as a eutectic of A and B. Except at high temperatures, *alloy* (2), when molten, consists of two liquids, their compositions being given by DN and DM. Thus at T_2 the alloy consists of two liquids L_1 and L_2 of compositions N^1 and M^1, respectively, and in the proportion $L_1/L_2 = D^1M^1/D^1N^1$. On reaching T_m the liquid compositions are N and M, respectively; this temperature is maintained until all the liquid of composition M has been converted to that of N by the crystallisation of pure B. Thereafter solidification continues as in alloy (1).

THERMODYNAMICAL RULES OF ALLOYING

Alloy equilibria conform to the phase rule that

$$P + F = C + 2,$$

where P is the number of phases, C is the number of components, F (or V) is the number of degrees of freedom, that is the number of the variables pressure, temperature and concentration, which can be independently changed without altering the equilibrium; or, put in another way, the variables which must be specified to fix the conditions of equilibrium. In solid-liquid alloy systems the vapour phase and pressure variations are ignored; the pressure is regarded as remaining fixed at one atmosphere. Thus the rule can be simplified to $P + F = C + 1$, which in binary systems becomes $P + F = 3$.

The phase rule shows that no more than two phases can exist at equilibrium in binary alloys, except at invariant positions (Fig. 77). Eutectic, eutectoid and peritectic horizontals, for example, are invariant. In the alloys concerned, at these temperatures three phases can exist in equilibrium, but neither the temperature nor the composition of the phases can be altered without the disappearance of at least one phase.

The phase rule has little direct value in the interpretation and

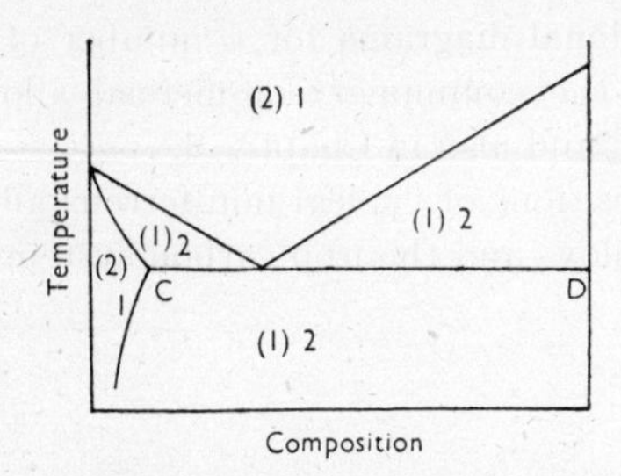

FIG. 77. Degrees of freedom in a binary system. The unbracketed number indicates the number of phases present, and the bracketed number the degrees of freedom (the variables being temperature and concentration). *CD* is an invariant line.

practical utilisation of alloy constitutional diagrams. In the determination of the diagrams, although the phase rule makes no predictions, the results have to be in agreement with the rule, and in this way it imposes valuable restraint. It is clear that an advantage of the phase rule is that it is independent of any theories of alloying.

Another thermodynamical consideration is that of free energy. The structure taken up in an alloy is that of lowest free energy, and on a free-energy basis it is possible to derive the general basic forms of constitutional diagrams, as was done originally by Roozeboom at the end of the last century. Only general forms are possible, because specific free-energy values cannot be calculated. Free-energy considerations also enable limitations to be imposed on experimental results as to the slope of certain curves in the diagrams. Thus with regard to phase boundaries, it can be shown that the continuation of a boundary must be in a two-phase region and not in the single-phase region (Fig. 78).

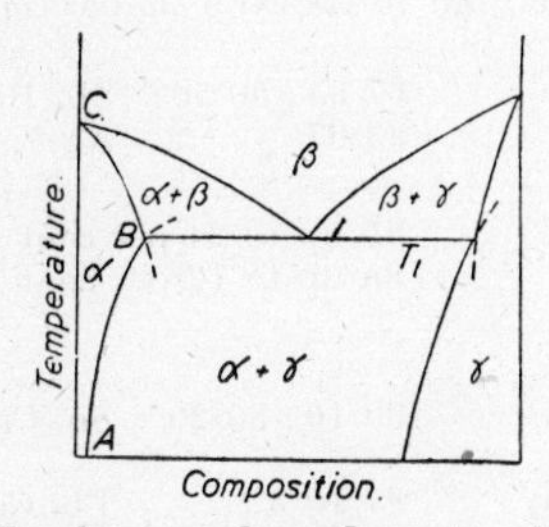

FIG. 78. The lower α-boundary is of correct form, whereas that of the γ-phase is incorrect. From H. Lipson and A. J. C. Wilson, *J. Iron & Steel Inst.*, 1940, 142, 108.

Specific constitutional diagrams for a number of binary systems including some of the commoner commercial alloys are given in Appendix 2, p. 500, and also in Chapter 8.

Industrial compositions of typical non-ferrous alloys are given in Table 7 ; ferrous alloys and the iron carbon system are discussed in Chapter 10.

TABLE 7. TYPICAL INDUSTRIAL NON-FERROUS ALLOYS

Name	Essential metals	Examples of important basic compositions per cent	Other additions	Ref. to binary constitutional diagram when given
Brass	Copper-zinc	85/15 ; 70/30 ; 65/35 ; 60/40	Fe, Mn, Al, Sn, Ni, Pb, Si	Fig. 392 p. 510
Tin bronze	Copper-tin: phosphorus is present in most cases up to about 0·7 per cent.	95/5 ; 90/10	P, Pb, Zn, Ni	Fig. 391 p. 509
Gunmetal	Copper-tin-zinc	88/10/2; 85/5/5/5Pb	Pb, Ni	
Aluminium bronze	Copper-aluminium	95/5 ; 90/10	Mn, Fe, Ni, Si, Pb	Fig. 383 p. 502
Beryllium bronze	Copper-beryllium	Cu – 2 to 2·5% Be	Ni, Co	Fig. 384 p. 503
Copper-nickel		98/2 90/10 80/20 ; 60/40 70/30 ; 30/70	Al, Si, Fe, Mn	Fig. 387 p. 506
Nickel-silvers	Cu 45–80 ; Zn 10–35; Ni 5–35 per cent.			
Solder	Lead-tin	67/33 ; 50/50 ; 33/67	Sb, Bi, Cd, Ag	Fig. 398 p. 513
Type metals	Lead-antimony-tin	Sb up to 24 per cent Sn up to 12 per cent		
Babbitt or white-metal bearing alloys	(*a*) lead-antimony. (*b*) tin-antimony invariably with copper	90/10 ; 80/20 87/10/3 89/7/4	Sn, Cu Pb, Cu	Fig. 397 p. 513 Fig. 401 p. 514

TABLE 7. TYPICAL INDUSTRIAL NON-FERROUS ALLOYS

Name	Essential metals	Examples of important basic compositions per cent	Other additions	Ref. to binary constitutional diagram when given
Aluminium Alloys*:				
1. Aluminium-copper		92/8 ; 88/12	Si	Fig. 381 p. 500
2. Aluminium-silicon		95/5 ; 88/12	Cu	Fig. 382 p. 501
3. Aluminium-magnesium		97/3 ; 93/7	Mn, Zn	
4. "Dur-alumin"		4 Cu/0·5 each of Mn, Mg, Fe, Si		
5. Y-alloy		4 Cu/2 Ni/1·5 Mg/0·7 Si/0·6 Fe/0·2 Ti		
"Elektron"-Magnesium Alloys*				
1. Magnesium-manganese		Mn 1–1·5		
2. Magnesium-aluminium-manganese		Al 1–12/Mn 0·1–1	Zn	

* Light alloys.

NOMENCLATURE OF ALLOYS

Extract from the *Journal of the Institute of Metals*; January 1944 :

"The report of the Institute's Committee on the Nomenclature of Alloys, published in 1914 (*Journal*, Vol. II, pp. 45–56), recommended that alloys should be denoted by the names of their component metals, placed in the order of increasing numerical importance from the point of view of chemical composition by weight.

In general, the Institute has endeavoured to follow this system in its publications, although familiar terms in universal use in English, such as brass, bronze, nickel silver, have naturally been retained where appropriate. The system recommended in 1914 has not, however, been widely accepted, and the contrary method of placing first the metal present in largest proportion is fairly common in this country and is general in America and other countries. The Council has therefore decided, on the recommendation of its recently constituted Nomenclature Committee, that in future the practice of the Institute's publications shall conform with current usage elsewhere.

The following rule will therefore be adopted forthwith in the *Journal* and other publications of the Institute :

When an alloy is named by stating the chief elements it contains before the word " alloy ", the elements will be given in the order :

(1) the element present in largest proportion, followed by

(2) the other elements present. These will be stated in order of descending proportion by weight, except in a very few cases where another order is well established. In such cases the customary order will usually be followed.

It will be observed that the Institute has made this rule for its own guidance, and that the use of established terms and expressions such as brass, bronze, leaded gun-metal, is not in any way affected.

The following examples illustrate the nomenclature to be adopted by the Institute :

96% aluminium, 4% copper—an aluminium-copper alloy.

90% copper, 10% lead—a copper-lead alloy.

94% aluminium, 5% zinc, 1% magnesium—an aluminium-zinc-magnesium alloy.

88% lead, 12% tin—a lead-tin alloy.

94% magnesium, 5% aluminium, 1% zinc—a magnesium-aluminium-zinc alloy."

ADDITIONAL READING

1. *Metallography*, by C. H. Desch. (6th Ed., Longmans, 1944).

2. *Metals*, by (Sir) H. Carpenter and J. M. Robertson. (Oxford Univ. Press, 1939).

3. *Theoretical Structural Metallurgy*, by A. H. Cottrell. (Arnold, 1948).

4. *An Introduction to X-ray Metallography*, by A. Taylor. (Chapman and Hall, 1945).

5. *Structure of Metals*, by C. S. Barrett. (2nd Ed., McGraw-Hill, 1952).

The following are recommended as reference works for specific equilibrium diagrams other than those given in this book :

6. *Metals Handbook*, 1948 Edition (American Soc. for Metals).

7. *Metals Reference Book*, C. J. Smithells (Edit.). (Butterworths, 1949).

8. *Aufbau der Zweistofflegierungen*, by M. Hansen. (Julius Springer, 1936).

9. *Equilibrium Diagrams of Binary Copper Alloys*. (Copper Development Assoc., 1948).

10. *Equilibrium Data for Tin Alloys*. (Tin Research Institute, 1949).

CHAPTER 5

EFFECTS OF STRESS ON METALS

WHEN metals are stressed, they become deformed. The deformation may be wholly temporary, that is *elastic*; or, in addition, permanent deformation may result. The subject may be considered from two major aspects: (1) permanent deformation intentionally carried out, as in working and shaping processes; and (2) the behaviour of metals in service under stress.

The fundamental considerations in each case will be common to both. Before entering into details, certain terms used to describe the behaviour of metals under stress are defined below. The tests used in assessing these characteristics are described in Chapter 13.

Strength is a term used in the general sense to indicate the resistance to applied stress of any form. The term also has a narrower meaning, namely, the highest tensile stress withstood, when a specimen is loaded continuously until it breaks. Strictly, this value is known as the **ultimate tensile stress (U.T.S.)**. **Tenacity** is also used to denote the degree of resistance to tensile stress. A factor which correlates strength and lightness is the **specific tenacity**, the ratio of tensile strength to density.

An important property of metals is their ability to undergo considerable permanent strain or deformation before breaking. The power of deforming in this manner under tensile stresses is termed **ductility**; when deformation is due to compression, the property is termed **malleability**. A measure of ductility is given by the elongation and also the reduction in area in the tensile test, usually expressed as a percentage of the original length and area, respectively. High ductility generally goes with high malleability, and both properties are associated with low or moderate tensile strength and low hardness.

Hardness is the resistance to abrasion, scratching and indentation. It is usually assessed by the resistance to indentation, the size of impression made under standard conditions being measured and expressed as load divided by the impressed area of the indentation.

Guidance as to the **resistance to fracture** is given by the notched-bar test, a common form being the Izod. Here, the energy absorbed in breaking a notched specimen with a swinging hammer is measured.

A **brittle** metal has poor resistance to fracture, is hard, has little ductility and low or moderate tensile strength. Material having in addition low hardness is " friable " or crumbly rather than brittle, a condition not commonly realised with metals. **Toughness**, on the other hand, is associated with high tensile strength and resistance to fracture, moderate or high hardness, and moderate or low ductility. It should be noted, however, that in certain cases brittleness, as denoted by poor resistance in the notched-bar test, occurs in material with good ductility as indicated by elongation values.

PERMANENT DEFORMATION

With purely elastic strain, the original internal state and external form of the metal is recovered after the stress is removed. Permanent or plastic deformation is accompanied by changes in the internal state, and although the original dimensions may be recovered by further deformation, this causes further changes internally.

Permanent deformation involves distortion of the crystal- and micro-structures. Provided the distortion is not removed, as deformation proceeds the distortion and the resistance of the metal to deformation increase, while the capacity for deformation is reduced. However, the distorted structure is unstable and the metal tends to *recrystallise*, that is, to regain an unstrained structure and essentially its original capacity for permanent strain. Recrystallisation usually involves reorientation of the atomic arrangement from that which existed before straining, and change in the crystal-boundary configuration. The tendency to recrystallise varies with different metals, but in all cases increases with rise in temperature and severity of straining. Some metals, lead for example, recrystallise rapidly at room temperature ; whereas in others, such as iron and nickel, the tendency is extremely slight at room temperature, and noticeable effects are not obtained until an appreciably higher temperature is maintained, of the order of 500° C. in the case of iron.

Metal which has been permanently strained, and in which recrystallisation is not proceeding (or takes some time to manifest itself) is said to be **strain-** or **work-hardened**. Deformation under these conditions is known as **cold-working**. On the other hand, when metal is worked at such temperatures that recrystallisation keeps pace with deformation, the operation is known as **hot-working**. Thus lead is hot-worked at room temperature, although for most metals, especially those used for service under stress, this is cold-working.

FIG. 79. Slip in a single crystal without constraint. Figs. 79, 85 and 89 are reproduced from *Structure of Metals*, by C. S. Barrett. McGraw-Hill.

As a number of factors are involved, this section is conveniently treated in stages under the following subheadings: (*a*) cold-working single crystal pure metals (excluding consideration of after effects); (*b*) cold-working polycrystalline pure metals; (*c*) changes occurring in cold-worked pure metals; hot-working; (*d*) alloys; cold-working and changes following; hot-working.

(*a*) **Cold-working single crystal pure metals.** By confining attention first to single crystals composed of the same kind of atoms, the effects of the presence of different kinds of atoms, of marked orientation changes, and grain boundary zones are avoided.

Slip. Single crystals of pure metals begin to deform plastically at low stresses. Deformation is essentially the same for different forms of stress. The most usual mode of deformation is by **slipping**; that is, one part of the crystal moves, glides, or slips over another. This slipping takes place on certain atomic planes or layers in the crystal, although general cohesion is maintained; it results in visible steps on the surface of the crystal (Figs. 79 and 80). The distance

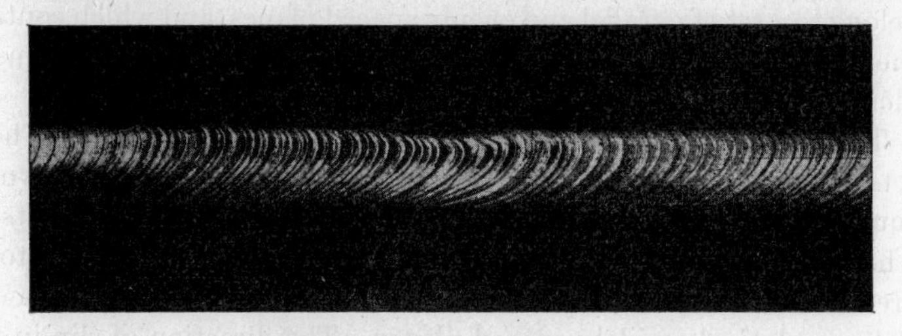

FIG. 80. Photograph of elongated single crystal showing steps on surface produced by slip. From *Distortion of Metal Crystals*, by C. F. Elam. Oxford Univ. Press.

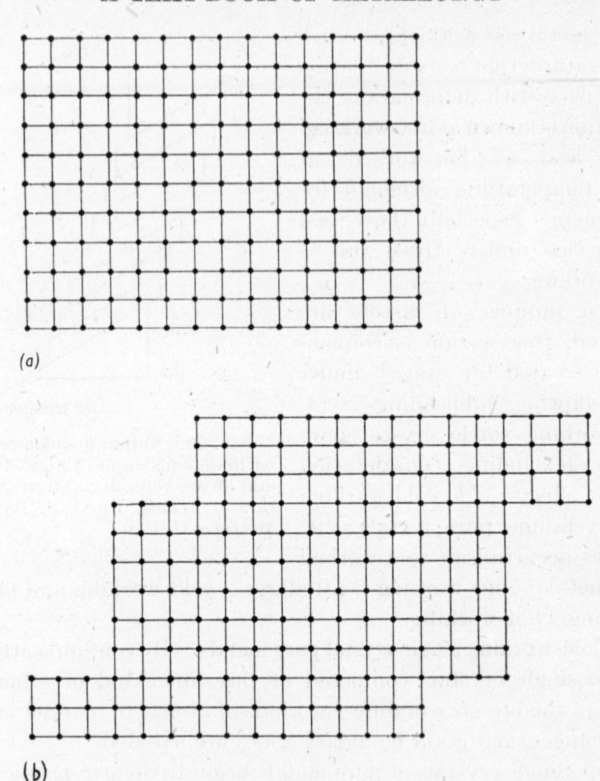

FIG. 81. Diagram illustrating slip, with respect to crystal structure.

moved during slip is in whole-number increments of the unit spacing between the atoms (Fig. 81).

A crystallographic or atomic plane is a plane passing through the centres of atoms. The planes of particular interest are those which belong to a **set** of parallel and evenly spaced planes, and which contain the centres of all the atoms (Fig. 82). The arrangement of atoms is identical on each plane of a set.

There are a number of possible sets in any crystal structure. Those sets which are similar although inclined to each other are known as **equivalent sets.** Slipping usually takes place in the set or sets in which the individual planes are farthest apart, and in which the atoms are closest together. Slip does not occur on adjacent planes in a set, but on relatively widely-spaced planes. The direction of slip in the planes is along the direction of closest packing of the atoms (Fig. 83). For convenience and precision in crystallography each set of planes

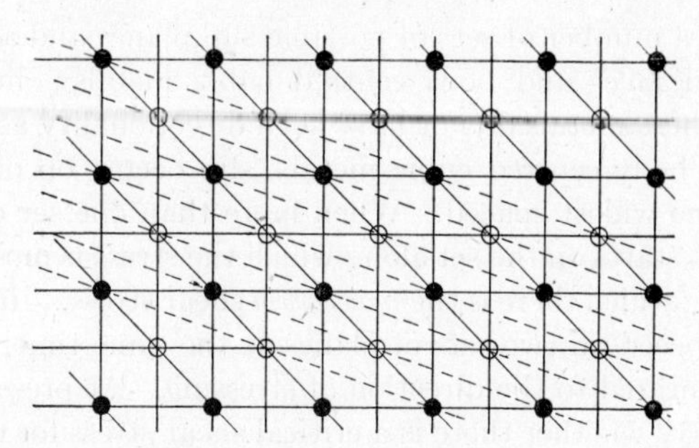

FIG. 82. Sets of atomic planes in body-centred cubic structure. The dark circles represent the atomic centres in one layer, and the light circles those in the next layer; subsequent layers are merely repetition.

is denoted by so-called Miller indices, which refer the planes to three standard axes in cubic structures, and three or usually four (Miller-Bravais) axes in hexagonal structures. The three or four whole-number indices are enclosed in rounded brackets; thus the (111) planes in the face-centred cubic structure are the densest layers. Directions in planes are indexed in a similar manner, the indices being enclosed in square brackets. The present treatment, however, is not sufficiently detailed to warrant the use of Miller indices.

In metals with the hexagonal close-packed structure, such as zinc and magnesium, there is only one set of slip planes at room temperature, and these are the basal planes; the direction of slip is along any of the diagonals (Figs. 83 and 84). This fact gives rise to pronounced directional properties in single crystals of hexagonal metals, for if the slip planes are normal or parallel to the direction of application of the stress, little or no deformation can occur: maximum plasticity is obtained when the slip planes are at 45° to the stress direction.

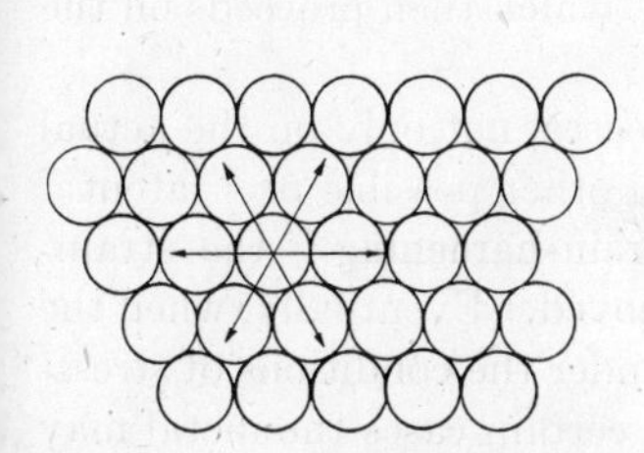

FIG. 83. Directions of slip in close-packed layer of face-centred cubic or close-packed hexagonal structures.

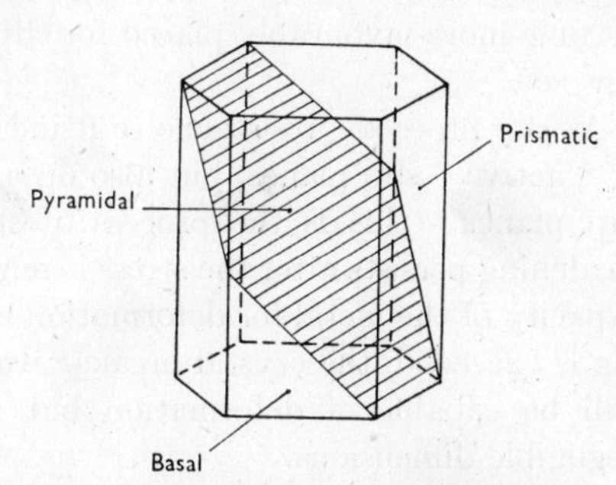

FIG. 84. Planes in hexagonal structure.

There are a number of sets of possible slip planes and a number of directions in face- and body-centred cubic metals; hence single crystals of these metals do not have such directionality as hexagonal metals. In body-centred cubic metals, slip occurs on other planes as well as the widest spaced. When more than one set of planes is possible, slip starts on the set along which the stress is most effective, that is, along which there is the *maximum* shear stress. In some cases slip may proceed on two sets of planes at the same time, if they are equally orientated to the direction of stressing. At present it is not possible to say whether there is a critical shear stress for each metal, which must be exceeded before slip will start. If such does exist, the values will be very low and they will be affected by time and temperature. It does appear that, for fairly rapid straining, there is some shear stress at which appreciable gliding starts, and values of this are quoted in the literature. Gliding appears to be independent of the form or value of the stress normal to the gliding planes.

When one-direction stresses are applied, or the metal is forced to flow essentially in one main direction, the crystal becomes elongated, and the slip planes are forced round to follow the direction of flow (Fig. 85). The result is reorientation of the crystal with respect to the direction of application of the stress, and eventually at least, if not at first, distortion of the atomic arrangement. If a single crystal is deformed in a tensile testing machine, the portions held in the grips will retain the original orientation and exert some restraint on the deformation of the rest of the crystal. Consequently a distorted region will exist between the two orientations, and in this the slip planes will be curved (Fig. 85*b*); the deformation taking place in these regions is sometimes known as " flexural gliding ". Similar warping may be produced by bending a crystal. The re-orientation resulting from deformation may cause another set of planes, if present, to become more favourably placed for slip, which then proceeds on the new set.

As slip proceeds, resistance to it increases, not only on the actual or " active " slip planes, but also on all other possible or " latent " slip planes; this is the process of **strain-hardening**; the strain-hardening persists after the stress is removed. Eventually, when the capacity of the metal for deformation under the conditions of stressing is exceeded, the crystal breaks. In certain cases the metal may still be capable of deformation but may have thinned down to negligible dimensions.

Twinning. Plastic deformation may also occur in metals by

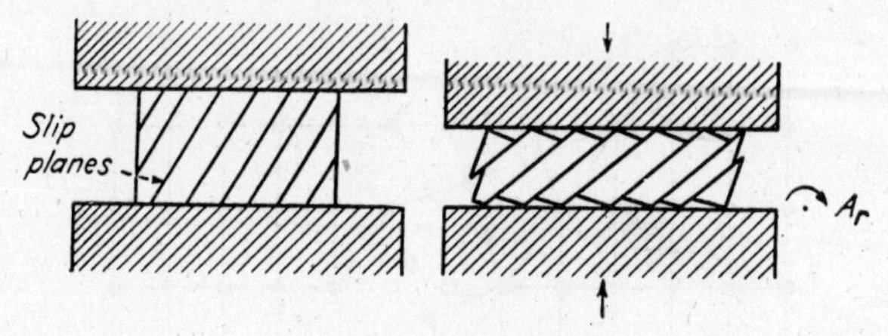

(a) Under compression.

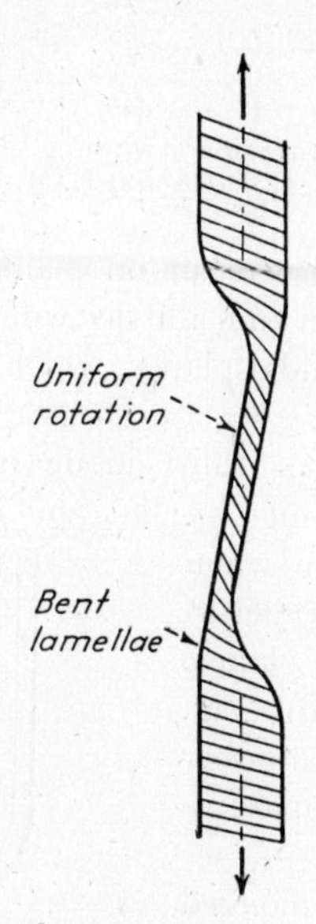

(b) Under tension.

FIG. 85. Rotation of planes of slip by one-direction stress. From Barrett.

twinning, and in some cases twinning is considered to be the principal mode, as, for example, in antimony and bismuth. Twinning may be regarded as a special form of slip; it involves movement in the same direction on a number of adjacent slip planes, so that the distance moved on each subsequent plane is greater by a constant amount than that on the previous plane (Fig. 86). The distances moved in the planes may be in fractions of the unit atomic spacing. Twinning results in re-orientation of the zone in which it occurs; like slip, it uses up the capacity for deformation, but because of the re-orientation may introduce further planes favourably arranged for ordinary slip, or it may improve the orientation of existing

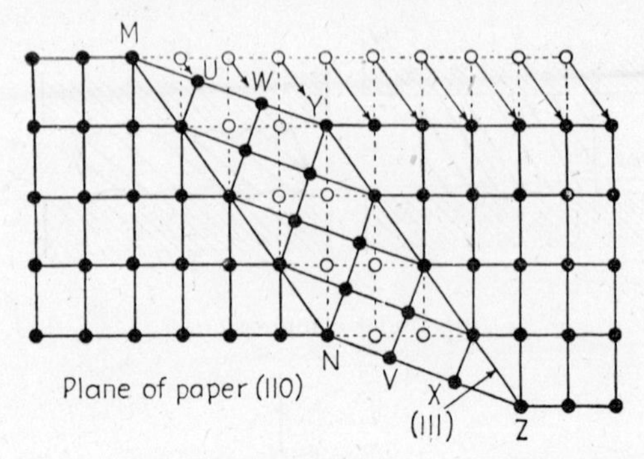

FIG. 86. Diagram illustrating twinning. From *Principles of Physical Metallurgy*, by G. E. Doan and E. M. Mahla. McGraw-Hill.

planes. Twinning may also occur on planes on which slip is not occurring. For example, in zinc a little twinning may occur at room temperature on the pyramidal planes, which are only active for slip at higher temperatures.

Orowan has described a third mode of plastic deformation, namely *kinking*, occurring in single crystals of cadmium when compression is applied parallel to the slip planes (the basal planes, as cadmium is hexagonal) (Fig. 87); he suggests that in a number of cases ordinarily glide may be preceded by kinking.

Under conditions of prolonged stressing at comparatively high temperatures, viscous flow, as described in the next section, may occur in single crystals.

Mechanism of slip and theories of work-hardening. Originally it was considered that during slip there was bodily movement of one part of the crystal over the other, and this is in agreement with visual observations. However, comparison of the calculated values of stress theoretically required for this form of slip with

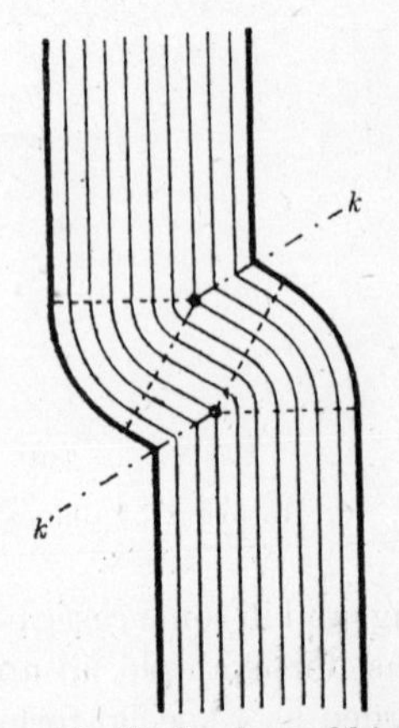

FIG. 87. Mechanism of kinking. The thin parallel lines represent the glide planes. On compressing parallel to the glide planes, the crystal suddenly collapses in the way shown, so that in the planes of kinking (dash-dotted lines k and k') the slip planes are sharply bent. The broken lines indicate the boundary of wedge-shaped regions of flexural glide. From E. Orowan, *Nature*, 1942, **149**, 643.

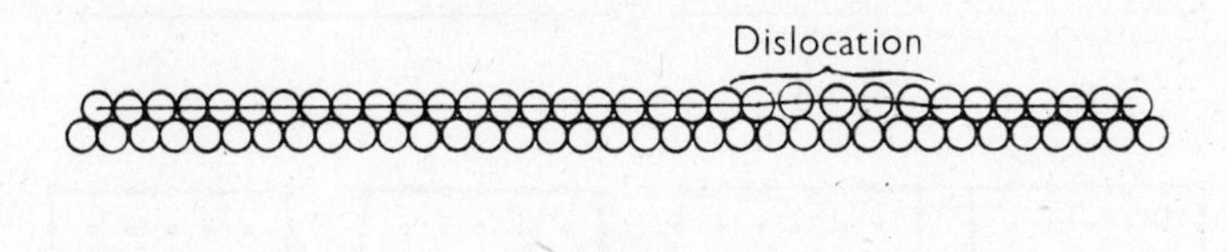

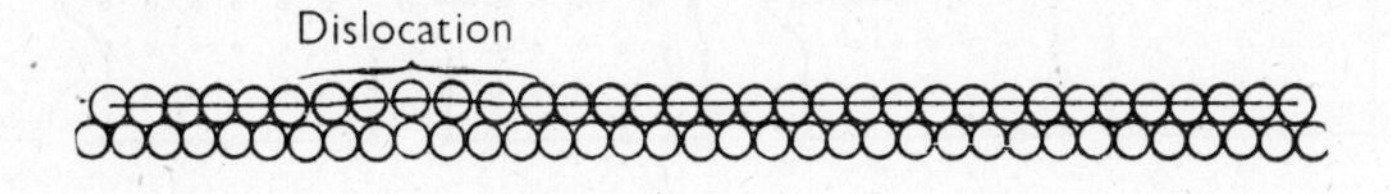

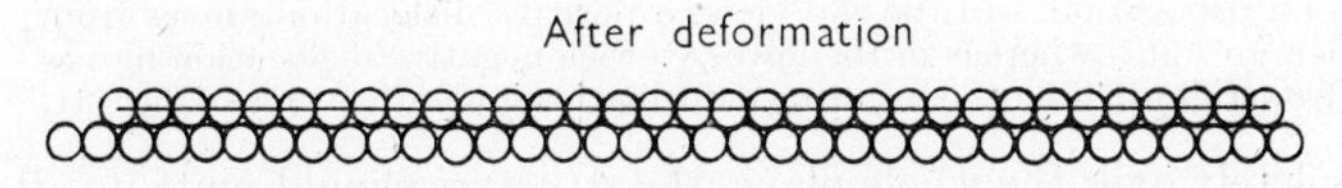

FIG. 88. Simplified picture of slip by means of a dislocation.

those stresses actually necessary (which are considerably lower) has warranted an alternative mechanism. The modern view is that slip takes place step by step by the movement of so-called **dislocations** (Figs. 88 and 89). The dislocations are imagined to extend through the crystal, although not necessarily in a straight line. The application of the dislocation theory to metals was due to Orowan, Polanyi, and Taylor in 1934. There is no direct experimental evidence of this mechanism, but it is in accordance with known facts, and on its basis a useful theory is being built up.

It is generally agreed that the energy required to form a dislocation in an ideal crystal would be greater than that required initially to propagate one already present. The initial softness of single crystals is attributed to the inherent presence of imperfections (page 8), either as dislocations, or in a form easily convertible to dislocations. There is some experimental evidence of the presence of dislocations as growth faults in metal crystals.

It may be taken that twinning is likely to proceed also by the movement of dislocations.

In the first stages of plastic deformation, it appears that the crystal structure may not be greatly distorted. It will be seen from the representations of slip (Figs. 81, 88 and 89) that, provided slip occurs

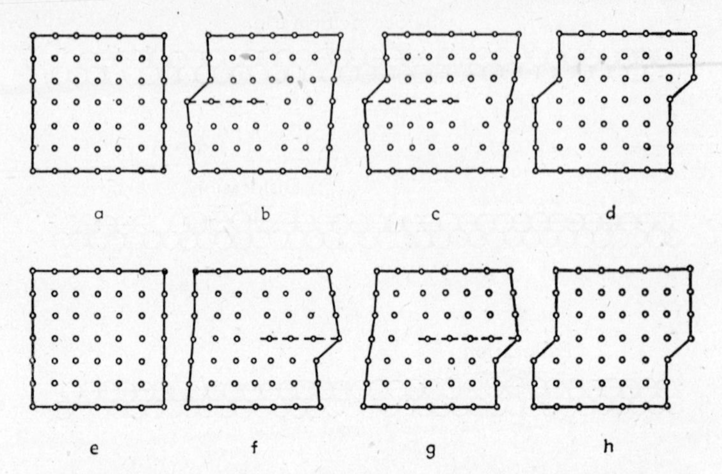

Fig. 89. Convential representation of the generation and movement of a dislocation. In the top views a positive dislocation moves from left to right, whereas in the lower views a negative dislocation moves from right to left; the resulting deformation is identical. From Barrett.

completely over the whole plane, the structure should mate up afterwards and continuity be regained without an increase in hardness, the dislocations passing out of the crystal. However, some dislocations remain in the metals and it is suggested that hardening results from their mutual interference and " jamming up ". For the continuation of deformation fresh dislocations have to be formed and propagated, although some may be reflected at the crystal surface or boundary, serving for more deformation. Mott and Nabarro point out that the experimental results indicate that increasing hardness is due to the increasing difficulty of moving dislocations against the " stuck " ones, rather than that of forming fresh dislocations, since the state of strain existing should favour their formation, although hindering their motion. It will be apparent how irregularities in a lattice due to alloying result in increased hardness. As deformation proceeds, the crystal structure as revealed by X-rays becomes distorted, planes appear to become bent and the lattice fragmented into small crystallites, clearly making continued deformation more difficult.

With regard to the older theories of slip, where it was imagined that simple gliding occurs, the first important explanation of strain-hardening was that of Beilby, namely the " amorphous metal theory ", which was later adopted and modified by Rosenhain in Britain and Archer in America. Beilby's theory originated from his earlier suggestion that the polishing (by abrasive means) of metal produced a *thin surface layer of flowed or amorphous metal.* It was presumed that something in the nature of melting occurred during polishing followed by drastic undercooling, the metal retaining an irregular random atomic arrangement similar to that in the liquid state. Applied to strain-hardening, it was suggested that, during slip, amorphous metal was produced along the slip planes. At first, slip was made easy while the amorphous metal was mobile ; but on its becoming rigid and hard, slip was prevented and forced to occur on other slip planes. When all the possible planes were used up, the metal ruptured. Hardness increased with the amount of amorphous metal. However, the theory was not regarded as explaining properly the point that latent slip planes harden as much as the active ones. No really complete alternative theory was offered. It was agreed that ease of deformation depended on an undistorted crystal structure, and that distortion caused by previous cold deformation increased the difficulty of further deformation. There is still no complete theory of the effect ; the whole problem is very complex, but the dislocation view is a likely base.

The amorphous metal concept was applied also to conditions at grain boundaries in polycrystalline metal. It was suggested that the grains were " cemented " together by zones of amorphous metal in thickness of the order of 100 atoms. It is more generally accepted now that the grain boundary zones consist of a transition structure existing over several inter-atomic distances, unless extended by the presence of impurities, which segregate here, especially in cast metal.

It will be appreciated, with regard to crystal boundaries and plastic deformation, that the difference in thought today from the amorphous metal view is largely one of degree. The viscous flow mechanism of creep has much in common with Beilby's concept. Electron diffraction techniques indicate that the structure of the polished surface (of the order of 30 A. thick) of a metal approaches the amorphous state, or is composed of extremely tiny grains.

(*b*) **Cold-working polycrystalline pure metals.** The mechanism of deformation inside each crystal is essentially the same as in single crystals, although certain modifications are introduced by the boundaries and changes in orientation. It is suggested that dislocations are likely to be generated at grain boundaries. It is apparent that the dislocations are more likely to be retained in the metal in the polycrystalline state.

The main effect of the varying orientation on the different grains may be summarised by stating that in polycrystalline metal each

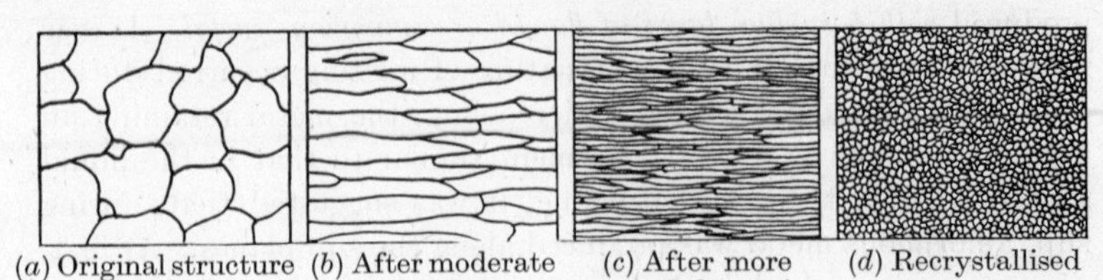

FIG. 90. Effect of cold work on the grains of a pure metal.

grain restricts the deformation of its neighbours, for the metal deforms as a whole, while cohesion between the grains is maintained. Hence, polycrystalline metal is usually stiffer than single crystals, and appreciable plastic deformation does not begin until higher stresses are reached. With the slipping mechanism, it is difficult to imagine exactly what happens during deformation at the boundaries of a grain surrounded on all sides by others. It can be shown that the slip planes become bent near the boundaries. It is likely that some flow movement occurs at the boundaries. The restraining effect at the crystal boundaries is clearly shown by experiments carried out on special samples one crystal in diameter, of polycrystal tungsten wire ; after extension under tension, the wire assumed the shape of a bamboo rod. Similar results were obtained with molybdenum and other metals.

Normally the grains are elongated by working (Fig. 90), and there is a tendency in each one for the slip planes to be aligned into the direction of flow. Due to this movement, the grains are shown up at the surface. With large grains a noticeably rippled surface results. In very plastic metals, continued deformation results in the production of a fibrous microstructure (Fig. 90 and 96*a*). Under cold-working conditions, metals usually break ultimately across the grains, that is, in a transcrystalline manner (Fig. 91*a*). If weak impurities are present at the boundaries, especially in the form of continuous films, there may be intercrystalline fracture (Fig. 91*b*) ; this may also occur at fairly high temperatures, and under stress-corrosion conditions.

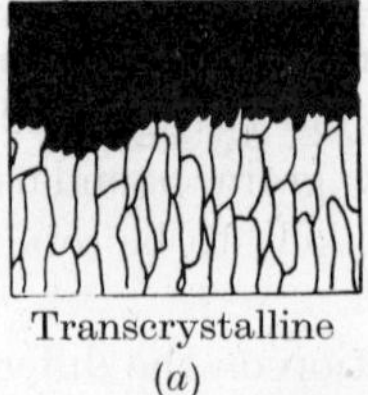

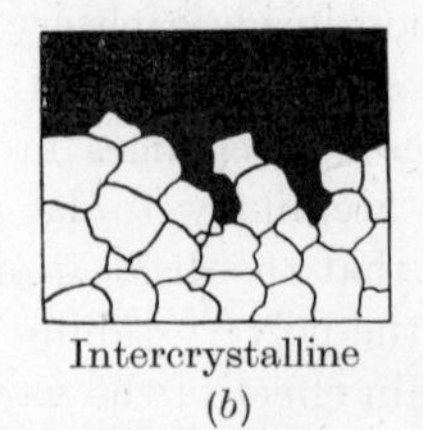

FIG. 91. Fracture in polycrystalline metal.

If the surface of a polycrystalline metal is polished, and then permanently deformed so that the polished face is not spoilt, slip bands or steps may be seen on this face under the microscope; polishing is necessary unless the surface is initially smooth, or the grains are extremely large. The bands run parallel across each grain and change direction from grain to grain (Fig. 92). The bands are small steps on the surface similar to those produced in single crystals only smaller; repolishing removes them. Recently it has been found that optically visible slip bands in aluminium, when examined by means of the electron microscope, are resolved into clusters of finer lines or steps.

FIG. 92. Slip bands in aluminium. ×100. From G. R. Wilms and W. A. Wood, *J. Inst. Metals*, 1949, **75**, 698.

Similar markings may be seen on a polished and etched section of cold-worked metal, and may be referred to as strain lines. Strain lines are small grooves etched in the surface (Fig. 97*b*), and forming the trace of the slipping planes in the plane of the section. Strain lines continually reappear with repeated polishing and etching. The preferential attack yielding strain lines would appear to be due to the distortion of the crystal structure in the neighbourhood of the planes. As a general rule, distorted metal dissolves more than undistorted; grooves are formed also at grain boundaries during etching.

In the case both of slip bands and strain lines, more than one set may be visible in any grain; if the lines are wavy, this is sometimes attributed to simultaneous slip on two sets of planes, although it may be caused by elongation of the crystals. It has been quite commonly accepted that although slip bands are revealed on the surface of metal after fairly slight deformation, it is necessary to produce comparatively severe deformation before strain lines are seen after polishing and etching. It is probable that slip may occur to some extent without its being possible to show up strain lines, but their detection is very dependent on the care and method of preparation and examination. It should be noted that the terms " strain line " or " band ", and " slip line " or " band " are very loosely used. Other strain markings are found in various cases, but the above, together with twins, are most common.

Preferred orientation. The grains of cast polycrystalline metal may be orientated at random ; this condition gives the least difference in mechanical properties between different directions. Columnar growth in cast metal usually produces some similarity in orientation, known as **preferred orientation.** Polycrystalline metal, especially that with hexagonal crystal structure, with preferred orientation has directional properties. Preferred orientation may also be produced from working, for the tendency is to force the slip planes of each grain into the direction of flow. The preferred orientation may or may not be removed by recrystallisation.

Preferred orientation does not reach the conditions in single crystals. Thus, for example, in the preferred orientation produced in face-centred cubic metals by wire drawing, corresponding atomic directions in each grain may be parallel or tend to be parallel to the drawing direction.

(*c*) **Changes following deformation in pure metals ; hot-working.** In the main, these changes apply equally well to single- or poly-crystals.

Recovery. Cold-worked metal may soften gradually without change in microstructure at comparatively low temperatures, depending on the metal ; the phenomenon is known as " recovery ". Internal stresses are also removed and this may occur without softening. Recovery is masked generally in commercial softening operations in which full recrystallisation occurs. Recovery may be an important factor at times in the behaviour of metals under prolonged stress. It is suggested that the mechanism of recovery involves the diffusion out of the metal of the dislocations produced during deformation.

Recrystallisation. At higher temperatures recrystallisation occurs, the atoms reverting to a regular arrangement, but of new orientation.

TABLE 8. TYPICAL RECRYSTALLISATION TEMPERATURES OF PURE METALS (COMMERCIAL PURITY)

Metal	*Temperature*
Iron	450° C.
Nickel	600° C.
Gold	200° C.
Copper	200° C.
Aluminium	150° C.
Magnesium	150° C.
Tungsten	1200° C.
Zinc	Room temperature
Lead	Below room temperature
Tin	Below room temperature

The cold-worked structure disappears and is replaced by a new set of regular undistorted grains having a regular crystal structure (Figs. 90*d*, 93, 96 and 97), although there may be similar imperfections in the crystal structure to those described for cast metal. Recrystallisation commences in the more distorted regions such as grain boundaries and slip planes ; the orientation of the nuclei may be at random or there may be some preference. As the temperature of cold-worked metal is raised, the tendency to recrystallise increases. The temperature at which this first occurs within a reasonable length of time such as is suitable for a practical operation is known as the **recrystallisation temperature** ; some examples are given in Table 8. The

FIG. 93. Partial recrystallisation in super-purity aluminium. ×100. By courtesy of the Director of the National Physical Laboratory and *La Revue de Metallurgie*.

tendency to recrystallise increases with severity of straining as well as with temperature, but is decreased by the presence of soluble impurities. The approximate beginning of recrystallisation may be detected from the microstructure, by X-ray examination, by hardness or some other mechanical test (Fig. 105); but the stages at which recrystallisation is first detected by different methods will not necessarily correspond. At each temperature for each metal there will be a minimum stable and even grain size increasing with the temperature and decreasing with severity of cold-working, and recrystallisation may be taken as the whole process of obtaining this condition. Initially, recrystallisation will involve the growth of the new crystals into distorted metal; but later there will usually be some growth into recrystallised metal, that is, some of the larger recrystallised grains will absorb smaller ones until the stable grain size is reached. If heating is continued at the recrystallisation temperature after a stable grain size has been reached, or at a higher temperature, the grains will gradually become larger, some being absorbed by others; this is known as **grain** or **crystal growth.** Sometimes, with continued heating, there is sudden preferential growth of certain of the grains, which eventually absorb all the others; this phenomenon is known as **secondary recrystallisation** or **secondary grain growth.** The growth of one crystal at the expense of another merely involves change in orientation of the atoms of the absorbed crystal to that of the growing crystal. For experimental purposes, by utilising the right conditions, polycrystalline metal may be converted by recrystallisation and crystal growth into a single crystal. The latter is the most stable state, and crystal growth results apparently from a tendency to reach this form.

At any temperature of recrystallisation, increased previous strain leads to reduced crystal size. However, after slight amounts of deformation of some metals an abnormally large grain size is produced, larger than that obtained with less or more strain; this is referred to as **abnormal grain growth.** The connection between this and secondary recrystallisation is not clear.

A feature of the microstructure of certain metals in the recrystallised state is the presence of twin markings in the grains. The differently orientated zones produced by twinning, on polishing and etching, have different reflecting powers from the rest of the grain, and show up under the microscope as contrasting darker or lighter bands. The twin markings may run completely or partly across a crystal. Straight-edged twins are very commonly seen on many of the grains of recrystallised face-centred cubic metals (Figs. 96 and 97); in fact they are a sure indication of recrystallisation. Twins are not normally visible in aluminium, although they may be seen in certain instances. In face-centred cubic metals twins do not usually appear until after recrystallisation ; for this reason they are sometimes known as " annealing twins ", although it is considered that they are initiated during deformation. Twinning marks are not generally apparent in body-centred cubic metals, although under certain conditions they may occur. Twins are common in hexagonal metals both in the cold-worked condition (" deformation twins "), and in the recrystallised condition. The deformation twins may have wavy boundaries, whereas after recrystallisation they may have straighter edges.

The general effects of cold-working recrystallised metal are essentially the same as for primitive cast metal. With regard to microstructure, slip markings are developed in twins, of different direction from those in the rest of the crystal, giving good indication of the different orientation. With elongation of crystals, twins become bent (Fig. 97*b*). Recrystallisation and crystal growth also proceed again in a similar manner. Cold-worked recrystallised metal will have superior properties to cold-worked cast metal.

In practice, when it is required to soften cold-worked metal so as to permit further working, or for service, the metal is heated to cause recrystallisation. The heating treatment is known as " annealing ", although this term has other meanings. It is apparent that by proper regulation of the degree of straining and the temperature and time of annealing, the grain size of finished material can be controlled. Generally, for further working, such as in sheet for cold pressing and deep-drawing, a medium grain size is required ; it must not be too small, or else the metal is stiff, and not too large or else the surface becomes roughened on working, producing the so-called " orange-peel " effect. Nevertheless, the grain size will be considerably smaller than in the cast state. For example, Jevons has stated that a mean grain diameter of 0·035–0·045 mm. is suitable for the deep-drawing and pressing of many shapes from sheet of most of the metals which can be shaped in this way. In general, fine-grained metal has better mechanical properties and resistance to applied stress at cold-working temperatures than coarse-grained metal.

It is desirable for service that the microstructure should be uniform, and for this thorough working and heating are necessary. In some cases strung-out membranes of insoluble impurities may mechanically prevent crystal growth during annealing, and zones of very fine grain size will be produced. This is undesirable, in sheet for example, for it will cause directional properties. Zoning in extruded lead pipes is an interesting example of uneven grain size resulting from other causes (page 415).

Generally, recrystallisation does not occur when cast metal is reheated, nor is there any change in grain-boundary configuration. This is to be expected, for the grains should not be strained, and, being formed at the highest possible solid temperature, should be essentially stable. Further, impurities at the grain boundaries will also tend to restrain grain growth. It is not unlikely, however, that prolonged heating of very pure metals may cause some growth.

If cast metal is cooled very drastically, pronounced internal stresses will be stored up in the metal. These stresses may relieve themselves by plastically deforming the metal so that hot-working occurs during cooling after solidification, or recrystallisation on reheating; or they may result in hot-working on annealing. It has been shown by Boas and Honeycombe that cycles of cooling and reheating may cause plastic deformation in non-cubic metals such as zinc due to the different expansion and contraction in different directions; this is known as " thermal fatigue ". Recrystallisation of cast metal may result from such treatment.

Sub-recrystallisation or *polygonisation* sometimes may be observed in the form of small sub-grains within the main ones (Fig. 94). Such

FIG. 94. Polygonised structure in super-purity aluminium, developed by creep at 200° C. ×100. By courtesy of the Director of the National Physical Laboratory and *La Revue de Metallurgie*.

structure also results, even in cast metal, although from a different cause, apparently preferential precipitation ; it is sometimes referred to as veining.

Strain ageing. So far, the phenomena following cold-working have resulted in softening. The remaining outstanding effect is "strain ageing", which results in an increase with time, at room or higher temperature, in hardness and ultimate tensile strength after straining has ceased. Strain ageing is pronounced, for example, in commercial iron and steel (Fig. 95), although it also proceeds in other metals. Strain ageing may be important in creep and fatigue behaviour.

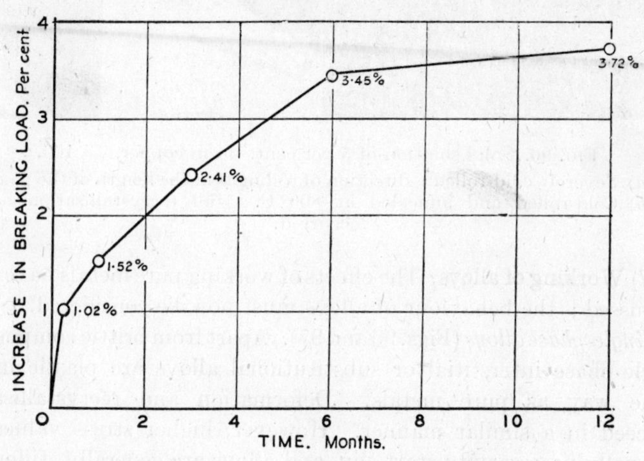

Fig. 95. Strain ageing of cold-drawn mild steel wire at room temperature. From J. C. Hudson, *Iron & Steel Inst.*, Spec. Rep. No. 8, 1935, 195.

Hot working. Resistance to slip decreases with increase in temperature. In certain cases, new sets of planes may become active with rise in temperature ; for example, at higher temperatures the pyramidal planes become active in magnesium and zinc, and this is utilised in practice Further, in hot-working, the effects of strain hardening are removed by recrystallisation as deformation proceeds. As a result of these various factors, deformation is easier hot than cold, and more can be carried out in one operation. Similar microstructures result from hot-working as from cold-working and annealing. In practice, wherever possible the bulk of working is carried out hot.

FIG. 96. Solid solution of 5 per cent. tin in copper. ×100.
(a) Severely cold-rolled : direction of rolling is in the length of the page.
(b) Cold-rolled and annealed at 800° C. ; full recrystallisation has occurred.

(d) **Working of alloys.** The effects of working pure metals have been discussed ; the behaviour of alloys must now be considered.

Single-phase alloys (Figs. 96 and 97). Apart from brittle compounds, single-phase interstitial or substitutional alloys are plastic in the same way as pure metals. Deformation and recrystallisation proceed in a similar manner. However, higher stress values are generally necessary to start slip, and alloys are generally stiffer and harder, with less total plasticity, than pure metals ; although some solutions may have increased capacity for deformation while being somewhat harder than the basis metal. The hardness of solid solutions increases with the amount of lattice distortion caused by the solute. Recrystallisation temperatures are higher for alloys ; few soften at room temperature after cold work. Hot-working or cold-working and annealing promote homogenity in alloys.

Two-phase or duplex alloys. Alloys, consisting of particles of a hard and brittle constituent embedded in a relatively soft matrix, are stiff to work ; the stiffness increases with the amount of hard constituent and the fineness of its dispersion. In cold-working such alloys, flow takes place in the matrix, and its crystals are elongated, and at the same time the particles of hard constituent may be broken up into smaller pieces, which are strung out in the direction of flow. When a continuous network of brittle phase is formed, the alloy becomes brittle and unworkable.

On the other hand, when the two constituents are plastic, they both undergo deformation, and by the same amount if they are equally plastic. If one is harder, the behaviour depends on the relative proportions and distribution of the two phases. When the structure consists of small amounts of the harder constituent existing as separate particles in a background of the softer one, there is a tendency for the latter to flow around the harder particles during deformation, and undergo proportionately more straining. The behaviour is similar in this respect to the first case considered above, except that in the present consideration the second constituent will not break up but will be deformed, although to a lesser extent than the softer. With the opposite type of structure, that is, soft particles embedded in a stiffer phase, the behaviour depends essentially on the properties of the latter. The above considerations refer to cold working.

Summing up, it will be seen that the behaviour of duplex aggregates is governed primarily by the properties of that phase which is continuous throughout the alloy, although when the alloy consists

(a) (b)

FIG. 97. Solid solution of 30 per cent zinc in copper. ×150.
(a) Recrystallised condition.
(b) Same material after 40 per cent reduction in thickness by cold rolling (direction of rolling is along length of page). From M. Cook and T. Ll. Richards, *J. Inst. Metals*, 1943, **69**, 364.

of hard particles in a soft matrix the behaviour is considerably affected by the dispersion of the harder phase.

Similar results are obtained with hot-working alloys in which two phases are present, except that relatively greater plasticity is obtained. Recrystallisation will proceed in one or both plastic constituents, depending on the temperature. The subsequent workability of an alloy consisting of hard particles in a soft matrix may be considerably improved by hot working, due to the breaking up of the hard particles. There is a tendency for broken particles to become rounded during heating, especially if they have some solubility in the matrix. Essentially the same structural effects are produced by cold-working and annealing.

Certain two-phase alloys become single phase on heating and it is usually advantageous to break these down hot if not to hot-work them completely. A difference in microstructure results, depending on whether the alloys are worked completely as single phase, or containing small amounts of second phase. The working of α–β brasses around 60 per cent copper, 40 per cent zinc will be taken as an example. In the cast state, these alloys have a Widmanstätten structure (Fig. 62*a*-*c*). If they are hot-worked as all β, the

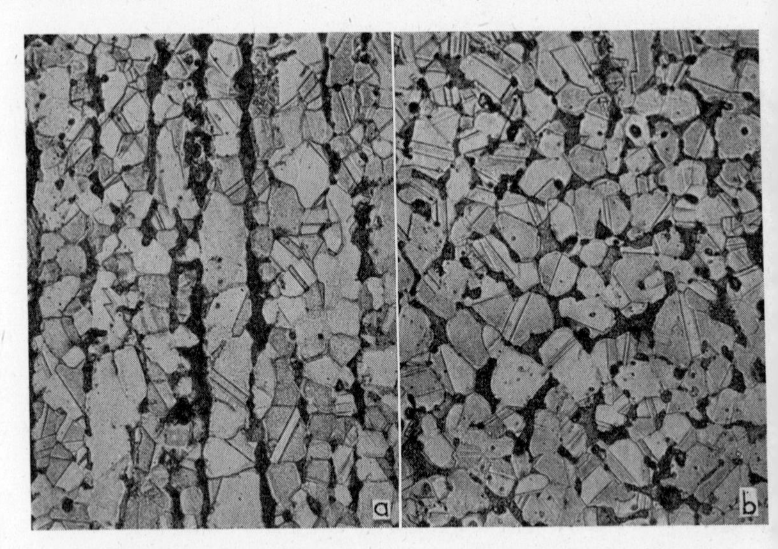

FIG. 98. Microstructure of α–β brass after hot-working in two-phase condition. $\times 350$.

(*a*) Longitudinal section with direction of working along length of page.

(*b*) Cross-section.

structure after working is recrystallised β, and on cooling a Widmanstätten structure is again formed, although usually finer than in the cast state. If the brasses are worked at such a temperature that the structure is nearly all β plus a small amount of α, the hot-worked structure consists usually of twinned α, and β, elongated in the direction of working (Fig. 98); the β may or may not show recrystallisation. In many cases there is no sign of the changes in composition and proportions of the α and β with fall in temperature, but sometimes precipitated α may be seen as well as the twinned α. In practice, due to heat losses, metal is hot-worked at decreasing temperatures, and thus in extruded α–β brass the structure may vary along the length of the extrude with the forms described above.

Also in this type of alloy the grain size may be refined by careful re-heating into the single-phase region, when smaller grains may be formed than existed previously; the changes involved should be distinguished from recrystallisation. The formation at room temperature of a metastable structure in duplex alloys by fast cooling may make the alloy unworkable.

BEHAVIOUR OF METALS UNDER STRESS IN SERVICE

The following factors affect the behaviour of metals under stress:

(*a*) actual value of the stress or range of stresses;

(*b*) type of stress and mode of application;

(*c*) time of application, or in the case of repeated stress, the frequency;

(*d*) temperature of the metal;

(*e*) composition and condition of the metal;

(*f*) environment.

Some of these factors have been discussed already under the conditions of intentional plastic deformation. The behaviour of metals will now be outlined from the aspect mainly of their ability to withstand stressing in various ways. The changes in mechanical characteristics that result from stressing will also be described. Unless otherwise stated, it should be assumed that the effects described refer to polycrystalline metal.

Elasticity. Part of the strain produced on stressing is elastic and disappears on removal of the stress. However, it is considered unlikely that there is an ideally elastic range, from zero stress to some definite limit, in which strain is directly proportional to stress and is temporary. But, on a practical basis at room or moderate temperatures, an elastic range may be regarded as existing in a number of metals used for their strength, especially, for example, in various steels. On the other hand, cast copper, and cast iron, even under conditions of practical testing, have little or no elastic range.

In practice, to determine the *extent* of the elastic range, for example, in tension, measurements are made on a length of metal of uniform cross-section. The bar is stressed and unstressed along its length to gradually increasing values. If the original length is regained when a particular stress is removed, the metal is considered to be still in the elastic range. The stress at which the metal first fails to regain the original length is taken as the **elastic limit**; and no consideration is given to the internal state. It is apparent that the value obtained depends on the sensitivity of the measuring instrument. It also depends on the time of application of the stress. Elastic limit determinations are made with fairly brief applications of the stress, no greater than a few minutes. If the stress is applied for a long time, gradual deformation or " creep " may occur. Creep becomes pronounced at elevated temperatures relative to the melting point. With most structural metals at room and moderate temperatures under stresses, at least within the apparent elastic range, if not at somewhat greater values, creep may be disregarded from a practical aspect. Marked creep occurs at low stresses even at room temperature in low-melting point metals such as lead and tin.

Stress-strain curves : elastic region. A common method of representing and assessing behaviour (from certain angles) of metals under uniform stressing of one kind is to plot a graph of stress against strain from measurements made during the testing of specimens of the metal. For all practical purposes, stress* is calculated on the original load-supporting area of the specimen, and strain† in the case of tension or compression on the original length. For fundamental considerations this may lead to false conclusions; *true* stress (calculated on actual load-bearing area), and *true* strain (each increment based on the length from which it was produced) graphs should be used. Where pronounced creep is involved, the stress-strain diagram is unfortunately limited, for it does not show the effect of time. In such cases behaviour can be properly assessed only by considering in addition a number of strain-time curves for particular stresses.

Fig. 99 shows the general form of stress-strain curve obtained in

* Load divided by original area.
† Change in length divided by original length.

tension; the slope and characteristic values vary from metal to metal. Similar curves are obtained by plotting stress against percentage elongation or percentage reduction in area. The discussion here applies to the cold-working temperature range. The initial straight-line portion OE of the curve represents the elastic range, E being the elastic limit. Accurate determination of the first part of the stress-strain curve is another method for determining the elastic limit. An index to the elastic properties is given by the slope of OE, which is known as the **modulus of elasticity** or **Young's modulus** (Table 9).

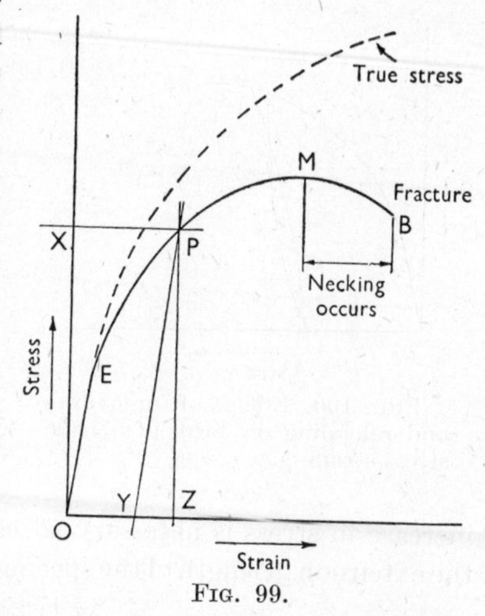

FIG. 99.

TABLE 9. YOUNG'S MODULUS OF ELASTICITY FOR PURE METALS (CARPENTER AND ROBERTSON)

Metal	Modulus
Nickel	30×10^6 lb. per sq. in.
Iron	30×10^6 lb. per sq. in.
Copper	16×10^6 lb. per sq. in.
Aluminium	10×10^6 lb. per sq. in.
Magnesium	$6{\cdot}25 \times 10^6$ lb. per sq. in.

Plastic region of tensile stress-strain curve. At E (Fig. 99) plastic straining begins and proceeds according to the mechanism described in the early part of this chapter. At any stress X the amount of plastic strain is given by OY, where YP is parallel to the straight-line portion OE, and the elastic strain by YZ. If the specimen is unloaded, it will contract along PY, although there may be some lag. On reloading, the curve essentially follows YP, and then PMB. It may be taken that this applies approximately in a number of cases provided there is no strain ageing, and the stress and strain are *always* calculated on the original dimensions of the unstressed specimen. However, it has been shown that the loading and unloading curve may form a closed loop (Fig. 100), and that the curve may be modified considerably by previous compressive straining.

The stress-strain curve shows that the resistance to stress of the specimen increases up to a maximum known as the maximum stress, or **ultimate tensile stress** (Table 10); it then decreases, with the result

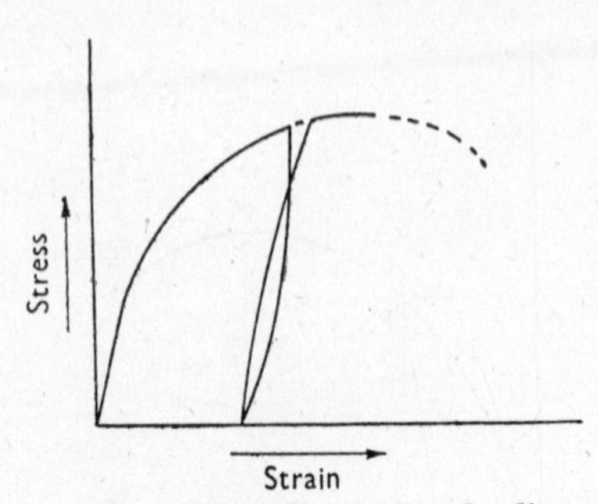

FIG. 100. Effect of unloading and reloading on form of tensile stress-strain curve.

that the breaking stress *B* is less than the maximum sustained by the specimen. The increased resistance to stress results from work hardening—the steeper *EM* the greater the work hardening. Actually, the resistance of the metal to stress increases continuously until rupture occurs, and this is shown when the true stress is plotted (Fig. 99). Up to the maximum *M*, although the load-bearing area is reduced, the work hardening is such that an increase in stress is necessary to carry on fairly rapid deformation; the extension in length of the specimen results in a uniform contraction

TABLE 10. TENSILE CHARACTERISTICS OF PURE METALS (high purity) IN RECRYSTALLISED CONDITION

Metal	Ultimate tensile stress tons/in.^{2}	Elongation percentage on 2 in.	Reduction in area (at point of fracture) (per cent)
Iron - - -	18	45	75
Copper - -	14	58	73
Aluminium -	4	60	95
Magnesium -	11	5	6

in area. The portion *MB* corresponds to the local thinning down or "necking" of the specimen (Fig. 101), which occurs in many cases; here, although the intrinsic resistance of the metal to fairly rapid straining still increases, it is no longer sufficient to compensate for the reduced area, and the load necessary to continue deformation decreases. The uniform extension is high when the rate of strain-hardening is high; considerable local elongation is obtained when strain hardening is not appreciable. Thus a metal may give good elongation figures in test, but be stiff to work; a high reduction of area indicates easy cold-working. Sometimes there is no necking, for example, in β-brass, and the breaking stress and ultimate stress coincide; the capacity for deformation is exhausted before the resistance of the specimen decreases. A high sustained stress below the ultimate may cause failure by creep.

In certain conditions, materials consisting largely of pure iron

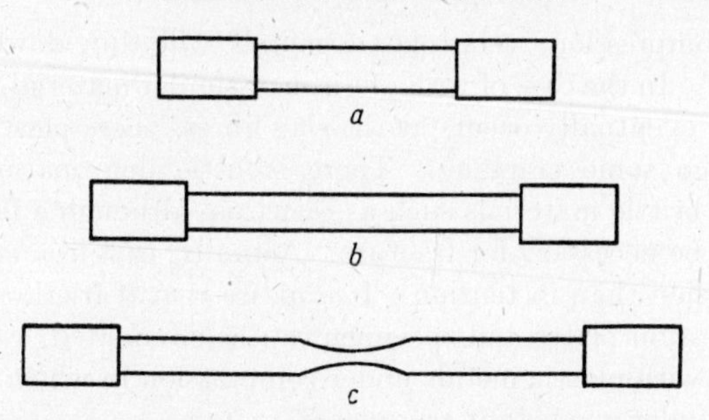

FIG. 101. Extension of test-piece. (*b*) uniform, (*c*) local.
Figs. 101, 103 and 104 from *Metals*, by (Sir) H. Carpenter and J. M. Robertson. Oxford Univ. Press.

crystals, such as ingot iron, "Armco" iron, wrought iron, and mild steel show a pronounced yield point (Fig. 102); prior to this the amount of permanent deformation is small. The deformation during yielding is uneven and gives rise to surface markings known as **Lüder's lines.**

Tensile fractures are generally transcrystalline, but under some conditions they may be intercrystalline.

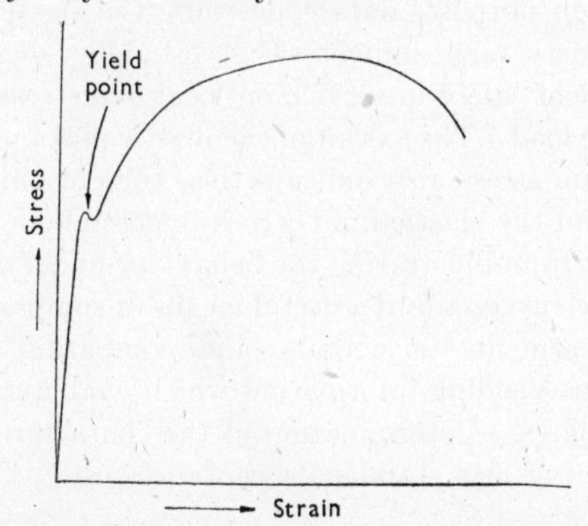

FIG. 102. Stress-strain curve for mild steel, showing yield point.

Stress-strain relations for compression. Compression stress-strain curves for polycrystalline metal have essentially the same form as those for tension, except that there is no portion corresponding to MB in the tensile curve (Fig. 99), for in compression the load-supporting area increases during testing. Torsional straining may also give a similar form of curve. The modulus of elasticity in compression is usually of the same value as that in tension. There is also a modulus for uniform compression in all directions, known as the **volumetric modulus**; its value differs from that of Young's modulus. The shear modulus is also different.

Under compression, very plastic metals will thin down almost indefinitely. In the case of wrought iron or similar material, cracking or splitting eventually occurs at the slag fibres. Less plastic metals also undergo some cracking. There is little deformation before fracture in brittle materials such as cast iron, although a fairly high stress may be necessary for fracture. Actually, cast iron is stronger in compression than in tension. It appears that if friction between the compression plates and specimen can be eliminated, a condition is attained with plastic metals under compression in which straining continues under a constant true stress.

Stress-strain curves on single crystals vary with the orientation of the crystal, especially in the case of hexagonal metals. However, it has been shown with a number of metals that if shear stress is plotted against shear strain along the slip planes, the differences can be eliminated. The same curve for different orientations and different forms of stressing is obtained.

General value of stress-strain curves. Stress-strain curves do not show the effect of time; but where creep is not important, they supply for design purposes data concerning the elastic range. The extent of the plastic range indicates the workability of the metal, and its ability to yield safely in service on local overstressing, and thus redistribute the load. The extent of the plastic portion and the value of the maximum stress also indicate the range of emergency overstraining beyond the elastic limit which is possible in a structure in service. Apart from illustrating the behaviour under certain aspects of stressing, the curves afford a useful means of comparing the effects of various treatments on metals, and comparing also different metals and thus yielding information which enables the production of improved alloys. Determination of the characteristics of tensile stress-strain curves is a standard acceptance test.

EFFECT OF VARIOUS FACTORS ON STRESS CHARACTERISTICS

In general, *alloys* are stronger and tougher, though with less ductility, than pure metals. Although the elastic limit is usually raised by alloying, it is difficult to generalise about Young's modulus. In the plain carbon steels the modulus is not markedly affected by carbon content or heat treatment, nor does it change much in the low-alloy steels. On the other hand, noticeable differences, depending on the crystal structure and composition, may occur in non-ferrous alloys.

Grain size, temperature and previous working. The remarks which follow with regard to the effects of grain size, temperature and previous working apply both to pure metals and alloys.

The effect of grain size varies; in many cases, at cold-working temperatures, polycrystalline metal is stiffer and tougher than single crystal, the stiffness increasing with decreasing grain size. At relatively elevated temperatures the position may be reversed. With polyphase alloys the effect of the fineness of the microstructure has already been pointed out.

There is usually an increase in tensile strength, elastic limit (or similar characteristic) and modulus of elasticity with fall in *temperature*, and a decrease with rise; elongation generally increases with rise in temperature. In some cases special phenomena may affect the behaviour. Thus, for example, strain ageing may cause an increase in strength and decrease in elongation at first with rise in temperature (Figs. 103 and 104). Many non-ferrous metals, such as copper, aluminium and nickel, and alloys based on them, retain their toughness and ductility (sometimes showing increases), together with increased tensile strength at very low temperatures, but iron, carbon steels and some alloy steels become brittle, whereas other alloy steels do not (Table 11). With low-carbon (ordinary) steels and iron, the brittleness is first indicated by low impact figures, often long before there is noticeable diminution in elongation; in some cases this brittleness is manifested around 0° C.

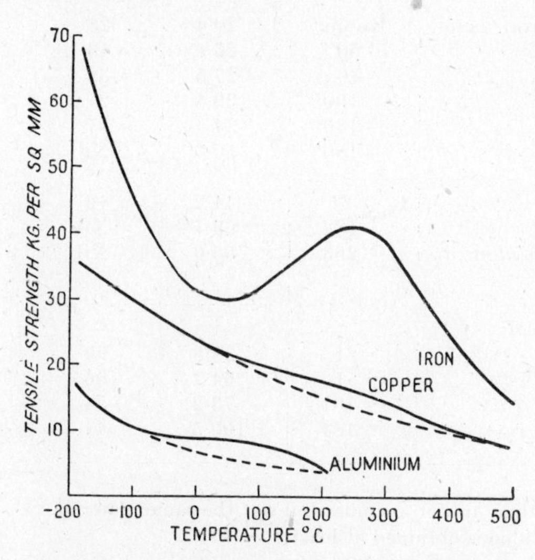

FIG. 103. Variation of tensile strength with temperature in pure metals. From Carpenter and Robertson.

TABLE 11. MECHANICAL CHARACTERISTICS OF METALS AT LOW TEMPERATURES

Metal	Temperature (° C.)	Ultimate tensile stress (tons per in.^{2})	Elongation percentage on 2 in.	Izod impact value (ft. lb.)
Pure aluminium, rolled and annealed	Room	4·4	36	19
	−40	5·2	40	19
	−120	6·3	40	21
	−180	9·3	44	27
Aluminium alloy, Al−4% Cu; 0·5% Mg; 2% Ni in heat-treated condition	24	29·7	12·3	7*
	−80	30·8	14	7·5
	−180			8
Copper, annealed	24	14·0	48	43
	−80	17·2	47	44
	−120	18·4	45	44
	−180	22·7	58	50
Monel. 28·86% Cu, 0·28% Mn, balance Ni. Annealed	24	31·6	41	90
	−80	38·1	40	90
	−180	50·4	51	97
"Armco" iron, as received	Room	20·4	28	78
	−50	26·5	43	
	−70	27·5	38	4†
	−100	29·8	27	
	−120	34·4	17	
	−180	50·0	Nil	1·5
Carbon steel, 0·78% C, 0·10% Mn. Annealed at 800° C.	21	44·2	12	
	−182	69·1	Nil	
	−253	55·0	Nil	
Stainless steel, 0·06% C; 18·25% Cr, 9·7% Ni. Annealed	21	38·8	69	119
	−51	64·2	66	117
	−101	73·2	54	
	−184	100·5	44	119

* Impact values are for a similar but not the same material.

† This low value is obtained at least at −40 °C.

Note: In those metals which become brittle with no elongation the yield stress or equivalent rises to the same value as the ultimate stress.

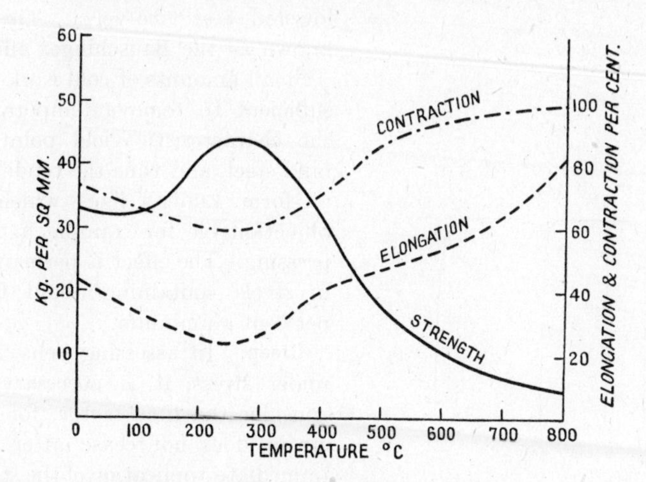

FIG. 104. Effect of temperature on mechanical properties of carbon steel. From Carpenter and Robertson.

The effect of the polymorphic transformation on the low-temperature properties of tin has been discussed in Chapter 1.

In general, if specimens are cut from *cold-worked* metal, the elastic limit and ultimate tensile stress will be higher than those for the metal in the cast or recrystallised state ; but the total ductility will be less (Fig. 105). However, although the elastic limit under tension is raised by previous tensile strain, the limit under compression is

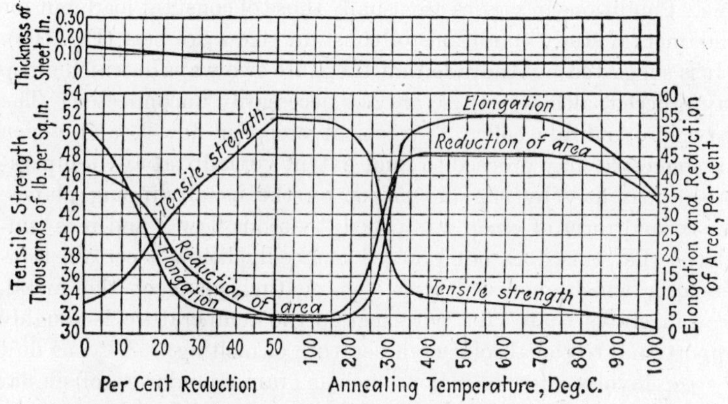

FIG. 105. Effect of cold rolling and annealing on the mechanical properties of copper. From *The Principles of Physical Metallurgy*, by G. E. Doan and E. M. Mahla. McGraw-Hill ; after Mathieson and Thalheimer.

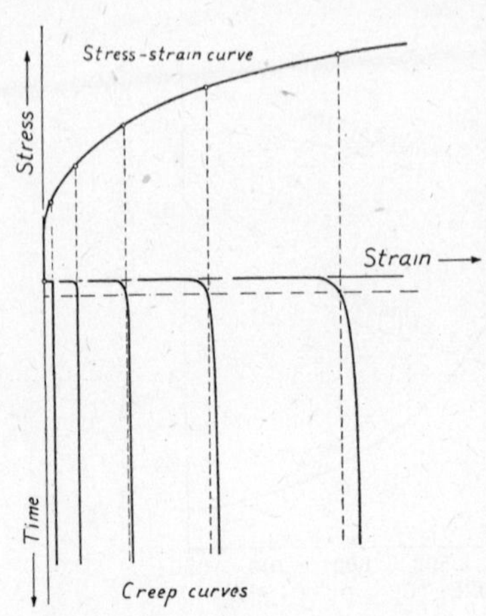

FIG. 106. Creep curves corresponding to loads at various points of the stress-strain curve. Figs. 106 and 108 are reproduced from E. Orowan, *J. West Scot. Iron & Steel Inst.*, 1946–47, 54, 45.

lowered, and vice versa. This is known as the **Bauschinger effect.**

Small amounts of cold work are sufficient to remove temporarily the characteristic yield point of mild steel, and thus the tendency to form Lüder's lines which is objectionable, for example, in cold pressing. The effect is permanent in steels containing about 0·05 per cent aluminium.

Creep. In assessing behaviour under stress, it is necessary to consider the *time* factor, for the strain does not cease after the immediate application of the stress but continues with time and may eventually lead to fracture (Figs. 106–108). This continuous deformation under prolonged stressing, that is, **creep,** may occur under any type of static stress such as tension, compression, bending, torsion or shear ; but it has been mainly studied with axial loading in tension under conditions of constant load. Weights are hung on one end of the specimen, while the other end is held fixed, and the extension read at regular intervals ; extension is then plotted against time. Conditions in service are usually those of constant load, but for fundamental study conditions of constant stress are best (Fig. 108).

It is suggested by Andrade that there are two ways in which creep may proceed, although these are not necessarily unconnected. The first type Andrade called " transient creep or flow ", and which it is suggested may proceed to some extent virtually at any temperature, apparently by slip movement on the usual slipping planes. The second form of creep was called " viscous flow " and it is considered that this does not proceed markedly below a certain temperature, which increases with the melting point of the metal. Orowan states that " for pure metals the temperature is roughly proportional to the absolute temperature of melting." Viscous flow or creep involves flow in regions such as grain boundaries, of similar nature to that which occurs in amorphous solids, such as pitch, under sustained stress (pitch will flow gradually under its own weight). With metals, such as pure lead at room temperature, it is found that at appropriate temperatures creep increases with decrease in grain size, that is, increase in the proportion of grain boundary material. Further, micro-examination of the test specimens

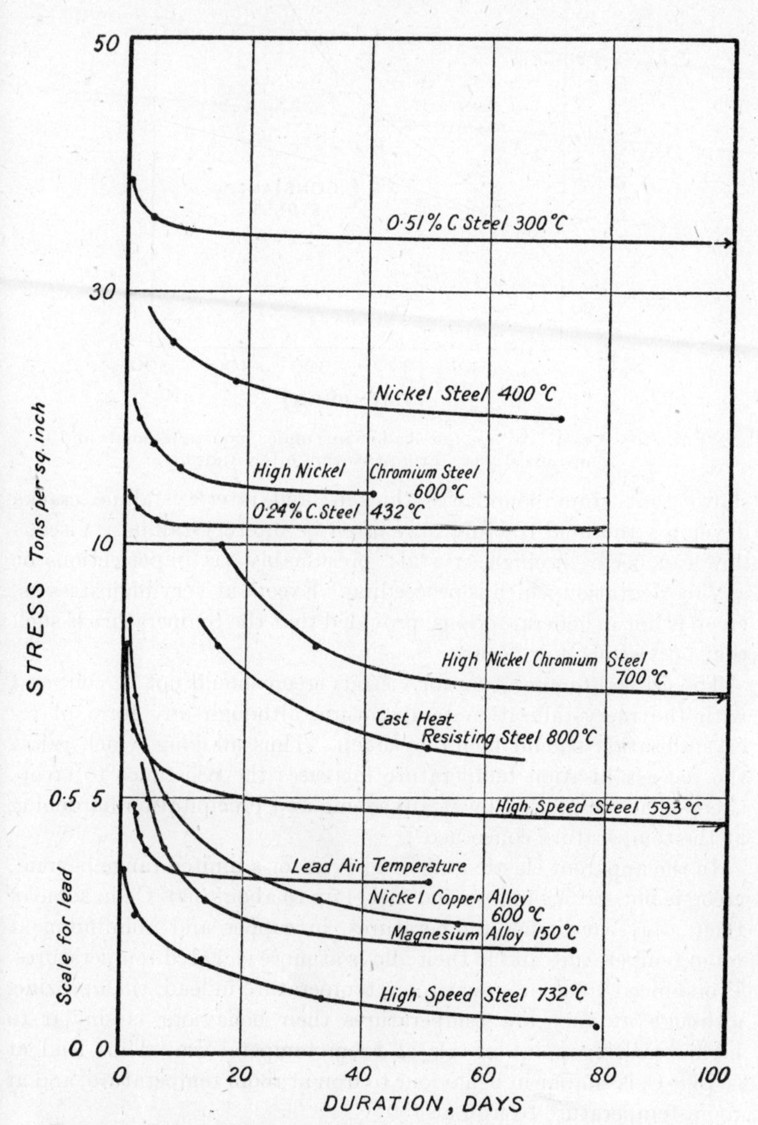

FIG. 107. Relations between stress and time to fracture for various metals. Figs. 107 and 111 from *The Creep of Metals*, by H. J. Tapsell. Oxford Univ. Press.

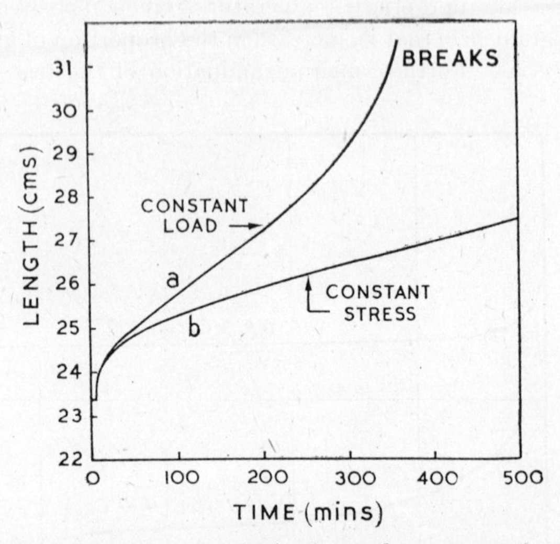

FIG. 108. Creep curves for lead wire under constant load and constant stress. From Orowan, after Andrade.

shows that grain boundaries thicken, and intercrystalline cracks develop ; the final fracture may often be intercrystalline. Viscous flow can occur in single crystals, presumably via imperfections or any reorientation which is proceeding. Except at very high stresses, creep is not in general serious, provided that the temperature is such that no viscous flow occurs.

The critical temperature for viscous creep should not be confused with the recrystallisation temperature, although any form of recrystallisation should facilitate creep. Thus alloying which raises the recrystallisation temperature increases the resistance to creep. Creep is also inhibited by strain ageing and precipitation hardening at the temperature concerned.

In the apparent elastic range and even for a limited range beyond, creep is not serious in iron and nickel up to about 350° C., in some of their alloys at higher temperatures, in copper and aluminium at room temperature and in their alloys at more elevated temperatures. Pronounced creep occurs at room temperature in lead, tin, and zinc, although at very low temperatures their behaviour is similar to higher melting point metals at room temperature. Thus lead at – 180° C. is similar in behaviour to iron at room temperature, and at room temperature to iron at 450° C.

Fatigue. In service, metal is frequently called upon to operate under various conditions of repeated stress. The stress repetitions may take the form of repeated impact, twisting, tension, or compression, or alternate twisting or bending backwards and forwards, or of alternate tension and compression. There may be a mean stress of zero or some definite value. In addition, there may be steady imposed loads. Under the above conditions, "fatigue" failures may occur and the upper stress value may be well below the ultimate tensile stress of the material. The resistance to fatigue is known as **endurance.**

The fatigue behaviour of metals has been studied under a variety of conditions, but the bulk of the work has been carried out with the Wöhler type of test (Fig. 109), in which a specific load is applied to one end of a rotating specimen, and the stress changes from a certain value in tension (+) to the same value in compression (−), so that the mean stress is zero. The conditions of stressing are essentially the same until failure commences; then when the effective area is reduced, the stress rises. The usual method of testing is to determine the number of reversals required to cause failure at various stresses. The value of the stress range R or S, or usually $R/2$, is plotted against the number of reversals, N, to cause failure (or log scales are used). At room temperature, for a number of metals including steel, it is found that the curve becomes horizontal (Fig. 110). The value of R at which this occurs is known as the **fatigue range, limiting range of stress,** or **endurance range.** Expressed as $\pm R/2$, it is known as the **fatigue** or **endurance limit,** or **limiting stress.** In the fatigue range, life is indefinite. The results obtained apply specifically to the condition of the specimens used, although affording guidance for practical conditions. At room temperature with steel, the limit is reached at about 10^7 reversals; with some non-ferrous metals a limit has been obtained at 5×10^7 reversals (Table 12). In other cases limits have not yet been determined, and if they exist many more reversals are necessary for their determination. In the latter case an endurance limit may be quoted, qualified by the number of reversals the metal will withstand at this value.

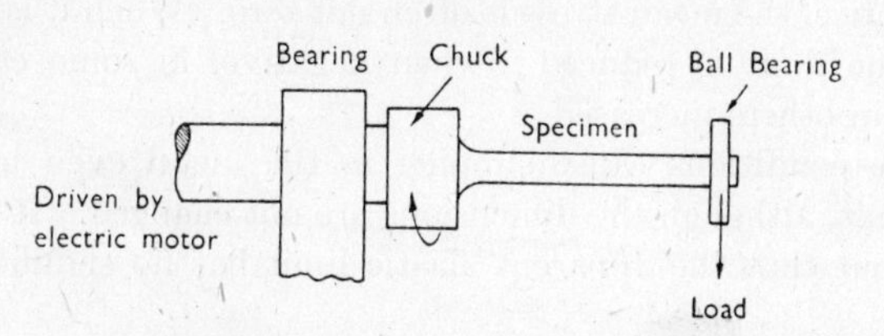

FIG. 109. Principles of Wöhler fatigue test. A revolution counter is arranged to record the number of cycles.

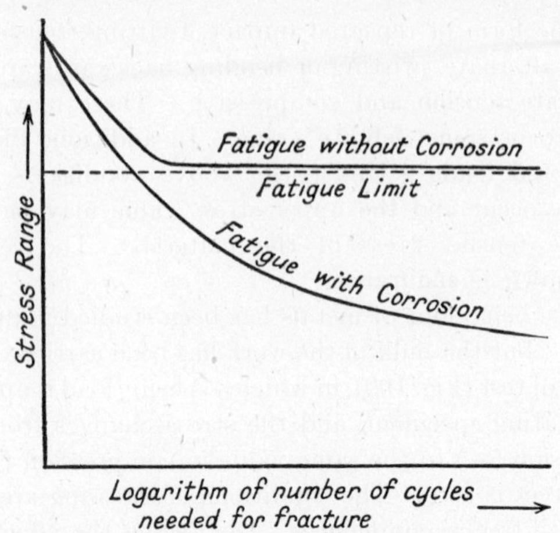

FIG. 110. *S*-log *N* curve, with and without corrosion. From *An Introduction to Metallic Corrosion*, by U. R. Evans. Arnold.

TABLE 12. FATIGUE LIMIT OF VARIOUS METALS IN POLISHED AND NOTCHED CONDITION. (After Carpenter and Robertson)

Material	U.T.S. tons/in.²	Fatigue limit	
		Polished	Notched
Brass - - - - -	21·8	8·9	8·9
Mild steel - - - - -	22·3	12·1	9·5
Mild steel - - - - -	34·3	17·2	11·4
Stainless steel - - - - -	43·0	15·2	15·2
Nickel-chromium steel annealed	46·8	29·9	19·1
Medium carbon steel - -	63·5	26·7	17·2
Nickel-chromium steel, hard -	68·6	34·3	19·1
Nickel-chromium-tungsten steel, hard- - - - - - -	103·0	43·8	20·3
Cast iron (grey) - -	7·4	4·5	4·5
Cast iron (grey) - - -	15·8	8·9	8·9

In practice, the mean stress is often not zero. When it is positive, the fatigue limit is reduced ; when negative, in some cases it is reduced, in others increased.

Fatigue conditions cause slipping in the metal even below the elastic limit, although the dimensions are not changed. It has been pointed out that the apparent elastic limit has no significance for fatigue.

Above the fatigue limit, cracks eventually develop in the slip areas, the stress is concentrated at them, and they are propagated through the specimen. Fatigue fractures usually show two areas, one where failure is due to fatigue, and the other where rapid failure has occurred when the stress rises due to the reduction in load-supporting area. At room temperature in structural metals, fatigue cracking is transcrystalline; but at elevated temperatures it may become intercrystalline. Fatigue failure in lead at room temperature is intercrystalline. The factors distinguishing between failure and survival in fatigue are not known. X-ray examination gives no definite information on this point. Indeed, no method of examination is yet known which will detect whether metal is in the safe range or not, although this may become possible with damping capacity measurements.

TABLE 13. EFFECT OF VARIOUS WORKSHOP FINISHES ON FATIGUE STRENGTH OF 0·33 PER CENT CARBON STEEL (Thomas)

Type of finish	Estimated maximum reduction in fatigue strength compared with finely polished surface (per cent)
Turned - - - - -	12
Coarse file - - - -	18 to 20
Bastard file - - - -	14
Smooth emery - - -	7·5
Coarse emery - - - -	6
Fine "Carborundum" - -	2 or 3
Accidental scratches (maximum found) - -	16

A number of factors profoundly affects fatigue behaviour, such as surface conditions and contours, the frequency of stress changes, temperature, corrosion and pre-stressing of various kinds. Sharp changes of section or cracks cause stress concentration and markedly reduce the fatigue limit (Table 12); this is referred to as **notch sensitivity.** In a similar manner the **surface finish** is very important (Table 13). The fatigue limit generally increases with the ultimate tensile stress, and is thus raised by any factors which improve the strength of the metal, such as by alloying, precipitation hardening, or cold working. Compressive surface stresses, due to nitriding or shot peening, for example, are also known to improve fatigue resistance. However, the notch sensitivity increases with the fatigue limit. Notch sensitivity decreases with increase in plasticity, for a plastic metal has the ability to give and redistribute the stress if it builds up anywhere. In practice, a balance must be struck between good fatigue resistance and low notch sensitivity.

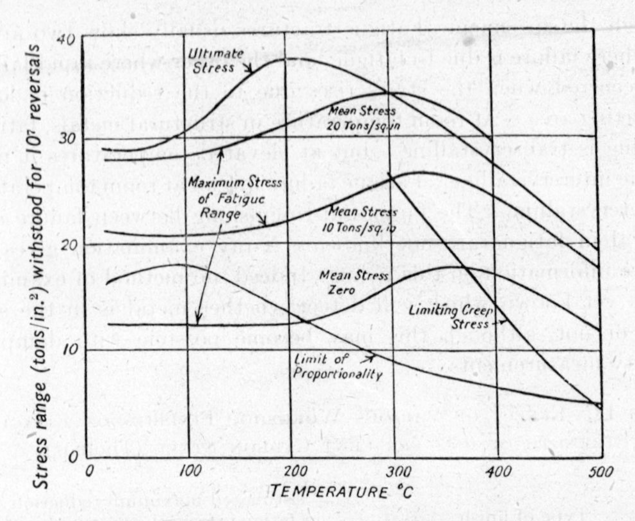

FIG. 111. Effect of temperature on fatigue ranges of 0·17 per cent. carbon steel. From Tapsell.

At low or moderate temperatures with respect to the melting point, the rate of application of the stress (up to at least about 6000 cycles/min.) does not appear to be important, though the limit may be raised at extremely high frequencies. At elevated temperatures the frequency is important.

The fatigue limit appears to increase with fall in temperature and decrease with rise in temperature, although strain ageing may cause a rise at first as in steel (Fig. 111). It is doubtful whether there is a fatigue limit at relatively elevated temperatures. At elevated temperatures, creep becomes important with regard to life in service (creep resistance decreases with rise in temperature) especially if the mean stress and dead load are not zero, when creep predominates, although fatigue resistance is the criterion at low temperatures. Creep resistance increases with increase in grain size; hence coarse-grained metal may be preferable at high temperatures, whereas fine grain is best at low temperatures for good all-round mechanical properties.

Damping capacity. The possibility of indefinitely sustaining repetitions of stress in the fatigue range is associated with the damping capacity of metal, which is its internal ability to cause vibrations in it to die out. Such vibrations may be set up in service, and unless damped by the metal itself or external factors, they may under certain conditions rise to dangerous sizes.

Effect of environment. Pronounced corrosion or oxidation of a metal under stress may reduce the effective load-supporting area, and thus increase the value of the stress ; eventually, if attack is marked, failure may occur. Also, stress may intensify corrosion or oxidation by breaking or flaking off a protective skin of reaction product, and thus expose the underlying metal for further attack.

However, more marked effects result when stress and corrosion act virtually simultaneously.

In the case of sustained static stress, the phenomena are known as **stress-corrosion.** Stress-corrosion failures may be intercrystalline, when normally fracture would be transcrystalline ; they generally occur in alloys. Examples are known in some magnesium-base and aluminium-base alloys, copper-zinc alloys and certain ferrous metals. A notable example is a brass containing about 30 per cent zinc, 5 per cent aluminium, and $1\frac{1}{2}$ per cent each of iron and manganese, balance copper (that is, a high-tensile brass). This brass consists of grains of β-electron compound plus well-distributed small particles of an iron-bearing compound. In the cast condition, the alloy has an ultimate tensile stress of 50 tons per square inch ; in air it will sustain tensile stresses almost up to this figure for forty days, and afterwards in ordinary tensile test will manifest no weakness (fracture is transcrystalline in both cases). If, however, the brass is subject to sustained stress in contact with sea water or dilute sodium chloride solution, intercrystalline cracking and failure may occur within a few days at stresses as low as 35 tons/sq. in. and possibly lower. Under constant load the fractures are usually only of intercrystalline inception, for once the effective section has been reduced by cracking the increased stress on the remainder will cause rapid transcrystalline failure.

No such weakness is found if the metal is left unstressed in contact with the sodium chloride solution, and then stressed after washing and drying. If an ordinary short-time tensile test is carried out with the specimen in sea water, low results are obtained and a tendency to intercrystalline cracking is observed. Similar stress-corrosion failure is experienced with bending.

Fatigue behaviour is also very susceptible to environment, and failure is intensified by simultaneous corrosion, known as **corrosion-fatigue.** Under such conditions a fatigue limit is not generally obtained (Fig. 110). The resistance to corrosion-fatigue can be improved by various surface treatments and coatings.

Molten metals, such as solders, may seriously penetrate stressed metal.

Internal stresses. Orowan defines internal or residual stresses "as those existing in bodies upon which no external forces are acting". Internal stresses may arise in a number of ways. For example, in cold-working, it will be appreciated that on the small scale the existence of dislocations or similar distortions in the crystal structure results in a state of internal stress ; on a larger scale uneven working produces internal stress. Internal stresses are also produced by rapid and uneven cooling, and arise from constitutional changes in alloys. Orowan points out that a polyphase alloy, on account of different coefficients of expansion of its phases, may be stress-free only at one temperature, namely that at which the structure was formed.

The presence of internal stress in a metal may cause distortion and even cracking, and is likely to affect behaviour under stress. Internal stresses are useful when they oppose service stresses but harmful if they supplement them. In corrosive environments they may give rise to stress-corrosion phenomena.

It should be noted that the presence of equal tensile stresses acting in three perpendicular directions in a metal inhibits plastic deformation, and conditions approaching this in practice, from service stresses or combined with residual stresses, will cause brittleness.

An outstanding example which is attributed to (internal) stress-corrosion is the **season cracking** of cold-worked high zinc alpha-phase brass, such as Cu70/Zn30. Such brasses are frequently used in the cold-worked condition, preceded by hot-working, or cold-working and annealing. Internal stress is introduced by the final cold-working and, unless removed, the brass is susceptible to spontaneous intercrystalline cracking even in the atmosphere. The corrosive agents are not fully known, although moist ammonia is severe in effect (for standard test see page 470). Another phenomenon, which has been explained in the same way, is the intercrystalline cracking or "caustic-embrittlement" of stressed mild steel in contact with hot solutions of caustic alkalis.

Internal stresses in both cast and wrought metal can generally be relieved by low-temperature annealing without affecting the mechanical properties. Thus the susceptibility of cold-worked brass to season cracking is minimised by annealing at about 250°–300° C. This treatment does not reduce the hardness obtained by cold-working ; in fact there may be a slight increase. Controlled mechanical work may also redistribute and reduce internal stresses, although this is not generally so effective as thermal treatment.

ADDITIONAL READING

1. *Metals,* by (Sir) H. Carpenter and J. M. Robertson. Vol. I. (Oxford Univ. Press, 1939).

2. *The Physics of Metals,* by F. Seitz. (McGraw-Hill, 1943).

3. *Structure of Metals,* by C. S. Barrett. (2nd. Ed. McGraw-Hill, 1952).

4. *The Distortion of Metal Crystals,* by C. F. Elam. (Oxford Univ. Press, 1935).

5. *Properties of Metallic Materials at Low Temperatures,* by P. Litherland Teed. (Chapman & Hall, 1950).

6. *The Fracture of Metals.* (Institution of Metallurgists, 1950).

7. *Fracturing of Metals.* (American Soc. for Metals, 1948).

8. *Properties of Metals at Elevated Temperatures,* by G. V. Smith. (McGraw-Hill, 1950).

9. *The Creep of Metals,* by E. Orowan. *West of Scotland Iron and Steel Inst.,* 54, pp. 45–96, (1946–47).

10. *Metallic Creep,* by A. H. Sully. (Butterworths, 1949).

11. *The Failure of Metals by Fatigue.* (Cambridge Univ. Press, 1947).

12. *An Introduction to Metallic Corrosion,* by U. R. Evans (includes chapter on effects of stress and corrosion). (Arnold, 1948).

13. *Symposium on Stress-Corrosion Cracking of Metals,* 1944. (American Society for Testing Materials and American Institute of Mining and Metallurgical Engineering, jointly, 1945).

14. *Symposium on Internal Stresses in Metals and Alloys,* Monograph and Report Series, No. 5. (Institute of Metals, 1948).

15. *Damping Capacity : A General Survey of Existing Information,* by F. C. Thompson. Research Reports of the Brit. Non-Ferrous Metals Research Association, No. 637 (1944).

16. *A Brief History of the Science of Metals,* by R. F. Mehl. (American Institute of Mining and Metallurgical Engineers, 1948).

17. *Progress in Metal Physics,* B. Chalmers (Edit.). Vol. 1. (Butterworths, 1949) ; Vol. 2. (Butterworths, 1950) ; Vol. 3 (Pergamon, 1952). Vol. 4. Pergamon, 1953).

References 16 and 17 are also general references for physical metallurgy.

CHAPTER 6

PHYSICAL EXAMINATION OF THE INTERNAL STRUCTURES OF METALS

THE intention in this chapter is to give the student a brief yet broad idea of the various methods used for studying the micro- and crystal-structure of metals. It does not set out to give full practical instructions.

MICROSCOPIC EXAMINATION

Microscopic examination of polished and etched sections of metal is carried out to determine the arrangement and size of the grains, the existence of permanent deformation, the distribution of the phases in polyphase alloys, as well as the presence of impurities, flaws and abnormalities. The structure seen is referred to as the **microstructure,** whereas that visible to the naked eye or under a low-power lens is known as the **macrostructure.** Up to the present in this book the distinction has not been made, and microstructure has applied to all aspects of the grain and crystal arrangement. The term **metallography** is sometimes applied to the study of macro- and micro-structures, although it is also used to embrace almost the complete field of physical metallurgy.

There is no real fundamental distinction between the macro- and micro-structure of a metal, for each supplies part of the picture. In the case of single-phase metals, there is only one type of crystal present ; and whether such crystals are resolved at low power depends on their size. Even if the crystals are very fine, the macroscopic appearance will often indicate whether or not they are uniform in size. Micro-examination of solid solutions may reveal heterogenity in the crystals not apparent from macro-examination. With alloys containing more than one phase, the grains may be distinguished on the macroscopic scale ; but generally microscopic study is necessary to reveal the inner arrangement of the different phases in each grain.

Useful information may be obtained from the study of fractures, using eye and lens. Recently a technique has been introduced by Zapffe in which fractured surfaces are studied under the microscope; it has been called **fractography.** This technique may yield information not obtained from prepared plane sections. However, a complete "library" of experience will have to be built up and correlated with the results of the usual microscopic technique.

The following account will be concentrated on the preparation of plane sections and their microscopic study, although some of the matter is not irrelevant with respect to macro-examination. Certain macro-techniques are discussed in Chapter 13.

Preparation of specimens for microscopic examination. A section is selected and a piece of convenient size containing the area required is cut off. Great care is necessary to obtain a representative sample. Several samples may be necessary with material that is likely to be heterogeneous. The usual practice is to select micro-samples in conjunction with macro-examination. For wrought metals, a longitudinal section should always be taken, that is, in the direction of working. Unless the edges of the specimen are of particular interest, they may be chamfered to avoid catching on emery papers or polishing cloth; similarly, the top edges may be made more comfortable to hold.

Small specimens such as sections of wire, thin sheet or surface coatings are best mounted in plastic before preparation and examination. Mounting gives a specimen of reasonable size to handle during preparation and affords protection to edges, preventing bevelling in polishing, although best protection is obtained from an electroplated metallic coating (for example, iron or copper) applied before mounting. For studying thin coatings, inclined mounting is advantageous in giving a wider area for examination. "Bakelite" and "Perspex" are commonly used for mounting: simple presses can be employed (Fig. 112), and the temperatures required are low. In those cases where heating is likely to affect the structure, cold-setting materials can be used: these can be cast in a metal ring around the specimen (Fig. 113). Prior to the introduction of plastics for mounting, low-melting point alloys were used, also cast in a ring, and still may have application in certain instances. A pronounced disadvantage of metallic mountants is that electrolytic effects may be set up during etching. In many laboratories all specimens are now mounted in plastic, where size permits. Sheet, plane or coated, sections can be conveniently handled without mounting by bolting between blanks and polishing together (Fig. 114).

The required surface is flattened by careful machining, grinding or

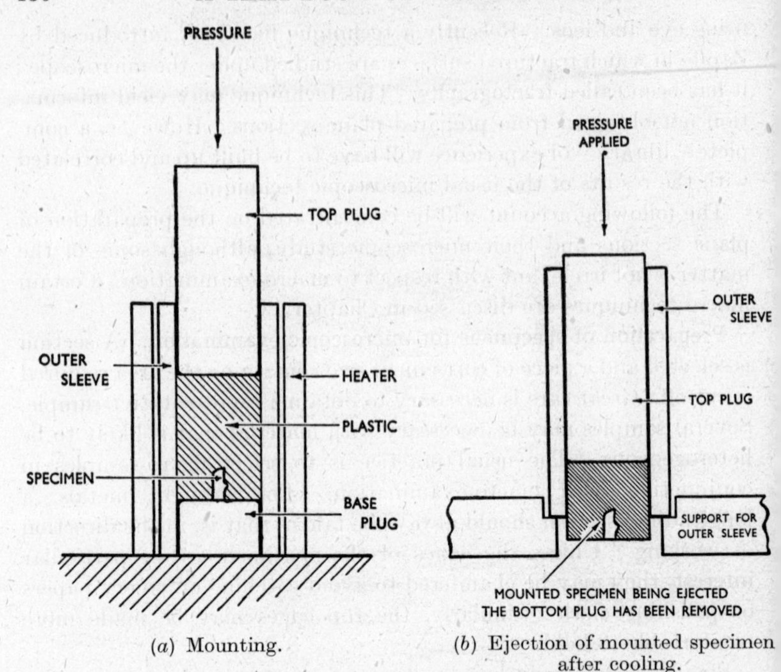

(*a*) Mounting. (*b*) Ejection of mounted specimen after cooling.

FIG. 112. Method of mounting micro-specimens in plastic. By courtesy of Cooke, Troughton & Simms Ltd.

filing, and then rubbed backwards and forwards on progressively finer emery papers, supported on a flat holder, until the surface is relatively smooth from the finest emery paper. The direction of rubbing is changed with each paper, so that the removal of the previous grinding marks can be followed. It is advisable that the rub-

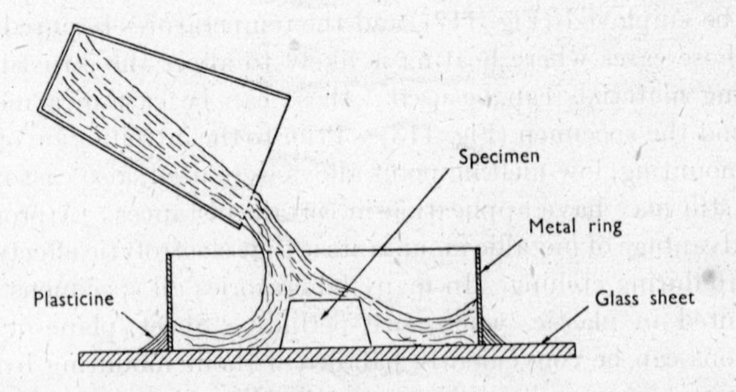

FIG. 113. Method of mounting in cold-setting plastic or low-melting point alloys.

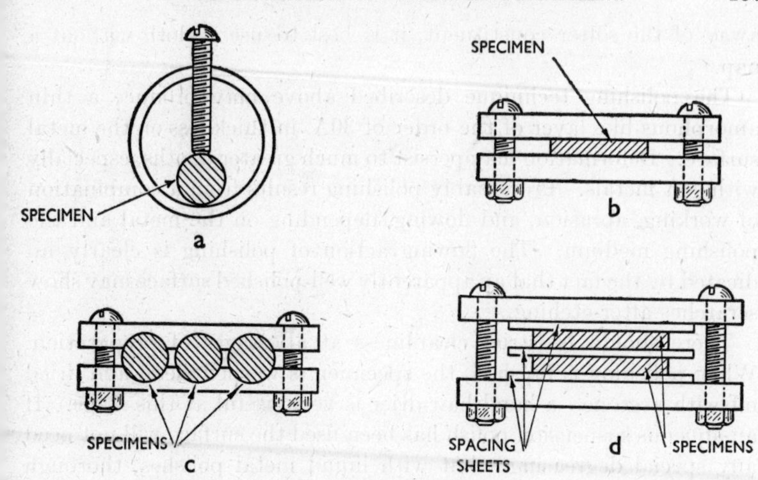

Fig. 114. Devices for holding small micro-specimens.
By courtesy of Cooke, Troughton & Simms Ltd.

bing each time should be continued after the previous scratches have been removed, because there is no doubt that the effects produced go deeper than the visible scratches. Severe distortion or overheating of the specimen should be avoided at all stages. With soft metals and those containing brittle constituents, a lubricant such as paraffin oil may be used to advantage on the emery papers ; paraffin is also useful in preventing overheating of the surface. This initial grinding may also be carried out on rotating grooved laps of paraffin wax or lead, the abrasive being added as a suspension ; during grinding some of the abrasive is temporarily imbedded in the lap.

After grinding with emery paper, the surface may be finally polished by fine powders, or electrolytically. In the former case the specimen is rubbed on a cloth such as serge, velvet or " Selvyt " (a proprietary cloth similar to velvet), which is covered with the polishing medium. This consists of a paste or suspension in water of very fine abrasive such as alumina (Al_2O_3) or magnesia (MgO), or sometimes commercial varieties of liquid metal polish may be used. The final polishing may be carried out in one stage or more, using several grades of polish. The cloth is held on a flat surface and the specimen rubbed on it by hand, or the cloth may be on a rotating horizontal wheel and the specimen held against it by hand or some mechanical means. The specimen should be rotated during polishing ; the pressure should be moderate to avoid smearing or burnishing the surface. Where relief polishing is likely, due to the greater wearing away of the softer constituent, it is best to use a cloth without a nap.

The polishing technique described above may produce a thin amorphous-like layer of the order of 30A. in thickness on the metal surface. Deformation may persist to much greater depths, especially with soft metals. Presumably polishing results from a combination of working, abrasion, and flowing, depending on the metal and the polishing medium. The flowing action of polishing is clearly indicated by the fact that an apparently well-polished surface may show scratches after etching.

There should be strict cleanliness at all stages of preparation. When polishing is finished, the specimen is washed clean and dried off with acetone—a hand hair-drier is very useful at this stage. If an aqueous suspension polish has been used the surface will not need any special degreasing; but with liquid metal polishes, thorough degreasing with acetone or a paste of fine magnesia or alumina is necessary.

Improved results can be obtained at the last stage by etching and repolishing before final etching. This treatment may remove a distorted layer and can be repeated several times to advantage. For soft metals, such as lead, in which distortion may be very severe, particularly from cutting and grinding, and which recrystallise at room temperature, this treatment is essential to remove the spurious top structure and obtain the true structure. The nitric acid—ammonium molybdate etch (Table 14) is most suitable for this purpose with lead; it is possible to remove the top surface with long etching, although alternate polishing (with metal polish on "Selvyt" cloth) and etching are better. With grey cast iron numerous repetitions of polishing and etching are recommended for satisfactory preparation of the graphite.

Excellent scratch-free virgin surfaces can be obtained in final polishing by using an aqueous suspension of fine alumina incorporating a small amount of etching solution. For example, a few drops of ammonia or ferric chloride may be added for copper and its alloys. Success depends on correct balance of etching reagent addition, grade of alumina and pressure of polishing; and a number of trials is necessary to establish the best conditions. It should be stressed that this technique does not yield an etched surface; the amount of reagent added should be insufficient for this. The conditions should be such that as fast as etching occurs the results are abraded away and vice versa. However, the two phases in duplex alloys may be distinguished if they have different reflecting characteristics.

Alumina for polishing can be made by roasting aluminium sulphate for an hour or more. A soft variety consisting essentially of the gamma-modification, is produced by roasting at around 650° C., and one with greater cutting power, in which the alpha-phase predominates, around 1200° C. In both cases it is possible to produce material with even action. After roasting, leaching in boiling water and sieving or elutriation may improve the product, but in many cases the alumina may be used directly in the roasted condition. The advantage of washing is that residual acidic sulphate is removed; this is desirable if the *p*H of the suspension is required to be controlled accurately, as in polishing zinc coatings on steel, which otherwise may stain due to electrolytic effects.

Magnesium is stained by water, and thus a simple aqueous suspension is not suitable for polishing. It has been found very satisfactory to polish magnesium and its alloys in an alumina suspension in dilute potassium dichromate solution which does not attack magnesium. Alternatively, most commercial liquid metal polishes can be used, as they do not stain magnesium.

Diamond powder is used for polishing very hard materials such as sintered tungsten carbide, for which the normal powders are not suitable. Also it has been demonstrated that in softer metals, relief polishing between constituents of different hardness is minimised by using diamond dust, because owing to its much greater hardness the difference in hardness between the constituents is masked. More recently, diamond abrasives have been shown to be advantageous for general work.

A good surface can be prepared on lead and other very soft metals by carefully cutting with a microtome, chisel or lathe tool. If the grains are coarse, little or no subsequent polishing will be needed. Care must be taken that any distorted layer is etched off; however, sometimes the grains show through as cutting proceeds, the cutting producing varying reflecting power for the different grains. With careful machining the latter effect can be obtained with harder metals. If low-melting point metals are cast on to a clean smooth sheet of glass, the metal solidifying in contact with the glass has an excellent surface suitable for direct microscopic examination, or after etching.

Electrolytic polishing. Electrolytic etching has been used for a considerable time, but more recent is the introduction of electrolytic smoothing and brightening, that is, polishing, which has commercial as well as metallographic applications. Probably the greatest individual contribution to the success and development of electrolytic polishing has been made by Jaquet, by whom it was introduced.

In electrolytic polishing, the specimen is made the *anode* in an electrolytic cell, and anodic dissolution under specific and often critical conditions results in smoothing and brightening. Numerous electrolytes are available ; for example, phosphoric acid for copper and its alloys, and mixtures of perchloric acid and acetic anhydride for steels and aluminium and its alloys. Care is necessary in mixing and using the second electrolyte ; the precautions given in the literature should be carefully observed. Generally, each operator has to spend time in getting used to a specific technique.

Best results are obtained in electrolytic polishing with single-phase materials. It should be noted that an electrolytically polished single-phase metal is structure-free and must be etched for the grains to be revealed. The presence of insoluble impurities or other phases generally causes relief polishing, due to different rates of solution. However, with care and minimising the amount of electrolytic polishing necessary, good results can be obtained with polyphase metals. For micrographic work it is best to start at least from finest emery paper, and quickest if some preliminary polishing is given first.

The particular advantage of electrolytic polishing is that an excellent scratch-free and undeformed surface can be obtained, although the surface may be slightly contaminated from the electrolyte. For routine work where satisfactory abrasive techniques are established, electrolytic polishing offers little gain ; but for special work or where difficulty is experienced, it is very valuable.

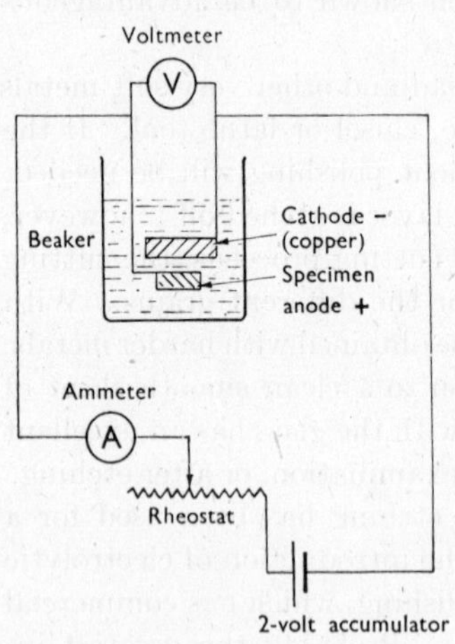

FIG. 115. Arrangement and circuit for electrolytic polishing of copper and its alloys.

To illustrate further the process of electrolytic polishing, the technique for copper and its alloys will be described, as only simple apparatus is called for. For details of other techniques the literature should be consulted. The circuit for copper comprises a 2-volt accumulator, ammeter, voltmeter, rheostat and the polishing cell consisting of the specimen and copper cathode arranged horizontally about 2–3 cm. apart in a beaker of the electrolyte (Fig. 115). Unless the specimen is mounted in " Bakelite ", the other surfaces should be " stopped-off " with lacquer. The electrolyte used is ortho phosphoric acid (H_3PO_4),

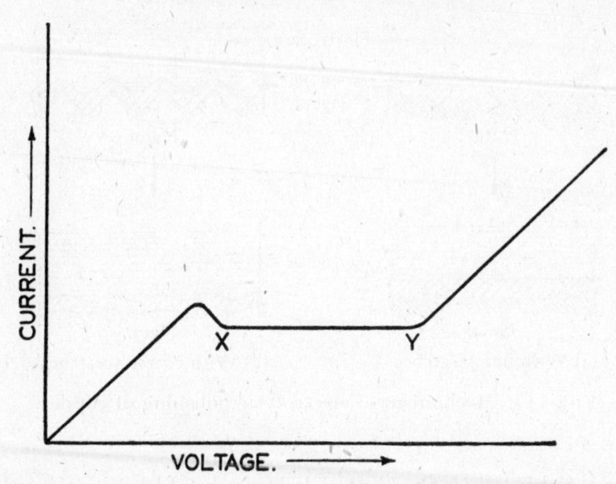

FIG. 116. Form of current/voltage curve obtained in electrolytic polishing of a number of metals including copper. By courtesy of Cooke, Troughton & Simms Ltd. Up to about X a dull etched surface results. Between X and Y is suitable for polishing. Beyond Y gassing occurs giving uneven polishing, although at very high current densities the gas bubbles do not adhere and a smooth polish may be obtained.

3 parts by volume of acid to 2 parts of water. Polishing can be controlled by the voltage, which lies in the range 1·4–2 volts, occasionally greater, depending on the specimen and the electrode spacing.

The correct voltage is determined by experiment ; a voltage is selected, say 1·8, and the circuit adjusted to give just over 1 volt initially. After a short time the voltage rises and is adjusted to the predecided value. Meanwhile there is a pronounced fall in the current. When the voltage and current become steady, polishing has started and will continue indefinitely provided the voltage is suitable, when the surface stays bright apart from a thin green film of electrolyte which adheres to it. If the voltage is too low, the surface will discolour (a form of etching occurs) ; if too high, gas bubbles will form and adhere to the surface, causing uneven polishing (Fig. 116). In both cases it may be necessary to remove the specimen and roughly re-prepare the surface before trying another voltage ; although in the case of a discoloured surface, satisfactory polishing conditions may be established by increasing the voltage gradually until the discolouration disappears. The optimum voltage in the polishing range can be found only by continued experiment.

Once polishing has started, a good surface is obtained in a minute or so with metal that has been roughly polished with liquid metal

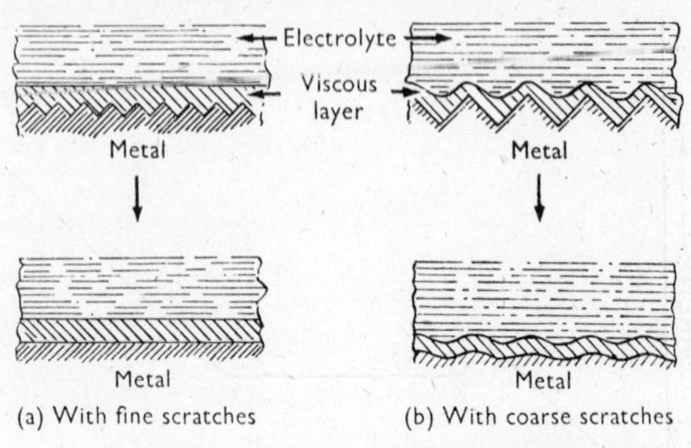

FIG. 117. Mechanism of electrolytic polishing of copper.

polish on " Selvyt " cloth ; but polishing should be continued longer to ensure removal of any deformed metal. It is found with this technique that although brightening and some smoothing will be produced from a very rough surface (such as from a file or coarse emery), the surface will not become completely level (Fig. 117).

With alloys such as brass it is advisable to remove the specimen from the electrolyte and rinse off that still adhering, before disconnecting the supply, otherwise copper may be precipitated on to the surface. The electrolyte can be used for a considerable time before renewal.

The polishing of copper and its alloys can be explained as follows. If fresh electrolyte is used, a thin green layer of electrolyte rich in copper will be seen to form on the surface of the metal when polishing starts. This layer is very viscous and of high resistance ; hence the rise in voltage and fall in current on its formation. If the undulations of the surface are not too great, the surface of the viscous layer remains level over the surface (Fig. 117). The current then takes the shortest path, and the peaks of metal within the layer are worn away. If the contours are pronounced, the viscous layer will follow them to some extent, and they will be perpetuated, although rounded off.

Etching. Etching is generally necessary to reveal the full features of the microstructure of a metal, although in certain alloys relief effects between constituents or different reflection characteristics will cause some aspects of the structure to be shown up on the polished surface. Cracks, porosity and inclusions will also be revealed ; and specimens should always be examined in the polished state. Normal grain etching will usually attack inclusions and destroy their characteristics. Elaborate etching procedures have been developed for distinguishing the various foreign inclusions in steel; similar procedure is adopted with regard to the constituents present in complex alloys, for example, the compounds that are found in many aluminium-base alloys.

The usual method of etching is by chemical means, using solutions which preferentially and delicately attack the metal (Table 14). An alcohol base is advantageous in numerous cases because attack is slower and more even, and slight traces of grease are dissolved off. Etching in solution is best done by immersion with the surface upwards. It is easier to etch in short stages until a satisfactory structure is obtained rather than for any fixed time, except in cases where comparison of etching rate is required. A slight bloom appearing on the surface is good indication that the etch is taking, where the grains are small and not apparent by eye. For microscopic work severe etching usually spoils the appearance of the structure. Long etching may develop small regularly shaped "etch pits", related geometrically to the crystal structure.

TABLE 14. STANDARD ETCHING SOLUTIONS

Etching Solution	*Application*
2 per cent HNO_3 in alcohol	Cast iron and steel Magnesium and its alloys Zinc and its alloys Tin and its alloys
Alcoholic ferric chloride, $FeCl_3$, 5 gm.; alcohol 95 ml.; conc. HCl, 2 ml.	Copper and its alloys Nickel and its alloys especially with copper Tin and its alloys
Water 95 ml.; conc. HCl, 1·5 ml.; conc. HNO_3, 2·5 ml.; HF (48%) 0·5 ml.	Aluminium alloys
Water 90 ml.; sodium hydroxide, 10 gm.	Aluminium alloys
Nitric acid—ammonium molybdate. Solution *A*: 80 ml. conc. HNO_3 in 220 ml. water Solution *B*: 45 gm. ammonium molybdate in 300 ml. water; for use—mix *A* and *B*, 1 : 1.	Grain-etch for lead
Alkaline sodium picrate: picric acid, 2 gm.; sodium hydroxide, 25 gm.; water, 100 ml.	To distinguish iron carbide and ferrite in steel: used boiling for 5–10 min.: carbide is darkened, ferrite unaffected.

Although, generally, etching is best done by immersion, specimens can be etched by swabbing on the reagent with cotton-wool, or by rubbing the specimen on polishing cloth which has been soaked in the reagent. The etched surface should not usually be touched after etching, unless a film is formed which requires removal.

In a few instances an etching reagent may be used to produce virtually a polished surface. Thus 1 part by volume of 100 vol. hydrogen peroxide and 3 parts of glacial acetic acid (freshly mixed and free from water) will smooth and brighten a rough-polished or grain-etched surface of lead, providing an excellent base for delicate grain etches ; the effect is most distinctive. Another example is 10 per cent nitric acid in alcohol, which produces similar effects with certain magnesium-base materials.

A varying number of factors contributes in revealing the structure of a metal by etching in solution. First, any flowed or amorphous-like layer will be dissolved. Then preferential attack at the boundaries between crystals of the same and different phases forms grooves which scatter the light differently from the body of the crystals. On the other hand difference of level from grain to grain may be produced, and if this is pronounced there may be steps at the boundaries rather than grooves ; although this effect will not on its own cause difference in brightness in the ordinary microscope from grain to grain, it will show up with the phase-contrast and the electron microscopes. Contrast is mainly developed between areas of different orientation in the same phase (grains and twins) because an extremely fine pattern is etched in the surface and the inclination of this pattern, hence the reflecting power, vary with the orientation (Fig. 118). Confirmation of this is obtained by rotation of the specimen under the microscope, when the grains lighten and darken as the inclination of the etch pattern to the

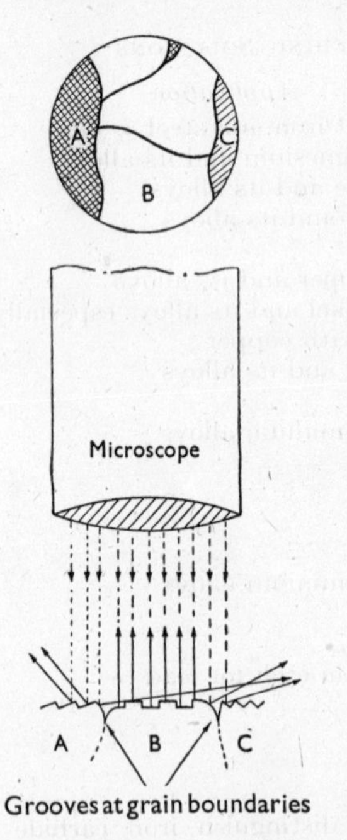

Fig. 118. Effect of etching in developing structure of single-phase metal.

incident light changes. When the grains are large enough to be distinguished by eye, it will be found that the brightness of any grain is altered by moving the specimen, or altering the position of the eyes or the light. In addition, with polyphase alloys, difference in reflection characteristics and particularly relief effects due to differential attack are important in showing up the structure ; in single-phase alloys heterogenity such as coring is also revealed by differential etching. Finally, there may be some differential oxidation, staining or deposition during etching. The effect of oxidation is particularly noticeable when etching copper-base alloys with a freshly made mixture of strong ammonia, 20-vol. hydrogen peroxide and water (1/1/2). This etch is most useful for revealing coring ; the structures in Figs. 38a and 39 (p. 56 and 57) were etched in this way.

Other forms of etching. *Heat-tinting.* If the polished metal is heated moderately in the air, differential oxidation may occur. This may explain in some cases, lead and copper, for example, the appearance of grain markings on the surface of as-cast metal ; the structure on the copper specimen shown in Fig. 10 (p. 10) certainly appeared to be due to this effect. The technique is useful for distinguishing different constituents in alloys.

Thermal-etching. When a metal is heated to a fairly high temperature in a vacuum or an atmosphere with which it does not form a stable compound, the grains are often shown up on smooth surfaces ; grooves may be formed at the boundaries, and sometimes striations on the surface. The effect is thought to be due to the transfer of atoms from one part of the surface to another ; it may be of considerable value in hot-stage microscopy.

The phenomenon of thermal-fatigue described on page 110, may reveal some aspects of the grains. The grain markings seen on the surface of zinc ingots without any preparation may be due to differential contraction ; ridges can be clearly seen at the grain boundaries (Fig. 9. p. 10).

Electrolytic-etching. Anodic dissolution in numerous electrolytes can be made to give an etched surface, as well as polishing.

A useful procedure for microscopic examination of the surface structure of large objects, such as rolls, is to polish and etch a small area and take a plastic replica, which can then be examined by transmitted light under a microscope.

METALLURGICAL MICROSCOPES

The usual form of metallurgical microscope uses ordinary white light. The principles of image formation for visual work are shown in Fig. 122 ; for simplicity, the lenses are shown as single elements, whereas in fact each has more than one component to give improved results, such as correction of objectives for chromatic and spherical aberration.

As the metal specimens are opaque, they are examined by reflected light. Two main forms of illumination are used, namely, oblique and direct. In oblique illumination the angle of incidence is large (Fig. 120*a*), whereas in direct illumination much of the incident light is more normal to the surface (Fig. 120*b*) ; this results in differences in appearance of the structure. Thus surface irregularities

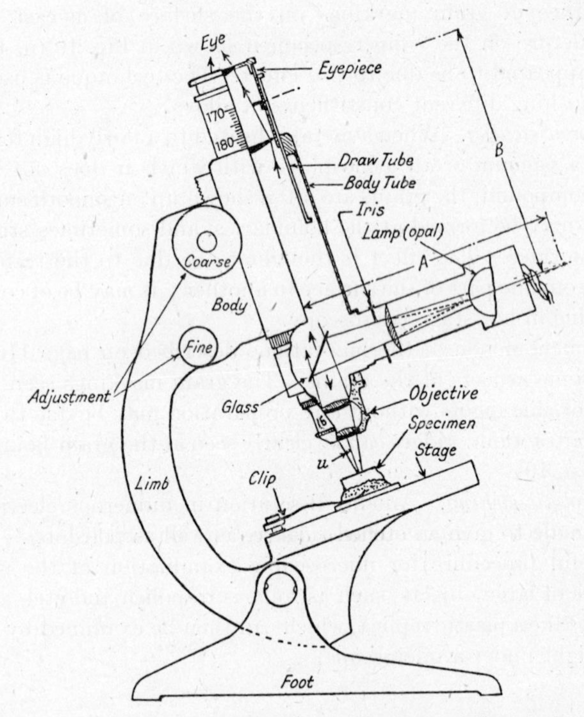

FIG. 119. Typical metallurgical microscope. The specimen is levelled in " Plasticine " held on a glass slide ; with specimens mounted in plastic this may not be necessary. From *Metallurgy for Engineers*, by E. C. Rollason. Arnold.

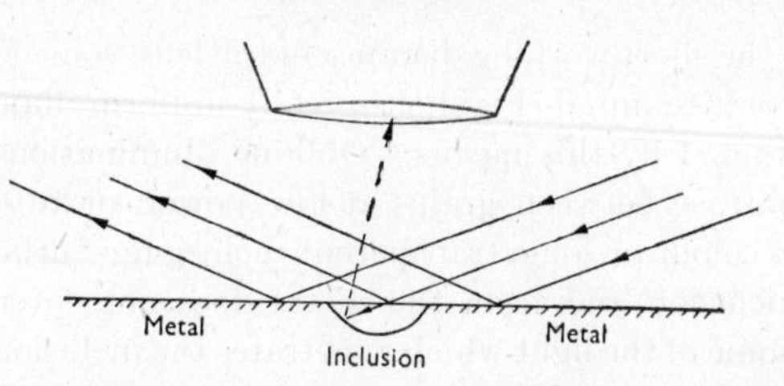

(*a*) oblique illumination ; the diagram shows how the true colour of a transparent inclusion is revealed by this form of illumination.

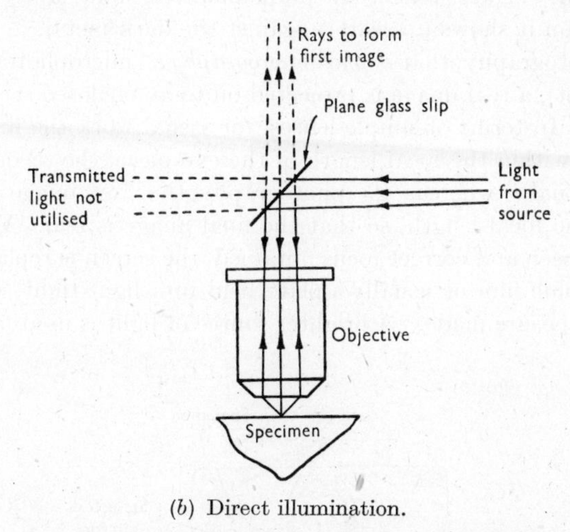

(*b*) Direct illumination.

Fig. 120. Illumination for metallurgical microscopes.

under oblique illumination look bright against a dark background, but under direct illumination the position is reversed (Fig. 9*a* and *b*, p. 10).

Direct illumination is most generally used ; it is usually obtained by a plane glass slip incorporated in the microscope tube (Figs. 119 and 120*b*). The illumination is supplied by a small lamp fixed in a tube attached to the microscope or by a larger lamp arranged in a separate housing. The best results are obtained with " critical illumination ", in which the condensers on the light source in conjunction with the objective focus the light source on the surface of the specimen, and at the same time the complete aperture of the objective is filled with light.

For low-power work a metal surface may be obliquely illuminated by directing the light from a lamp on to it. For high-power examination, due to the short working distance of the lens, some form of built-in illuminator is required (Fig. 121); really uniform illumination can only be obtained by this means. Oblique illumination is useful to improve contrast between grains at low power, or to show up the transmitted colour of some transparent inclusion; surface reflection from the inclusion and from the metal does not enter the microscope, but some of the light which penetrates the inclusion is scattered up into the objective (Fig. 120*a*). Thus cuprous oxide (Cu_2O) in copper appears a varying greyish purple under direct illumination when surface reflection preponderates, but under oblique illumination it shows up scarlet against the dark metal.

For photography, that is *photomicrography* ("microphotography" is incorrect), a real image is projected on to an enclosed screen (Fig. 122–124). In terms of simple lenses, for visual work the first image is formed within the focal length of the eye-piece, the second image being virtual; whereas for photography the first image must lie beyond the focal length, so that the final image is real. When the field is chosen and correct focus obtained, the screen is replaced by a photographic film or usually a plate held in a light-tight container, and an exposure made. A brighter source of light is used for photo-

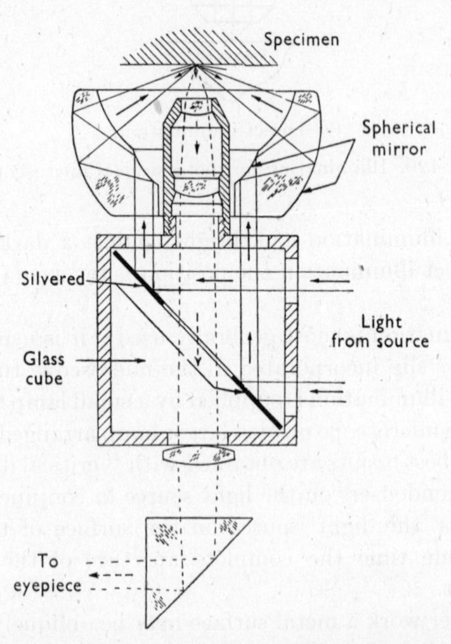

FIG. 121. Principles of a built-in oblique illuminator.

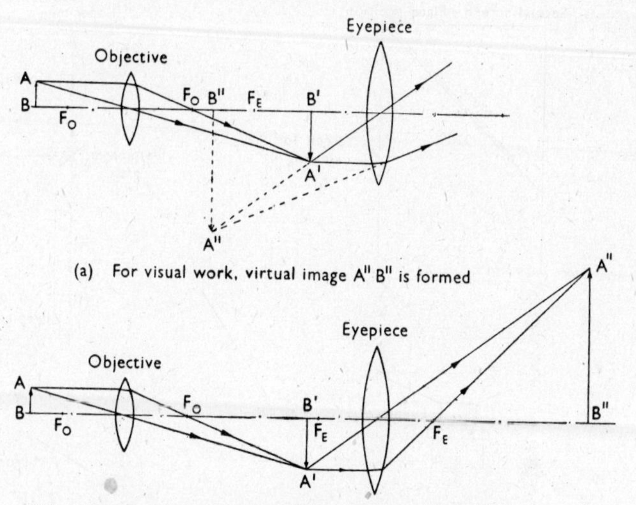

Fig. 122. Image formation in the microscope.

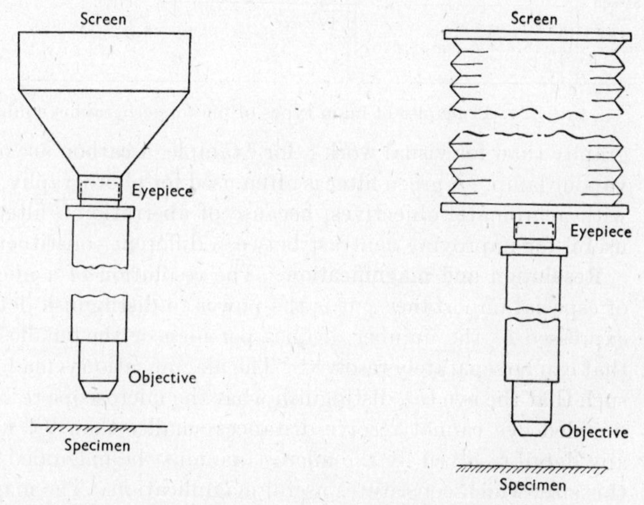

Fig. 123. Principles of simple photomicrographic equipment

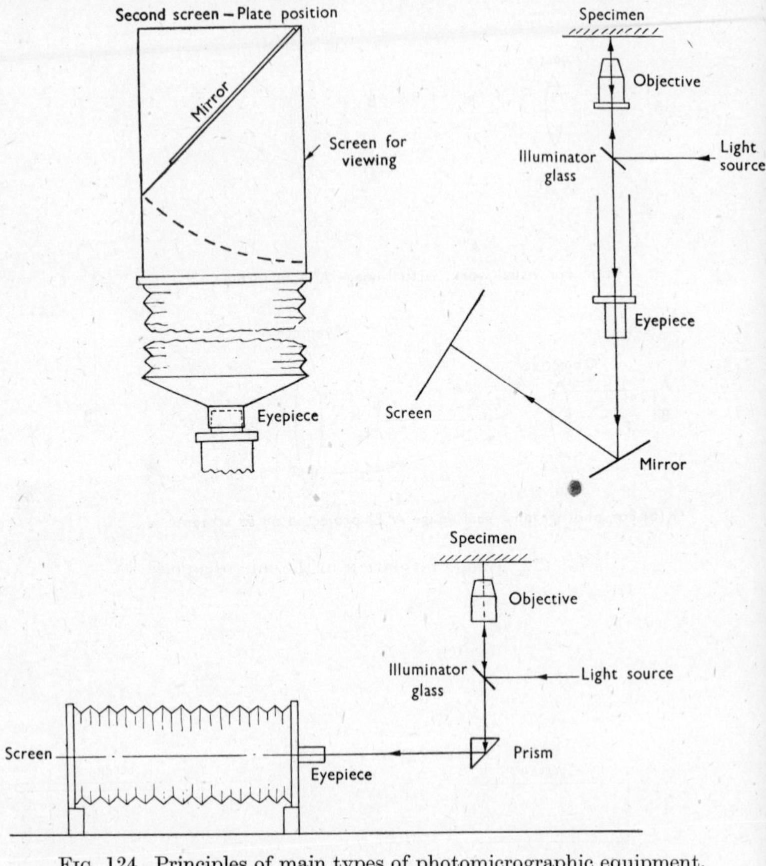

FIG. 124. Principles of main types of photomicrographic equipment.

graphy than for visual work ; for example, a carbon arc or mercury vapour lamp. A green filter is often used for photography, especially with achromatic objectives, because of aberration ; filters are also useful for improving contrast between different constituents.

Resolution and magnification. The resolution of a microscope is of especial importance ; it is the power to distinguish detail, and is expressed as the number of lines per inch or the smallest distance that can be separately resolved. The magnification is made primarily such that the eye can distinguish what the microscope resolves. The unaided eye cannot resolve distances smaller than 0·1 mm. Thus any detail resolved by the microscope must be magnified to at least this size, which constitutes useful magnification. The magnification is often increased somewhat beyond the minimum to ensure that there is no strain on the eye, and in the case of photomicrography to reduce the effects of curvature of field. In the latter case, it is convenient to be able to increase the magnification so as to give a balanced picture for a specific size of film or plate.

Magnification is obtained in the microscope in two stages: the objective produces an image, which is further magnified by the eyepiece. Standard objectives are obtained with focal lengths of 32, 16, 8, 4 and 2 mm., ranging in magnification from about $\times 4$ to $\times 95$. The usual eye-pieces have magnifications of $\times 6$ and $\times 10$. The lenses are made to work at specific tube lengths of from 160 to 250 mm.; for metallography the higher values are usual. In photomicrography the magnification is increased by projection.

Three classes of objectives are generally available, namely achromatic, fluorite and apochromatic, given in order of increasing correction. The best known type of eyepiece is the Huyghens, with two separated simple lenses (Fig. 119). The compensated eyepiece, used especially with apochromatic objectives, is similar but one or both lenses are compound.

The resolution of the ordinary microscope is controlled by three factors, namely, the effective aperture of the objective lens, the nature of the medium between the lens and the specimen, and the wavelength of the illuminating radiation, approximately according to the following formula:

$$\delta = \frac{0{\cdot}5\lambda}{N.A.},$$

where δ is the smallest distance that may be resolved, λ is the wavelength of the illumination, and $N.A.$ is the numerical aperture of the objective, which is an index of the effective aperture. Thus the resolution may be improved, that is δ reduced, by making λ smaller, and by increasing the numerical aperture.

The numerical aperture of an objective lens is equal to $\mu \sin \alpha$, where μ is the refractive index of the medium between the lens and the specimen (in most cases this is air, with $\mu = 1$), and α is half the angle subtended by the maximum cone of rays entering the objective (Fig. 125). The numerical aperture, and therefore the resolution, are increased by increasing μ and α.

Of the three factors by which the resolution may be improved (namely λ, μ and α) the greatest potentiality lies with λ, the wavelength of the illumination. It is clear that α must be less than 90°, with a sine of less than 1, and the possibility of increasing the refractive index of the lens/specimen medium is restricted.

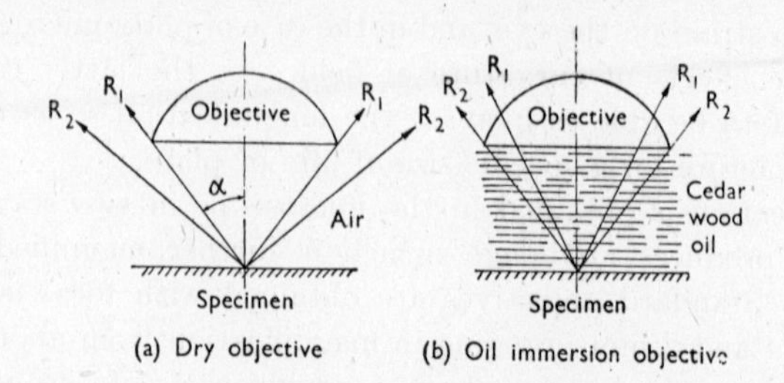

FIG. 125. Showing increase in effective aperture of objective by immersion in cedar wood oil.

By using a lens corrected to work immersed in cedar wood oil ($\mu = 1{\cdot}5$) (Fig. 125) the resolution may be considerably improved. There are not many suitable liquids with refractive indices higher than 1·5; for they must be stable, not too viscous and non-corrosive. Cedar wood oil is practically the only liquid used. In practice, a good 2-mm. oil-immersion objective gives a numerical aperture of between 1·3 and 1·4, which is very close to the absolute maximum of 1·5 which could be obtained if α could be made 90°. Such lenses which have in white light a resolution of about 140,000 lines per inch, or $\delta = 1/140{,}000$ in. $= 0{\cdot}00018$ mm., are in regular use; the minimum magnification necessary is about $\times 600$, and for visual work there is no need to exceed $\times 1000$, although for photography with these lenses magnifications up to and even greater than $\times 2000$ are used. For photomicrography, Vilella recommends that in general the magnification be arranged between 400 and 1000 times the numerical aperture of the objective.

A special immersion lens has been developed employing monobromo naphthalene (refractive index 1·66) as immersion fluid. This objective works in blue light, which has the shortest wave-length of the visible range, and gives an effective $N.A.$ of 1·60, resolving about 180,000 lines per inch.

The remaining variable is the illumination. White light is composed of a range of wave-lengths from approximately 4000 to 7500

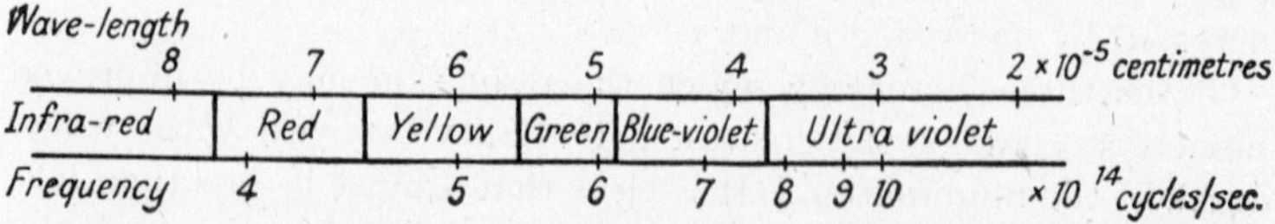

FIG. 126. The visible spectrum. From *The Physical Examination of Metals*, Vol. I., by B. Chalmers. Arnold.

Angstrom units (1 Angstrom unit, A. $=10^{-8}$ cm.), and is the general illumination for everyday metallurgical microscopes, although filters are used in photomicrography. Increase in resolution is obtained by reducing the wave-length of the illumination. Some small improvement may be made by using lenses designed to work in the short-wave end of the visible spectrum, namely visible blue light, as in the objective described above. Further improvement results from the use of *ultra-violet light*. However, the eye cannot detect ultra-violet light, and ordinary glass lenses are opaque to it. Quartz lenses may be used down to about 2000 A. wave-length, and the image photographed ; the image can be focused on a fluorescent screen, or by using a special set of interchangeable glass lenses and focusing with these in white light. Fluorite lenses can be used down to about 1300 A. ; the reflection microscope (see below) also offers possibilities in this direction. A very limited amount of metallurgical investigation has been carried out with ultra-violet light. Wrighton and Smiles used light with a wave-length of 2750 A., and obtained a resolution of about 200,000 lines per inch. The general conclusion so far has been that the results do not warrant the effort. The development of the electron microscope, employing a beam of electrons with a very short effective wave-length as illumination, has given a means of very high resolution microscopy.

DEVELOPMENTS IN METALLURGICAL MICROSCOPY

Hot-stage microscopy. By this technique, metal can be studied at elevated temperatures. The specimen is contained in a small furnace and examined by a microscope through a transparent heat-resisting window, of mica, for example. The furnace is evacuated or may contain a suitable atmosphere. The microscope objective is usually cooled by some means. The technique has considerable possibilities for studying recrystallisation and crystal growth, phase changes, and for work on constitutional diagrams. A limitation of magnification arises because of the short working distances of high-power lenses. The use of the reflection microscope should eventually overcome this problem.

Reflection or mirror microscope. Dr. C. R. Burch has developed and constructed a microscope using a mirror-pair objective (Fig. 127). The mirrors are made of polished speculum metal, or glass on which is deposited a thin film of aluminium. The reflecting objective is achromatic, and has a relatively long working distance ; for example, 13 mm. at a magnification of 500–700 (*N.A.*, 0·65)

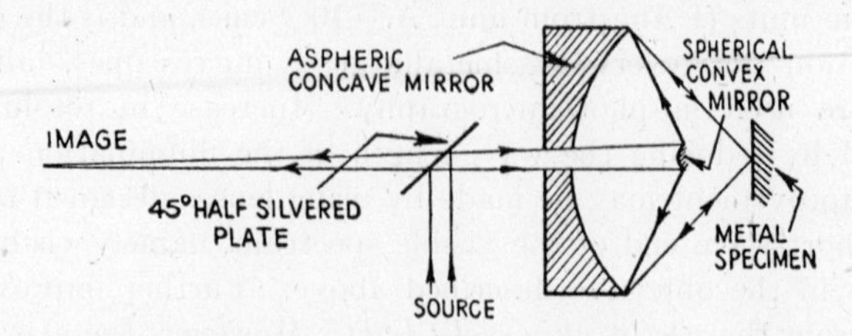

FIG. 127. Principles of reflection microscope. From K. W. Keohane, *Iron and Coal Trades Review*, 1948, **156**, 1296.

has been quoted, giving similar performance to a glass lens of the same magnification and numerical aperture with a working distance of the order only of 0·5 mm. From this aspect the potentialities of the reflecting microscope for examining hot surfaces are clear; preliminary application has been made to oxidation studies.

Another considerable advantage is that the reflecting microscope could be used well down in the ultra-violet, at least to about 1000 A.; the lens remains in focus for any wave-length from the ultra-violet to the infra-red. So far the aperture quoted above has been obtained in white light, but further developments are being made. The preparation of the mirrors is a difficult process.

Phase-contrast microscope. Phase changes occur when light passes through transparent materials or on reflection from surfaces (Fig. 128). The eye or photographic plate can distinguish intensity changes in light, but not phase changes. The phase-contrast microscope converts relative differences in phase into intensity differences. The optics are complicated and will not be described. The technique

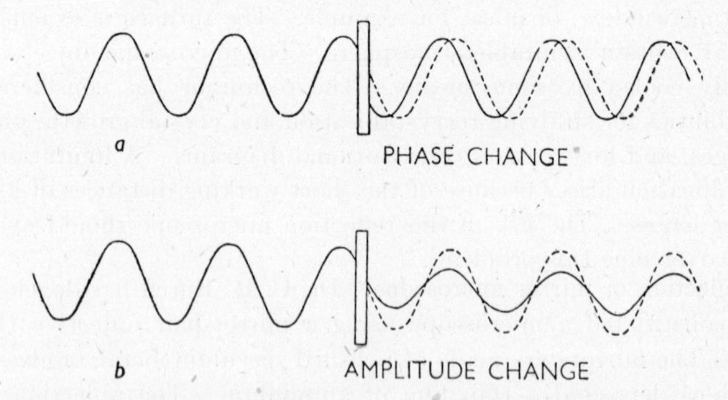

FIG. 128. Passage of a light wave through: (*a*) a non-absorbing transparent material; (*b*) an absorbing material. From R. Barer, *Brit. Sci. News*, 1948, **1**, (9) 11.

may be applied to the examination by transmitted or reflected light, and ordinary microscopes can be adapted for it. In the case of metal specimens, differences in level produced by etching cause phase differences on reflection (as may different constituents even when there is no difference in level). The raised areas show up bright, and the attacked areas of lower level, dark. The phase-contrast microscope has been shown to give improved contrast and to be more suitable for studying differences in level than the ordinary microscope, although the resolution is no better.

Interference methods. These methods can be used for studying the topography of surfaces, as well as phase-contrast and electron-microscope methods.

Use of polarised light. Polarised light is used considerably in the study of rocks, minerals and crystals. In comparison, application in metallography has been limited, its main use being in the study of inclusions, but interest and applications are increasing.

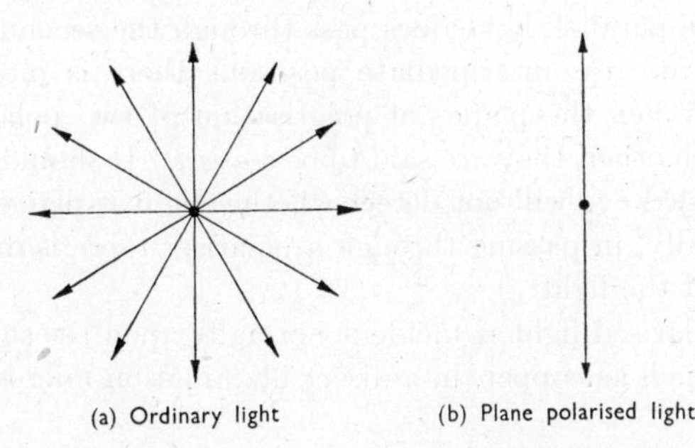

FIG. 129. Distinction between ordinary and polarised light. The direction of the ray in each case is normal to the paper.

If light is regarded as a wave motion, it may be said that ordinary light is vibrating in all planes at right angles to its direction. In contrast, plane-polarised light vibrates only in one plane, its plane of polarisation (Fig. 129). Reflection from certain surfaces and transmission through certain substances will cause polarisation. There are two transparent substances commonly used for microscopic work, namely, naturally-occurring calcite (Iceland spar), and " Polaroid ", an artificial material consisting of crystals of periodide of quinine sulphate arranged between sheets of transparent plastic. The latter is used in the form of fairly thin filters, but the former must be cut and prepared as shown (Fig. 130), when it is known as a Nicol prism.

When light is polarised by one prism or a " Polaroid " filter, and

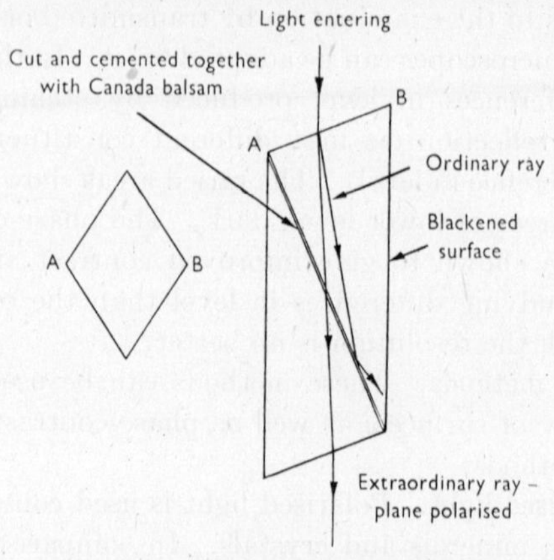

FIG. 130. Principle of Nicol prism.

then passed through another the plane of polarisation of which is at right angles to that of the first, no light passes ; whereas if the planes of the two are parallel, light does pass through the second polariser (Fig. 131) ; at any intermediate positions there is intermediate brightness. When the planes of polarisation of two polarisers are normal to each other, they are said to be *crossed*. It should be noted that the unaided eye will not detect whether light is plane polarised or not. Usually, in passing through a polariser there is diminution of intensity of the light.

If plane polarised light is incident normally upon the surface of a cubic metal such as copper, in a direct illumination microscope, the

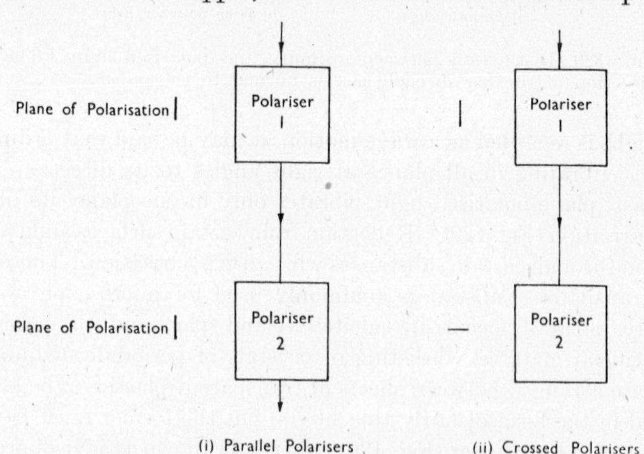

FIG. 131. Effect of parallel and crossed polarisers.

light is reflected essentially without change in polarisation. A specimen may be illuminated with polarised light by arranging a polariser in front of the light source ; the polariser should be arranged in the position giving the brightest light—this then minimises interference due to polarising effects of the plane glass slip illuminator. If a second polariser known as the analyser is fixed to the eyepiece of the microscope, and crossed with the first, the light from the metal surface will be cut out, and it will appear to be dark. Cuprous oxide particles (which are scarlet in transmitted light) in copper have a purple to grey appearance under direct illumination and may be confused with other inclusions. Oblique illumination may reveal the true scarlet colour and thus confirm the nature of the particles. Similarly, under crossed prisms cuprous oxide shows up scarlet against the blacked-out copper. Surface reflections are cancelled out and the particles are viewed with light that has been reflected from the oxide-metal interface and which has been partly depolarised.

Hexagonal and other non-cubic materials are anisotropic (different properties in different directions in the crystal) to light. Thus if a differently orientated polycrystalline hexagonal metal, such as zinc, is examined under crossed polarisers, the grains will show up in contrast. The grains will vary the plane of polarisation of the incident light on reflection depending on their orientation, and it will not be possible to cancel out reflections from all the grains at the same position. Rotation of the specimen, or either polariser, will cause changes in shade. The grains may be made to show up without etching, provided the surface distortion is not too great. Similar effects may be obtained after deep etching with cubic metals, which are normally isotropic.

A specific characteristic of anisotropic materials is that if the specimen is rotated through 360° while being examined under crossed polarisers, lightening and darkening occur four times. This offers a useful point of distinction between inclusions ; thus, Fe_2O_3 is hexagonal and anisotropic, whereas FeO and Fe_3O_4 are cubic and isotropic. Another example is anisotropic and transparent stannic oxide, SnO_2, which may occur as needle-shaped inclusions in brasses, and bronzes which have been improperly deoxidised. Under oblique illumination the crystals have a rainbow appearance, and similarly under polarised light. Full confirmation is obtained by the lightening and darkening on rotation.

Polarised light has been used for examining the distribution of strain in some transparent substances in studying the processes of plastic deformation ; the effect on the plane polarised incident light varies with the strain. This is of course the basis of photoelastic stress-analysis of plastic models. Similar principles are utilised in testing lenses. There has been little practical success with such methods in the study of strain distribution in metal.

Sensitive-tint illumination. By incorporating a special gypsum filter in the optical system, variations in the polarisation of the reflected light are shown by colour differences instead of brightness differences. The colour of the specimen is uniformly purple if there is no change when the polarisers are crossed. A combined illuminator is marketed with which direct, oblique, plane polarised or sensitive-tint illumination is easily obtained.

It has been shown that it is possible after special preparation to reveal with polarised light the varying orientation in aluminium and its alloys, which are optically isotropic. The specimen is polished and then anodically oxidised. The oxide film resulting is optically active and its characteristics are related to the orientation of the underlying metal. The surface is examined with sensitive-tint illumination (or crossed polarisers) and, due to the selective wave-length extinction, grains of different orientation appear of different colour. By this means preferred orientation can be detected. From experimental evidence it appears likely that the effect is due to the surface topography of the oxide film rather than to its optical anisotropy. The structures shown in Fig. 93, p. 107, and Fig. 94, p. 110 were revealed in this way.

Electron microscope. Electrons behave like wave motion, and rays produced by a voltage of 60,000, for example, have an effective wave-length of 0·05 A. It is apparent, therefore, that the use of electron rays as illumination in microscopy has immense potentiality with regard to resolution. Glass lenses cannot be used for focusing as they are opaque to electron rays; but in 1926 Busch showed that focusing is possible with magnetic and electrostatic fields. As a result of development since then, there is available to-day the electron microscope, with a possible resolution down to about 25 A. (or even as low as 10 A.), which is about eighty times better than that obtained with the best optical microscope. The average resolution obtained is between about 50 and 100 A., and about 200 A. in metals which have to be studied by a replica technique. The best figure for the electron microscope is far larger than that theoretically possible from consideration of the effective wave-length of the electron beam. Limitation is due to the fact that electron lenses are prone to similar defects as glass lenses, such as spherical and chromatic aberration; and very small apertures must be used to overcome them, with resulting impairment in resolution, although yielding good depth of focus (considerably better than with the optical microscope). Severe reduction in aperture is possible because the illumination can be made so intense. Chromatic aberration also is reduced by keeping the accelerating voltage very constant, and thus producing rays of essentially one wave-length.

Specimens may be viewed by reflected radiation, and in a few cases the metals have been heated and made to emit their own electrons; but the usual method is to use transmitted radiation. In the case of metals, this involves the preparation and examination of thin transparent replicas (with thickness of about 500–1,500 A.) of the polished and etched surface, as electrons are easily stopped by matter.

The arrangement of the lenses and specimen in the electron microscope using transmitted illumination is analogous to that in the optical microscope in which the specimen is viewed by transmitted light (Figs. 132 and 133). Magnetic lenses have been most successful

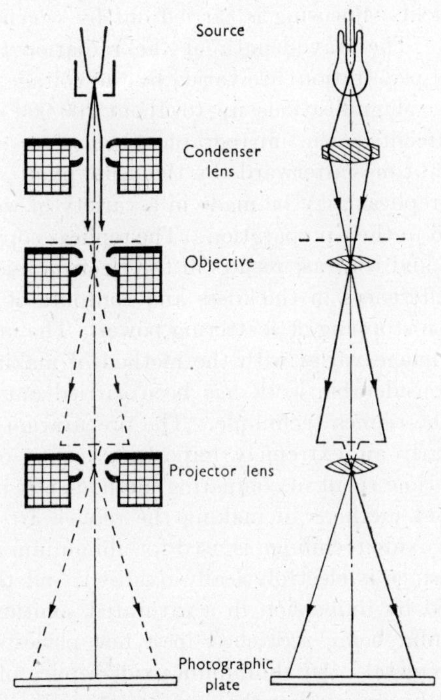

FIG. 132. Comparison of electron and optical microscope systems. By courtesy of the Institute of Physics.

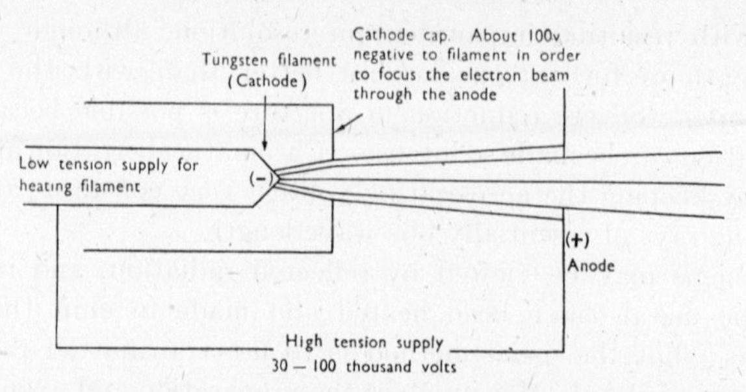

FIG. 133. Principle of "electron gun" used in electron microscope.

so far, and most generally used ; in the latest instruments there are more than three lenses. The microscope must be evacuated to allow the free passage of the electrons. The images produced may be viewed by focusing them on a fluorescent screen and then photographed. The specimen and plate holder are introduced through air locks so that the whole instrument need not be evacuated each time. The replica is supported on a fine grid—one opening covering the field. Focusing is carried out by varying the current to the lenses. The wave-length of the radiation, and thus the resolution (and penetration) are varied by the voltage applied to the electron tube. Magnifications up to about 100,000 are possible in modern instruments ; the micrographs themselves are frequently enlarged several times afterwards by the usual photographic means.

The surface replicas may be made in a variety of ways, and great care is required in their preparation. The replicas copy the contours of the surface, and contrast results in the electron micrograph from the relative differences in thickness and contours of the film, and thus its electron stopping or scattering power. The intensity distribution in the image varies with the method of making the replica (Fig. 134) ; considerable work has been carried out to check the reliability of the replica technique. The preparation of the etched surface is clearly an extremely important aspect of the replica technique and time spent in comparing methods will be well repaid. Three important methods of making the replica are illustrated in Fig. 134. The oxide technique is used for aluminium and its alloys. The etched surface is electrolytically oxidised, and then the oxide film is removed by immersion in a saturated solution of mercuric chloride, the film being scratched in a few places to admit the solution to the metal. An aluminium oxide replica of other metals can be formed by impressing the surface into soft aluminium foil, from which the oxide replica is then made.

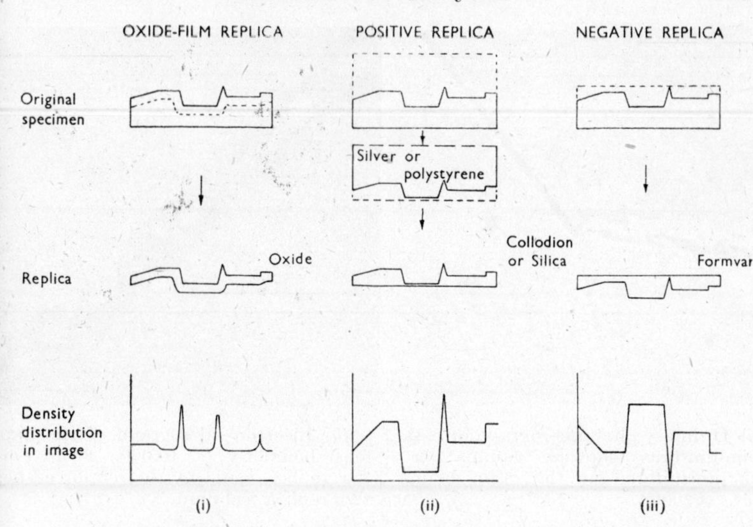

FIG. 134. Methods of preparing replicas of etched surfaces for the electron microscope. (After Zworykin).

Two processes for making a positive replica are shown: (1) A fairly thick layer of silver is evaporated on to the surface in a vacuum. The silver is stripped off mechanically and a drop of collodion solution is applied to it. When the film formed has dried, the silver is dissolved away with dilute nitric acid. (2) A polystyrene moulding is taken of the etched surface. Silica is evaporated in a vacuum on to the moulding, then the latter is dissolved away.

In the negative technique, the specimen is dipped into a dilute solution of "Formvar" or collodion in a volatile solvent. When the film is dry it is stripped off mechanically. The first film may be reinforced before stripping by a second film which is afterwards dissolved away.

Allen has pointed out that the replica material must not adhere strongly to the metal, it must have sufficient strength to withstand stripping and the effects of the electron beam, as well as being electrostatically stable in the beam. Further, the material must have a fine and uniform molecular structure (as this restricts the resolution), and be free of any grain structure.

Apart from improved resolution, increased contrast is likely with electron photographs compared with ordinary photomicrographs. Contrast with plastic replicas can be improved by shadowing the replica by evaporating metal on to it from one side.

The electron microscope has been applied to the study of de-

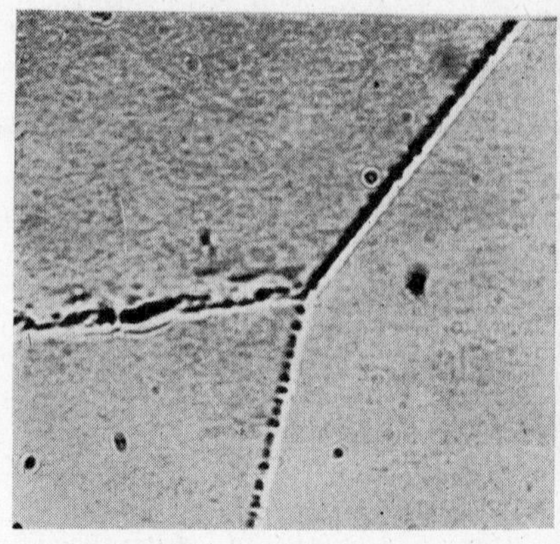

(*a*) Ordinary photomicrograph of beta aluminium-brass showing gamma particles precipitated at the grain boundaries. ×2000.

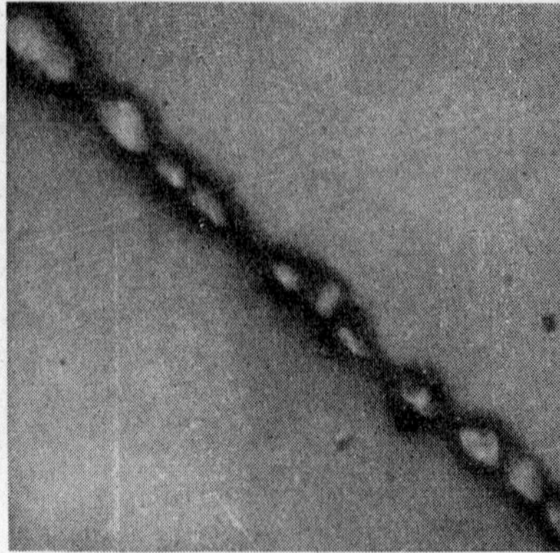

(*b*) Electron micrograph of the upp most boundary. ×10,000. From For var replica made by the reinforced-neg tive replica technique.

Fig. 135. Comparison of light and electron micrographs. From G. L. J. Bailey and S. Vernon-Smith, Symposium on "Metallurgical Applications of the Electron Microscope". Inst. of Metals, 1950.

formation, precipitation processes, and the structure of fine non-equilibrium constituents. It is especially useful for detecting small amounts of second phase (and impurities) (Figs. 135 and 136), and this should prove valuable in equilibrium diagram work. Other applications include metal powders, and surface contours in connection with problems on wear; the good depth of focus has been utilised to advantage in the examination of fractures. In conclusion, it must be stressed that the electron and light microscopes should be used as complementary instruments, and a certain amount of overlap of observations is very useful.

Recently a new principle of electron microscopy has been worked

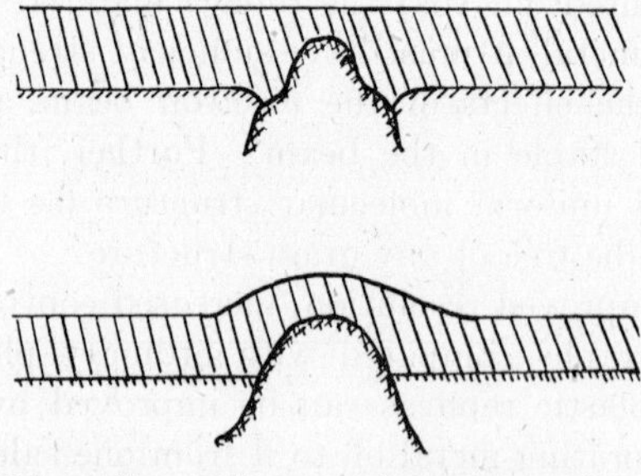

Fig. 136. Possible replica sections causing contrast shown in Fig. 135(*b*). From Bailey & Vernon-Smith

out by Gabor to give improvement in resolution. The method involves the production of a type of electron diffraction photograph without focusing lenses ; from this a magnified image is optically synthesised (using white light and glass lenses).

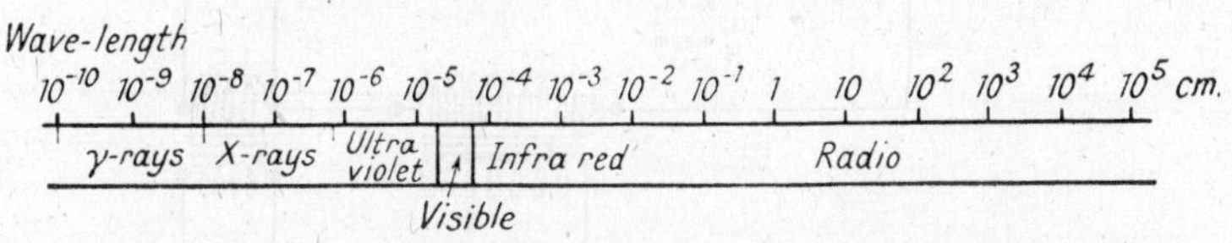

FIG. 137. The electromagnetic spectrum. From *The Physical Examination of Metals*, Vol. 1, by B. Chalmers. Arnold.

Production of X-rays. X-rays are produced when a metal target is bombarded with high-velocity electrons. For crystal structure analysis the electrons are accelerated by applied voltages, usually between about 30 and 70 thousand volts. Two kinds of X-ray tubes are used : (1) cold-gas tubes, and (2) hot-cathode tubes (Figs. 138 and 139). Both kinds have two electrodes, the target or anti-cathode, and the cathode, between which the accelerating potential is applied. The bulk of the energy of the electrons impinging on the target is converted into heat (only a small fraction is converted into X-rays) ; for this reason the targets are specially cooled by air, oil or water. Typical target materials are copper, silver, iron, nickel, cobalt, chromium, tungsten and molybdenum.

The cold-gas tubes contain a small amount of gas at low pressure. Initially the electrons come from the gas, but eventually from the cathode, made usually of aluminium and which should be efficiently

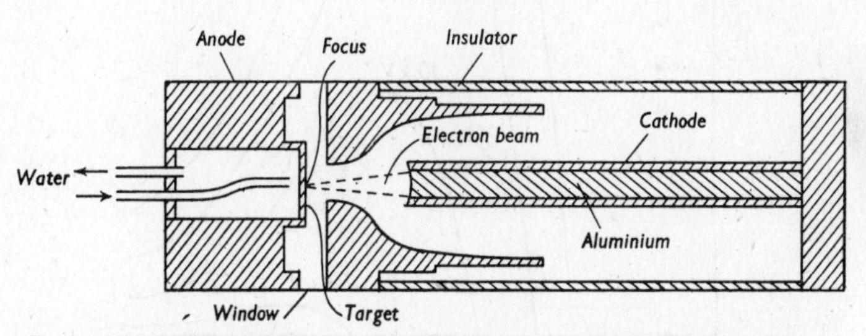

FIG. 138. Cold-gas X-ray tube. The X-rays come off at an angle through the windows shown. The tubes are made of metal and glass. Figs. 138, 140 and 141 are from *The Interpretation of X-ray Diffraction Photographs*, by N. F. M. Henry, H. Lipson and W. A. Wooster. Macmillan.

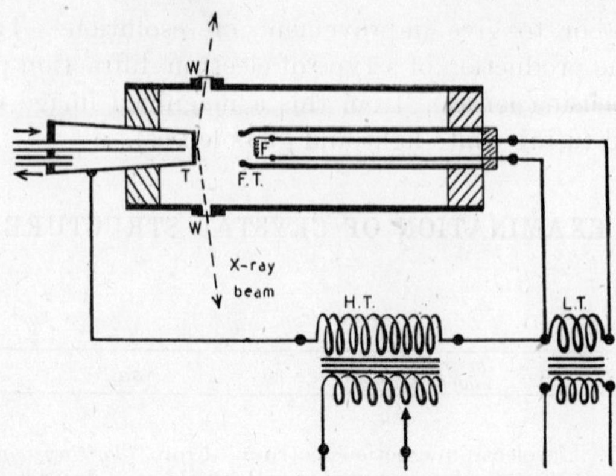

FIG. 139. Hot-cathode X-ray tube, with electrical circuit: the tube is self-rectifying. *T*, water-cooled target; *F*, incandescent tungsten filament; *F.T.*, focussing tube; *W*, window of thin aluminium foil, beryllium or Lindemann glass; *H.T.*, high-tension transformer; *L.T.*, low-tension transformer. Figs. 139, 146 and 150 are from *An Introduction to X-ray Metallography*, by A. Taylor. Chapman & Hall.

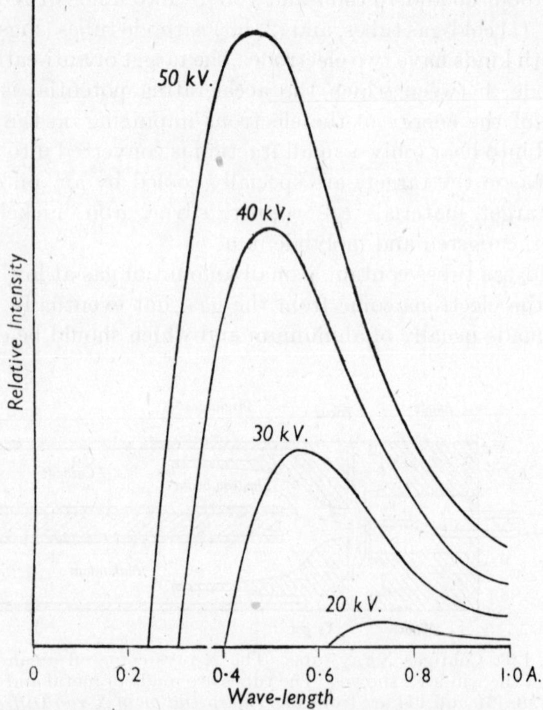

FIG. 140. Continuous X-ray spectra from tungsten target, at various potentials. From Henry, Lipson and Wooster.

cooled. Cold-gas tubes may be sealed off, but usually are worked off pumps which maintain the correct pressure in the tube. In hot-cathode tubes, which are more common, the electrons are emitted from a tungsten wire cathode heated by the passage of a current of electricity. The tubes are evacuated and may be sealed off or demountable. Sealed-off hot-cathode tubes are used for radiography.

X-ray spectra. Two spectra may be formed. The first is a continuous range of wave-lengths known as continuous or white radiation, with a definite short-wave limit (Fig. 140). The value of this limit is determined by the voltage, becoming shorter with increase in voltage ; it is independent of the target material. However, the maximum intensity peak becomes shorter the higher the atomic number of the target metal.

When a certain voltage, critical for each target material, is exceeded, characteristic radiation appears ; that is, there are marked rises in the intensities of certain wave-lengths (Fig. 141). In practice, there is an optimum voltage for contrast between the characteristic and continuous radiation. The wave-length of corresponding characteristic radiation becomes shorter the higher the atomic number of the target. The longer wave-length characteristics are generally absorbed in the tube material. The two shortest-wave characteristics are known as $K\alpha$ and $K\beta$ (each usually consists of more than one component close together).

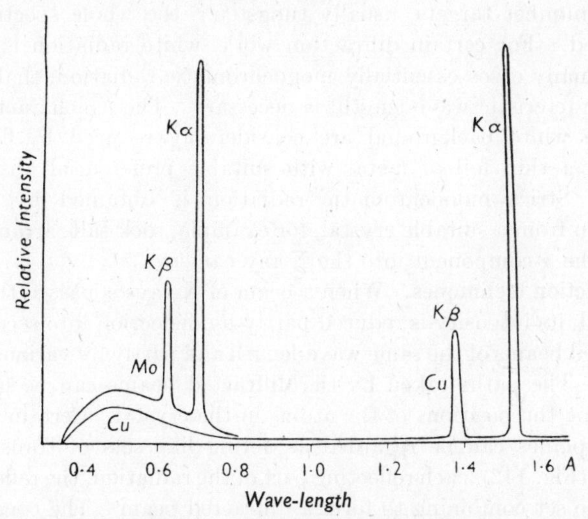

FIG. 141. X-ray spectra at 35,000 volts with targets of molybdenum and copper. That for molybdenum is due to Ulrey, and that for copper is hypothetical. From Henry, Lipson and Wooster.

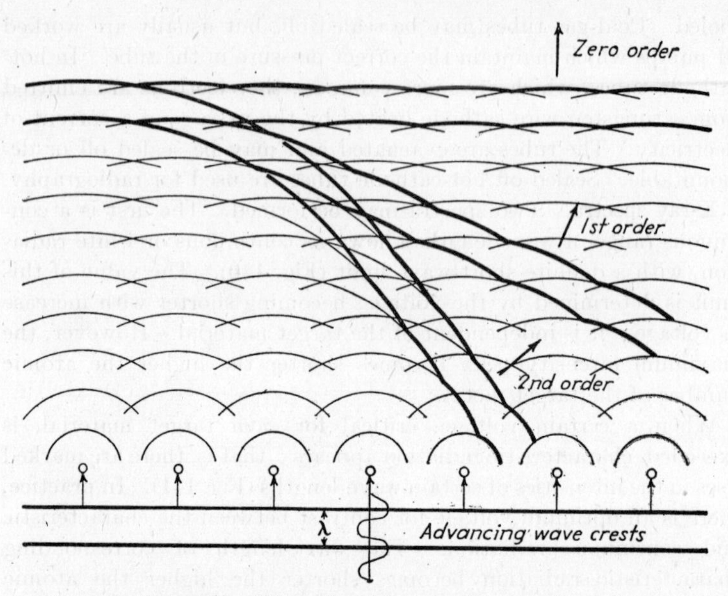

FIG. 142. Diffraction of X-ray beam by row of atoms. From *Structure of Metals*, by C. S. Barrett. McGraw-Hill.

Penetration of matter by X-rays increases with decrease in wave-length. Hence for radiography, high voltages are used, and high atomic number targets, usually tungsten; the whole spectrum is employed. For certain diffraction work, white radiation is used; but in many cases essentially monochromatic radiation, that is, of one characteristic wave-length, is necessary. The $K\beta$ characteristic and the white background are considerably reduced by filtering through a thin foil of metal with suitable preferential absorbing power. Strict monochromatic radiation is obtained by Bragg reflection from a suitable crystal, for example, rock-salt, arranged to reflect the α-component into the X-ray camera.

Diffraction techniques. When a beam of X-rays is passed through a crystal, its intensity is reduced partly by deflection into secondary diffracted beams of the same wave-length and partly by various other effects. The paths taken by the diffracted beams can be used to determine the positions of the atoms in the crystal. Certain sets of atomic planes can be regarded as acting like sets of transparent mirrors (Fig. 142), each reflecting part of the radiation, the reflections from one set combining to form a diffracted beam. The conditions that must be satisfied for reflection for rays of a specific wave-length are given by Bragg's law, which states that $n\lambda = 2d \sin \theta$,

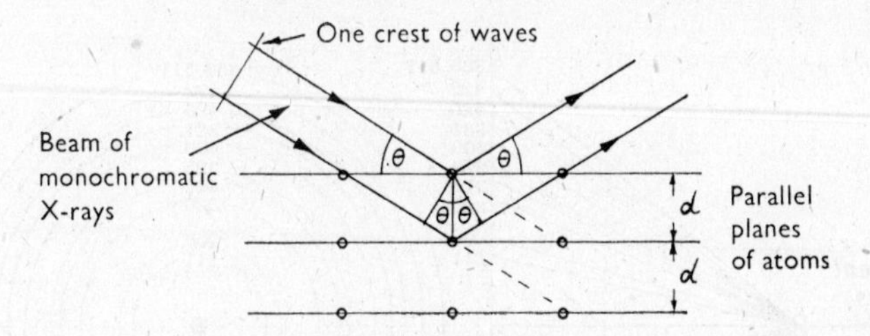

FIG. 143. Illustrating Bragg's law.

where n is a whole number (order of reflection (Fig. 142)), λ is the wave-length of the X-rays, d is the spacing of the diffracting planes, θ is $90°$ – angle of incidence of primary beam on the planes (Fig. 143).

The intensity of a diffracted beam depends among other things on the crystal structure of the material, and the set of planes producing the diffraction. In crystal analysis, therefore, intensities have to be measured as well as the angle θ. It may be satisfactory to measure the relative intensities of the diffracted beams on a photograph with a photometer. Intensity may be measured absolutely and more accurately by the Bragg ionisation spectrometer, which depends on the ionisation of gases by X-rays.

In practice, to ensure that the required conditions for reflection with monochromatic radiation are obtained, a single crystal is rotated or a small polycrystal is used, which with its varied orientation is bound to be arranged with some planes suitable (Fig. 144–146). In the Laue technique (Figs. 147 and 148) a fixed single crystal is analysed with white radiation, giving a range of wave-lengths, the various planes diffracting different wave-lengths. The emergent beams in each case are photographed as shown in the figures. Each technique has its particular applications.

Analysis of the dimensions and pattern of the crystal structure becomes an involved question of finding the arrangement that fits in with the recorded detail. In addition grain size can be estimated from the nature of the spots or lines, and distortion and internal stress can be studied. Preferred orientation can be detected from uneven intensity in the diffraction rings (Fig. 149). In addition, chemical analysis is also possible. Further, X-ray analysis is extremely valuable in equilibrium diagram work, both in analysing the structure of phases and intermediate reaction products, and in determining solid phase boundaries in the diagrams. High-temperature cameras have been developed for this purpose.

Micro-radiography. This is an X-ray technique for revealing the

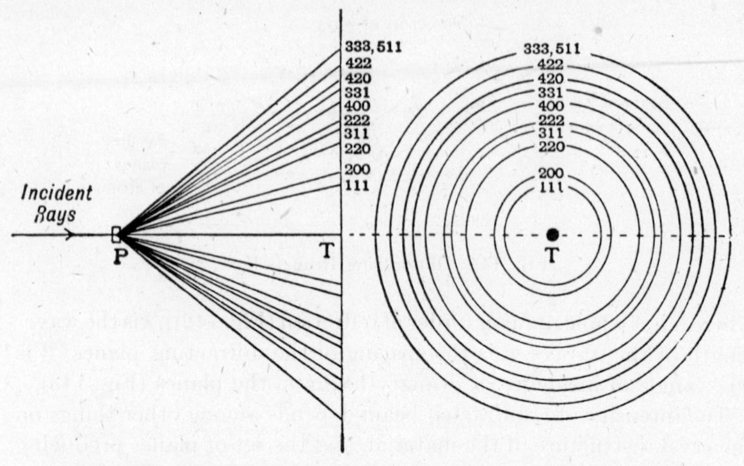

FIG. 144. Powder method, using photographic plate or flat film for recording. The diffracted beams are traced as rings in the photograph, as shown on the right. The spectrum is typical of a face-centred cubic metal. The specimen, *P*, is a small polycrystalline sample, or fine powder in a very thin glass tube or coated with adhesive on to a hair. From *The Crystalline State*, by W. H. and W. L. Bragg. Bell.

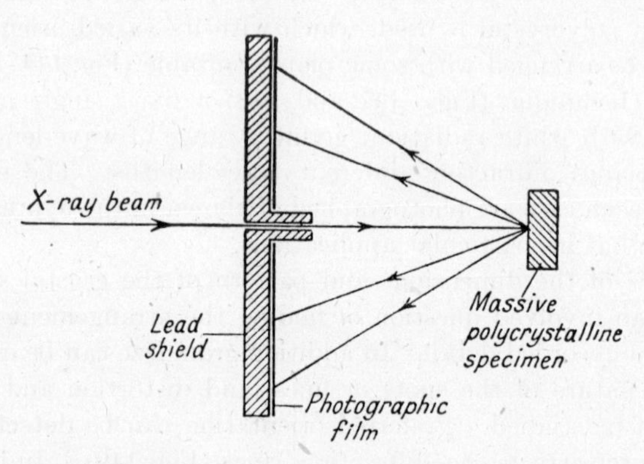

FIG. 145. Back-reflection technique. Figs. 145 and 147 are from *The Physical Examination of Metals*, Vol. II., by B. Chalmers and A. G. Quarrell. Arnold.

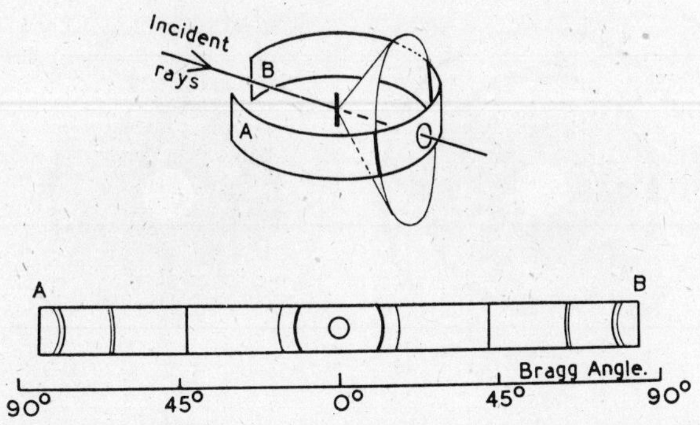

FIG. 146. Powder technique with cylindrical film, *A B* , recording the whole spectrum. The best results are obtained in the powder method if the specimen is rotated during exposure. From Taylor.

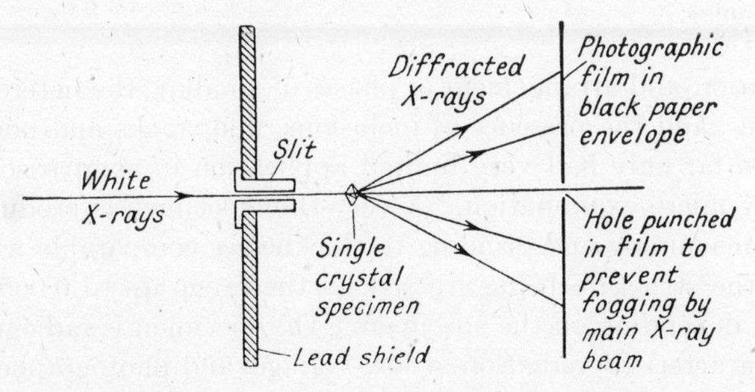

FIG. 147. Laue method. From Chalmers and Quarrell.

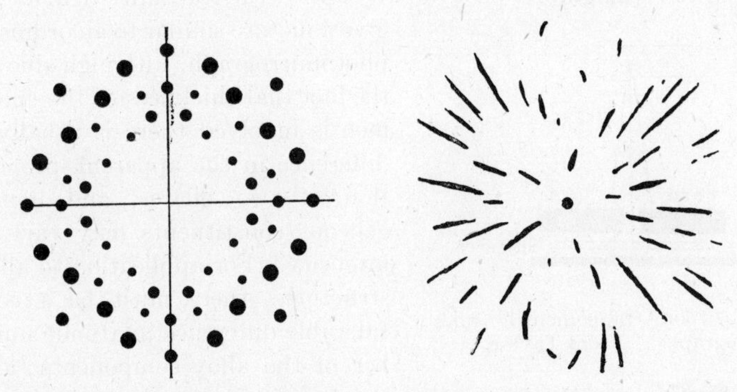

(*a*) Crystal of rock salt (NaCl). From *Physics of Metals*, by F. Seitz. McGraw-Hill. The diameters of the spots are proportional to their intensity.

(*b*) Distorted crystal. From Barrett.

FIG. 148. Laue patterns.

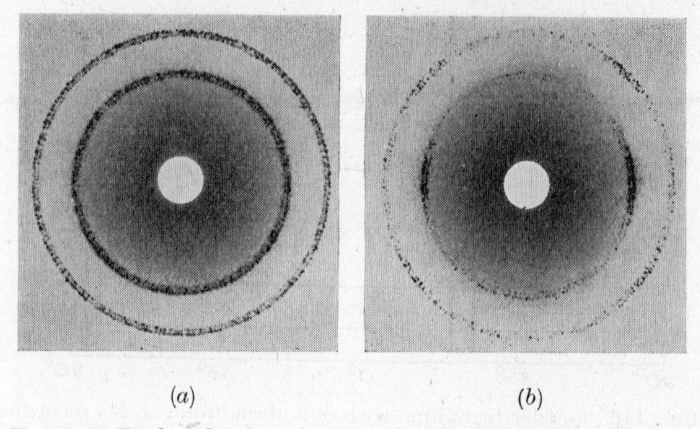

FIG. 149. Back-reflection photographs of copper-nickel alloy sheet. (*a*) Fairly uniform. (*b*) Showing preferred orientation. By courtesy of The Research Laboratories of the General Electric Co., Ltd., Wembley.

distribution and arrangement of phases in an alloy, the heterogenity of phases, and the presence of inclusions, fine cracks and porosity ; it has so far only had very limited application in comparison with ordinary micro-examination. A very thin specimen is produced by careful machining and grinding to thicknesses comparable with the size of the structure being studied, in the range up to 0·005 in. or greater, depending on the specimen. The specimen is radiographed with characteristic radiation at low voltage, and photographed on a special high-resolution plate (Fig. 150). The radiograph is then moderately magnified on a microscope (with transmitted light) to give a picture similar to an ordinary photomicrograph, although due to the fact that thickness of the specimen is involved there is usually a difference in the apparent proportion of two phases, and homogeneous constituents may vary in intensity. For application to alloy structures, there must be a considerable difference in atomic number of the alloy components ; and thus in X-ray absorption, the radiation is arranged to emphasise the latter difference.

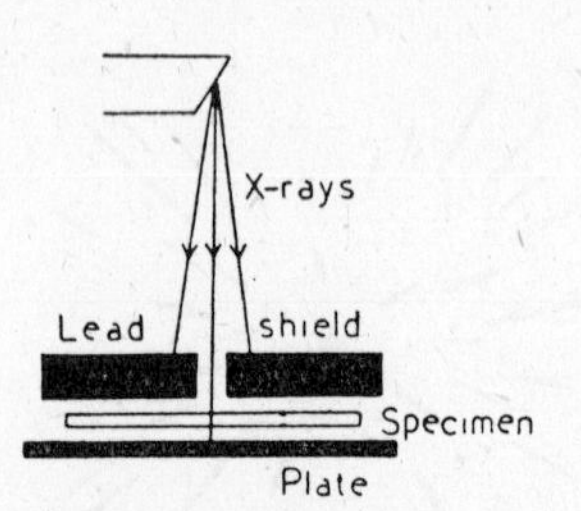

FIG. 150. Arrangement for micro-radiography. From Taylor.

X-ray microscopy. Bragg reflection from a crystal in suitable circumstances will also produce an image which can be magnified 50–100 times. The technique may reveal aspects of structure not readily observed by ordinary optical microscopy ; the techniques should be used in a complementary manner.

Electron and neutron diffraction. Electron rays have wave-like characteristics, and are diffracted by crystals in a similar manner to X-rays, and can be used for analysis. The great advantage of electrons is that their penetration is very slight, and they can be used especially for studying surface conditions. The limit of penetration at voltages normally used is about 500 A. Both reflection and transmission procedures are used on actual metal samples.

A very recent development is the use of **neutron diffraction** for the study of crystal structures. Neutrons are uncharged particles and are constituents of atomic nuclei. Whereas X-rays are diffracted by the extra-nuclear electrons of the atoms in a crystal, neutrons are diffracted by the nuclei, although their interaction cannot be calculated but must be determined from experiments on known structures. With combinations of light and heavy elements, it is difficult to locate the position of light atoms by the usual X-ray technique, because the scattering of the X-rays by the heavy elements predominates. Thus the positions of the hydrogen, carbon, nitrogen and boron atoms in combination with iron and other transition elements cannot be detected ; hence although the pattern of the metal atoms can be determined, that of the lighter atoms has to be deduced theoretically. On the other hand, there is no connection between atomic weight and scattering power of neutrons, light atoms having quite high scattering power, and thus it is easy to locate them by neutron diffraction.

DETERMINATION OF EQUILIBRIUM DIAGRAMS

A brief summary can now be given of standard methods for the determination of equilibrium diagrams, showing the use in particular of microscopic and X-ray techniques. The copper-silver was one of the first diagrams to be determined, by Roberts-Austin in 1875. Primitive technique was used, temperatures being measured by calorimetric methods. Since then there have been marked improvements in technique, but many diagrams still need accurate determination.

The *liquidus* is determined by thermal analysis. Precious metal thermo-couples are used for temperature measurement ; for very high temperature work, disappearing filament pyrometers are suitable. Great care must be taken to have the temperature uniform in the sample, and by continually stirring to avoid undercooling. For accurate work the actual sample used should be analysed ; this applies with all techniques. An alternative procedure is to draw off through a small refractory tube a sample of the metal just before the arrest occurs ; the temperature can be determined by taking a preliminary cooling curve. If there is a considerable tendency for undercooling and arrests are slight, samples may be held at a suitable number of temperatures for sufficient time to reach equilibrium, and then a sample of the liquid drawn off and analysed. The analysis gives the composition of the liquid at a specific temperature, that is, the liquidus value at that temperature.

Cooling curves are not generally suitable for determination of the *solidus* for the arrests are slight, unless, for example, substantial amounts of eutectic are present, although heating curves may be used with small ingots free from segregation. A general method consists in quenching a number of specimens of the same composition from a series of temperatures, followed by microscopic examination for signs of melting, that is, rapidly chilled liquid at grain boundaries. The technique is known as " bracketing ", for the final temperature is determined as lying between two values. Apart from the accuracy of instruments and measurements, the accuracy of the results depends on the temperature intervals used. The above procedure is repeated for a series of compositions. An interesting method that has been used for the solidus is to observe the temperature of collapse of slowly heated specimens under a light load ; collapse should occur as soon as melting starts.

For *conditions in the solid state*, standard " tools " are microscopy and X-ray analysis. It is generally agreed that these two techniques are complementary. Thermal analysis is not generally suitable for changes in the solid state, as sufficient heat is not usually evolved ; although it may be used in certain cases, as with steel. Both microscopic and X-ray techniques may be used for phase boundaries, X-rays being especially useful at low temperatures. X-ray analysis is the only method for determination of the crystal structure of the phases (and the occurrence of ordering), and of any intermediate products in solid reactions, although indications may be obtained from the microstructure. In addition, X-rays are particularly valuable for studying changes, such as that shown in Fig. 70, page 84. The preparation of X-ray samples calls for great care, and errors may be introduced at this stage. The particular advantage of microscopy is that it reveals the distribution of the phases ; it may also give useful information about intermediate reaction products and the type of reaction occurring.

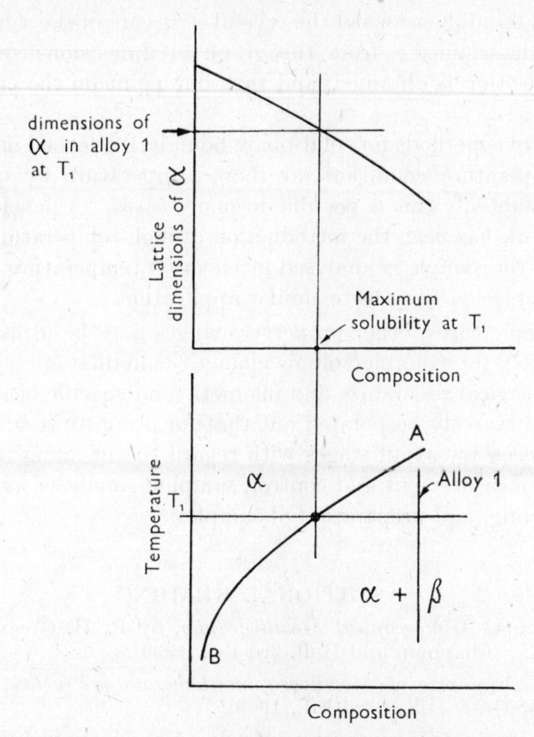

FIG. 151. Lattice dimension method for phase boundary determination.

The microscopic method for phase boundaries employs a " bracketing " technique. A set of samples of the same composition is annealed to reach equilibrium at a series of temperatures overlying the actual one, then quenched, prepared and examined for signs of the second phase.

An accurate X-ray method for phase boundaries utilises measurements of the dimensions of the crystal structure of one phase. Thus, to determine the limit of solid solubility *AB* (Fig. 151), the dimensions of the crystal structure at various compositions in the solid-solution range are first measured ; this may necessitate quenching specimens from the temperature of maximum solubility. Dimensions are then plotted against composition. In many cases there is a regular change with composition due to the incorporation of two sizes of atoms on the one structure ; the method is only applicable if this is so. To determine the boundary at any temperature, a two-phase alloy is annealed and quenched from this temperature, and the dimensions of the crystal structure of the solid solution present determined; from the graph of dimensions/composition, its composition is obtained, and thus one point on the curve is determined.

The above methods for solid-phase boundaries depend on retaining high-temperature conditions at room temperature by quenching, and undoubtedly this is possible in many cases. A development in X-ray work has been the introduction of high-temperature cameras in which the sample is analysed at elevated temperature; the hot-stage microscope may have similar application.

In specific cases, other property changes may be utilised for the solid state; for example volume changes as in dilatometry (used for steel), electrical resistance, and magnetic and specific heat changes.

It need scarcely be pointed out that for accurate results extreme care is necessary at all stages with regard to annealing times, temperature measurement and control, sampling, analysis, avoidance of undercooling, and preparation of samples.

ADDITIONAL READING

1. *Practical Microscopical Metallography*, by R. H. Greaves and H. Wrighton. (Chapman and Hall, 3rd Ed., 1939).

2. *The Principles of Metallographic Laboratory Practice*, by G. L. Kehl. (McGraw-Hill. 3rd Ed., 1949).

3. *The Physical Examination of Metals*: Vol. I. Optical Methods, by B. Chalmers, 1939. Vol. II. Electrical Methods, by B. Chalmers and A. G. Quarrell, 1941. (Arnold).

4. *Metallographic Technique for Steel*, by J. R. Vilella. (American Society for Metals, 1938). (Considerable metallographic detail is also given in *Metals Handbook*, 1948 Edition, published by this Society).

5. *The Use of Diamond Abrasives for a Universal System of Metallographic Polishing*, by L. E. Samuels, *J. Inst. Metals*, **81**, 471 (1952–53).

6. *Electrolytic Polishing of Metallic Surfaces*, by P. A. Jaquet. *Metal Finishing*: Part I, May 1949, Part II June 1949. (Also discussed in (2) above).

7. *A Simple Reflecting Microscope for High-Temperature Metallography*, by D. W. Dewhirst and M. J. Olney, *J. Iron and Steel Inst.*, **169**, 221, (1951).

8. *The Study of Recrystallisation in Zinc by Direct Observation*, by G. Brinson and A. J. W. Moore, *J. Inst. Metals*, **79**, 429 (1951).

9. *Polarized Light in Metallography*, G. K. T. Conn and F. J. Bradshaw (Editors). (Butterworths, 1952).

10. *Metallurgical Applications of the Electron Microscope*, Monograph and Report Series, No. 8. (Institute of Metals, 1950).

11. *Structure of Metals*, by C. S. Barrett. (McGraw-Hill, 2nd Ed., 1952).

12. *An Introduction to X-ray Metallography*, by A. Taylor. (Chapman and Hall, 1945).

13. *Crystals and X-rays*, by K. Lonsdale. (Bell, 1948).

14. *The Crystalline State*. Vol. I. *A General Survey*, by Sir Lawrence Bragg. (Bell, 1949).

15. *Applied X-rays*, by G. L. Clarke. (McGraw-Hill, 3rd Ed., 1940).

16. *A Simple Method of X-ray Microscopy and its Application to the Study of Deformed Metals*, by R. W. K. Honeycombe, *J. Inst. Metals*, **80**, 39, (1951–52).

17. *Determination of Equilibrium Diagrams*, by G. V. Raynor. *J. Birmingham Metallurgical Society*, **28**, 3 (1948).

18. *Metallurgical Equilibrium Diagrams*, by W. Hume-Rothery, J. W. Christian and W. B. Pearson. (Institute of Physics, 1952). Deals mainly with determination of the diagrams.

19. *The Determination of Equilibrium Diagrams by X-ray Methods.* Joint Discussion with Institute of Physics, *J. Inst. Metals*, **60**, 1 (1943).

20. *The Application of X-ray Methods to the Determination of Phase Boundaries in Metallurgical Equilibrium Diagrams*, by E. A. Owen and D. P. Morris, *J. Inst. Metals*, **76**, 145 (1949).

21. *Researches into the Structures of Alloys*, by A. J. Bradley, W. L. Bragg and C. Sykes, *J. Iron and Steel Inst.*, **141**, 63*P* (1940). This paper gives outline of investigation of equilibrium diagrams of alloys of Fe with Co, Ni, Cr, Cu and Al, by X-ray methods.

22. *The Equilibrium Diagram of the System Chromium-Manganese*, by S. J. Carlile, J. W. Christian and W. Hume-Rothery, *J. Inst. Metals*, **76**, 169 (1949). This describes high-temperature work with disappearing filament pyrometer.

23. *High-Temperature Thermal Analysis using the Tungsten/Molybdenum Thermocouple*, by H. T. Greenaway, S. T. M. Johnstone and M. K. McQuillan, *J. Inst. Metals*, **80**, 109 (1951–52). See also, H. T. Greenaway, *ibid.*, p. 589.

Techniques for the Determination of Equilibrium Diagrams are also discussed in some detail in the references (11) and (12) above.

CHAPTER 7

METAL WINNING: OCCURRENCE AND ORE-PREPARATION

Occurrence. Metals occur mainly in the earth's crust, sometimes in the "native" or free elemental form, but usually as compounds with other elements. Naturally-occurring elements and compounds are known as **minerals**; compound minerals are referred to by proper names (Table 15).

TABLE 15. IMPORTANT MINERALS OF SOME COMMON METALS

Magnetite (Fe_3O_4).	Chalcocite (Cu_2S).
Hematite (Fe_2O_3).	Covellite (CuS).
Limonite ($2Fe_2O_3 . 3H_2O$).	Bornite (Cu_5FeS_4).
Siderite ($FeCO_3$).	Chalcopyrite ($CuFeS_2$).
	Enargite (Cu_3AsS_4).
Galena (PbS).	Cuprite (Cu_2O).
Sphalerite (ZnS).	Malachite ($CuCO_3 . Cu(OH)_2$).
Cassiterite (SnO_2).	Native Copper (Cu).
Magnesite ($MgCO_3$).	
Diaspore ($Al_2O_3 . H_2O$).	
Native Gold (Au).	
Calaverite [$(AuAg)Te_2$.]	
Native Silver (Ag).	
Argentite (Ag_2S).	
Cerargyrite ($AgCl$).	

Generally minerals are homogeneous crystalline solids; some have fairly definite composition, others exist over a range of composition. They may contain extra elements in solid solution. Strictly defined, minerals are inorganic in the sense that they are considered never to have passed through the changes known as life and growth; however, rigid adherence to this qualification is not always practised. Rocks are aggregates of one or more minerals, and have different characteristics corresponding to their period and mode of formation.

Minerals of economic value are classed as **metallic or non-metallic.** Metal-bearing compound minerals may be put in either class according as they are to be utilised as source of metal or non-metal (or, as is often the case, in their natural form, utilising their inherent properties). Aluminium oxide (hydrated) and magnesite are minerals which are utilised both as source of metal and in compound form as refractory and abrasive.

TABLE 16. APPROXIMATE COMPOSITION OF EARTH'S CRUST (accessible)

Element	*Percentage*
Oxygen	46·7
Silicon	27·7
Aluminium	8·1
Iron	5·0
Calcium	3·6
Sodium	2·8
Potassium	2·6
Magnesium	2·1
Titanium	0·6
Manganese	0·1
Hydrogen	0·1
Barium	0·05
Chromium	0·04
Carbon	0·03
Nickel	0·02
Vanadium	0·02
Copper	0·01
Zinc	0·004
Lead	0·002
Tin	0·0001
Silver	0·000001
Gold	0·0000001

Metallic minerals occur in association, generally close, with other minerals (Figs. 152–154). Sometimes two or more economically important minerals occur together in worthwhile amounts. It will be seen from Table 16 that, apart from iron, aluminium and magnesium, the commercially utilised metals constitute an exceedingly small proportion of the earth's crust. Generally, only deposits in which the metallic mineral predominates due to concentration by natural means are of commercial value (Table 17).

TABLE 17. CONCENTRATION OF METALS IN WORKABLE DEPOSITS IN RELATION TO THEIR AVERAGE PERCENTAGE IN THE EARTH'S CRUST (from Carpenter and Robertson)

Metal	*Concentration*
Aluminium	4 to 5 times
Iron	5 to 10 times
Nickel	50 to 250 times
Copper	100 to 700 times
Vanadium	150 to 500 times
Chromium	250 to 800 times
Gold	2,500 to 7,500 times
Silver	4,000 to 15,000 times

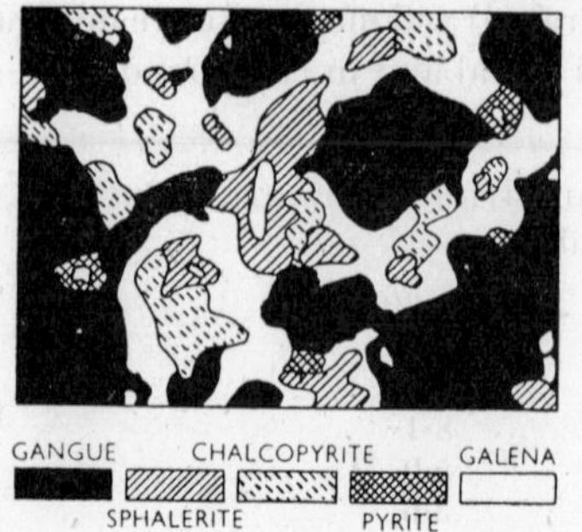

(*a*) Non-ferrous sulphide ore. ×50.

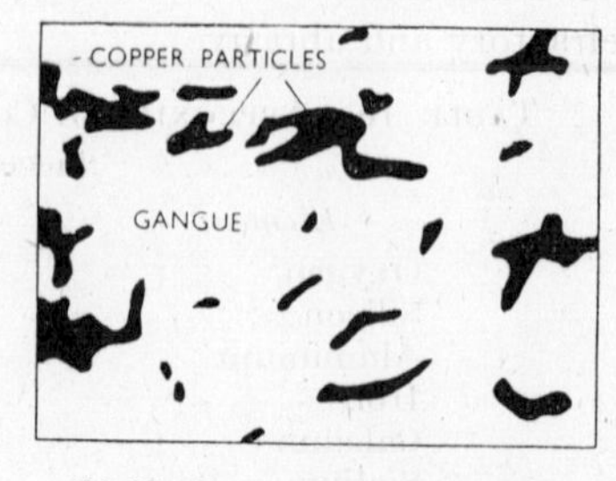

(*b*) Native copper ore. ×40.

FIG. 152. Microstructures of non-ferrous ores.

Usually in mining the valuable mineral, a certain amount of waste in the form of other associated or neighbouring minerals, and known as the **gangue** must inadvertently be included. Common gangue minerals are silica (SiO_2) as quartz and various silicates, aluminium oxide as such, but often as silicate, calcite ($CaCO_3$), dolomite ($MgCO_3CaCO_3$), barytes ($BaSO_4$), fluorspar (CaF_2) and various iron compounds. The desired mineral or minerals, together with the gangue, constitute the **ore**. Thus ore can be defined briefly as a mineral aggregate containing one or more metals in profitable form. The metallurgical field generally commences with the as-mined ore.

Ores are frequently classed according to the nature of the valuable mineral. Thus in native ores the metal is present in the elementary form; sulphide ores contain the metal required in the form of a sulphide. In oxidised ores the valuable mineral may be present as oxide, sulphate, silicate, carbonate or some hydrated form of these. Complex ores are those containing profitable amounts of more than one valuable mineral. Ores are also qualified by the nature of their gangues, such as calcareous (lime rich) or siliceous (silica predominating).

Fig. 153. Microstructure of calcareous iron ore (Frodingham) containing about 21 per cent iron. ×20. The structure largely consists of limonite ooliths embedded in calcite.

The factors which control the suitability and value of mineral deposits as sources of metal, considered together with the available winning techniques, are:

(1) accessibility of the deposit and nearness to fuel, power and water supplies, etc.;

(2) actual form the metal takes and its predomination;

(3) demand for, and value of, the metal;

(4) nature of the gangue;

(5) aggregation and dissemination of the valuable mineral.

Aggregation and dissemination are associated in meaning and refer to the size and distribution, respectively, of the valuable mineral among its associates, namely the texture of the ore. In some cases the valuable mineral may be coarsely aggregated, so that the particles can be seen by eye. But often there is fine dissemination, and microscopic examination is necessary to study the occurrence (Figs. 152–154).

The minimum metal content for a deposit to qualify as an ore varies from metal to metal, and according to the factors enumerated above. Often base non-ferrous metal ores contain, as mined, as little as 1 per cent metal; tin ores are worked at much lower figures. Gold and silver may be recovered profitably from ores containing as little as 0·02 oz. per ton and 1 oz. per ton, respectively. In contrast, iron ores range from about 20 to 60 per cent metal, the former being considered low grade.

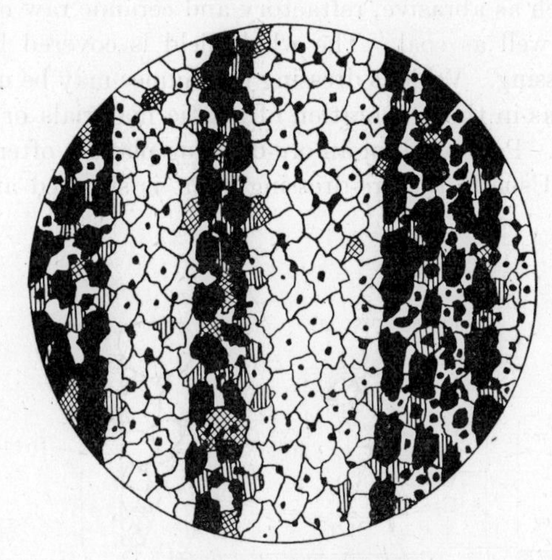

FIG. 154. Norwegian magnetite ore, containing 30–32 per cent iron as magnetite; hornblende is a complex silicate. ×25. From J. Kraft Johanssen, *J. Iron and Steel Inst.*, 1949, 162, 4.

ORE-PREPARATION

Physical methods : ore-dressing. " As-mined " or " run-of-mine " ore consists of valuable metallic mineral or minerals and waste. The remaining metal-winning operations have as their function removal of the waste and separation of the metal from the mineral. Ore-dressing follows mining, and prepares the ore for extraction. Apart from regulating the particle size of the ore, it functions as a cleaning operation, removing as much of the waste as possible consonant with maintaining economic efficiency. Cleaning is carried out by utilising differences in physical properties between the valuable and gangue minerals, such as those of appearance, density, magnetic and surface nature. If the ore contains worthwhile amounts of more than one valuable mineral, it is usually the object of ore-dressing to separate them. Further, dressing may remove particular minerals containing undesirable elements which may be difficult or impossible to remove in extraction or refining. Ore-cleaning is a necessary prelude with most non-ferrous metal ores and is continually increasing in importance. In comparison, due to the high-grade deposits that have been available, generally cleaning has not been a serious item with iron ores, although interest and use are now growing. However, size control has had considerable application to iron ores. Non-metallic minerals such as abrasive, refractory and ceramic raw materials are dressed, as well as coal. The whole field is covered by the term **mineral-dressing.** Various dressing techniques may be used in other ways, such as in the preparation of plastic materials or in cleaning metal scrap. Part or all of an ore-dressing plant is often referred to as a **mill.** Usually the ore-dressing plant is situated at the mine ;

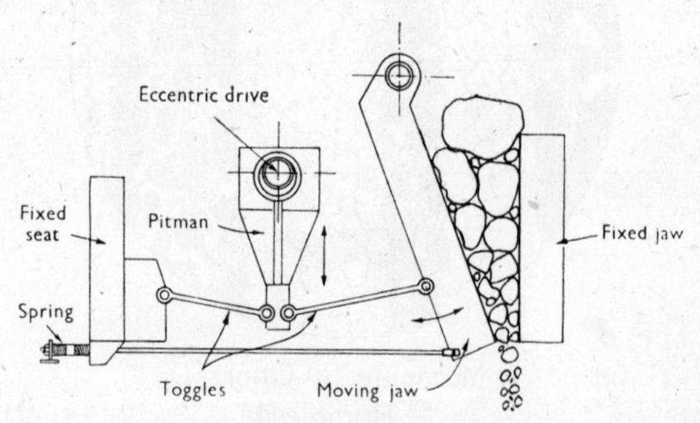

FIG. 155. Principles of typical jaw breaker : made in various sizes with mouth opening up to 7 ft. × 10 ft. : the ore is usually broken dry.

although a **custom mill** treats ore from a number of mines in the locality.

As-mined ore is usually irregular in size and may contain very large pieces up to several feet across. For extraction there is, depending on the process, some limitation to particle size and its irregularity. Thus most important in ore-dressing are the size-reduction and grading treatments, which are also necessary prior to the actual cleaning. Size control may be the only treatment applied to rich ores (sometimes, especially in the past, there may be no preliminary treatment of rich ores). However, when, as is frequently the case with non-ferrous ores, cleaning precedes extraction, the ultimate size must be primarily such as to ensure sufficient release of the valuable mineral from the associated minerals. The extent of reduction then depends on the aggregation of the valuable mineral. In some instances the requirements of the available cleaning process may be the paramount factor controlling size, and may necessitate reduction to smaller sizes than is warranted for mineral release.

During dressing or handling of both rich and low-grade ores, all or part of the ore may be rendered too fine for efficient extraction, and special agglomerating treatments may be necessary.

Comminution. This term is applied to the various size-reducing processes ; it includes breaking, crushing and grinding, which may be arbitrarily distinguished on the following size basis : breaking converts run-of-mine ore to any size between about 6 in. and 2 in. ; crushing reduces material in this range to between about 1 in. and $\frac{1}{8}$ in. ; grinding reduces ore of about $\frac{1}{4}$ in. or smaller size to the range 0·02–0·002 in., or less.

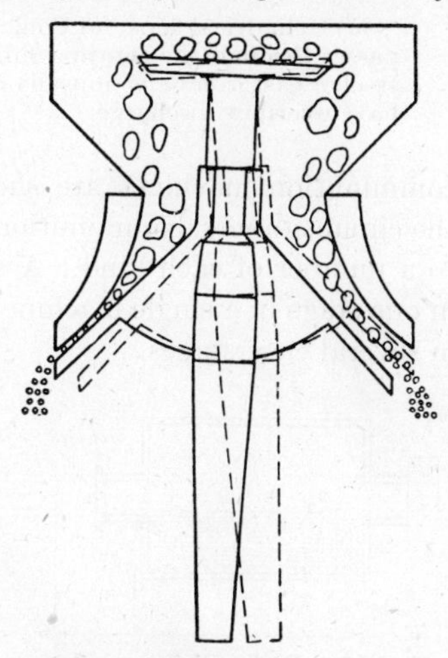

FIG. 156. Symons cone crusher. Feed is usually dry. Figs. 156, 157*a*, and 158 are from Hardinge in *Handbook of Non-Ferrous Metallurgy*. McGraw-Hill.

As indicated above, the extent of comminution is governed in a rich ore by the size requirements of extraction. With low-grade ores, joint consideration of the following two factors is necessary : (1) aggregation of the valuable mineral, and (2) size requirements of the concentration process to be employed.

The principles of some typical

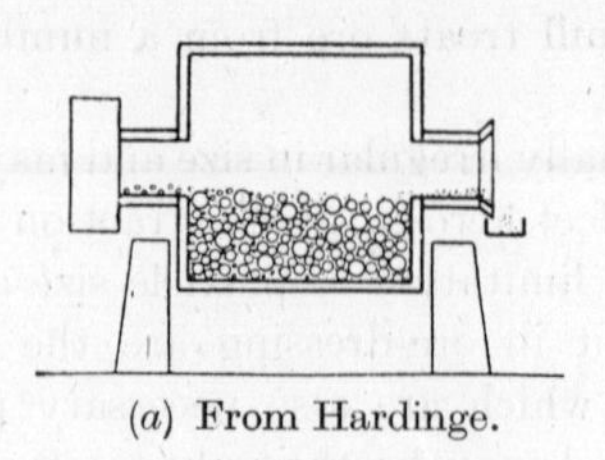

(*a*) From Hardinge.

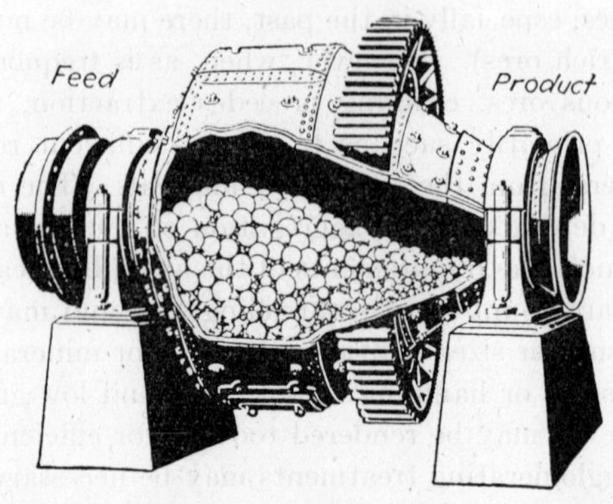

(*b*) From *Principles of Mineral Dressing*, A. M. Gaudin. McGraw-Hill.

FIG.157. Ball mills for grinding.

(*a*) Cylindrical type. (*b*) Conical type. The ore, generally as a pulp, passes through the rotating mill and is ground by the action of the steel or cast iron balls (initially often 3-4 in. dia.). Both types shown have overflow discharge.

comminution machines are shown in Figs. 155–58. Depending on the circumstances, comminution systems vary from a single machine to a number of each kind. A specific size-reduction may be made in one stage in a single machine, or by graded or stage-comminution in several easy stages.

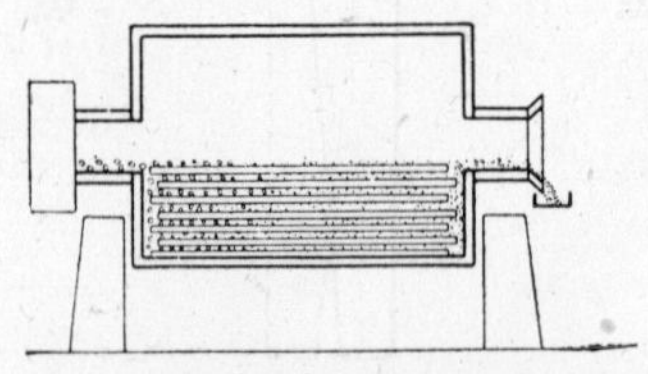

FIG. 158. Rod mill for grinding. The grinding medium is steel rods. To avoid contamination of the product with iron, pebble mills containing flint pebbles may be used. From Hardinge.

Sorting or grading. The particles in as-mined or comminuted ore usually have a wide size-range. With rich as-mined ore, sorting can be used to remove coarse sizes for comminution and fine sizes for agglomeration. Sorting divides comminuted ore for cleaning into fairly close-sized groups, as the cleaning machines usually work most efficiently on feed of this kind.

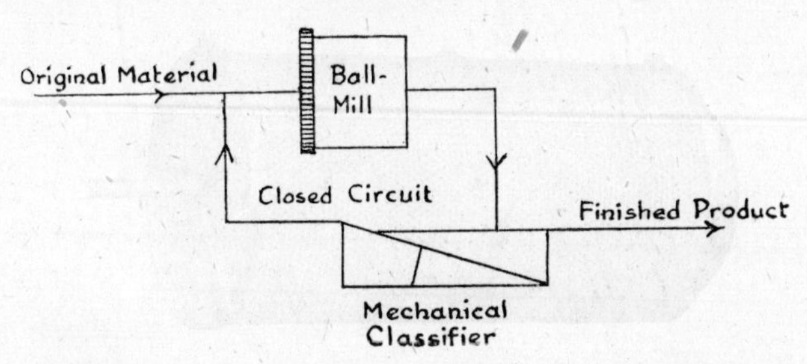

Fig. 159. Closed-circuit grinding. Most of Figs. 159–180 are from *A Text-Book of Ore-Dressing*, by S. J. Truscott. Macmillan.

In addition, previous sorting is often employed to remove material already fine enough from comminution feed at any stage, even from run-of-mine ore. Sorting devices are also used in closed-circuit comminution, especially grinding. Closed-circuit working imposes a size control on grinding, for most machines are not positive. At the same time, over-comminution of the finer sizes is avoided. The ore leaving the grinder is sorted and the over-size returned for further reduction (Fig. 159). The avoidance of over-grinding is important, because there are lower as well as upper size limits for the feed to the various cleaning processes.

For sizes down to about 0·05 in., ore is sorted by screening or sieving, that is, sorting by size or " sizing ". The screens may be made of woven steel or other metal wire, steel rods, punched steel plate, or of steel or cast-iron bars, depending on the size of ore being handled. The bar screens used for coarse material are known as **grizzlies** ; they may be stationary or moving or made of rollers. Usually the other types of screens for finer material are shaken by mechanical or electrical means ; the **trommel** is a rotating cylindrical screen (Fig. 160). Feed to screens may be wet or dry ore.

Screen aperture is best expressed directly, but various mesh scales are in use. For woven-wire screens, the mesh number is the number of holes per linear inch and the actual aperture clearly depends on the diameter of wire employed. When mesh numbers are quoted without referring to the wire diameter or specific scale used, a very rough approximation of the order of the aperture is obtained by assuming the wire diameter to be the same as the opening size ; thus the aperture is taken as the reciprocal of twice the mesh number.

Screens are not generally efficient for sizes smaller than about 0·05 in., and fine material is sorted by utilising the different rates of fall of the various particles in water and sometimes in air : this is

(*a*) Cylindrical trommel.

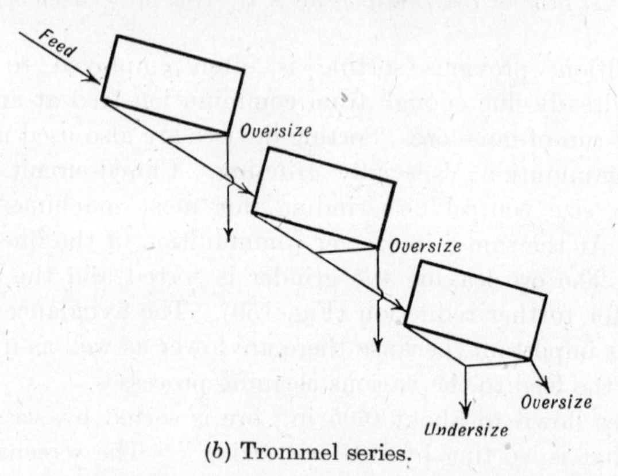

(*b*) Trommel series.

Fig. 160. Screening by trommels. From Truscott.

known as **classification**. The rate of fall in water is affected by density and shape as well as size, and thus classification is not true sizing (Fig. 161).

Under the simplest conditions in classification, the particles fall *freely* in water ; but in practice often the pulp is used at such density that conditions of *hindered-settling* result. The effective density of the fluid and thus the size ratio of particles of equal falling-rate are increased. Hindered-settling classification is, therefore, advantageous in preparation for certain gravity concentration, such as tabling. On the other hand, in closed-circuit grinding, where sizing is the aim of classification, free-settling conditions are preferable.

It will be seen that classification of the different classes of screened material should give separation, and this result is obtained in concentration by jigging. Reciprocally, screening of classified groups should have a similar result. However, at the fine sizes concerned, screens are not efficient, and in practice a film sizing technique (see p. 195) can be employed.

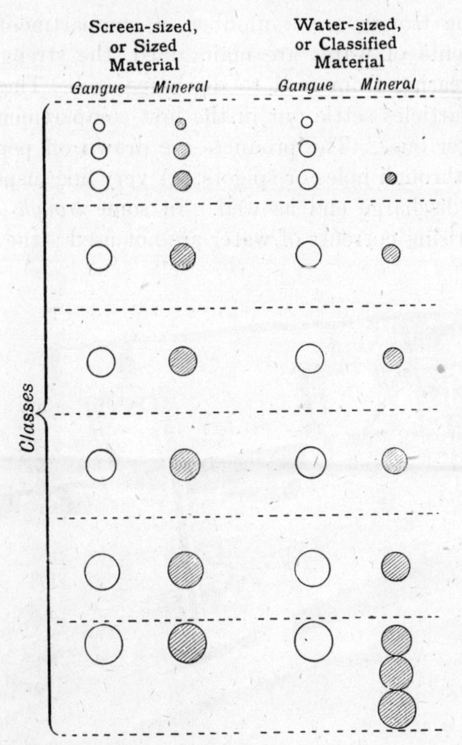

FIG. 161. Showing ideally the difference between sized and classified material; the latter consists of particles of equal falling-rate. From Truscott.

A typical water classifier for dividing up comminuted ore for feed to various cleaning machines consists of a trough along which the ore is carried as a pulp in a horizontal water current (Fig. 162). In the

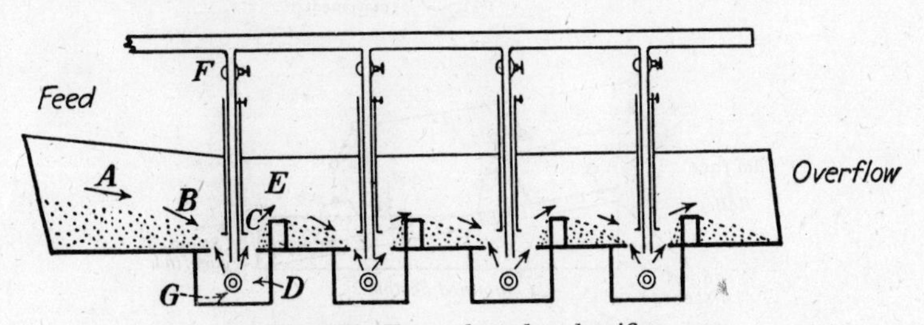

Fig. 162. Evans launder classifier.

Extra water is introduced through the pipes controlled by valves F. G represents the discharge openings or spigots. From Gaudin, after Taggart.

bottom of the trough are a number of compartments in which uprising currents of water are maintained, the strength of these currents decreasing from feed to discharge end. The larger and heavier ore particles settle out in the first compartments, and the smaller in later ones. The products are drawn off periodically or continuously through holes or spigots. A very fine suspension overflows at the discharge end as well. In some *trough-* or *launder-classifiers*, uprising currents of water are not used; the pulp passes

(*a*) Phantom view

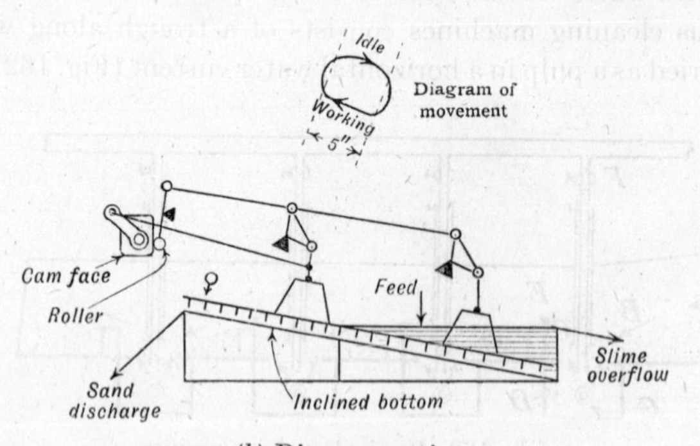

(*b*) Diagrammatic.

Fig. 163. Dorr rake classifier. Typical size is 16 ft. long × 5 ft. wide, with the rakes making 10 strokes per min. From Truscott.

in a horizontal current along a trough and the particles gradually fall out into pockets situated in the bottom.

The so-called *mechanical classifiers* are used particularly in conjunction with grinding machines in closed-circuit operations. These classifiers consist of an inclined trough into which the ore pulp is charged about half-way up. The fine particles stay suspended and overflow at the lower end as **fines**. The heavier and larger particles, which settle to the bottom, are conveyed up the trough by some form of mechanism and are discharged at the top as **sands**, which in closed-circuit work are returned for further grinding. The sand conveyance may be by rakes (Fig. 163), or by a revolving spiral mechanism. The conveying action keeps the fine material suspended and reduces the likelihood of fines being mechanically entrapped in the sands.

Various **thickeners** and **settling tanks** may also be regarded as classifiers. They are used in de-watering cleaned ore prior to extraction, to decrease the water content of ore pulps at any stage if

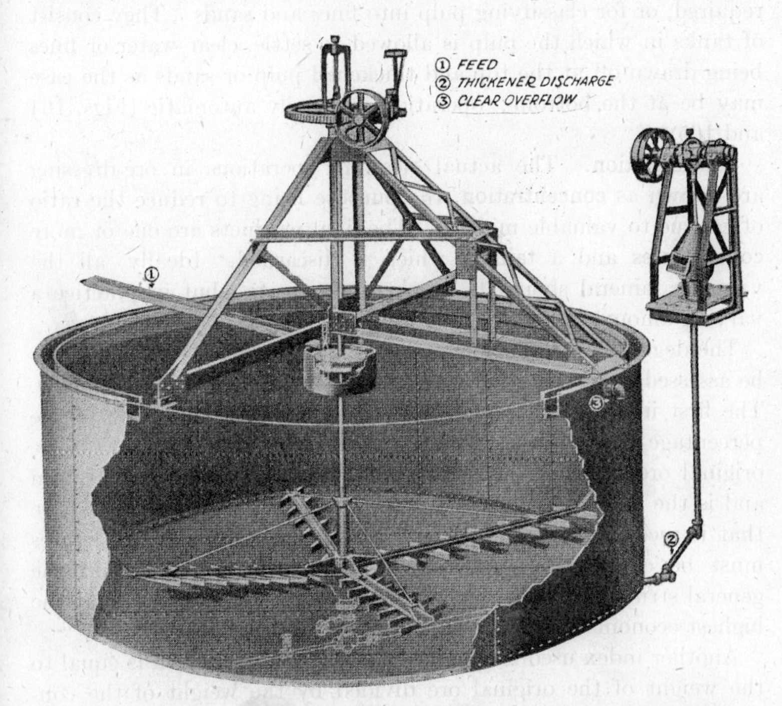

Fig. 164. Dorr thickener. The settled material is moved towards the central discharge by the slowly moving rakes; the tank is 6–10 ft. in depth, with a wide range of diameters. From Truscott.

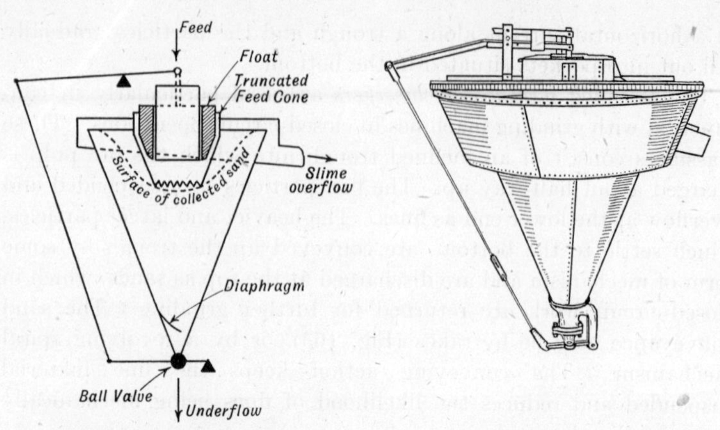

FIG. 165. Allen cone classifier ($3\frac{1}{2}$–8 ft. dia.). The valve discharge is actuated by the float when the sands have risen sufficiently. From Truscott.

required, or for classifying pulp into fines and sands. They consist of tanks in which the pulp is allowed to settle, clear water or fines being drawn off at the top and thickened pulp or sands as the case may be at the bottom; operation is usually automatic (Figs. 164 and 165).

Concentration. The actual cleaning operations in ore-dressing are known as **concentration,** the purpose being to reduce the ratio of gangue to valuable mineral. The final products are one or more **concentrates** and a **tailing,** which is discarded. Ideally, all the valuable mineral should be in the concentrates, but in practice a varying amount is lost in the tailing.

The degree of technical success of a concentrating operation may be assessed from the *ratio of enrichment* and the *percentage recovery*. The first indicates the amount of cleaning and is the ratio of the percentage of valuable material in the concentrate to that in the original ore. The second shows the loss entailed in concentration and is the percentage of the valuable mineral contained in the ore that is recovered in the concentrate. In practice, the two figures must be considered together with extraction demands and the general structure of the industry, and a balance struck so that the highest economic efficiency is maintained.

Another index used is the *ratio of concentration*, which is equal to the weight of the original ore divided by the weight of the concentrate. This index and the ratio of enrichment would be equal if there were no loss in the tailing.

The three figures are connected in the following way :

ratio of enrichment = ratio of concentration × recovery (expressed as a fraction).

The greater the value of the metal, the greater are the average figures obtained for the ratio of enrichment, for the lower is the grade of deposit that generally is economically workable. Further, it is apparent that the lower the grade of the ore the higher will be the likely enrichment ; the same is also true of the ratio of concentration. Typical values for the indices are given in Chapter 9.

As well as yielding concentrate and tailing, an intermediate product known as **middling** is usually produced. A middling may be made as a practical safeguard against loss, or arise from the nature of the ore and the mineral release obtained. In a " chatty middling " or " chat ", the valuable mineral and gangue are intergrown to such an extent that sufficient release has not been obtained at the sizes in question. Middlings may be re-treated in a separate, especially adjusted machine, or they may be returned to the same machine ; but particularly in gravity concentration there is a considerable tendency for reformation, and generally the former method is best. Chatty middlings will need further comminution before re-treatment, and in such cases a different type of machine may then be used for their treatment.

With low-grade ores a certain amount of cleaning is necessary, for there is a limiting metal content below which extraction may be neither metallurgically nor profitably practicable. The value is not the same for different metals or for different processes with the same metal ; nor again is it necessarily constant in any one case, because it is partly dependent on available techniques and current demand and prices (examples are given in Chapter 9). Beyond the respective minimum figures, cleaning is continued generally so long as it is more expensive to remove the same waste in extraction, although in some cases there may be an optimum upper limit to the metal content. The physical processes of ore-dressing are generally cheaper than the chemical ones of extraction in removing waste, especially when large proportions are present. Moreover, as the extraction plant is often situated at a considerable distance from the mine and associated dressing plant, saving in transport costs usually results from the reduction in bulk.

With ores that as-mined are already rich enough for extraction, the extent of further cleaning, if any, is also dependent on the factors outlined above. In most cases today a certain amount of size reduction and grading at least are carried out, so as to increase the efficiency of extraction.

It must be pointed out that although the above remarks stand as generalisations, in application they are subject to some modified interpretations according to the structure of the particular industry and winning processes used.

CONCENTRATION PROCESSES

One of the oldest forms of concentration is **hand-picking** or **-sorting**, in which the valuable mineral is separated from the waste, or vice versa, by hand. It depends on there being coarse aggregation of the valuable mineral (it is practicable with sizes down to about 2 in.) and a marked difference in appearance between the minerals. Hand-picking is further dependent on cheap labour ; it is practised to a limited extent today mainly as a preliminary treatment. In addition to separating minerals, harmful substances or refuse may be removed.

Washing is another process of early origin, being the fore-runner of modern gravity processes. With suitable ores, the smaller and lighter particles are washed away by a current of water, the action of which may be sufficient to give mineral release as well. " Washing " is sometimes used to include all the various classification and gravity concentration processes, especially in connection with coal cleaning, but usually the term is reserved for the more elementary operations.

The most important modern methods of concentration are: (1) **flotation**, in which use is made of differences in surface conditions ; and (2) **gravity concentration** in water ; air is sometimes used as a medium, but rarely with ores. **Magnetic methods** of separation are also of importance. There is a number of comparatively minor processes in addition, such as table-flotation, electrostatic and centrifugal concentration, but these will not be described.

The principal factors governing choice of concentration process are :

(1) Differences in physical properties that exist between the minerals ; and

(2) Aggregation of the valuable mineral(s).

The complete scheme of concentration may utilise two or more processes of the same or different nature, depending on the conditions.

Gravity concentration. Differences in density between minerals are exploited to effect their separation (Table 18).

TABLE 18. APPROXIMATE SPECIFIC GRAVITIES OF COMMON MINERALS

Mineral	Spec. gravity	Mineral	Spec. gravity
Garnierite (hydrated Ni.Mg silicate)	2·5	Barytes ($BaSO_4$)	4·5
Quartz (SiO_2)	2·65	Covellite (CuS)	4·6
Calcite ($CaCO_3$)	2·7	Pyrite (FeS_2)	5·0
Magnesite ($MgCO_3$)	3·05	Hematite (Fe_2O_3)	5·1
A number of gangue silicates have spec. grav. around 3.		Magnetite (Fe_3O_4)	5·2
		Cerargyrite (AgCl)	5·55
		Chalcocite (Cu_2S)	5·65
Fluorite (CaF_2)	3·1	Arsenopyrite (FeAsS)	6·0
Diaspore ($Al_2O_3 . H_2O$)	3·4	Cuprite (Cu_2O)	6·0
Limonite ($2Fe_2O_3 . 3H_2O$)	3·8	Anglesite ($PbSO_4$)	6·25
Siderite ($FeCO_3$)	3·85	Cerussite ($PbCO_3$)	6·5
Sphalerite (ZnS)	4·0	Cassiterite (SnO_2)	7·0
Malachite ($CuCO_3 . Cu(OH)_2$)	4·0	Wolframite ((FeMn) WO_4)	7·3
Bornite (Cu_5FeS_4)	4·15	Argentite (Ag_2S)	7·3
Chalcopyrite ($CuFeS_2$)	4·2	Galena (PbS)	7·5
Enargite (Cu_3AsS_4)	4·45	Calaverite ((AuAg) Te_2)	9·0

In **jigging, tabling** and **vanning** the minerals are stratified by agitation in water and then separated. The difference in specific gravity between the minerals to be separated should best be 1 or greater; particle size and shape also affect separation.

Jigs deal efficiently with ore in the size range 1·5–0·08 in., tables 0·08–0·008 in. and vanners can be used for finer sizes, although not less than about 0·0004 in. These figures indicate approximate overall ranges of application; there is, of course, some overlapping. Usually, for efficient working, closely sized feed is required, and a number of machines will be used to cover the complete range, each treating a sorted fraction.

Jigging. The plunger type fixed-sieve jig well illustrates the principles of this form of concentration (Fig. 166 and 167). The ore is fed on to a screen which is submerged in water and contained in a tank. The ore is stratified by means of pulsion (upward) and suction (downward) currents of water passing through the screen. The water action is produced by a plunger driven by an eccentric and operating in an adjacent and connected chamber. Extra water is supplied to the plunger compartment. Concentrate is removed from the screen by a gate mechanism. A valuable "hutch" product composed of fine particles that have been drawn through the screen

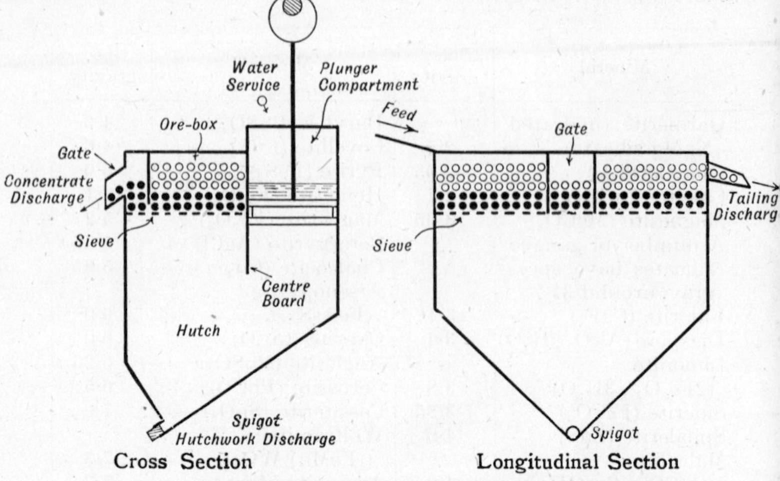

FIG. 166. Principle of fixed-sieve jig. Typical size of ore-box is 2 ft. × 3 ft. The plunger makes 100–300 strokes per min. of 0·2–3 in. length. From Truscott.

collects at the bottom of the tank. Tailing is discharged at one side of the machine.

The fixed-sieve jig employs the technique of "jigging on the sieve". During the pulsion stroke the conditions are similar to those of hindered-settling classification, enhanced by the plunger action (Fig.

FIG. 167. Exterior view of two-cell Harz jig. The two gate discharges and the final tailing discharge can be seen. From Truscott.

168). With closely-sized material the suction stroke is made slowly to avoid drawing down gangue particles faster than valuable mineral. However, if the ore is not so closely-sized, strong suction will be useful in drawing the fine overlapping mineral particles into the concentrate. The technique has been practised on screened feed down to about 0·3 in.; the screen aperture is slightly smaller than the smallest particle.

Fixed-sieve jigs contain one or more jigging compartments (two, three or four are common) connected together, each with a sieve and plunger, and separated by cross partitions. Some of the material in one compartment overflows as feed to the next. The amplitude of jigging decreases from the first cell. Generally, when concentrating one valuable mineral, concentrate is made in the first cell and the useful products of the others are treated as middlings. In the separation of two or more valuable minerals, the first cell would make concentrate of the heaviest mineral, the second cell middling, the third concentrate of the second valuable mineral and so on.

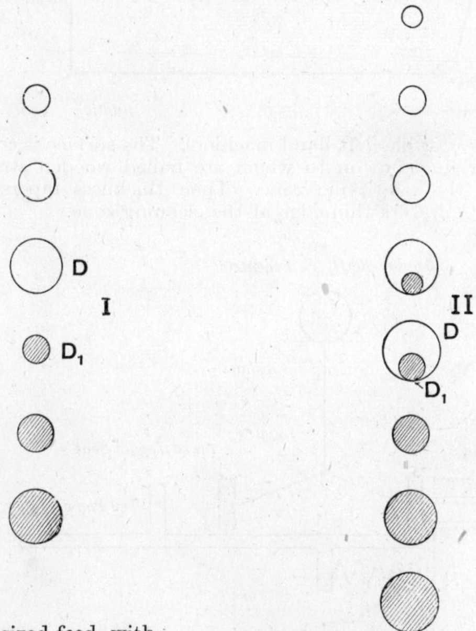

I. Closely-sized feed, with $\frac{D}{D_1} < \frac{d_1 - 1 \cdot 5}{d - 1 \cdot 5}$

II. Less closely-sized feed, so that $\frac{D}{D_1} > \frac{d_1 - 1 \cdot 5}{d - 1 \cdot 5}$

FIG. 168. Effect of pulsion stroke during jigging. D = diameter of largest particle of density d. D_1 = diameter of smallest valuable mineral particle of density d_1. From Truscott.

In the Richards fixed-sieve pulsator jig, suction is eliminated and pulsion is caused by inserting a rotating valve on the water supply, thus obtaining surges of water through the screen.

In movable-sieve jigs such as the Hancock, which are used on finer material, pulsion and strong suction are produced by moving the screen up and down in the water. Jigging is "through the screen", the products being obtained from compartments in the bottom of the tank ; only one separation is possible.

This kind of jigging can also be carried out on material smaller than 0·3 in. in Harz fixed-sieve jigs.

Tabling. The "Wilfley" is the best-known form of concentrating table. It consists of a partly smooth and partly riffled or shallow

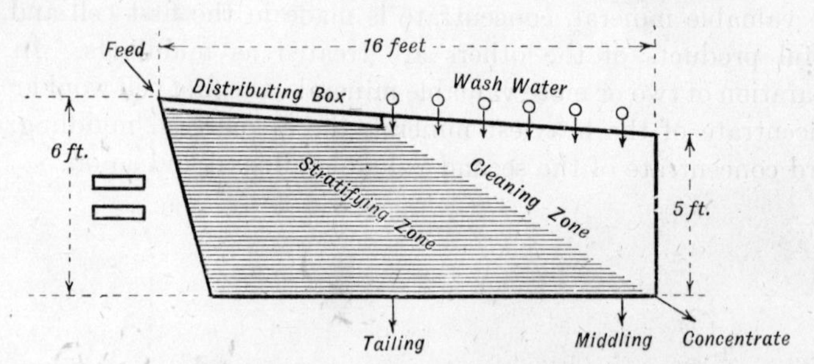

(*a*) Plan view of table (left-hand machine). The surface is covered with rubber or linoleum on to which are nailed wooden strips or riffles to form the stratifying zone. Their thickness tapers from between $\frac{1}{4}$ and $\frac{1}{2}$ in. to a thin edge at the cleaning zone.

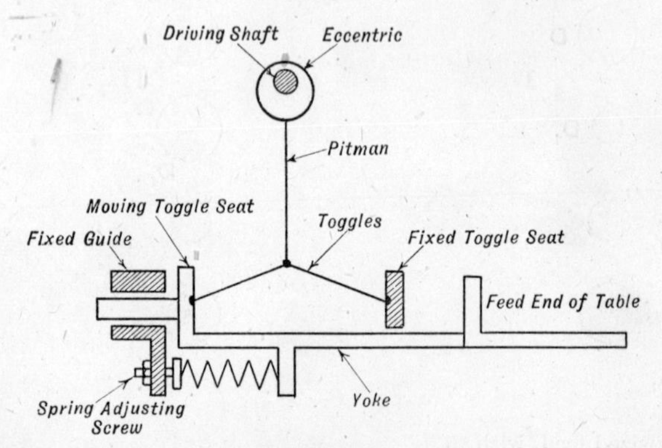

(*b*) Mechanism: the up-and-down movement of the pitman produced by the eccentric drive is transmitted to the table as a horizontal movement by means of the toggles. The length of stroke is adjusted by raising or lowering the fixed toggle-seat. A typical stroke is $\frac{3}{4}$ in., made 240 times per min.

Fig. 169. Diagrams of Wilfley table. From Truscott.

Fig. 170. General view of Wilfley table (right-hand machine.) From Truscott.

ribbed surface, which is slightly inclined to the horizontal plane (Fig. 169 and 170). In operation, the table is shaken rapidly backwards and forwards in the direction of its length with such acceleration that particles on it receive an impetus to move from one end to the other. The ore pulp is fed across the table down the slight slope (on to the riffled portion). Due to the shaking motion, the ore is stratified with the heavier valuable mineral at the bottom, where it is well protected behind the riffles from the water flowing down the table (extra water is fed as shown). As the ore is moved along the riffles by the shaking motion, the top-lying gangue is washed away by the water to discharge as tailing. The underlying valuable mineral continues to move along, gradually becoming less protected with more gangue being removed. Finally, the valuable mineral comes to the plane portion of the table, where it drops from rib to rib, undergoing more cleaning, and discharging as concentrate ; a middling is also made.

Vanning. The vanner is the most outstanding example of a once important class of concentrators that has been rendered nearly obsolete by flotation. The simplest consisted of a stationary sloping surface of wood, cloth or rubber. The pulp was fed down the slope with water, whereupon the slower moving valuable mineral settling to the bottom tended to be held by the surface, while the lighter gangue was washed away. A *film-sizing* effect is involved (Fig. 171). Operation of these tables or "buddles" was intermittent, concentrate being scraped off regularly. Corduroy blanket tables are used in modern practice for recovering free gold in the treatment of gold ores.

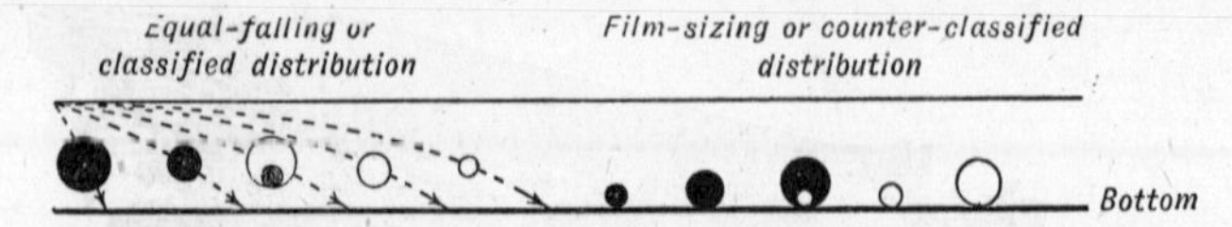

FIG. 171. Difference, ideally, between classification and film-sizing in horizontal water current. Classification depends on falling-rate. Film-sizing results because the lighter particles are moved more easily along the table surface ; and because the velocity of the flowing water decreases to zero at the bottom, that is, at the table surface, so that there is the greater action on the larger particles. From Truscott.

The Frue vanner is the best known continuous kind ; it consists of a slightly inclined endless belt moving up the slope while being shaken sideways. Ore and water are fed near the top ; the gangue is washed down and discharged as tailing at the bottom, the concentrate being discharged at the top (Fig. 172).

In this machine the stratification from the shaking supplements the film-sizing effect. In the Wilfley table, in addition, the protective effect of the riffles is utilised, increasing capacity.

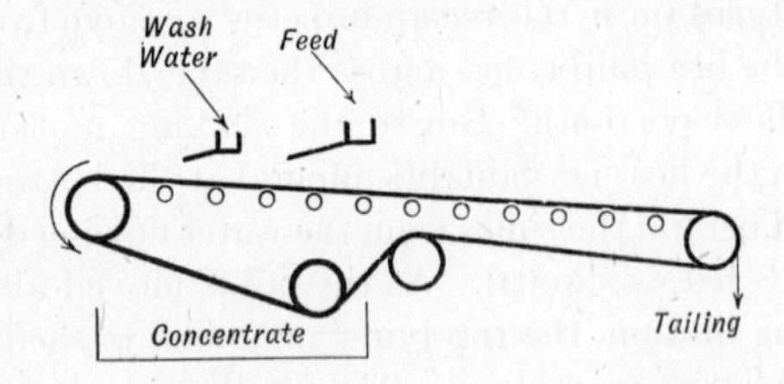

FIG. 172. Diagram of Frue vanner. From Truscott.

Jigging, tabling and vanning systems and applications. Because of their size range, jigs can only be used with ores in which there is coarse or moderate aggregation of the valuable mineral in part or wholly. Small plants may use one jig as sole concentrator, in which case no special attention is paid to the fine sizes. However, in general practice, after comminution the feed is sorted and the finer sizes sent to other suitable processes. The coarse fraction is divided up and distributed to a series of jigs. The concentrates may be taken as final or re-treated in other jigs. The middlings may need comminution before re-treatment in a separate jig or by another process. The tailings from the jigs may be discarded, but if there is fine dissemination of valuable mineral as well as coarse, comminution and re-treatment are likely to be profitable. For treating the fine sizes either as directly formed in the first comminution, or afterwards from intermediate jig products, vanning may be used, although in most cases, flotation offers a more efficient method and is widely used. Tabling may be used to advantage between jigs and fine concentrators, or in some cases with jigs alone, and with ores of finer dissemination concentration can start on tables.

Jigs can also be employed for removing coarsely aggregated waste minerals. The concentrated material is then comminuted further and treated usually by flotation.

The once dominating position of water-gravity concentration is now occupied by flotation. Jigs and/or tables may be used in conjunction with flotation as outlined above, although sometimes it is found more efficient to comminute the whole ore finely and treat by flotation irrespective of dissemination; this is especially so with complex ores. Jigs and tables without flotation still predominate in cases where flotation is not yet applicable or economical, as with cassiterite, chromite, and non-magnetic iron ores. They are also of importance in coal cleaning (jigs are used for much larger sizes than with ores) and other non-metallic applications. Tables are useful for various separations as opposed to concentration. Vanners are largely obsolete except for the fine sizes of ores where flotation is not yet applied, the principal application being with cassiterite. Typical flow-sheets are given in Chapters 9 and 10.

Sink-and-float process (or **heavy-media separation**). This is a comparatively recent process especially for ores and is now soundly established. Gravity is essentially the only factor involved in separation. The comminuted ore, generally with finer sizes removed, is put into a fluid having a specific gravity intermediate between those of the minerals to be separated. Close sizing of the feed is not necessary.

In the case of ores, the valuable mineral is recovered as **sink** and the waste as **float**. The upper size limit for sink and float is not rigid, but is set by the ore to about 1–2 in., for effective release of the minerals is not likely at larger sizes. For some time the lower limit was about 0·25 in., but it is reported that this has been considerably reduced and as low as 0·06 in. is apparently operated; eventually it is hoped to reduce this to about 0·006 in. Sink-and-float requires less difference in specific gravity between the minerals to be separated than the other gravity methods; a figure as low as 0·1 has been claimed.

Due to the high specific gravities of most ore minerals, the media in commercial work consist of suspensions of fine dense particles in water; such suspensions have a high effective specific gravity. Typical materials are magnetite (effective specific gravity of medium

2·5), galena (4·3) and ferro-silicon (2·5–3·5, depending on composition); they are ground to less than about 0·006 in. In a mill treating galena-bearing ores a portion of the flotation concentrates is suitable as medium. The usual suspensions contain about 70–85 per cent solids by weight. Sand suspensions and calcium chloride solution (S.G. 1·4) are used commercially for coal cleaning, and an organic liquid has been tried; organic liquids are employed in laboratory testing of ores.

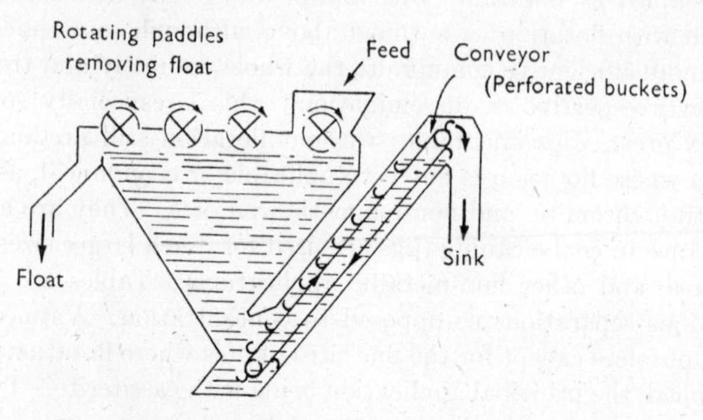

FIG. 173. Tank suitable for heavy-media separation.

Separation is carried out in tanks (Fig. 173). The floating material overflows or is scraped into a trough. The settled minerals are removed mechanically from the bottom of the tank or drawn off in some way. A middling may be made by varying the density of the medium from top to bottom of the tanks. Currents in the medium may cause particle size and shape to play some part in separation. The medium must be recovered from the concentration products, and the range of usefulness of sink-and-float must justify the cost of the apparatus necessary. The first stage consists in draining and washing on screens, followed by thickening and cleaning of the medium for re-use, for which classifiers and concentrators are used. A point in favour of ferrous media is their easy recovery by magnetic means. At present the lower size limit of about 0·06 in. is due to the fact that this is about the lowest screen aperture which is practicable for the separation of medium and product. Finer sizes may be separated by concentrators.

For ores, sink-and-float is generally used in conjunction with other concentration processes. With non-ferrous ores it is often necessary to comminute the sink-and-float concentrate further and clean it, together with the fine portions of the ore; its function is thus to remove waste liberated at coarse sizes (Fig. 223, p. 297). With coal and iron-ores, sink-and-float makes final concentrate (Fig. 237, p. 325); a fine concentration adjunct may often not be used. An attractive feature of heavy-media separation is the smallness of density difference required. In some cases it may replace other gravity methods; in other cases it is worked in conjunction with them.

At present it is used commercially with lead, zinc and iron ores, cassiterite, magnesite, coal and other non-metallics, for example.

Flotation. Flotation concentration has been evolved since the end of the nineteenth century. The ore is first obtained as a fine suspension in water by fine grinding in ball or rod mills in closed circuit with mechanical classifiers. The particle size is generally best less than about 0·01 in. yet greater than 0·0002 in. The dilution of the pulp ranges from about 5 to 40 per cent solids by weight. Air is bubbled through this pulp contained in a cell or tank and, due to the previous addition of various chemicals and proper agitation, the valuable mineral particles become attached to the air bubbles and are carried by them to the surface to form a fairly stable mineralised froth, which is skimmed off. The gangue particles are unaffected and remain in the pulp.

Agitation of the pulp brings about encounter between the valuable mineral particles and the air bubbles. The froth itself consists of air bubbles attached to one another by regular thin water walls. In the mineralised froth, the mineral particles are attached at the air/water interfaces. **Frothing agents** are added to produce a dry, regular, strong and fairly stable froth. The frothing agents are complex organic compounds containing one part with a strong affinity for water (a wettable, water-avid or polar complex) and the other with reverse properties (a non-wettable or non-polar group). Their molecules concentrate at air/water interfaces, and reduce the surface tension of the water. Typical examples are cresylic acid, pine, eucalyptus and camphor oils; very small quantities are used, of the order of 0·001–0·01 per cent.

In addition, **collecting** or **promoting agents** must be introduced to give the desired mineral the right kind of surface for flotation. Modifying agents are also added, notably depressants which prevent collection of certain minerals, and activators which remove the effects of depressants or make certain minerals respond to collection when otherwise they would not do so.

Certain substances may have intrinsically non-wettable surfaces, but most ore minerals require special treatment to acquire such surface properties and give them the power to become attached to air bubbles. Sulphides appear to have the greatest tendency to be non-wettable and these are the easiest minerals to float. But, even with sulphides, collecting agents are necessary. Xanthates, such as potassium or sodium ethyl, butyl or amyl xanthates, are the commonest commercial collecting agents. They are somewhat similar in nature to frothing agents and are also added in small quantities (about 0·002 to 0·1 per cent). However, frothing agents themselves should have no collecting power. It is suggested that collecting agents form the desired non-wettable surface on a mineral either by reaction or more likely by adsorption at the mineral surface with the collector molecules so orientated that the non-polar parts are outwards.

Once given non-wettable surfaces and proper encounter with air bubbles, the mineral particles will become attached, carried up and gathered into the froth. The complete mechanism of attachment of the non-wettable surfaces to the air bubles is not fully understood. In the Direct-Contact theory, it is suggested that if good contact is made between an air bubble and a non-wettable surface, there will be little tendency for displacement of the air by water. It is apparent that a wettable surface will always tend to become covered with water, thus displacing any air present. It should be appreciated that one valuable mineral particle may reach the surface by the aid of a number of air bubbles. Such conditions are desirable, especially in the froth, as they allow for exclusion of mechanically entrapped particles or gangue particles with weakly wettable surfaces. On the other hand, the Gas-Precipitation theory is based on the idea that the pulp is saturated with air, which is precipitated selectively at non-wettable surfaces, thereby forming mineralised bubbles. A continued supply of air keeps the pulp saturated. It is possible that both mechanisms may be operating at the same time, or one or other may predominate. Electrostatic effects are not thought to be of importance.

The most outstanding modifying or conditioning treatments are **activating** and **depressing**; they are in many cases complementary. Depressing makes a surface wettable and prevents collection by maintaining the wettability. Activation makes a surface responsive to collection and removes deliberate wettability. A variety of inorganic reagents is used in similar proportions to the other reagents. Their mode of action may be similar to those of collectors; in addition, surface coatings may be dissolved. The two treatments are used in selective flotation. Thus, for example, with lead-zinc sulphide ores, zinc sulphate, sodium cyanide or sodium sulphite is used to depress the zinc sulphide, while the lead sulphide is floated off to form one concentrate. The zinc sulphide is then activated by copper sulphate and floated off as a second concentrate. Pyrite present in these ores can be depressed with lime and afterwards activated by sodium sulphide or sulphuric acid. Depressants may also be used to prevent the flotation of specific gangue minerals; and activators to aid collection of difficult minerals. Dispersing agents such as sodium silicate are used to prevent the formation of slimy gangue coatings on the desired minerals.

Flotation is generally carried out in alkaline solutions (pH 7–13). The pH is controlled by additions of reagents such as lime and soda ash, which may also precipitate impurities such as soluble iron salts introduced in the water or ore. **pH control** is a very important factor, especially in selective flotation.

The various flotation reagents may be added in the grinding mills, classifiers, during the flow to the cells, in special conditioning tanks or actually in the flotation cell, depending on the time required for their action.

There is a large number of proprietary flotation machines or cells available. They all consist essentially of a tank provided with means for introduction of air and causing agitation, and through which the pulp flows (Fig. 174). The mineralised froth overflows or is scraped by paddles into troughs, where it is broken down by sprays of water. First concentrates may often be cleaned and sometimes recleaned. Middlings are re-treated in the same or a different machine. Tailings

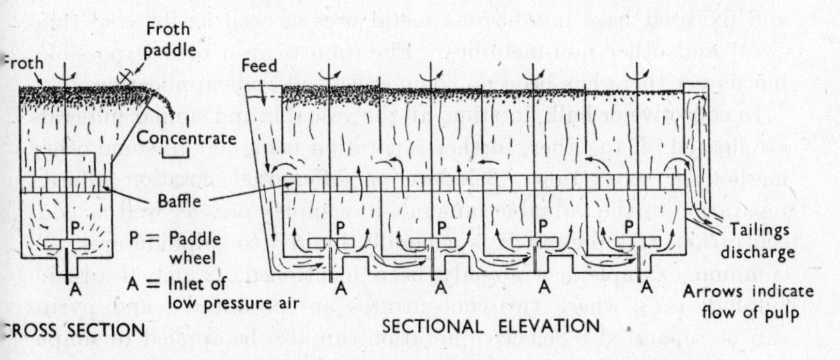

Fig. 174. Flotation machine: mechanically agitated, with four connected cells (section of each cell, 2–4 ft. sq.). An alternative method for introduction of air in this type is to draw it down through the paddle shaft, by the vortex created around the paddles. Sufficient time (5–15 min.) must be allowed for the flotation.

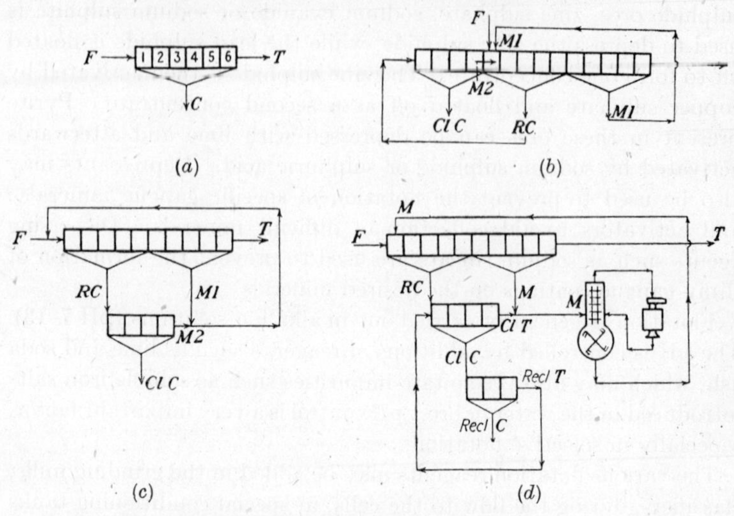

FIG. 175. Typical flotation circuits. F = feed. C = concentrate. M = middling. T = tailing. RC = rougher concentrate. From Gaudin.

may be scavenged by a separate treatment. Intermediate products may be reground before re-treatment (Fig. 175).

Flotation is the most important modern concentration process. It may be used in conjunction with gravity concentration or often for complete concentration. The major applications are with copper, lead, zinc and nickel sulphide ores, as described in Chapter 9. Flotation is also employed with native copper, gold and silver, and oxidised base non-ferrous metal ores as well as for coal (fine sizes) and other non-metallics. Flotation of iron ores is possible, but as yet there has been no commercial full-scale application.

In **collective** or **bulk flotation,** all the valuable and similar minerals are floated off together, further separation being left to some other method or extraction. **Selective** or **differential flotation** affords separation of the valuable minerals in complex ores as well as concentration. At present it is generally limited to sulphide ores. A common example has already been mentioned, namely lead-zinc sulphide ores, where two concentrates are produced; and pyrite can be separated. Selective flotation can also be applied to simple ores if any gangue mineral has to be definitely depressed. In some cases flotation is used just to remove undesirable minerals from ores or concentrates (made in other ways). Thus base sulphides, for example of iron and copper, are removed from cassiterite ores, which are concentrated by gravity. Another case is the removal of undesirable minerals from gold ores before cyaniding. Two interesting applications during extraction are mentioned on page 222.

Magnetic separation and concentration. Minerals are non-magnetic, weakly magnetic or strongly magnetic, and are referred to as diamagnetic, paramagnetic and ferromagnetic, respectively (Table 19).

TABLE 19. RELATIVE MAGNETIC ATTRACTIBILITY OF SOME MINERALS

	Mineral	Relative Attractibility
Strongly Magnetic	Iron (taken as standard)	100·0
	Magnetite (Fe_3O_4)	40·2
	Ilmenite ($FeTiO_3$)	24·7
Weakly Magnetic	Pyrrhotite ($Fe_{11}S_{12}$)	6·7
	Siderite ($FeCO_3$)	1·8
	Hematite (Fe_2O_3)	1·3
	Limonite ($2Fe_2O_3 . 3H_2O$)	0·8
	Pyrolusite (MnO_2)	0·7
	Manganite ($Mn_2O_3 . H_2O$)	0·5
Non-Magnetic	Quartz (SiO_2)	0·4
	Cerussite ($PbCO_3$)	0·3
	Argentite (Ag_2S)	0·3
	Pyrite (FeS_2)	0·2
	Sphalerite (ZnS)	0·2
	Bornite (Cu_5FeS_4)	0·2
	Magnesite ($MgCO_3$)	0·15
	Chalcocite (Cu_2S)	0·09
	Cuprite (Cu_2O)	0·08
	Galena (PbS)	0·04
	Calcite ($CaCO_3$)	0·03

Magnetic concentration implies the separation of valuable mineral from gangue; whereas **magnetic separation** may indicate the separation of minerals, gangue removal being carried out by other means, as in separation of iron- and tungsten-bearing minerals from cassiterite.

There is a variety of magnetic machines using drums or belts to bring the ore into the magnetic field and to remove the attracted material (Figs. 176–78). Direct-current electro-magnets are used, high intensity for attracting weakly magnetic and low intensity for strongly magnetic minerals. Often a number of magnets are arranged together with alternating poles, an arrangement which gives better opportunity for mechanically entrapped non-magnetic

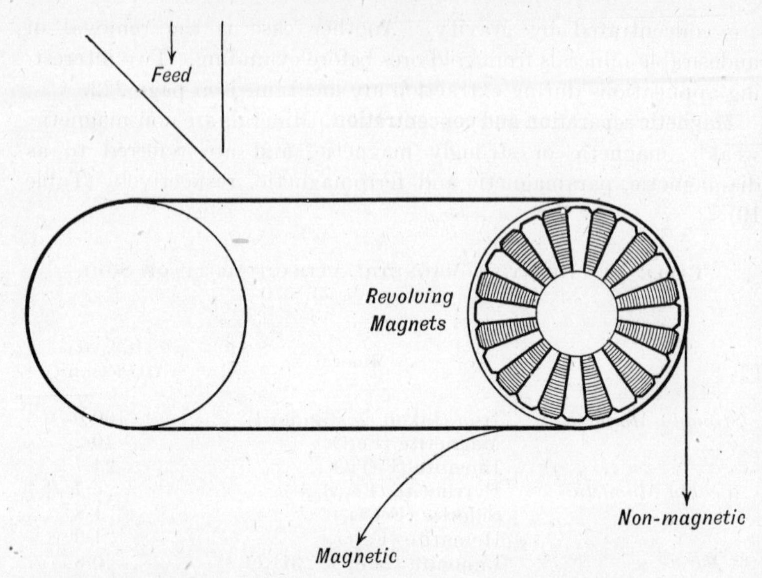

FIG. 176. Magnetic pulley, suitable for removing scrap iron from ore or for concentrating magnetite ores. From Truscott.

particles to escape. The feed may be wet or dry ore ; the machines usually work on either type but not both. The main factor governing size is that adequate release of valuable mineral should have been made. The lower size limit is about 0·003 in., and generally the closer the sizing the better. Although magnetic properties are the primary factor involved, in practice other properties such as specific gravity, size and purity are also involved. After magnetic treatment, demagnetising may be desirable to prevent the formation of magnetic " flocs " in subsequent treatments.

In connection with magnetic processes, various roasting treatments may be carried out on ore to convert a mineral to a more magnetic form. Thus oxide and sulphide minerals of iron may be converted to the strongly magnetic Fe_3O_4 by roasting under appropriate conditions.

The principal application of magnetic concentration is to magnetite ores, and other iron ores after a magnetising roast. It is also applied to nickel-iron sulphide ores, pyrolusite (MnO_2), chromite (Cr_2FeO_4) and franklinite (a complex iron-zinc-manganese-oxide mineral used in the production of zinc oxide). As indicated above, magnetic means may be used in removing certain minerals from other concentrates and for miscellaneous separations. An important use is

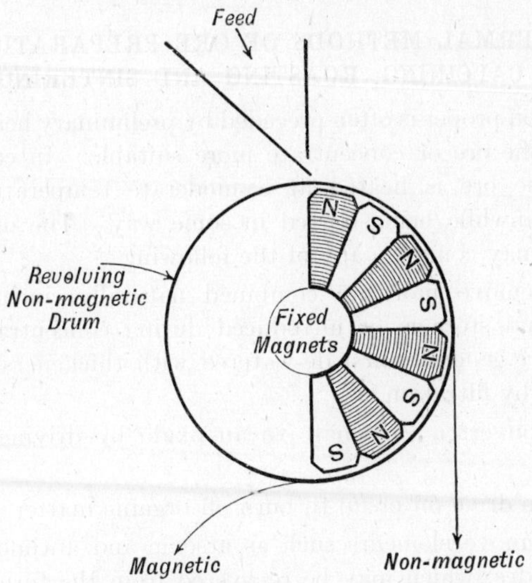

FIG. 177. Drum type magnetic separator. For dry, coarse and strongly magnetic material. From Truscott.

the removal of "tramp" or scrap iron (broken mining and comminution equipment) from ore to prevent damage to subsequent machines. Iron may also be removed from non-ferrous metal scrap. In the non-metallic field, there are applications in removal of undesirable iron-bearing and other materials from refractories, glass and pottery materials, plastics, abrasives and coal.

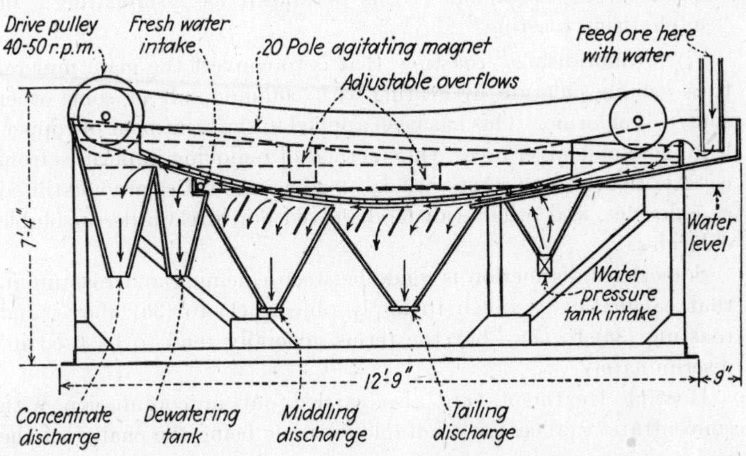

FIG. 178. Wet belt-type magnetic separator. From Gaudin.

THERMAL METHODS OF ORE PREPARATION : CALCINING, ROASTING AND SINTERING

Extraction proper is often preceded by preliminary heat treatment to render the ore or concentrate more suitable. In calcining and roasting the ore is heated at a moderate temperature without fusion, meanwhile being stirred in some way. The object of the treatment may comprise any of the following :

(1) To remove moisture combined naturally, included during handling and storage, or introduced during concentration. Concentrates are generally first de-watered with thickeners followed in some cases by filtration.

(2) To convert a carbonate to an oxide by driving off carbon dioxide.

(3) (*a*) To drive off or (*b*) to burn off organic matter.

(4) To remove elements such as arsenic and antimony as their volatile oxides, which may be recovered from the furnace flues or from the flue gases.

(5) To oxidise a sulphide to an oxide ; for example

$$2PbS + 3O_2 \rightarrow 2PbO + 2SO_2$$

$$2ZnS + 3O_2 \rightarrow 2ZnO + 2SO_2 ;$$

or to burn off part of the sulphur prior to matte-smelting (roaster gases are often used for sulphuric acid manufacture).

(6) By careful control of roasting conditions to produce a soluble sulphate from a sulphide ; this is known as " sulphating " or " sulphatising roasting ".

(7) " Chloridising " roasting, that is to convert the main mineral to a soluble chloride by heating with common salt or some other source of chlorine. This has been applied in the treatment of copper, lead, gold and silver ores. One method of removing impurities from cassiterite ores is to roast with salt : some impurities are volatilised as chlorides, and others can be dissolved out afterwards as soluble chlorides.

Sometimes distinction is made between calcining and roasting in that calcination is taken to imply objects (1) to (3*a*) above, and roasting (3*b*) to (7) ; but the terms generally tend to be used indiscriminately.

Heating treatments are also carried out in conjunction with concentration processes, a notable example being the change of the metal-bearing compound to a more magnetic form. For example,

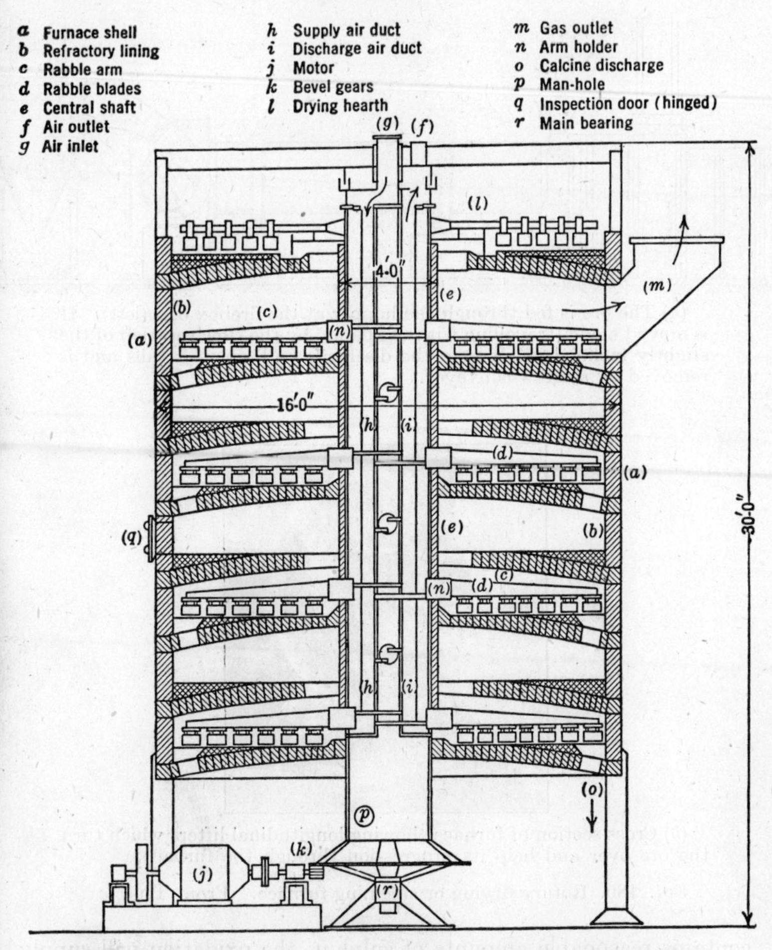

FIG. 179. Multi-hearth roasting furnace. A number of hearths are arranged one above the other, thus giving large capacity. The ore is fed in at the top and raked from hearth to hearth. The air supply to each hearth can be varied, and burners are provided where required. From *Non-Ferrous Production Metallurgy*, by J. L. Bray. Wiley.

hematite and limonite can be converted to the strongly magnetic Fe_3O_4 by roasting under controlled reducing conditions whereas siderite needs controlled oxidation. Pyrite can also be changed to Fe_3O_4.

Typical calcining and roasting furnaces are illustrated in Figs. 179–180. In **flash-** or **shower-roasting** of sulphides, fine ore is allowed to fall in a chamber through hot ascending air, when rapid roasting occurs. As with any method of roasting sulphides, provided the ore

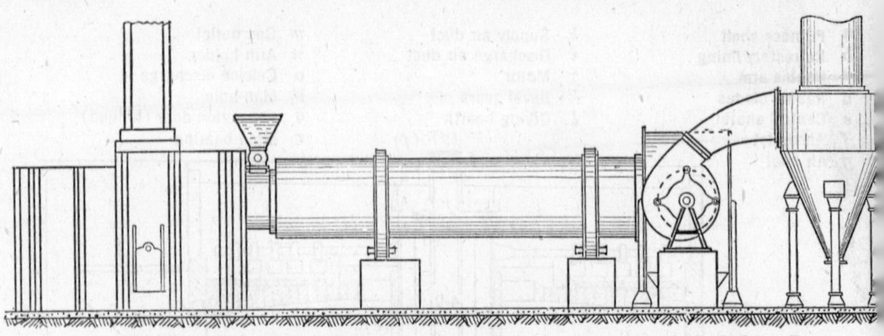

(*a*) The ore is fed through the hopper at the firebox end (left). It is moved along (travelling with the flame) by the slow rotation of the slightly inclined cylinder to the discharge end where it falls and is removed by a screw-conveyor.

(*b*) Cross-section of furnace showing longitudinal lifters which turn the ore over and help its progression through the furnace.

FIG. 180. Rotary drying or calcining furnace. From Truscott.

contains reasonable amounts of sulphur, the oxidation will supply substantially all the heat required, once the process has been started. At Trail, B. C., the air for flash-roasting zinc sulphide ores has been enriched with oxygen to advantage. A large part of the roasting in multi-hearth furnaces results from flash-roasting in the fall of ore from hearth to hearth.

Sintering and Blast-roasting. Sintering consists of the agglomeration of material too fine for efficient extraction in the blast-furnace, because of high dust losses. The treatment has considerable application with iron ores. There are two common machines, the " Greenawalt " and the " Dwight-Lloyd " ; the latter is best known and most used (Fig. 181). The ore is mixed with a proportion of fine coke and water, if not already sufficiently moist. It is then charged as a layer a few inches thick on to the endless belt of grates or pallets. Combustion is started under the ignition hood and is rapidly propagated by a current of air drawn through the ore by the wind box. The combustion is sufficient to cause partial or incipient fusion, fritting or sintering of the particles to produce a fairly strong cellular material, which is discharged at the other end of the pallet belt, fines being returned. The presence of a certain amount of moisture is necessary to give porosity to the sinter cake. Due to this porosity, sinter is very suitable material for smelting charges, giving good solid/gas contact.

The term "sintering" in connection with ore-preparation indicates the agglomeration of any ore. Specifically, *blast-roasting* implies the treatment of sulphides on a sintering machine, when roasting to oxide occurs as well as agglomeration. Generally, no additional fuel is required, the sulphur being sufficient. For complete roasting the material is re-cycled or a preliminary roast is given in some other furnace. Blast-roasting is standard practice for lead sulphide ores, where the fine flotation concentrates are put in a better form for the blast furnace; an additional advantage is that these ores tend to fuse at comparatively low temperatures, which is disadvantageous in ordinary roasting furnaces. In contrast, blast-roasting has not had the same application with copper ores, which are mainly smelted in reverberatory furnaces, this kind of furnace being able to deal efficiently with fine ore. However, the technique

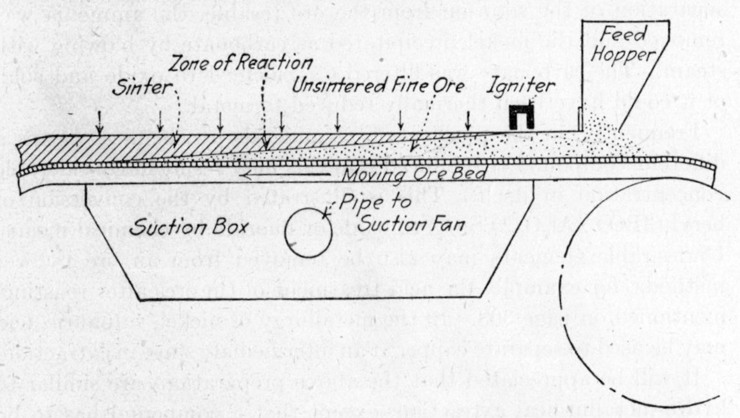

FIG. 181. Dwight-Lloyd sintering machine. For non-ferrous ores a typical length is 22 ft., but for iron ores the machines are considerably longer. From Dwight in *Handbook of Non-Ferrous Metallurgy*. McGraw-Hill.

O

is used to prepare concentrates when blast-furnaces are used for smelting. Blast-roasting is supplanting multi-hearth roasters for zinc ores, which are to be treated by distillation ; a reduction in cost and a better material for retort treatment are obtained.

Various products may be incorporated in sintering charges, such as flue-dust, dust from furnace gas-cleaning plants and even metal turnings. With lead ores the limestone for fluxing may be added. Sometimes additions may be made to assist the fusion in sintering.

CHEMICAL METHODS (WET) OF ORE PRE-TREATMENT

In some cases minerals may be purified or concentrated by chemical means. A notable example is the preparation of bauxite for electrolysis ; the aluminium oxide is dissolved out with caustic soda and then precipitated in a pure form from the solution. Similarly, in the production of tungsten, the ore is heated with sodium carbonate to form sodium tungstate. The latter is dissolved out with water and tungstic acid precipitated from it. Heating the acid yields a purified oxide, which is reduced thermally. Another example is the treatment that was applied during the Second World War to the Cuban nickel-bearing oxidised iron ores. The dried ore after grinding was given a reducing roast and then leached in an ammonia solution. During leaching the mixture was aerated to aid solution of the nickel and to oxidise and precipitate any dissolved iron. After separation of the solution from the ore residue, the ammonia was removed and the nickel precipitated as carbonate by blowing with steam. The carbonate was filtered off, calcined to oxide and sold, or it could have been thermally reduced to metal.

Frequently, in the purification of minerals by chemical means a different compound is produced and this may result in considerable concentration in itself. This is illustrated by the conversion of beryl ($3BeO . Al_2O_3 . 6SiO_2$) to oxide or fluoride by chemical means. Undesirable elements may also be removed from an ore by wet methods, for example, the acid treatment of tin ores after roasting, mentioned on page 303. In the metallurgy of nickel, sulphuric acid may be used to separate copper at an intermediate stage in extraction.

It will be appreciated that the above preparations are similar to hydro-metallurgical extraction, except that a compound has to be produced and not the metal.

The production of magnesium (page 309) also affords numerous examples of chemical treatments, and is of interest because one source of the metal is in a solution, namely sea water and natural brines.

ADDITIONAL READING

1. *Rutley's Elements of Mineralogy*, by H. H. Read. (24th Ed., Thomas Murby, 1948).

2. *Principles of Mineral Dressing*, by A. M. Gaudin. (McGraw-Hill, 1939).

3. *Textbook of Ore Dressing*, by R. H. Richards and C. E. Locke. (3rd Ed., McGraw-Hill, 1940).

4. *Handbook of Mineral Dressing*, by A. F. Taggart. (2nd Ed., Wiley; Chapman and Hall, 1945). This is a work of reference.

5. *Handbook of Non-Ferrous Metallurgy*, edited by D. M. Liddell. Vol. 1. (2nd Ed., McGraw-Hill, 1945).

6. *A Text-book of Ore Dressing*, by S. J. Truscott. (Macmillan, 1923).

7. *Principles of Extraction and Refining of Metals*. (Institution of Metallurgists, 1951).

8. *Recent Developments in Mineral Dressing*. Symposium 1952. (Inst. Min. and Met., 1953.)

9. See reference 8, Chap. 9.

CHAPTER 8

METAL WINNING: GENERAL METHODS OF EXTRACTION AND REFINING

Extraction comprises the various methods used to obtain and to consolidate metal from concentrates, ore, or some mixture, or from chemically purified mineral; sometimes the mineral may be first converted to a more amenable form. The procedure thus involves removal of remaining gangue, decomposition of the mineral if a compound, and agglomeration and collection of the metal. Extraction may be carried out in one or several stages.

Extraction processes may be classed under three main headings, namely:

(I) *Pyro-metallurgical methods*, in which thermal means primarily bring about decomposition of the feed material and separation and consolidation of the metal.

(II) *Hydro-metallurgical methods*, involving separation of the metal in aqueous solution from the rest of the ore, followed by precipitation in metallic form.

(III) *Thermo-electrolytic methods*, in which electrical energy is used to decompose the pure mineral in the molten state or dissolved in a mixture of molten salts.

A number of metals, generally those produced and used in small quantities, are recovered as by-products in the treatment of the common non-ferrous metals. This is the case especially when pyro-metallurgical extraction is used, although, for example, there is by-metal recovery in the hydro-metallurgy of zinc.

Considerable amounts of gold are obtained indirectly in the production of the base non-ferrous metals, and the majority of the world's silver is obtained in a similar way; bismuth is recovered during lead winning, and cadmium is largely a by-product from zinc, copper and lead. This position is due to the fact that the minerals of the metals in question occur in close association with the principal mineral, and these metals are concentrated into the main metal during extraction, being recovered later in refining, or if volatile from furnace gases. There is such good concentration of precious metals into copper and lead during their thermal extraction that admixture with a base ore may be regarded as one method of dealing with a primary precious metal ore. The same principle is utilised in the fire assay of gold and silver ores, where the ore is mixed with lead oxide, reducing agents and fluxes, and heated slowly in a crucible. At the correct time the temperature is raised so that the oxide is reduced and the molten lead descends as a "rain" through the charge, collecting the precious metals. The melt is cast, the lead button is separated from the top slag layer, and is cupelled to separate the gold and silver from the lead.

The once important amalgamation process for gold and silver extraction in a sense utilises similar principles. As the process does not fit easily into the classification of extraction processes adopted, it will be convenient to give a brief description here. The finely comminuted gold ore pulp is brought into contact with mercury; for example, by passing the pulp over a brass plate coated with the mercury. The mercury dissolves the free gold, forming an amalgam with it. Periodically the amalgam is removed and the mercury and gold separated by distillation.

Reverting to by-metal recovery: generally, as pointed out, the by-products are recovered during refining, and this factor will seriously affect the choice of refining process. However, volatile materials are also recovered from roaster and extraction furnace flues and by filtration of the flue gases. In the case of hydro-metallurgical extraction, as with zinc, the by-metals will dissolve with the main metal; then selective precipitation follows.

PYRO-METALLURGICAL TECHNIQUES

Direct smelting of ores. This is mainly applied to ores in which the metal occurs as an oxide, as with iron and tin, or in which the mineral has been converted to an oxide, for example, by roasting a sulphide, as with lead. The ore is heated with reducing agent and fluxes in a furnace to produce molten metal and slag. Often the reactions lead to the production of gases which may be used as sources of heat elsewhere in the plant. The process may be represented in general terms as follows:

$$\text{Mineral} + \text{gangue} + \text{reducing agent} + \text{flux} + \text{heat} = \text{metal} + \text{slag} + \text{gas.}$$

A few oxides are unstable and decompose on heating within practical temperatures at normal pressure, examples being the oxides of silver, platinum and mercury. Generally, however, a reducing agent having a greater affinity for oxygen under the conditions of treatment is necessary to make thermal reduction possible. The ease of reducibility, and thus the minimum temperature for reduction by a particular reducing agent, vary from oxide to oxide. Carbon as coke (or coal) is the usual commercial reducing agent in smelting, although silicon, aluminium and hydrogen are also used in small-scale reduction processes. The reaction with carbon may be represented by :

$$MeO + C \rightarrow Me + CO \quad \text{. ....(1)}$$

The effective reducing agent in most processes at the order of temperatures used is carbon monoxide, as follows :

$$MeO + CO \rightarrow Me + CO_2 \text{ ; } \quad \text{......................(2)}$$

but above about 900–1000° C. the bulk of the carbon dioxide is reduced :

$$C + CO_2 \rightarrow 2CO, \quad \text{............................(3)}$$

so that the net reaction is as represented in equation (1). Theoretically, an equilibrium mixture of the two oxides of carbon will be obtained, but it will be mainly the monoxide. There is a tendency for some reducing agent, if soluble, to dissolve in the metal. Thus iron dissolves several per cent of carbon in the blast-furnace ; on the other hand, none is dissolved in the smelting of lead, in which carbon is not soluble. However, due to its greater affinity for oxygen, preferential oxidation in a subsequent fire-refining operation offers a means of removing dissolved reducing agent, and this is utilised in dealing with iron.

The function of the smelting flux or fluxes is to combine with and neutralise the gangue and products of decomposition, apart from gases, making a product which is fusible and easy to handle and separate from the metal at the temperature of working ; that is, to form a *slag*. Where fuel is burnt in association with the ore, the slag must dissolve the ash produced. A certain amount of furnace lining also enters the slag. The slag is usually lighter than the metal, and being immiscible with it, forms a layer on top. The difference in density and the fluidity should be sufficient to ensure good separation. The metal and slag are easily parted then by tapping separately from the furnace, or by some simple method after tapping.

The slag should be as stable as possible so that co-reduction of gangue minerals and loss of valuable mineral in the slag by combination are minimised. The oxides to which smelting is applied are of moderate stability. Fortunately, common gangue minerals such as alumina, calcium carbonate and silica are very stable, especially the former two, and have little tendency to be reduced under the conditions necessary for the reduction of the valuable mineral. However, the reduction may be facilitated to some extent if the product is readily soluble in the basis metal; thus in iron smelting a small amount of silica is reduced, the silicon entering the metal.

Associate minerals of similar stability to the valuable mineral have greater tendency to be reduced and contaminate the metal, especially if they readily alloy with it. For example, if copper sulphide ores with their associated iron sulphide were roasted to oxides and smelted direct to metal, a copper high in iron would result; whereas this trouble does not arise in the smelting of roasted sulphide ores of lead, with which iron does not easily alloy. Co-reduction is affected to some extent by the affinity of the compound concerned for the slag.

Co-reduced impurities in small amounts are not serious if the metal can be efficiently refined after smelting. More reactive elements are less difficult to remove, because the common technique of fire-refining utilising preferential oxidation is available. When contaminants are present in large amounts (and not required as alloying elements), unless they can be satisfactorily removed during dressing of the ore, modification of the smelting procedure to a larger or smaller extent will be necessitated. Thus with tin oxide ores, because of associated iron compounds, smelting is usually in two stages. In the first the reducing conditions and temperature are moderate so as to minimise co-reduction and obtain comparatively pure tin, but the loss of tin in the slag is high. This slag is, therefore, smelted again under stronger reducing conditions; the tin resulting is impure and needs considerable refining. Another example is with the copper sulphide ores mentioned above. A smelting process is used to remove the gangue as slag from the sulphides. In a subsequent operation the sulphides are separated and the copper sulphide is reduced to metal.

The very stable metallic oxides (and other compounds) require high temperatures and powerful reducing agents. Special thermal reduction processes, such as the Thermit, or other techniques, such as electrolytic reduction, are used. The compounds are thoroughly purified first, because the impurities will usually be less stable and thus at least considerably co-reduced, if not completely, and are difficult to remove after reduction from the more reactive metal.

TABLE 20. TYPICAL ANALYSIS OF SMELTING SLAGS

per cent

Type	SiO_2	CaO	Al_2O_3	FeO	MgO	MnO	PbO	ZnO	Cu_2O
1. Iron, direct-smelting in blast-furnace	35	44	15	1	3	1	—	—	—
2. Lead, direct-smelting in blast-furnace	35	20	3	29	2	1	1	6	—
3. Copper, matte-smelting in reverberatory furnace	39	1	8	46	1	0·5	—	2	0·5
4. * Tin, direct-smelting in reverberatory furnace	35	28	$Al_2O_3 + MgO$ 16	18					

* Tin smelting slags may contain considerable amounts of tin.

Smelting slags are usually silicates. The main constituents of slags in iron-making are silica, calcium oxide and alumina (and sometimes magnesium oxide). The slags in non-ferrous smelting contain in addition large amounts of iron oxide (Table 20). Many ore gangues are predominantly siliceous or " acid ": to these, limestone is the main flux addition ; dolomite is sometimes used. If the gangue is largely composed of basic metallic oxides or carbonates, silica in some form is added as flux. In non-ferrous smelting, iron oxide must also be added if sufficient is not already present. In special cases other fluxes may be used. Generally the additions are arranged to give a fluid slag with the lowest " free-running " temperature permitted by other considerations ; in iron-smelting the proportions are varied to some extent to control the composition of the iron. In large-scale smelting, cost is an important factor in the choice and form of the flux. Wherever possible, various mixtures of ores are made so that the combined different gangues go to make or produce actually a suitable slag. " Self-fluxing " ores are those which contain naturally the correct proportions of siliceous and basic materials. The binary phase relationships between silica and the oxides of calcium and iron, for example, are shown in

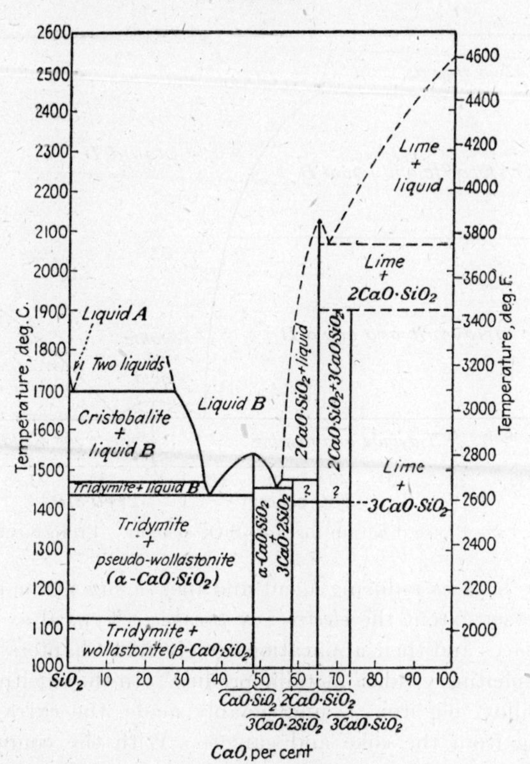

FIG. 182. Phase diagram for $CaO\text{-}SiO_2$ system. Figs. 182 and 183 are from R. B. Sosman, *Basic Open Hearth Steelmaking*. Amer. Inst. Min. Met. Eng.

Figs. 182 and 183. Generally, more complex combinations have lower melting points.

The temperature of smelting, apart from being sufficient to initiate and help propagate the required reactions, will be sufficient to melt the metal and slag and make their separation possible, although thermal reduction will often proceed below the melting point of the metal. The temperature should not be unduly high, for high temperature leads to increased wear on furnace linings, waste of heat, likelihood of greater co-reduction of gangue minerals, and in some cases volatilisation of valuable materials. Apart from the Thermit process, continuous external heating is usually necessary. The furnaces used for large-scale smelting are : (1) the *reverberatory*, in which oil, powdered coal or gas flames burn across and above the charge lying in a comparatively shallow hearth ; (2) the *blast-furnace*,

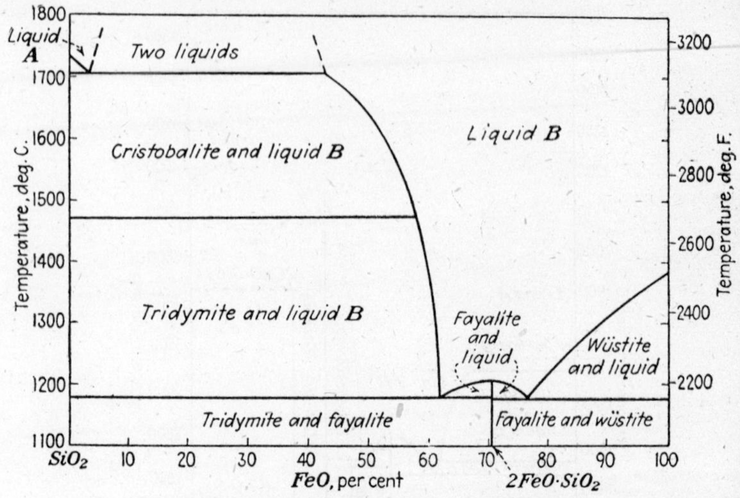

FIG. 183. Phase diagram for FeO-SiO_2 system. From Sosman.

using coke both as reducing agent and fuel *in situ* in the ore ; and (3) to a lesser extent the *electric arc furnace.* Typical examples of these furnaces and their application are given in Chapters 9 and 10.

Direct smelting yields a metallic product. In the smelting of iron ores, an alloy, pig iron, is unavoidably made, the extra elements originating from the coke and gangue. With the common non-ferrous metals, the aim is usually an elementary product. However, production may be easier if an acceptable alloy is made, and thus some copper-nickel ores are smelted to yield a copper-nickel alloy suitable for use ; beryllium may be produced as a " master " alloy with copper ; and aluminium-silicon and aluminium-copper " hardeners " have also been made. Considerable quantities of metals such as molybdenum, chromium and manganese are produced as ferro-alloys, which is convenient for alloying with steel and cast-iron.

Thermit Process. Aluminium in fairly fine granular form are used as reducing agent in the *Thermit* or *Aluminothermic process.* So much heat is generated that only initiation is necessary ; a mixture of barium peroxide and aluminium powder ignited by magnesium ribbon can be used for this purpose. Two particular advantages of aluminium as a reducing agent are that it is suitable for very stable oxides, and that metals which dissolve carbon can be produced free of this element ; some aluminium dissolves, but it can be minimised by careful control. High-grade raw materials are used ; and the oxygen ratio of the charge is important. Fluxes may be added but the slag is predominantly aluminium oxide ; it can be utilised as a refractory. The process is carried out in steel vessels lined with magnesia refractory (alumina can also be employed) on a small scale compared with normal furnace smelting of the common metals. The production of a good grade of manganese and chromium, and ferro-alloys such as ferro-columbium and ferro-vanadium, are examples of the application of the Thermit process.

Direct smelting of minerals other than oxides. The direct smelting technique may be applied to minerals other than oxides. Thus native copper ores are smelted with fluxes, a reducing agent being unnecessary. Carbonates, and hydrated oxides and carbonates, if not calcined first, soon become oxides in the smelting furnace. Nickel can be directly reduced from garnierite, the nickel-magnesium silicate (although considerable iron is also reduced from the gangue) ; alternatively, the mineral is converted to a sulphide and then treated as such. Copper silicate, which is not very common, is mixed with sulphides and matte-smelted or treated hydro-metallurgically. In the production of beryllium, the main mineral, beryl ($3BeO . Al_2O_3 . 6SiO_2$), is first converted to oxide or fluoride. The conversion of a silicate to simpler form results in concentration ; at the same time, in the examples above, the gangue is removed. In the production of metals, so far in small quantities, such as beryllium and titanium, thermal reduction of chemically prepared halide salts is utilised, although the processes can scarcely be designated as smelting. The two common examples of natural halides, namely those of magnesium and silver, are treated by other techniques.

Smelting of sulphide ores. As with oxides, a few sulphides decompose purely by heating. Thus one method of extraction of mercury from sulphide ores consists of heating the ore ; the temperature necessary is such that the mercury distils off.

In general, direct smelting to metal has not a great deal of commercial application with sulphides. Carbon and hydrogen have very limited suitability as reducing agents : calcium, magnesium, aluminium, manganese and iron have possibilities. Iron is actually used commercially as reducing agent in the smelting of antimony sulphide ore ; the reaction is :

$$Sb_2S_3 + 3Fe \rightarrow 2Sb + 3FeS.$$

Scrap iron may also be charged in the smelting of roasted lead sulphide ores with coke, its function being to reduce any unroasted sulphide :

$$PbS + Fe \rightarrow Pb + FeS.$$

A useful method of dealing with sulphides is to roast to oxide and then reduce thermally with carbon. This procedure is important with lead (where the reduction is a smelting process), and with zinc (where distillation is involved), but it is not suitable for copper or nickel sulphide ores.

The main source of copper is from sulphide ores, which contain considerable amounts of iron both in combination with the copper and sulphur, as in the minerals bornite (Cu_5FeS_4) and chalcopyrite ($CuFeS_2$), and as an associated mineral, pyrite (FeS_2). The bulk of the world's nickel comes from ores in which the nickel is present as a nickel-iron sulphide and in which copper is present as an associated sulphide. Although considerable amounts of the associated sulphide minerals in both cases can be removed by selective flotation, some still remain, and it will be appreciated that the physical processes of dressing cannot remove the combined iron in each case. In both instances the result of smelting the ore direct, or after roasting, would produce a metal high in iron, and the nickel would contain copper as well. Therefore, other means of concentration are adopted, involving more than one stage, but in each case commencing with *matte-smelting*.

Matte-smelting. This is essentially a thermal concentrating process for sulphides, whereby the ore is fused with fluxes producing a molten mixture of sulphides known as a *matte* and an immiscible slag in which most of the gangue is separated (some sulphur passes off with the furnace gases as sulphur di- or tri-oxide). The elements entering the matte are those with the greatest affinity for sulphur. Thus copper mattes are primarily copper-iron sulphides, and the more important nickel ones, nickel-copper-iron sulphides. A number of other minor elements present in the ore pass into the matte. A most valuable point is that among these are the precious metals, which stay associated with the main metal and are recovered during refining. The iron content of the mattes may be varied by preliminary roasting to convert preferentially some of the iron sulphide to oxide, in which form it joins the slag on smelting. Complete removal of iron in this way would not be practical. After matte-smelting, the copper and nickel sulphides have to be separated from their mattes and reduced to metal. The most important furnace for matte smelting is the reverberatory, although the blast-furnace is also used and, in one or two cases, the arc furnace.

An interesting modification being applied at the present time to copper concentrates is **flash-smelting**, which is a combination of flash-roasting and matte-smelting. The smelting is *autogeneous*, that is, no external heating is required, the heat being supplied by the oxidation of the excess sulphur.

A similar method of thermal concentration to matte-smelting, though not so involved, is practised in the "liquating" of antimony sulphide from its unfused gangue.

Smelting to yield a *speise* of arsenides or antimonides and slag may also be carried out, although the technique is not of great importance. An example of its application is in the production of cobalt. In matte-smelting, some speise may be produced as well, depending on the composition of the ore; and in direct smelting, for example of lead, a certain amount of both matte and speise may be formed: these are worked up afterwards for the important elements.

Treatment of mattes. In the case of copper matte, the iron sulphide is removed and the copper sulphide reduced by treatment in a converter. Air is blown through the molten matte contained in the vessel. Sometimes the term to *Bessemerise* is used to describe this type of operation. First the iron sulphide is oxidised to oxide, combining with an added siliceous flux, and is removed as iron silicate slag. When all the iron has been oxidised and slagged off, continued blowing reduces the copper sulphide. The reduction may be represented directly as:

$$Cu_2S + O_2 \rightarrow 2Cu + SO_2;$$

or by the double decomposition reaction:

$$Cu_2S + 2Cu_2O \rightarrow 6Cu + SO_2,$$

the cuprous oxide being formed according to the reaction:

$$2Cu_2S + 3O_2 \rightarrow 2Cu_2O + 2SO_2.$$

While iron sulphide is present, any Cu_2O formed is considered to be converted back to the sulphide by the reaction:

$$Cu_2O + FeS \rightarrow Cu_2S + FeO.$$

The relative affinities are such that iron sulphide cannot be reduced in the same way as copper sulphide.

Attempts to obtain copper by direct electrolysis of the matte have had no commercial success. Attention has been given to smelting high-grade concentrates directly in the converter, and as much as $\frac{3}{4}$ ton of concentrate/ton of molten matte has been successfully treated in one plant.

The iron sulphide is removed from nickel mattes in the same way as from copper mattes. But copper sulphide cannot be so removed, as continued blowing would oxidise the nickel; nor can the nickel sulphide be reduced via a double decomposition reaction. Although a copper-nickel alloy can be produced by roasting the sulphides (when low in precious metals) and reducing thermally with carbon, generally the sulphides are separated before reduction. There are various methods of separation ; the most important until recently was the Orford.

The Orford process utilises mutual immiscibility and density differences of the sulphides. The solidified copper-nickel matte is re-fused with sodium sulphide and then allowed to cool slowly and solidify in iron pots, when the nickel sulphide gravitates to the bottom, with the majority of the copper and sodium sulphides on top. The layers are easily separated and are treated for the nickel and copper, respectively.

An interesting method has been patented whereby the sulphides are separated by **selective flotation** (or other suitable physical method) after comminuting the carefully solidified matte to liberate the separate sulphide crystals, for on crystallisation there is immiscibility. Griffiths states that this technique is now replacing the Orford process, and that magnetic separators are used as well as flotation.

The use of dressing techniques has promise for other applications. Taggart has described the use of flotation for oxidised copper ores ; the mineral is reduced to metallic copper by a reducing roast and this is then floated off. Alternatively the copper can be floated off after the ore has been leached and copper precipitated in the separated solution.

Double-decomposition or Roast-reaction. This process, represented by the reaction :

$$MeS + 2MeO \rightarrow 3Me + SO_2,$$

as already indicated, is the likely progress of copper sulphide reduction in the converter ; lead sulphide can be reduced by similar reaction, but this is not practical in a converter. The roast-reaction was the basis of the old **Flintshire process** for lead carried out in reverberatory furnaces, and is involved in the process at the present time of lead smelting in a special furnace known as an **ore-hearth.** Rich ores are required and are treated directly ; a slag is made.

Distillation processes. In some cases of thermal reduction the reduction temperature is above the boiling point of the metal, which is thus produced as a vapour. This occurs for example in the reduction of zinc oxide and magnesium oxide (both with carbon), and mercury sulphide and oxide by heating only. Reduction is carried out in special retorts; the vapour is removed from the field of reduction, so that the reaction may continue, and is allowed to condense without oxidation. In the case of the reduction of magnesium oxide with carbon, the process is represented by the reaction:

$$MgO + C \rightleftharpoons Mg + CO.$$

It is operated at about 2000° C. Special measures have to be taken to prevent the reaction reversing when the products are cooled; this is done by chilling or quenching the magnesium vapour in hydrogen or natural gas. Ellingham points out that an advantage of aluminium or silicon as reducing agent for magnesium oxide is that the final gas phase is essentially magnesium, and hence difficulties do not arise on condensation.

Slag considerations similar to those in smelting do not arise in distillation processes. The residue in the retorts should be unfused and crumbly, so that it may be removed easily. With zinc, where high-grade concentrates are used, care is taken that ores which might flux each other at the temperature of working are not mixed. Stable oxides, such as those of lithium and magnesium, can be reduced with silicon in vacuum, yielding the metal as vapour. In these cases slag consideration arises in that, by adding lime to the charge, stable calcium silicate is formed with the silica, which aids the continued progress of the reaction, lowers the temperature necessary and prevents loss of the valuable compound as stable silicate. In the commercially operated **Pidgeon vacuum process** for magnesium, calcined dolomite is reduced with silicon (as ferrosilicon), the dolomite providing a fortuitous combination of lime and magnesia. The reaction may be represented as follows:

$$2(CaO \,.\, MgO) + Si \rightarrow 2Mg + 2(CaO).\, SiO_2.$$

In reactions such as this, in which a vapour phase is formed (or in which there is an increase in volume) reduction of pressure increases the tendency for reaction, and lowers the necessary temperature. The Pidgeon process for magnesium, and the reduction of magnesia with aluminium, have been carried out commercially under vacuum at considerably lower temperatures than otherwise would be required; vacuum technique is also used in the production of a number of rarer metals. On the other hand, the application of pressure is beneficial in reactions in which gases disappear, and although there has been as yet no application in full-scale metallurgical practice, such conditions have been obtained in producing small amounts of rarer metals by carrying out the reaction in an

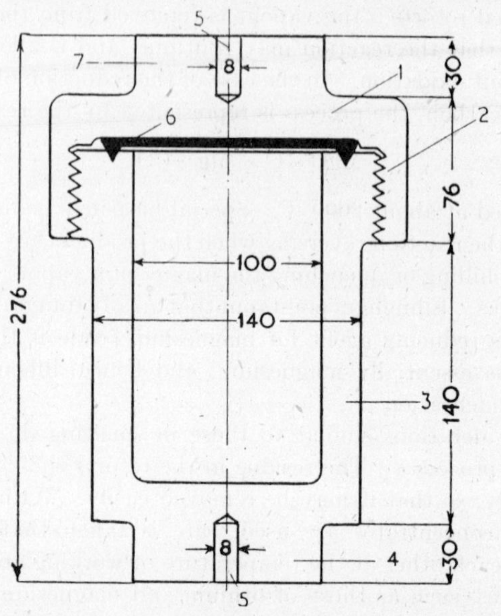

FIG. 184. Hunter steel bomb for special reductions. 5 is thermocouple hole and 6 is an iron gasket. (All dimensions are in mm.) From W. J. Kroll, *Met. Ind.*, 1948, 73, 283.

externally heated steel " bomb " (Fig. 184). The effect of pressure is illustrated by Kroll with respect to the following reaction :

$$ZrO_2 + 2Ca \rightleftharpoons 2CaO + Zr.$$

" In a vacuum, or at very high temperature at atmospheric pressure, zirconium reduces lime and calcium metal escapes in vapour form, but zirconium metal may be produced at a lower temperature in a bomb."

Other thermal processes. In contrast to distillation processes, with high melting-point metals such as tungsten and molybdenum, reduction may be carried out below the melting point. A gaseous reducing agent, such as hydrogen or carbon monoxide, is used. A pure compound is obtained by chemical means, and this is reduced at workable temperatures, yielding a powdered metal which is agglomerated by pressing and heating followed usually by hot working.

The **Mond process for nickel** is an interesting technique which does not involve fusion. It is applied to crude nickel oxide. The ground oxide is first reduced by hydrogen at about 350–400° C. and then treated with carbon monoxide at about 60° C., producing the volatile carbonyl [$Ni(CO)_4$]. The carbonyl is drawn off and passed over nickel shots at about 180° C., when the carbonyl dissociates. The nickel is deposited on the shot and the carbon monoxide is made available for re-use. This process is sometimes classed as refining.

In general, it would seem that the term " smelting " is best reserved for those fusion processes involving the production of a slag, and is used in that sense in this book. However, the term is sometimes used to describe some of the other thermal processes, notably zinc distillation.

PHYSICAL CHEMISTRY OF THERMAL REDUCTION (AND OXIDATION) PROCESSES

In the reduction of oxides, the aim is to cause the following reaction to proceed at a practical temperature and reasonable rate virtually to completion :

$$MeO + R \rightleftarrows Me + RO \quad (1)$$

As pointed out earlier, the reduction of oxides cannot generally be achieved solely by heating ; a reducing agent is necessary. The principal requirement is that under the conditions of operation the reducing agent shall have a greater affinity for oxygen than the metal, that is, its oxide shall be more stable. With regard to the above equation, if RO is more stable, that is, has a lower potential energy, than MeO, it should be possible under certain conditions to obtain transfer of the oxygen atoms. However, catalysis may be necessary and usually the reactants must be heated to activate them, that is, to give MeO sufficient energy to enable it to part fairly easily with its oxygen atoms.

Approximate guidance on the relative stabilities of oxides or other compounds may be obtained by considering the heats of formation at room temperature. The *heat of formation* of a compound (ΔH) may be defined as the heat evolved or absorbed at constant pressure when 1 gram molecule of the compound is formed from the elements (the same value is obtained whatever way the reaction proceeds). If the combining elements can exist in different forms, ΔH varies according to form, but the standard values are quoted for the elements in their normal state. The heat of transition is that involved in the change from one form to another ; similar remarks apply to compounds which can exist in more than one form.

From the thermodynamical aspect, heat changes are given a negative sign when heat is evolved, that is, lost to the system.

Therefore a minus value of ΔH indicates an evolution of heat ; on the other hand, frequently the heat of formation is referred to as $-\Delta H$; thus when the heat is evolved $-\Delta H$ is given by a positive number.

The more stable a compound is, the greater is its heat of formation (negative numeral). Typical heats of formation are given in Table 21. Stabilities must of course be compared on the values per gram molecule of oxygen, not per formula weight. The position of certain elements as reducing agents depends on the particular oxide which is formed.

TABLE 21. TYPICAL HEATS OF FORMATION AT 25° C.

Compound	$-\Delta H$ in k.cal./gm. mol. of compound	Compound	$-\Delta H$ in k.cal./gm. mol. of compound
Al_2O_3	380·0	MgO	146·1
Au_2O_3	− 11·0	MnO_2	125·4
CaO	151·7	NiO	58·4
CO (gas)	26·366	PbO	52·46
CO_2 (gas)	94·030	SiO_2 (cristobalite modification)	205·6
Cr_2O_3	268·9	SnO_2	138·0
CuO	38·5	ZnO	83·5
Cu_2O	42·5	Cu_2S	18·5
FeO	64·6	FeS	22·8
Fe_2O_3	195·2	NiS	20·4
Fe_3O_4	266·8		

The term " heat of formation " is, as in the above definition, taken generally to apply to conditions of constant pressure. One also speaks of the heat of reaction ΔH, which is the heat change involved in any reaction at constant pressure. The difference between ΔH, and the heat of reaction or formation obtained at constant volume, ΔU or ΔE, is due to the work done in expanding against the acting pressure, and which may be appreciable when gases are involved in the reaction. The difference is $PV = RT = 1{\cdot}987\,T$ cal. for every gram molecule of gas which disappears or is evolved in the reaction, under atmospheric pressure, and it is added to ΔH to give ΔU when a gas is evolved, and subtracted when gases disappear.

Equations containing heats of reaction can be handled by multiplying, adding and subtracting, etc. Thus, for example,

for Fe_2O_3, $-\Delta H = 195{\cdot}2$ k. cal./gm. mol.

and for Al_2O_3, $-\Delta H = 380{\cdot}0$ k. cal./gm. mol.

and the heat of reduction of Fe_2O_3 by Al is simply calculated :

$$2Fe + 3O \rightarrow Fe_2O_3 - 195{\cdot}2$$
$$2Al + 3O \rightarrow Al_2O_3 - 380{\cdot}0$$

Subtracting $$2Fe - 2Al \rightarrow Fe_2O_3 - Al_2O_3 + 184{\cdot}8,$$

or $$-Fe_2O_3 - 2Al \rightarrow -2Fe - Al_2O_3 + 184{\cdot}8$$

or $$Fe_2O_3 + 2Al \rightarrow 2Fe + Al_2O_3 - 184{\cdot}8.$$

That is, the heat of reduction $-\Delta H = 184{\cdot}8$ k.cal./gm. mol. (evolved).

It will be seen that the idea of affinities based on heats of formation implies that all processes occurring freely will do so with evolution of heat, whereas some are known which do so with absorption. Theoretically, affinities are governed by free energy considerations at the temperatures concerned.

The standard thermodynamical equation defining free energy change, ΔG, for a reaction at constant temperature and pressure is

$$\Delta G = \Delta H - T\Delta S \quad \text{.............................(2)}$$

or, $$\Delta H = \Delta G + T\Delta S,$$

where ΔS is the change in entropy ; $T\Delta S$ is then the change in bound energy at the temperature of the reaction. ΔG (or ΔF) is the portion of the energy change which is free or available for doing external work ; ΔG and ΔH become equal at absolute zero. If ΔG is negative, there is a decrease in free energy of the system. ΔG and ΔS are expressed in the same units as ΔH. Absolute values for G are not known ; it is the value of the change, ΔG, that can be determined.

An alternative description of the quantities in equation (2) is that ΔG is the *real* energy change of the actual reaction, whereas $T\Delta S$ is the energy change associated with changes in the state of *order* of the atoms in the participants.

For a reaction to be likely to proceed freely in a given direction under a given set of conditions, it should involve a decrease in free energy,the magnitude of which change indicates the driving force, and extent of the reaction (in a closed system). The value of the free energy change is altered by varying the conditions, such as temperature, pressure or relative concentrations.

Comparison of free energies of formation of oxides, for example, indicates suitability of elements as reducing agents. Thus for R to reduce MeO (equation (1) p.225), the free energy of formation of RO should have a greater (negative) value than that of MeO under the proposed conditions of reduction, the difference being the free energy change involved in the reduction.

It must be stressed that although a decrease in free energy indicates the likelihood of a reaction proceeding, it does not guarantee that it will actually proceed. Whether or not the reaction occurs at a particular temperature depends on a number of factors. For example, a catalyst may be necessary, or the temperature may not be sufficient to give the molecules sufficient activation energy.

From the above, it will be seen that an endothermic reaction is thermodynamically possible, for a high entropy factor can make ΔH positive, although there is a decrease in free energy in the reaction.

Theoretically, all chemical reactions are, to some extent at least, reversible. Thus in a closed system reactions do not go to completion but reach a dynamic equilibrium in which there are definite proportions of reactants and products, the velocities of the forward and reverse reactions being then equal. The extent of a reaction increases with the (–) value of the free energy liberated in reaching the equilibrium (when ΔG is zero). For example, in the oxidation of many metals, the free energy change is of considerable magnitude and the reactions are nearly complete. Thus aluminium is a vigorous deoxidant or reducing agent, its oxide having a high free energy of formation. On the other hand, the oxides of silver and mercury, for example, are unstable due to their small free energies of formation which are actually positive at moderate temperatures, when the oxides largely dissociate. The point is further illustrated by Fig. 185 which shows the extent of deoxidation of iron by different elements all of which form more stable oxides than does iron, but have varying deoxidising power depending on the respective free energies of formation of their oxides compared with that for iron oxide under the particular conditions. The graphs also indicate the effect of the concentration of the residual deoxidant.

The actual extent of a closed reaction is given by the equilibrium constant K, which is equal to the product of the concentrations of the products divided by that of the reactants. It is obtained from the **Law of Mass Action,** which may be stated as follows : " The velocity of a reaction at constant temperature is proportional to the product of the concentrations of the reacting substances " ; when gases are involved, the external pressure is important because of its effect on concentrations. Thus in the reaction :

$$A + B \rightleftharpoons C + D,$$

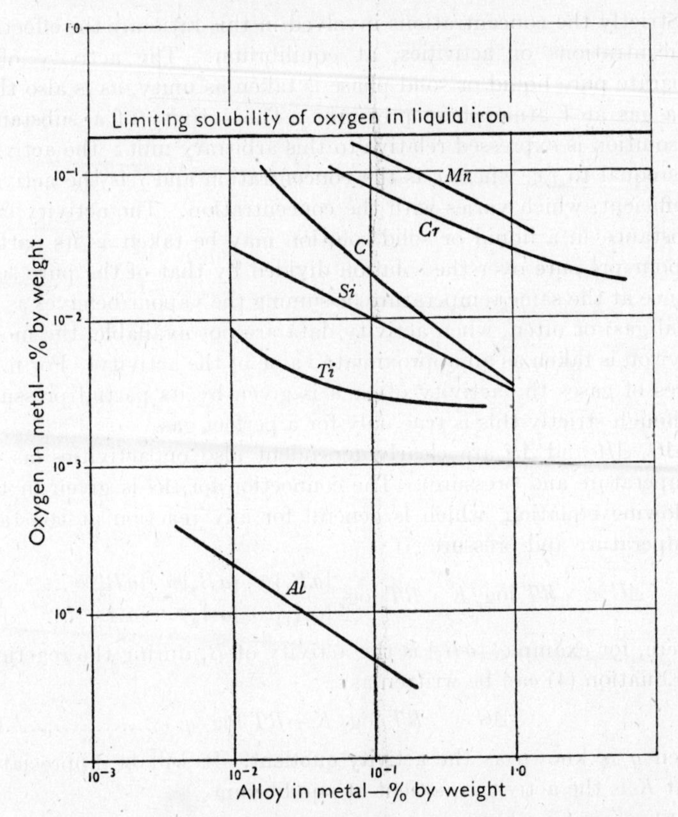

FIG. 185. Relation between residual oxygen and residual deoxidant in liquid iron, under equilibrium conditions at 1540° C.; established by laboratory experiments. From F. D. Richardson, *Brit. Sci. News*. 1949. 2, 380.

the velocity to the right is equal to $K_1[A]\times[B]$, and to the left $K_2[C]\times[D]$, where the square brackets mean concentration of the substance in question. But, at equilibrium the forward and backward velocities are equal, and

$$\frac{[C].[D]}{[A].[B]}=\frac{K_1}{K_2}=K.$$

With a more general equation:

$$x_1A_1+x_2A_2+x_3A_3\ldots\rightleftharpoons y_1B_1+y_2B_2+y_3B_3\ldots$$

$$K=\frac{[B_1]^{y_1}\times[B_2]^{y_2}\times[B_3]^{y_3}\ldots}{[A_1]^{x_1}\times[A_2]^{x_2}\times[A_3]^{x_3}\ldots}\quad\ldots\ldots\ldots\ldots\ldots\ldots(3)$$

K is known as the **equilibrium constant** of the reaction.

Strictly the concentrations involved in this ratio are the effective concentrations or **activities**, at equilibrium. The activity of a separate pure liquid or solid phase is taken as unity, as is also that of a gas at 1 atmosphere pressure. The activity of a substance in solution is expressed relative to this arbitrary unit ; the activity a is equal to $f.c$, where c is the concentration and f is the activity coefficient, which varies with the concentration. The activity of a substance in a liquid or solid solution may be taken as its partial vapour pressure over the solution divided by that of the pure substance at the same temperature (assuming the vapour behaves as an ideal gas) or often, when activity data are not available, the molar fraction is taken as an approximate value of the activity. For mixtures of gases the activity of each is given by its partial pressure, although strictly this is true only for a perfect gas.

ΔG, ΔH and ΔS are clearly dependent also on activities (as on temperature and pressure). The connection for ΔG is given in the following equation, which is general for any reaction at constant temperature and pressure :

$$\Delta G = -RT \log_e K + RT \log_e \frac{[aB_1]^{y_1} \, . \, [aB_2]^{y_2} \, . \, [aB_3]^{y_3} \ldots}{[aA_1]^{x_1} \, . \, [aA_2]^{x_2} \, . \, [aA_3]^{x_3} \ldots}, \qquad (4)$$

where, for example, $[aB_1]$ is the activity of B_1 during the reaction.

Equation (4) can be written as :

$$\Delta G = -RT \log_e K + RT \log_e q, \qquad \ldots\ldots\ldots\ldots\ldots\ldots(5)$$

when q is known as the **activity quotient.** It will be appreciated that K is the activity quotient at equilibrium.

When each of the substances involved in a reaction has unit activity, $q=1$ and the free energy change for the reaction, which is known as the **standard free energy** ΔG°, is given as follows :

$$\Delta G^\circ = -RT \log_e K, \qquad \ldots\ldots\ldots\ldots\ldots\ldots\ldots\ldots\ldots(6)$$

$$= -1{\cdot}987 \times T \times 2{\cdot}303 \times \log_{10} K.$$

Standard free energy values are used for comparing different reactions, on a common basis.

Free energy values vary with temperature, and Ellingham has prepared for oxides graphs showing this variation of the standard free energy (Fig. 186). For proper comparison the energy values are plotted for combination with 1 gm. molecule of oxygen (partial pressure 1 atmosphere). The diagram indicates at any temperature what is thermodynamically possible in thermal reduction processes, deoxidation and the reverse, namely preferential oxidation as utilised in fire-refining. At the point of intersection of two curves,

ΔG° is zero for the reaction and an equilibrium is reached at which K is 1. For example, up to about 1750° C., the tendency is for magnesium to reduce aluminium oxide, but above this temperature the reverse tendency holds ; magnesium and silicon show similar behaviour. The diagram clearly shows the selectivity of reduction or oxidation that may be expected.

Various factors affect the values for the free energy change in a reaction. Thus the formation of a stable compound with a reaction

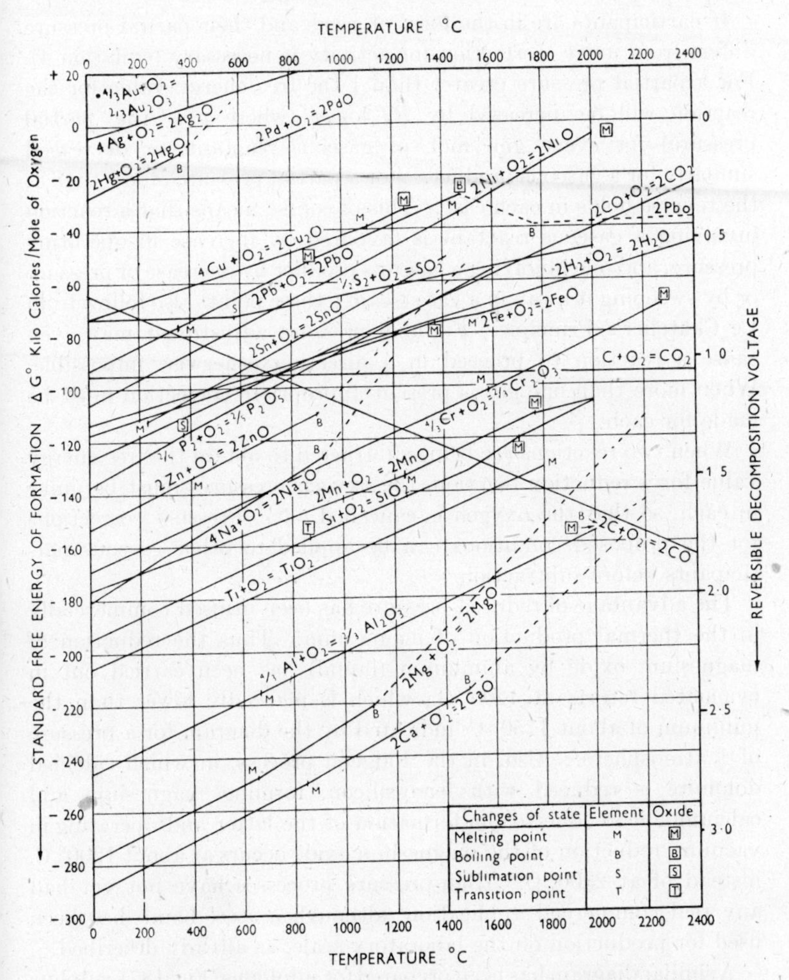

FIG. 186. Variation of standard free energy of formation of oxides with temperature. After Ellingham, and Richardson.

product liberates free energy to increase the total for the reaction; for example, in the Pidgeon process for magnesium, this advantage is obtained from the formation of the calcium silicate. Reaction between metal and reducing agent yields free energy, which may have an important effect on the course of a reaction. The curves represent conditions of unit activity, but mutual solubility among the substances, which is very likely in many cases, will affect the results due to activity corrections; further, consideration must be given to the presence of additional matter such as slag.

If participants are in the form of a gas and their partial pressure differs from unity, correction for activity is necessary (equation 4). For a partial pressure greater than 1 the free energy value for the reaction will be increased by $RT \log_e p$ (where p is the partial pressure) for every gm. mol. of gaseous reactant, or decreased similarly for a gaseous product. For a partial pressure of less than 1, the reverse holds in each case. This of course means that a reaction involving a gaseous reactant is favoured by increase in operating pressure, and one involving a gaseous product by decrease of pressure or by sweeping it away in a gas stream; these points also follow from Le Chatelier's Principle. Suitable pressure adjustment may even cause a reaction to proceed in a direction otherwise impossible. When more than one gas is present appropriate correction must be made for each.

When two reactions are being subtracted to obtain the free energy value for a reduction reaction, the oxygen pressures must be unity in each, so that the oxygen is cancelled out. Pressure corrections for the proposed conditions can be applied to other gaseous participants before subtraction.

The advantage of reduced pressure has been utilised commercially in the thermal production of magnesium. Thus the reduction of magnesium oxide by aluminium (liquid) has been carried out in evacuated retorts at 1200° C., which is markedly lower than the minimum of about 1750° C. indicated by the diagram for a pressure of 1 atmosphere. Also, in the Pidgeon process, in which calcined dolomite is reduced with ferro-silicon, forming magnesium and calcium silicate, due to the formation of the latter and operating in vacuum, reduction of the magnesium oxide occurs at about 1200° C. instead of at 2300° C. High-pressure processes have not yet had any real commercial application, although a steel bomb has been used for production on the laboratory scale, as already described.

A similar diagram has been prepared for sulphides (Fig. 187), sulphur being regarded at all temperatures as a gas (S_2), at a partial pressure

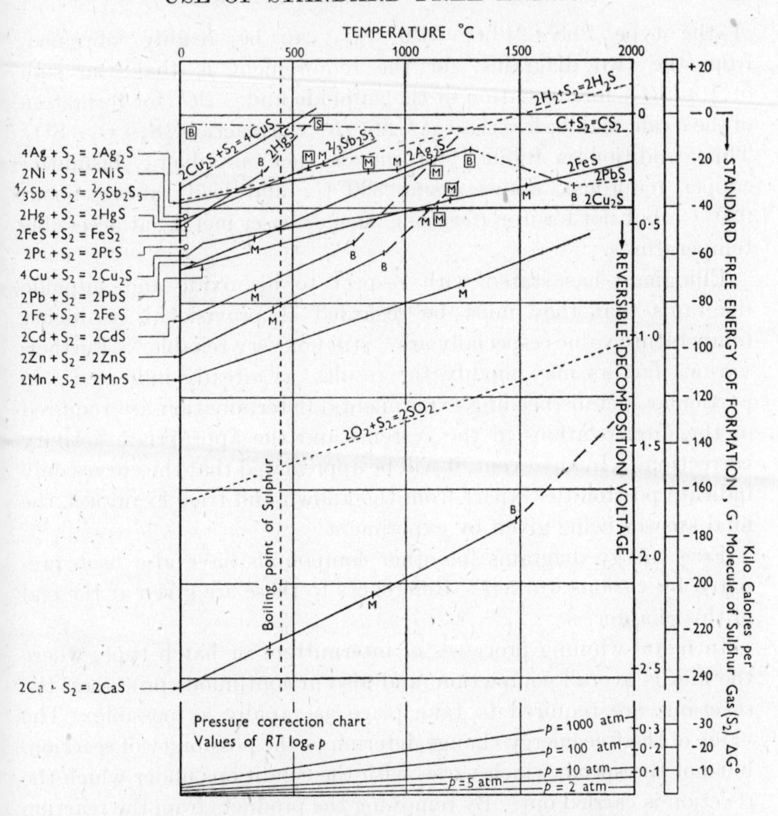

FIG. 187. Variation of standard free energy of formation of sulphides with temperature. From H. J. T. Ellingham, *J. Soc. Chem. Ind.*, 1944, 63, 128.

of 1 atmosphere. From this diagram the relative desulphurising and reducing powers may also be compared. Ellingham makes the following points :

(1) The sulphide curves are closer together than those for the oxides and mutual solubility between metals and their sulphides when molten is greater. Thus direct preferential reduction and separation from a mixture of sulphides is more difficult. Further, it can be seen that neither carbon nor hydrogen has much scope as a reducing agent. However, the position of the curve for the oxidation of sulphur indicates the good displacement that can be obtained by roasting, the oxides thus produced being more widely separated in stability and more suitable for reduction by carbon (or hydrogen).

(2) The condition for the occurrence of the " roast-reaction "

of the type $PbS + 2PbO = 3Pb + SO_2$ can be readily obtained, from the two diagrams, for the requirement is that the sum of $\frac{1}{2}(-\Delta G^\circ)$ for formation of the sulphide and $-\Delta G^\circ$ for formation of the oxide shall be less than $\frac{1}{2}(-\Delta G^\circ)$ for the reaction $\frac{1}{2}S_2 + O_2 = SO_2$. This condition is fulfilled for metals such as silver; bismuth; copper (cuprous), above about 800° C.; and lead, above about 930° C.; but not for iron (ferrous), zinc, or baser metals, at accessible temperatures.

Ellingham has stated with respect to his oxide and sulphide diagrams that they must be regarded as provisional, as higher temperature values especially are " still not very reliable." Further, various factors may modify the results, as already indicated; in particular, details needing experimental determination are required of the inter-relations in the systems and the appropriate activity corrections. In any event, it will be appreciated that the curves only indicate possibilities, apart from the known and tried examples, the final answer being given by experiment.

Free energy diagrams for other compounds have also been prepared by various workers. References to these are given at the end of this chapter.

In metal-winning processes of intermittent or batch type, where the aim is overall completion, and also in continuous processes, the reactions are required to take place as rapidly as possible. The value of the free energy change determines the possibility of reaction, but not the speed, which varies with the conditions under which the reaction is carried out. By removing the products from the reaction zone as fast as they are formed, and in appropriate processes by continuous supply of reactants, a reaction can be forced in the required direction and the general overall speed increased. In addition to concentration, temperature, catalysis, nature and viscosity of solvent medium and particle size are important factors. Pressure is also important when gases are involved, because of its effect on concentrations.

It is necessary to distinguish between **homogeneous** and **heterogeneous reactions.** Homogeneous reactions are those occurring in *one* phase, as between gases, or constituents dissolved in a liquid or solid; reaction results from collision or contact of sufficiently activated atoms or molecules. The collisions and proportion of activated molecules, and thus the rate of reaction, increase with temperature.

Heterogeneous reactions occur between *different* phases. Thus in extraction and refining processes, reactions may occur at gas-solid, gas-liquid and liquid-solid interfaces and between two immiscible liquids; those at solid-solid interfaces are not generally important in winning techniques. Progress of the reaction depends on the continued supply of reactants at the interface, and this in turn on diffusion through the adjoining phases. Frequently the rate of diffusion is the governing factor with regard to the net overall rate, rather than the intrinsic rate of the reaction at the interface. Rates may be increased by agitation or stirring providing more contact, or for example, by causing a gas to flow across a surface; but even in such cases some diffusion is involved. The rate of diffusion of product(s) from the reaction interface may also affect the speed of the process.

Further, a reaction may occur in one phase, yet fresh reactant may be supplied from an adjoining phase by diffusion, the reactant being soluble in both phases, for example from refining slag to metal; the same applies to the removal of products. Also, frequently, products of otherwise homogeneous reactions are precipitated as separate phases. Precipitation involves diffusion of reactants or products to precipitation sites; but the diffusion-rate and consequently the reaction-rate may be governed by the rate of precipitation.

In practice, a particular result may be achieved by a combination of different mechanisms. The actual mechanism in specific examples is generally uncertain.

On the basis of the above, with regard to speed, Chipman has distinguished three large groups of processes, namely, reaction-rate controlled, diffusion-rate controlled and precipitation-rate controlled; and has tabulated the effect of various factors on the rate (Table 22).

TABLE 22 (Chipman)

Variable	Diffusion-rate controlled	Reaction-rate controlled	Pptn.-rate controlled	
			Rate of nucleus formation	Rate of nuclear growth
Temperature increase	Small increase	Exponential increase	Varies	Increases rate
Viscosity increase	Decreases rate	No effect	Little or no effect	Decreases rate
Increased rate of stirring	Increases rate	No effect	Better distribution of nuclei; thus increase	Increases rate
Addition of nuclei	No effect	No effect	Increases rate	No direct effect

When a substance is soluble in two adjoining phases at a constant temperature under *equilibrium* conditions, the distribution is such that the ratio of the effective concentrations or activities in the phases is a constant, namely, the **partition coefficient**; in practice, of course, equilibrium is not usually attained. Examples of solubility in adjoining phases are oxygen and sulphur in slag and steel in the open-hearth furnace, and sulphur in pig iron and slag in the blast furnace.

HYDRO-METALLURGICAL EXTRACTION

In this technique the ore is soaked, **leached** or **lixiviated** for sufficient time in a dilute aqueous solvent of the mineral: the solvent power should be as selective as possible. The solution is then separated from the ore residue and the metal is recovered from the leach liquor by electrolysis with insoluble anodes or by precipitation (or *cementation*) by a less noble metal. Metal precipitation by electrolysis directly regenerates the solution, so that it can be re-used for leaching. Reactive metals, such as magnesium and aluminium, cannot be precipitated in the metallic state from aqueous solution; therefore the hydro-metallurgy technique cannot be applied for extraction, although it can be used as a means of purification of the mineral. Electro-deposition has the advantage that it gives a very pure metal, whereas metal precipitated by another is usually contaminated and needs purification.

The hydro-metallurgy technique is applicable to a number of minerals, especially oxidised and native ones; sulphides are usually first roasted to oxides, sulphates or chlorides. Notable commercial applications are to gold, silver, zinc, copper and cadmium (Table 23).

The extent of comminution and other preparation necessary prior to leaching depends on the ore. Zinc ores, for example, are in the form of fine concentrates which are roasted to a mixture of oxide and a small amount of sulphate. In the **all-sliming process** for gold ores, the ore is finely ground before leaching, or sands and fines may be separately treated. Gold ores also may be first concentrated; and "cyanicides", that is, substances which use up the valuable cyanide solution, may be removed by flotation, dissolved out with acid, or rendered innocuous by addition of lime (which neutralises free acid and precipitates soluble sulphates as insoluble calcium compounds unable to affect the cyanide); usually "protective alkalinity" is maintained during leaching by a small excess of lime. Gold ores in which the gold is combined with tellurium may be roasted first or treated in some other way to aid solution, which is more difficult than with native gold. With copper ores, application of leaching has been mainly to low-grade oxidised ores, as opposed to concentration (which is difficult) followed by smelting, and for which attention to size is the main factor.

Leaching is carried out in tanks, some with agitators, and may take up to several weeks. Sometimes gold ores are leached in filter presses, and also leaching may be started by adding the cyanide in the grinding mills. It is common to recover copper from mine drainage waters and the principle offers a direct method of treatment.

Another treatment used for copper ores is heap leaching in the open, where the weathering action converts sulphides to a readily soluble form. Many tons of ore are spread out on the ground, hollows are made for the solution, and ventilation and drainage to precipitation tanks are arranged; treatment time may be a number of years.

The leach liquors in tank leaching are separated from the waste by drawing and decanting off, thickening and filtering. In the case of zinc, for example, considerable purification of the solution from numerous interfering elements is necessary before the precipitation by electrolysis can be at all efficient.

Recently, a process has been developed for rapid leaching of sulphide ores, such as those containing nickel, copper and cobalt, under pressure in hot aerated solutions of ammonia or sulphuric acid. The metals can be selectively precipitated, as powders, from the hot leach liquors with hydrogen under pressure. The process can also be applied to the treatment of scrap metal.

TABLE 23. EXAMPLES OF HYDRO-METALLURGICAL APPLICATIONS

Ore	Leaching solution	Method of precipitation	Comparative importance of process
Zinc sulphide, high-grade concentrate roasted to mixture of oxide and sulphate	diluted sulphuric acid	electrolysis	important
Native gold ore containing as little as a fraction of an oz. of gold per ton. Silver ores are treated similarly but stronger solutions are used.	0·01 to 0·10 per cent sodium cyanide soln.	zinc is most satisfactory	major
Low grade oxidised copper ore	dilute sulphuric acid	scrap iron or electrolysis	minor

THERMO-ELECTROLYTIC EXTRACTION

Electrolytic extraction (from fused mineral or salt mixture) is applied mainly in the production of reactive metals such as aluminium, magnesium, beryllium, sodium and calcium, for which hydro-metallurgy is not practical and thermal extraction requires high temperatures and powerful and expensive reducing agents. The latter technique has been applied in a number of cases, for example with aluminium and magnesium, but electrolytic methods still predominate. For economic reasons, electrolytic processes are situated usually near sources of cheap hydro-electricity.

The metal-bearing mineral must be thoroughly purified before electrolysis to avoid unsatisfactory working and formation of low-grade metal difficult to refine; the usual fire-refining methods are not suitable for the reactive metals. The mineral may be converted by chemical means to another more suitable form; thus magnesium oxide is changed to the chloride. Impurities may also arise in electrolytic extraction from cell linings and from electrode materials, and care must be taken in selection of such materials.

If the mineral has a reasonable melting point and conductivity, it may be electrolysed on its own, but often mixtures of salts are necessary. The bath should not be viscous or else metal may be entrapped; and the density must be made sufficiently greater or less than that of the metal. The additions to the bath may also serve to inhibit the decomposition of the metallic mineral on heating; for example, normally on heating hydrated magnesium chloride ($MgCl_2 . 2H_2O$) the oxide is formed. Once the bath has been melted, it is usually kept hot enough by the heating effect of the electrolysing current.

Various cell arrangements are used in fusion electrolysis; frequently the metal is produced molten. For aluminium, the bath is of aluminium oxide dissolved in a mixture of sodium, calcium and aluminium fluorides at about 900° C., contained in a carbon-lined steel cell; carbon anodes are employed, which burn away, the heat supplementing that due to the current. The molten aluminium produced, being denser than the electrolyte, forms a layer at the bottom, where it acts as cathode (Fig. 227, p. 307).

In the electrolytic production of magnesium from a bath of calcium, sodium, potassium and magnesium chlorides contained in a steel vessel at about 700–750° C., using carbon anodes and steel cathodes (voltage 5–8), the metal is also produced molten; but in this case it floats on the top of the bath, whence it is removed regularly. In another type of cell, a cirulating molten lead cathode was used to dissolve the magnesium. The magnesium and lead were then separated by another fusion electrolysis.

Calcium is produced by the electrolysis of its chloride at about 800° C. with graphite anodes, and an iron contact cathode which is raised continuously, the depositing calcium freezing on to it ; the cell is lined with carbon. The calcium is protected from oxidation by a thin coating of chloride.

In special cases the metal may need to be deposited in the solid form because of the volatility of the electrolyte. Difficulties may arise in the separation of metal and electrolyte ; after squeezing out excess electrolyte, aqueous and acid separation or vacuum evaporation at high temperature may be used.

METAL REFINING

The impurities in primary extracted metal or alloy may be non-metals, metalloids or other metals ; they may be dissolved in, or combined with, the basis metal, or sometimes mechanically entrapped. The impurities originate in the ore as associated minerals, or arise from fuels, fluxes, the atmosphere and materials of plant construction. Whereas in one instance an element may be considered an impurity, in another it may be an essential constituent.

Impurities usually modify the properties of the metal to some extent and in a number of cases are definitely very harmful ; generally, therefore, it becomes necessary to remove or to control them to within permissible limits. Further, irrespective of their effect, the impurities may be of considerable value ; for example, precious metals in copper and lead, and bismuth in lead, when it often becomes a decided economic advantage to remove them.

The metal produced by smelting is usually impure, due in particular to co-reduction and solution in the molten metal of associated minerals ; and sometimes from elements in the fuel or fluxes, for example, most of the sulphur in pig-iron usually comes from the coke.

A relatively high-grade product (suitable in some cases for direct use) is usually obtained by distillation, for high-grade raw material is used and the conditions are conducive to good separation, although there is some co-volatilisation of impurities. With the other thermal processes, raw material of good purity is generally used, and the resulting metal is also fairly pure.

In hydro-metallurgy, other elements may dissolve with the metal. If these are in such quantities and of such nature that the metal cannot be selectively precipitated efficiently, the solution has to be purified, as is the case with zinc. Electrolytically deposited metal often requires no further treatment apart from melting and casting into ingots, although with copper the melting involves some refining, in particular with respect to the hydrogen content. Cemented metal is usually contaminated with the precipitating metal. Thus cemented copper is usually charged to the smelting furnaces ; and precipitated gold requires acid treatment to separate the zinc before final refining.

Metal produced by electrolytic reduction of a fused bath is of high purity. This is largely because the mineral is thoroughly purified before electrolysis, although a significant source of impurities is the cell linings and electrode materials, especially when the anodes are consumed as in aluminium practice, where impurities originate in the ash. However, the bulk of aluminium and all the magnesium is used without any real purification after electrolysis, apart from treatment to allow separation of entrapped electrolyte.

Refining may be defined as the removal of other elements from extracted metal for the purpose of improving the purity or adjusting the composition. Dannatt has pointed out that originally " fining " meant the first treatment applied to an ore to improve its purity, subsequent operations becoming " re-fining ". On this basis, flotation concentration of a copper ore becomes fining and matte-smelting the first refining (when there is no roasting). But with rich ores, matte-smelting may be fining, and converting becomes the first refining. However, it has become common in metal-winning terminology to apply the term " refining " to the purification of metal, and that use is adopted here.

Certain refining techniques as well as those used in extraction are applied to the purification of a complete charge of scrap metal. In the purification of primary extracted metal, especially by fire-refining, in some cases a proportion of scrap metal is incorporated in the charge. Some scrap may also be added to smelting charges.

REFINING TECHNIQUES

Fire-refining. This process can be used to remove more reactive elements from the molten metal by their preferential oxidation. The oxides are eliminated in the gaseous form, or as insoluble freely separating particles. The technique is suitable for metals such as iron, lead, tin and copper, but not for the more reactive metals, such as aluminium and magnesium.

In some cases the oxygen is supplied as air, which is blown through the metal, drawn over the surface, or the metal may be mechanically agitated and splashed to bring it into contact with the air. Interest is being taken in the enrichment of the oxygen content of the air used ; some individual examples are discussed in Chapters 9 and 10. The oxygen is also supplied from a solid compound ; for example, iron oxide is used in refining iron, and lead oxide and sodium nitrate with lead. Fluxes are often added to the metal to combine with non-volatile oxidation products to prevent reversion to the metal, and to make a slag which may be easily separated. Fluxes are generally used with solid oxidising agents, so that refining is carried out with a fluid oxidising slag.

In air oxidation, good contact is obtained by blowing the air through the molten metal or by agitating the bath. With slag refining, it is desirable that metal and slag should be well agitated also to give good contact. In the open-hearth process for steel, the gases evolved by certain of the reactions have this effect. Good contact is obtained in the Harris process for lead refining by pouring the lead through the slag. In the Perrin process, which may be used for dephosphorising (or deoxidising) steel, the molten steel is poured from a height of about 20 ft. into a bath of slag. Rotating furnaces also promote metal-slag intermixing. After agitation, it is necessary for the metal to stand tranquilly for some time to allow the separation of entrapped slag.

The manner in which the oxidation reactions proceed depends on whether oxygen is appreciably soluble in the molten metal being refined. When there is such solubility, as with copper and iron, it is considered that reaction will mainly occur in the liquid-metal phase between the dissolved impurity and dissolved oxygen, the oxides being precipitated as immiscible phases ; some reaction undoubtedly occurs at the interface between metal and air or oxidising slag. If oxygen solubility is negligible, the reactions will have to proceed at interfaces and will depend on diffusion of impurities to the interfaces.

The solubility of oxygen in molten lead and tin at moderate temperatures is so small that deoxidation is not considered necessary in normal melting practice ; the metal oxide forms and is essentially insoluble. The solubility increases with rise in temperature, but it is difficult to say which is the major mode of oxidation of the impurities in fire-refining. Actually, in the case of tin, as discussed later, it is doubtful whether straightforward oxidation is of great importance. However, it is clear that in both mechanisms agitation favours the oxidation by providing greater contact area with the oxygen supply, either for direct reaction or for entry of soluble oxygen. Similar queries as to the mechanism of reaction arise in the oxidising conversion of copper mattes.

With metals such as copper and iron in which there is appreciable solubility of oxygen, at the end of oxidation refining, deoxidation is necessary to remove the excess oxygen remaining in the metal. Deoxidation also depends on forming insoluble oxides ; elements with greater affinity for oxygen than the basis metal are added.

Other effects may be utilised under the heading of fire-refining. Thus copper is removed from molten lead or tin by stirring in sulphur and skimming off the material separating. Sulphur may be removed from molten pig-iron by treatment with sodium carbonate, with which it forms insoluble sodium sulphide ; in steelmaking, sulphur in the metal reacts with lime in the slag to form calcium sulphide, which is dissolved by the slag. Nickel may be desulphurised by adding magnesium which forms an insoluble sulphide, although this treatment is generally carried out at the melting stage. Small quantities of zinc may be separated from lead as zinc chloride by passing chlorine through the molten metal ; similarly zinc and aluminium may be removed from tin. Also, an important refining process for gold involves the preferential *chlorination* of the baser impurities.

Liquation. The term " liquation " is used to cover two types of processes : (1) those utilising liquid immiscibility ; and (2) those utilising melting-point differences. The efficiency and possibility of separation depend on the constitution of the metal-impurity system. In the following the principles will be outlined on a binary basis, although in practice the systems are more complex.

A method used to reduce the lead content of zinc illustrates the first type of process. Zinc and lead are partially miscible in the liquid state (Figs. 188–189), and if the crude zinc is held in a furnace at a temperature just above the melting point of zinc, two liquids exist, one rich in zinc and the other rich in lead. The latter, being considerably denser, gravitates to the bottom, and the two liquids can be tapped off separately. Theoretically the limit for this separation is 0·85 per cent lead ; the typical figures in Table 24 should be compared with this :

Table 24. Liquation Refining of Zinc (Robson)

	Per cent			
	Zn	Pb	Fe	Cd
Metal input - - -	97·8	2·0	0·10	0·05
Metal output - - -	98·8	1·1	0·025	0·05

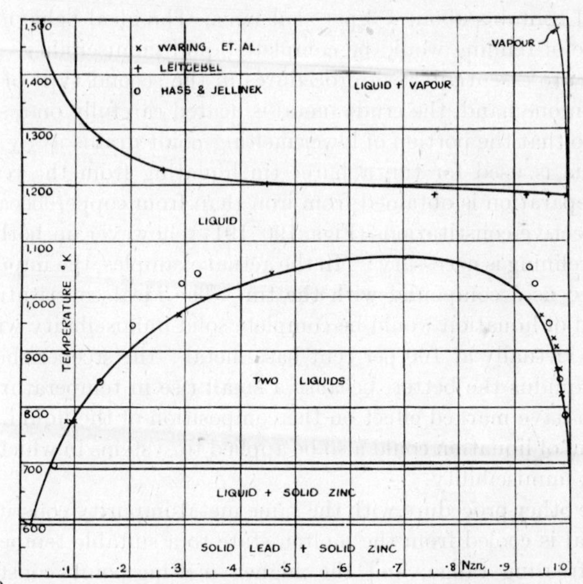

FIG. 188. Phase diagram for the lead-zinc system. Note that the temperature scale is in degrees absolute and the composition scale in mole fraction. From J. Lumsden, *Discus. Faraday Society*, No. 4, 1948, 62.

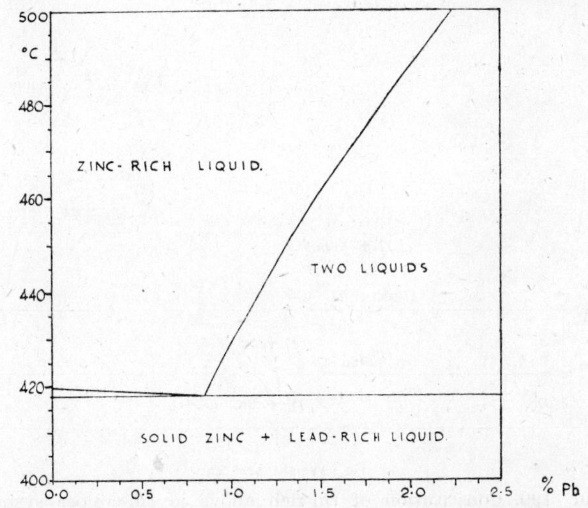

FIG. 189. Solubility of lead in liquid zinc. The monotectic point is at 0·85 per cent lead, and this figure is thus the theoretical limit for removal of lead from zinc by liquation. Figs. 189 and 195 are from S. Robson, *The Refining of Non-Ferrous Metals*, Inst. Min. and Met., 1950, 330.

The lead contains about 1·3 per cent zinc. The ideal behaviour for this type of refining would be complete liquid immiscibility.

There are essentially two procedures in the second type of liquation. On one hand, the crude metal is heated carefully on a sloping hearth so that the portion of lower melting-point drains away. This technique is used for tin, a purer tin liquating from the residue; better separation is obtained from iron than from copper because of the respective constitutions (Figs. 190–191); however, in both cases further refining is necessary. In the actual examples, the impurity is separated as a compound with the tin. The ideal constitution for this kind of liquation would be complete solid immiscibility with the eutectic virtually at 100 per cent base metal; the steeper the slope of the liquidus the better, because a small rise in temperature does not then have marked effect on the composition of the liquid phase. This form of liquation could also be applied to systems in which there is liquid immiscibility.

In the other procedure with the same metal-impurity constitution, the metal is cooled from the molten state to a suitable temperature in the freezing range, and the higher melting-point constituent which solidifies is removed, for example with perforated ladles, or, if it rises satisfactorily to the surface, by skimming. An example of the application of this refining method was the old Patterson

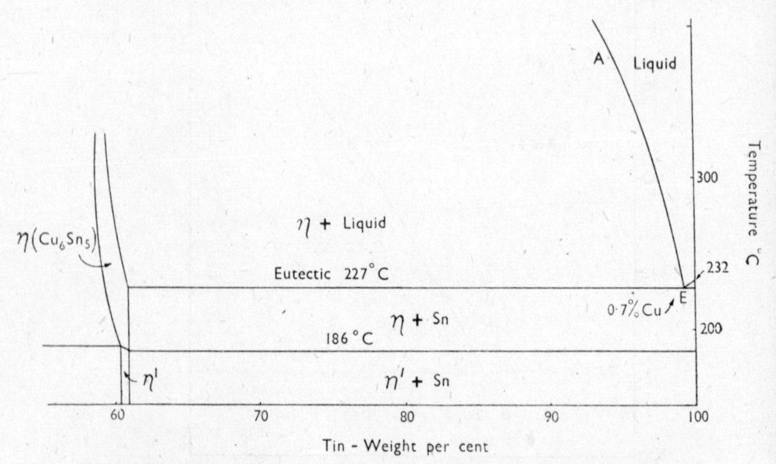

Fig. 190. Constitution of tin-rich alloys in tin-copper system. By heating the crude tin to just above the eutectic temperature it will form η and liquid of composition given by the liquidus *AE*. The absolute limit of copper removal by hearth liquation is thus 0·7 per cent copper.

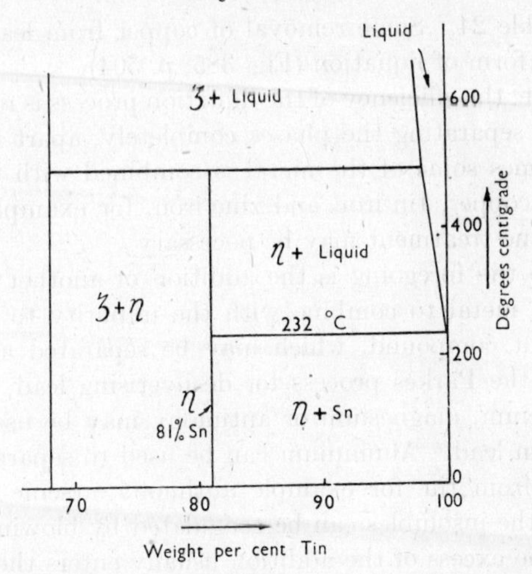

FIG. 191. Constitution of tin-rich alloys of tin-iron system. Because the eutectic point is considerably nearer to pure tin than in the tin-copper system, better separation of iron by hearth liquation is to be expected.

process of desilverising lead ; lead-rich crystals were separated, the silver concentration in the liquid being limited by the eutectic composition at 2·5 per cent silver. During the liquation of zinc (p. 242), a solid iron-zinc compound separates out to the top of the lead, whence it is removed ; the constitution of the zinc-iron system is shown in Fig. 192, and typical values for the refining obtained are

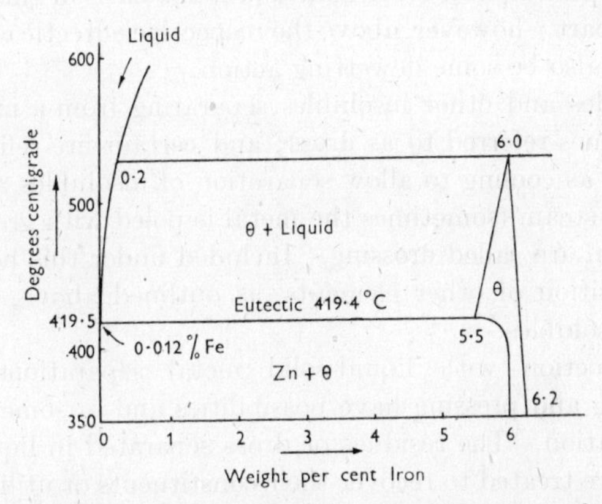

FIG. 192. Phase diagram for the zinc-rich alloys of zinc-iron system. Removal of iron by liquation is restricted to a theoretical limit of 0·012 per cent iron : actual results are given in Table 24.

given in Table 24. Some removal of copper from lead is obtained also by this form of liquation (Fig. 385, p. 504).

In practice, the efficiency of the liquation process is reduced by the difficulty of separating the phases completely, apart from the fact that sometimes some of the metal is combined with the impurity, as with tin-copper, tin-iron and zinc-iron, for example. Actually, more than one treatment may be necessary.

Similar to the foregoing is the addition of another metal to the molten base metal to combine with the impurity to form a high-melting point compound, which may be separated as solid. For example, in the Parkes process for desilverising lead, zinc is used; likewise calcium, magnesium or antimony may be used to remove bismuth from lead. Aluminium can be used to separate a number of elements from tin, for example antimony, arsenic and copper; in this case the insolubles can be coagulated by blowing with air or steam. Some excess of the addition usually enters the metal being refined; this is removed by appropriate methods, such as chlorination, oxidation or distillation.

Iron may be removed from molten tin by blowing with air or steam, when a dross forms on the surface; it has been suggested that this may be attributed to some "dewetting" action allowing the solid particles of iron-tin compound to become coagulated, rather than necessarily to direct preferential oxidation. This blowing treatment can be used for further removal of iron after hearth liquation. As mentioned on p. 242, copper is removed from tin and lead by stirring in sulphur and skimming. The formation of insoluble copper sulphide is without doubt the basis of this treatment, at least in part; however, above the respective eutectic compositions there may also be some dewetting action.

The oxides and other insolubles separating from a molten metal are sometimes referred to as **dross**; and certain fire-refining operations, such as cooling to allow separation of insolubles and blowing with air or steam (sometimes the metal is poled with green trees) of lead and tin are called **drossing**. Included under this heading may be the addition of other elements, as outlined above, in order to produce insolubles.

In connection with liquid-solid metal separations, filtering, centrifuging and pressing have possibilities and in some cases have had application. The residues or dross separated in liquation-type processes are treated to recover their constituents or utilised in some other way. Occasionally they may have direct metallurgical use; for example, a copper-tin compound may be used in alloy making.

When another metal is added to effect separation, it is usually recovered for re-use; thus in the Parke's process the zinc and silver are separated by distillation.

Distillation. Separation may be effected by utilising boiling point differences. However, the process is not so simple as merely heating to a temperature intermediate between the boiling points of the elements concerned and directly separating the pure constituents. Complete liquid miscibility is common in binary alloy systems, and often when there is partial liquid miscibility, full miscibility obtains at higher temperatures.

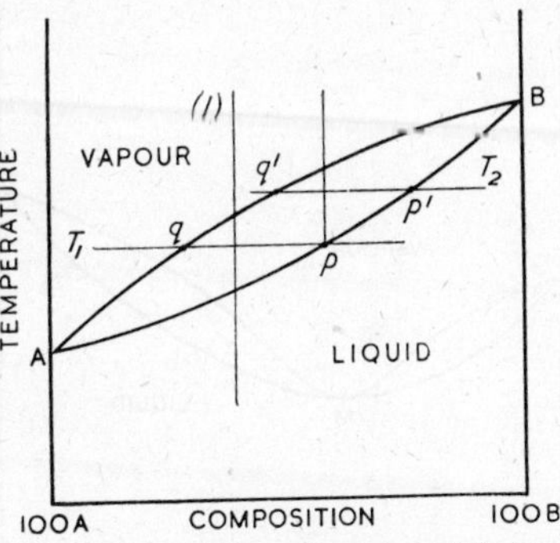

FIG. 193. Liquid-vapour equilibrium diagram.

The curves showing the equilibrium between vapour and liquid for conditions of liquid miscibility are of three kinds (Figs. 193–194). Considering alloy (1), in the first case if this is heated to T_1, at equilibrium there will be vapour of composition q and liquid of composition p. If the fractions are separated and the liquid heated, say to T_2, the liquid composition will be changed to p^1, though decreasing in amount; and some vapour of composition q^1 will be formed, the proportion of liquid to vapour obeying the usual rule. It will be seen that by taking repeated fractions, some liquid which is almost pure B in composition should be obtained. Similarly, by cooling the original vapour in steps and separating the fractions, almost pure A should be produced. To separate the whole of the original amount of alloy (1) into pure A and B would involve countless treatments on the various intermediate fractions, and hence the operation is impracticable. However, by using a reflux condenser or fractionating column, separation becomes possible as a continuous whole.

In practice, the vapours are passed up a tower in which a temperature gradient is maintained, the temperature of the top being just sufficient to volatilise the more volatile element. As the vapours move up from the furnace at the bottom of the tower, they get steadily cooler, and the proportion of the higher-boiling point element continuously decreases; the reverse happens to the condensate which runs down the column. Superimposed trays, through which the liquid descends, are arranged in the tower to promote good contact and equilibrium between the liquid and the uprising

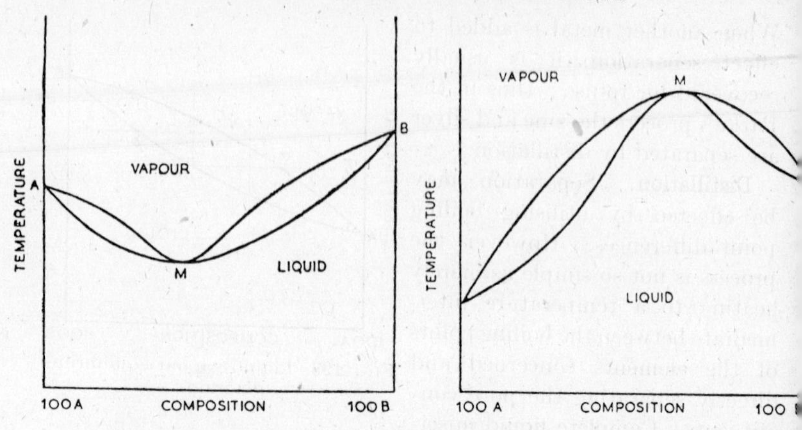

FIG. 194. Liquid-vapour equilibrium diagrams containing a constant boiling-point or azeotropic mixture, *M*. Figs. 194 and 196 are from C. W. Dannatt, *Met. Ind.*, 1948, 72, 5.

vapours. The vapour is led off from the column to a condenser; the liquid is tapped at the bottom of the column as required according to the manner of operation.

The other types of boiling-point curves show that only separation into one or other of the pure elements and the azeotropic or constant boiling-point mixture will be possible in each case. In practice, refining does not usually deal with binary materials, but similar principles apply in more complex metals.

The use of refluxing is standard for chemical separation, but only recently has it been applied to metals. The application origi-

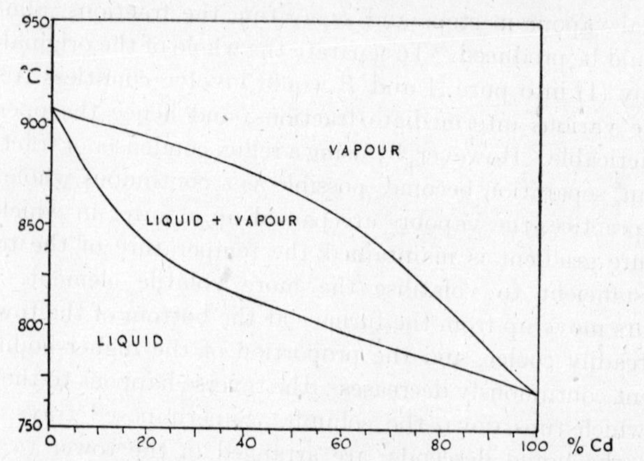

FIG. 195. Liquid-vapour equilibrium diagram for zinc-cadmium system. From S. Robson.

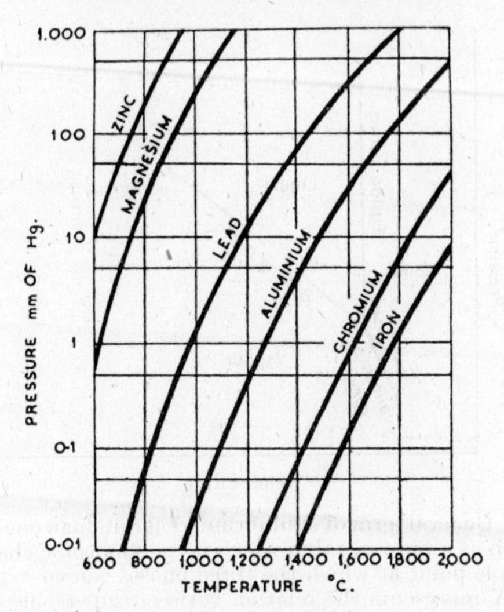

Fig. 196. Variation of vapour pressure with temperature. From Dannatt, after Kelly.

nated with zinc and is in full-scale commercial operation, giving 99·99 per cent purity. Separation is made principally from lead, iron and cadmium (Fig. 195 and Fig. 188) (*see also* p. 292). It is also possible to refine cadmium by refluxing to give the same high purity. Single redistillations have also been made to refine zinc and cadmium as well as arsenic and mercury, subject, of course, to the limitations described earlier. The particular shape of the zinc-lead boiling curves (Fig. 188) indicates good separation of lead by a single distillation.

Reduction of the surrounding pressure causes lowering of the temperature necessary for vaporization (Fig. 196), which is especially advantageous when dealing with the high boiling-point metals. **Vacuum distillation** refining techniques have been developed commercially. Under vacuum conditions **sublimation** may occur, that is, vaporization without melting (Fig. 197). For example, magnesium may be readily sublimed *in vacuo* at about 50° C. or more below its melting point, and small amounts of high-purity sublimed magnesium are made, though more than one treatment may be necessary. Kroll states that practical experience, for example, in the vacuum thermal extraction process for obtaining magnesium from dolomite, using silicon as reducing agent, has shown that there should be a minimum pressure drop of about 2 mm. between metal surface and condenser in order to obtain rapid flow of metal vapour from the evaporating surface. He points out that " few metals, except

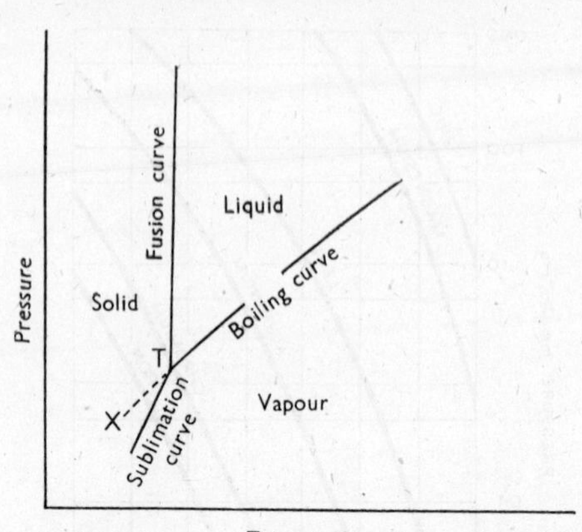

FIG. 197. General form of equilibrium diagram for a one-component system, such as a pure metal in which no polymorphic changes occur. T is the triple point at which the three phases can co-exist in equilibrium. TX represents the relation between supercooled liquid and vapour.

magnesium and calcium, have such high vapour pressure at their triple point".

An example of vacuum treatment with molten metal is the process developed by an American company for the removal of zinc from desilverised lead, and operated at more than one plant. The molten lead initially contains 0·5–0·6 per cent zinc and well over 90 per cent is removed by the treatment. The zinc distilled off condenses on the inside of the cooler top of the steel vessel in which the process is carried out. It contains some lead, as would be expected, and is suitable for re-use in the desilverising process.

Vacuum methods have also been applied, for example, to the purification of calcium, manganese and chromium; and vacuum melting is useful for degassing metals.

Several processes have been investigated and patented for the purification of aluminium by so-called **catalytic distillation.** The crude molten aluminium is brought into contact with an aluminium tri-halide so that the mono-halide is formed. The vapours are drawn off and cooled, when separation into the tri-halide and metallic aluminium occurs. The usual impurities are unaffected. The net effect is thus to lower markedly the temperature at which aluminium can be distilled. The process can be represented as follows:

$$2Al + AlF_3 \rightarrow 3AlF \rightarrow AlF_3 + 2Al.$$

This should be compared with the Mond process for nickel (p. 224).

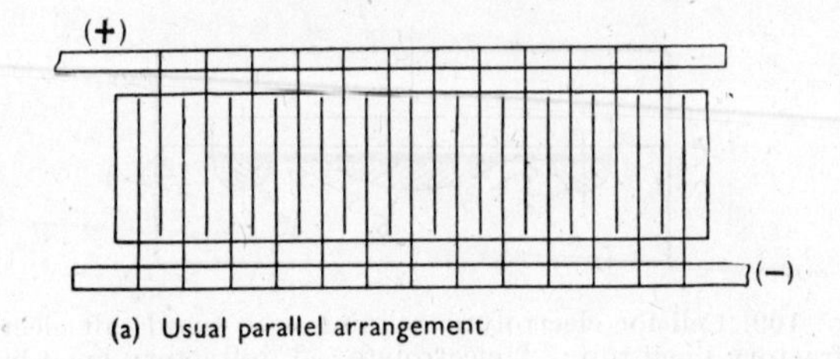

(a) Usual parallel arrangement

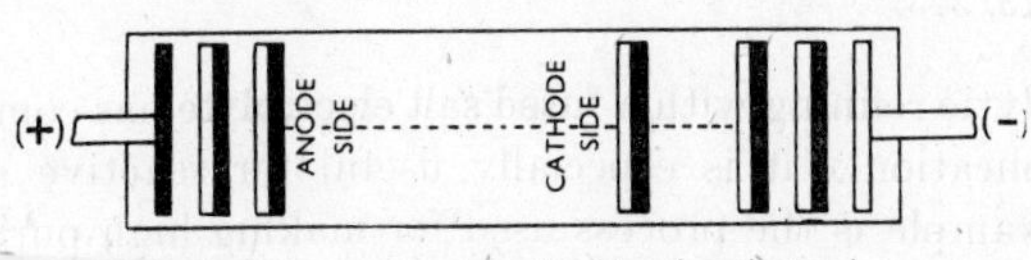

(b) Series arrangement using bi-polar electrode.

FIG. 198. Arrangement of electrodes for electrolytic refining (with aqueous electrolyte). In the series arrangement the electrodes are initially the crude metal which is gradually replaced by cathodically-deposited metal.

Electrolytic-refining with aqueous electrolyte. This method yields metal of high purity and is particularly useful for separating elements which are not removed by ordinary fire-refining. Costs are greater with electrolytic refining, but this is often offset by better recovery of valuable by-product metals.

The crude metal is frequently given some preliminary fire-refining before casting into anodes. The cathode starting sheets are usually of the same metal (of high purity) although sometimes another metal is used from which the deposit is stripped. The electrodes are generally arranged vertically in parallel or multiple although bi-polar electrodes in series have been used for copper (Fig. 198); in one cell used for silver, the electrodes are horizontal. The anodes have to be removed before they are completely dissolved; the amount removed is known as anode scrap and is returned to the anode furnace.

A coherent cathode deposit is usually obtained, except with silver, where the metal is deposited in granular form. The cathode metal is generally melted down and cast into ingots. With copper some refining is necessary at the melting stage. The more noble constituents of the crude metal are left as an insoluble residue or slime at the anode; this is worked up for these elements. The less noble elements dissolve with the main metal and thus the electrolyte generally needs regular purification. Specific details for important applications are given in Chapter 9.

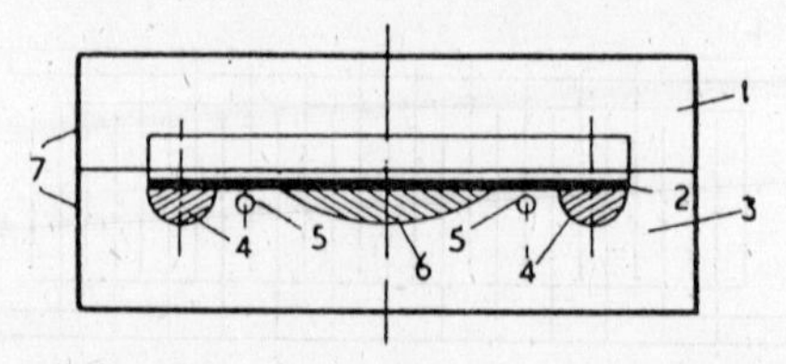

FIG. 199. Cell for electrolytic refining with fused salt electrolyte. 1, refractory lined top ; 2, electrolyte ; 3, refractory lined bottom ; 4, annular cathode of refined metal ; 5, water cooling ; 6, central pool of anode metal ; 7, iron shell. From W. J. Kroll, *Met. Ind.*, 1948, 73, 323.

Electrolytic refining with a **fused salt electrolyte** has comparatively small application ; it is especially useful for reactive metals. A notable example is the process used for making high-purity aluminium, described on page 308, in which both the anode and cathode are of molten metal. Another possible cell arrangement for this type of refining is shown in Fig. 199. Refining with solid electrodes producing solid metal is also possible for high melting-point metals.

THEORETICAL CONSIDERATIONS OF ELECTRO-CHEMICAL PROCESSES

Four electro-chemical techniques have been discussed in the preceding sections :

(1) Precipitation from aqueous leach liquors by replacement with another metal, or by electrolysis using insoluble anodes.

(2) Electrolytic refining with soluble anodes in aqueous electrolytes.

(3) Electrolytic extraction from a fused-salt bath using insoluble anodes, the metal entering the process in the form of a purified compound.

(4) Electrolytic refining with a fused-salt bath, the metal treated being in the form of a soluble anode.

Aqueous electrolysis. It is well known that when a metal is immersed in a solution of its salts at a specific temperature, it acquires a potential varying with the concentration of metal ions in the solution. The value in a particular case depends on the equilibrium set up between the passage of ions into solution from the metal electrode and the discharge of ions as atoms on to the electrode. Intrinsic values for the potentials cannot be measured, but comparison can be made with a standard. The standard adopted is that of the **hydrogen electrode,** which is taken as zero potential at any temperature in acid solution containing hydrogen ions at unit activity under atmospheric pressure. The potential difference developed between the metal in contact with a solution containing its ions and the hydrogen electrode is taken as the potential of the particular metal electrode. The metals are compared by tabulating their respective potentials at 25° C. (or 18° C.) for unit concentration (activity) giving the **electro-motive, electro-potential** or **electro-chemical series** (Table 25).

TABLE 25. ELECTRODE POTENTIALS AT 25° C. REFERRED TO HYDROGEN AS ZERO (for unit activities) (from Creighton and Koehler)

Element	Ion	Volts	
Li	Li^+	−2·96	[" Base " End]
K	K^+	−2·92	
Na	Na^+	−2·72	
Ca	Ca^{++}	−2·5	
Mg	Mg^{++}	−1·87	
Al	Al^{+++}	−1·35	
Zn	Zn^{++}	−0·76	
Cr	Cr^{++}	−0·6	
Cr	Cr^{+++}	−0·5	
Fe	Fe^{++}	−0·44	
Cd	Cd^{++}	−0·40	
Co	Co^{++}	−0·29	
Ni	Ni^{++}	−0·22	
Sn	Sn^{++}	−0·14	
Pb	Pb^{++}	−0·13	
Fe	Fe^{+++}	−0·04	
H	H^+	0·00	
Sb	Sb^{+++}	+0·11	
Cu	Cu^{++}	+0·34	
Cu	Cu^+	+0·52	
2Hg	Hg_2^{++}	+0·7986	
Ag	Ag^+	+0·7995	
Pd	Pd^{++}	+0·82	
Hg	Hg^{++}	+0·86	
Au	Au^{+++}	+1·3	[" Noble " End]
O_2	OH^-	+0·40	
I_2	I^-	+0·54	
Cl_2	Cl^-	+1·36	

The base metals are reactive, and for those at the top of the table, such as aluminium, magnesium, calcium and sodium, under ordinary conditions, electro-deposition from solution is impossible. With increasing nobility, inertness and ease of deposition increase. A metal will tend to replace a more noble one from solution, and this fact is utilised in practice ; for example, copper is precipitated from acid leach liquors by iron, and gold from cyanide solutions by aluminium or usually zinc. The electrode potentials of various gases have also been determined (Table 25) ; reference is made to them later.

Electrolysing voltage. The voltage in an electrolytic bath is such as to overcome the ohmic resistance of the electrolyte and various polarisation effects, as well as conductor and contact resistance ; in addition, it has to overcome any opposing E.M.F. developed by the electrodes, that is, carry out any chemical work involved. In general, the voltage needed for electrolysis is reduced by a low current-density and a high temperature ; but in practice, high output demands as high current-density as possible, and cost of heating must be considered ; temperature is obviously limited by vaporisation losses.

With fairly high-grade soluble anodes, as in refining practice, no overall chemical work is done in the bath, and this factor does not then enter into voltage considerations. Metal dissolves and an equivalent is deposited ; a graph of current versus voltage should be theoretically a straight line passing through the origin (Fig. 200a).

With insoluble anodes the position is somewhat different ; it is found that essentially no current flows until a certain voltage is reached, which is known as the **decomposition voltage** (Fig. 200b). The decomposition voltage is thus the minimum for electrolysis. The values vary according to the solution concerned and the nature of the electrodes involved, and other factors as indicated below.

Neglecting the resistance of the electrolyte (which is not involved until the decomposition voltage is exceeded), and provided there is no polarisation, the (*reversible*) *decomposition voltage is equal to the difference of the* (*equilibrium*) *electrode potentials* under the conditions

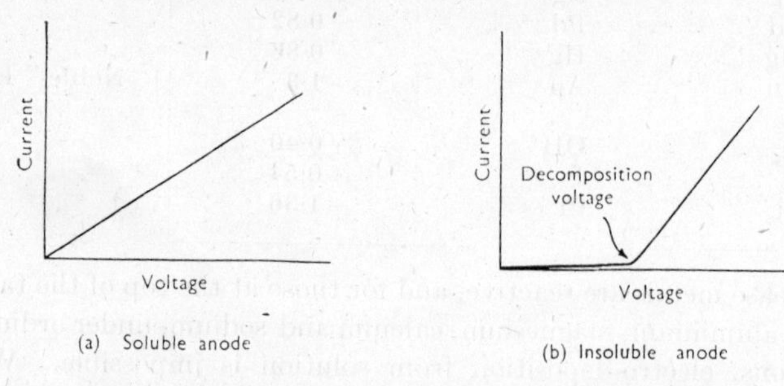

FIG. 200. Current-voltage relations in electrolysis.

of concentration, pressure and temperature obtaining. The electrodes to be considered are those of the products of electrolysis. Thus, in the case of dilute acid or water between platinum electrodes, hydrogen is evolved at the cathode and oxygen at the anode, and the electrodes become gas electrodes and the theoretical decomposition voltage becomes the difference of two gas potentials. In metallurgical electrolysis, a metal is liberated at the cathode and usually a gas at the anode ; these are therefore the potentials which must be considered. However, there is usually polarisation, especially when gases are evolved, and it will be found that the potential required to liberate the particular gas at an electrode will be higher than the theoretical potential. The difference is known as the **overvoltage** for the electrode concerned, or sometimes the **polarisation voltage.** The decomposition voltage thus becomes in practice the difference of the actual potentials and is increased by the polarisation effects. It should be appreciated that in the above, polarisation is used strictly in connection with the extra potential required for actual gas liberation. Polarisation is also used in another more general sense to indicate any opposing potential or back E.M.F., which may also be referred to as the polarisation voltage (*also see* concentration polarisation, p. 256).

Gas overvoltage values vary for different gases and for different electrode materials ; approximate values of the hydrogen overvoltage of a number of metals are given in Table 26. The values are affected by a number of factors, but, in particular, are increased by increase in current-density and decreased by rise in temperature, although that of hydrogen on platinised platinum is almost independent of temperature. Overvoltage effects are mainly experienced with gases. Appreciable polarisation is not generally obtained in the cathodic deposition of metals, although some is experienced with iron, nickel and cobalt.

TABLE 26. TYPICAL APPROXIMATE HYDROGEN OVERVOLTAGES FOR VARIOUS METALS WITH RESPECT TO THEIR POSITION IN THE PERIODIC TABLE (Creighton).

Group		Metals	Overvoltage
Group	I.	Copper, silver, gold	0·35 volts
,,	II.	Magnesium, zinc, mercury	0·70 ,,
,,	III.	Aluminium	0·50 ,,
,,	IV.	Tin, lead	0·45 ,,
,,	V.	Antimony, bismuth	0·42 ,,
,,	VI.	Chromium, tungsten	0·32 ,,
,,	VII.	Manganese	0·25 ,,
,,	VIII.	Iron, nickel	0·18 ,,

It will be seen from the foregoing that the decomposition voltage of any solution will vary, depending, for example, on the concentration of the electrolyte, the nature of the electrodes, the current density and the temperature. Typical decomposition voltages are given in Table 27.

TABLE 27. TYPICAL DECOMPOSITION POTENTIALS OF ELECTROLYTES: FOR NORMAL SOLUTIONS BETWEEN PLATINUM ELECTRODES AT ROOM TEMPERATURE

	Decomposition voltage
Cadmium sulphate	2·03
Calcium chloride	1·89
Cobalt sulphate	1·92
Copper sulphate	1·49
Lead nitrate	1·52
Nickel sulphate	2·09
Potassium chloride	1·96
Sodium carbonate	1·71
Sulphuric acid	1·67
Nitric acid	1·69
Hydrochloric acid	1·31

From examination of the electrode potentials, it would appear that metals baser than hydrogen in the scale could not be electrolytically precipitated, for in each case hydrogen would be preferentially precipitated. That metals such as zinc and cadmium can be electrodeposited is due to the values of their hydrogen overvoltage, which are such that hydrogen is not evolved at voltages at which the metals are deposited.

The applied voltage in soluble-anode processes has to overcome concentration polarisation. During electrolysis, metal ions are going into solution at the anode and others are precipitated on the cathode. Due to slowness of diffusion, the concentration of metal ions is increased at the anode and decreased at the cathode. This concentration difference results in a concentration potential acting against the applied potential. Concentration polarisation is reduced by stirring or circulation of electrolyte, and by raising the temperature. Marked polarisation is also obtained with soluble anodes, due to the formation of insoluble films. Thus in electrolysing anodes of crude gold, the presence of silver in the anode metal results in the formation of an anode coating of silver chloride. When the silver exceeds about 6 per cent, this becomes most serious in effect, and dissolution of the gold is prevented. This is overcome in practice by superimposing an alternating current, which causes the silver chloride to flake off.

Efficiency. Although theoretically Faraday's Laws hold for all electrolytic processes, in practice larger amounts of electricity are required than the theoretical, due to various losses. The **current efficiency** is the theoretical amount of electricity required, divided by the actual amount used, and multiplied by 100 to express it as a percentage. A typical value for copper refining is 90 per cent. The efficiency is further reduced by the fact that higher voltages than the theoretical are necessary. The energy efficiency is more generally representative than the current efficiency, and is equal to the latter multiplied by the ratio of the theoretical to the actual voltage.

Behaviour of metals and electrolyte during electrolysis. In the case of a refining process with a soluble anode, the main metal and the baser impurities go into solution, while the more noble are mainly insoluble and form the anode mud or slime, which is periodically removed from the tanks. The anodes may be surrounded with cloth bags in which the slime collects, as in the Moebius process for silver.

The position in practice is not so simple as the above would imply, because impurities in a metal are frequently combined with it in some way as compounds or solid solutions, for example, and it is the nobler constituents which remain. This is one reason why some of the main metal is found in the slimes ; for example, copper slimes may contain up to 50 per cent copper (some of this is also due to mechanical loss, arising from uneven solution causing pieces of the anodes to drop into the slimes ; also for example from the following reaction : $2Cu^{+} = Cu^{++} + Cu$). In a similar manner the main metal may have other elements, including more noble ones, in solid solution and which may be co-dissolved. Further, a more noble element may dissolve if, due to some polarisation effect at the anode, the potential rises. The soluble impurities which build up in the electrolyte necessitate its regular purification ; a portion is usually drawn off for treatment ; the adjustment may be continuous or periodic. The metal strength of the electrolyte is also likely to change and thus to need adjustment.

Of the impurities going into solution with the metal, only those with similar potentials under the existing conditions are likely to be co-deposited (unless concentration becomes excessive). Thus tin will dissolve and be co-precipitated during electrolytic refining of lead ; it is removed by fire-refining methods before or after electrolysis. The co-deposition of copper in nickel refining is prevented by surrounding the cathodes with porous cloth to act as a diaphragm. Pure electrolyte, free from copper, is fed to the cathode compartments, where some of its nickel is deposited. The rate of feeding is such that the electrolyte flows out of the compartments into the main cell and then overflows. In the main cell, copper is dissolving with the nickel from the anodes, but the solution containing the copper overflows. The overflow is purified, particularly of copper, and is then returned to the cathode compartments. Sometimes impurities may be precipitated as insolubles from the electrolyte. Thus in copper refining with copper sulphate—sulphuric acid electrolyte, dissolved lead and tin precipitate as sulphates, the former at once, the tin slowly; further, dissolved silver may be precipitated by the addition of hydrochloric acid, which also causes the precipitation of antimony and bismuth. A very high current-density may cause co-deposition of impurities due to depletion in metal (main) ions of the electrolyte near the cathode, diffusion not being sufficiently rapid.

In some instances the presence of other elements in the electrolyte may seriously affect the efficiency of the process and also the physical nature of the deposit. This is especially so with electrolysis of zinc, where according to Laist, for example, the presence of antimony to the extent of 1 mgm. per litre causes lowering of current efficiency and the development of sprouts on the cathode; if germanium is present, it causes pronounced fluctuations of current efficiency and sometimes prevents deposition of zinc. Zinc leach liquors are, therefore, carefully purified before electrolysis.

In deposition from leach liquors for which insoluble anodes are used, in general, separation can be obtained from elements the appropriate salts of which have higher decomposition voltages in the solution than that for the main salt, provided the elements do not have harmful effects. The electrolysis regenerates the solution, but the metal cannot be completely removed from the solution, because impurities would be deposited.

The following points should be noted regarding the metal and acid strengths in electrolytes:

(1) A high metal ion concentration enables the production of sound deposits at high current-density and reduces the tendency for co-deposition of impurities dissolved in the electrolyte.

(2) The conductivity of the electrolyte increases with the amount of free acid, but so also does the tendency for hydrogen to be evolved.

Apart from co-deposition of elements dissolving from the anode or during leaching, impurities in the cathode metal may arise from entrapping of insolubles such as slimes or precipitates, electrolyte, or hydrogen.

Electrolytes are usually stirred or circulated through the tanks during electrolysis. Circulation reduces concentration polarisation; gives opportunity for composition adjustments; helps to maintain an adequate supply of metal ions at the cathode, especially with high current-densities. The rate of agitation should increase with current-density, but should not be sufficient to disturb the slimes.

Physical nature of cathode deposit. The quality of the deposit is paramount in electro-plating. In process metallurgy, the cathodes are usually melted down and cast to ingots, and the requirement is a reasonably coherent deposit for handling, although uneven growth is, of course, undesirable. Actually, electro-refined silver is deposited in a granular form, in which form it is shovelled out of the tanks.

Many factors govern the nature of the cathode deposit; some of the more important are generalised below.

At relatively low values of *current-density*, the metal is coarse-grained: at first, increase of current-density gives finer grain size, but beyond a certain figure roughened and eventually incoherent deposits and pronounced evolution of hydrogen result. Increase in metal ion concentration and circulation rate generally increases the values of current densities possible.

Moderate increase of *temperature* aids diffusion in the electrolyte and gives smoother and finer grained deposits; but with continued increase, coarsening results.

The *smoothness* of a deposit can often be improved and grain size reduced by small additions of colloidal and other materials, for example, glue and gelatine. As pointed out above, the smoothness and soundness of a deposit may be adversely affected by the presence of certain impurities. In general, smoother deposits are obtained from complex ions (used in electro-plating). Smoothness is also improved by good circulation of the electrolyte.

Fused salt electrolysis. The essential principles are the same as with aqueous electrolytes. The conductivity of a fused electrolyte is usually noticeably greater than the same material in aqueous solution at room temperature; the same primary electrode products are generally obtained in both cases. Typical decomposition voltages are given in Figs. 186 and 187; there is a simple relation between decomposition voltage and free energy of formation. It has been pointed out that for various reasons the fused baths are usually mixtures of salts. The salts should have higher decomposition voltages than the metal source. Then, provided there is no interaction and the concentration of the latter is kept sufficient, the salts should not undergo decomposition. However, the position is often likely to be complicated by interaction.

Two phenomena which decrease the efficiency of electrolysis are the anode effect and the formation of a metal fog. The *anode effect* occurs especially with high current-densities in halide baths, and is characterised by marked increase in voltage and reduction in current. A gas envelope forms around the carbon anodes, preventing their being wetted by the electrolyte. The electrode seems to glow due to the many spark discharges which occur. The anode effect is stopped by stirring, raising the anode from the melt for a short time or reversing the current to remove the gas film. The loss of metal at the cathode due to the formation of a small amount of *metal fog* in the electrolyte is peculiar to fused electrolytes.

ADDITIONAL READING

1. *Principles of Extraction and Refining of Metals.* (Institution of Metallurgists, 1951).

2. *The Refining of Non-Ferrous Metals*, Symposium (1949). (Institution of Mining and Metallurgy, 1950).

3. *Textbook of Metallurgical Problems*, by A. Butts. (2nd Ed., McGraw-Hill, 1943).

4. *Elements of Physical Chemistry*, by J. Chipman. Chapter XIII of *Basic Open Hearth Steelmaking*. (American Inst. Min. Met. Eng., 1944).

5. *Metallurgical Thermochemistry*, by O. Kubaschewski and E. Ll. Evans. (Butterworth-Springer, 1951).

6. *The Physical Chemistry of Process Metallurgy.* Discussions of the Faraday Society No. 4 (Gurney and Jackson, 1948).

7. *Reducibility of Oxides and Sulphides in Metallurgical Processes*, by H. J. T. Ellingham, *J. Soc. Chem. Indust.*, **63**, 125, (1944).

8. *Thermodynamics of Substances of Interest in Iron and Steel Making. I. Oxides*, by F. D. Richardson and J. H. E. Jeffes, *J. Iron and Steel Inst.*, **160**, 261, (1948). *II. Compounds between Oxides*, by F. D. Richardson, J. H. E. Jeffes and G. Withers, *J. Iron and Steel Inst.*, **166**, 213, (1950). *III. Sulphides*, by F. D. Richardson and J. H. E. Jeffes, *J. Iron and Steel Inst.*, **171**, 165, (1952).

9. *The Thermodynamic Background of Iron and Steel Making Processes. I. The Blast Furnace*, by F. D. Richardson and J. H. E. Jeffes, *J. Iron and Steel Inst.*, **163**, 397, (1949). *II. Deoxidation*, by F. D. Richardson, *J. Iron and Steel Inst.*, **166**, 137, (1950).

10. *The Production of Pure Cerium Metal by Electrolytic and Thermal Reduction Processes*, by P. M. J. Gray, *Bull. Inst. Min. Met.*, **61**, 141 1951–52). Contains free-energy diagrams for chlorides and fluorides.

11. *Thermodynamic Data of the Metallic Chlorides*, by H. Villa, *J. Soc. Chem. Ind.*, **69**, *Supplementery Issue No.* 1, S9–S18, (1950).

12. *The Graphical Representation of Metallurgical Equilibria*, by C. J. Osborn, *J. Met.*, **188**, 600, 1388, (1950).

13. *The Physical Chemistry of Copper Smelting*, by R. W. Ruddle. (Inst. Min. and Met., 1953).

14. *Hydrometallurgy of Base Metals*, by G. D. Van Arsdale. (McGraw-Hill, 1953).

15. *Electrochemistry*, by H. J. Creighton and W. A. Koehler. Vol. I. *Principles*, by Creighton. (4th Ed., 1943). Vol. II. *Applications*, by Koehler. (2nd Ed., 1944). (New York, Wiley. London, Chapman and Hall).

16. *The Principles of Applied Electrochemistry*, by A. J. Allmand and H. J. T. Ellingham. (2nd Ed., Arnold 1931).

17. *Principles of Electro-Deposition*, by S. Field. (2nd Ed. 1949, Pitman).

CHAPTER 9

METAL WINNING: PRODUCTION OF NON-FERROUS METALS

Refractories. It is necessary first to discuss briefly the heat-resisting or refractory materials used in furnace construction, which are of considerable importance. They are mainly natural minerals in a fairly pure state, namely, **fireclay** (essentially kaolinite ($Al_2O_3 . 2SiO_2 . 2H_2O$) with excess silica or alumina), **silica** (in various forms), **alumina,** calcined **magnesite** and **dolomite, chromite** ($Cr_2O_3 . FeO$) and **graphite** ; although some are prepared synthetically, such as graphite, cokes, and **silicon carbide** which is made from coke and sand in electric furnaces. In certain instances metals are used.

The general requirements of a refractory include high softening and fusion temperatures, good strength at high temperature, ability to withstand changes in temperature, resistance to abrasion and imperviousness to the materials with which it is to come into contact. These are of course only obtained to varying degrees in any particular material. In addition, with regard to heat transfer, one of three particular characteristics is usually paramount, namely, good thermal conductivity as in distillation retorts, insulating power, or ability to store heat as in furnace regenerators.

For high-temperature processes using a combustible fuel, greater efficiency and higher temperatures are obtained by preheating the air for combustion, and sometimes the fuel when gaseous, by utilising the heat of the waste gases. There are two main methods, **regeneration** and **recuperation.** The former is an intermittent process (Fig. 205 and 216) ; the waste gases are passed through a honeycomb of brick-work (chequer brickwork) to which they give up much of their heat. After a period of perhaps half an hour, the gases are diverted to another regenerator which has been preheating the combustion air; the latter is then passed through the newly heated regenerator; the regular alternation is continued. If both gas and air are being preheated by regeneration, then two sets of double-compartment regenerators are necessary ; as an alternative to brickwork, metal plates may be used in regenerators. Recuperation is based on a counterflow principle (Fig. 201).

Sometimes a refractory is used in the form of blocks cut from the as-mined material. In a number of cases the mineral is crushed, mixed with bonding material, rammed into place and fired *in situ*. But, very often refractories are used in the form of bricks. Bricks and other pre-formed shapes are made as follows. The mineral is crushed and cleaned, mixed with water and bonding agent, shaped by casting, pressing or extruding, dried, and fired at high temperature to bond the particles together and put the mineral into a stable form. There are usually associated with the main refractory mineral small quantities of other minerals as impurities, and these act as bonding agents; but often definite additions in small amounts are made. For example, fireclay is added to silica, silicon carbide and magnesite; silica is bonded also with lime, and calcined dolomite with tar. The bonding resulting from firing is due to the formation of a small amount of "glass" cementing the particles together, and to other changes.

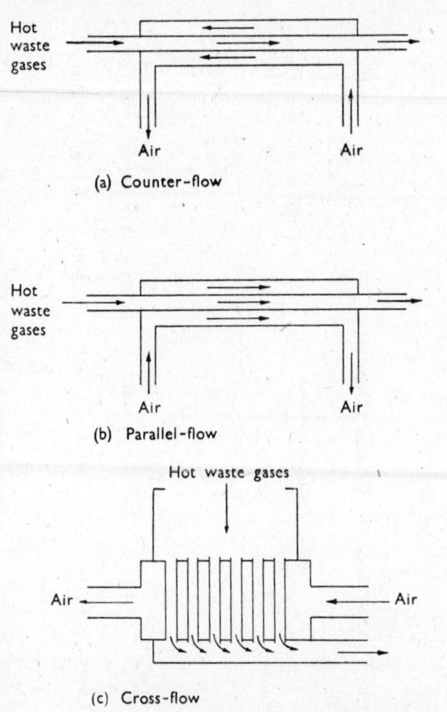

FIG. 201. Principle of recuperation. Both metallic and non-metallic materials are used. After W. Trinks.

In processes in which a slag is formed of definite acid or basic properties, it is usual to make the refractory in contact with the slag of similar nature in order to reduce interaction, unless the rate of reaction is slow. The procedure is well illustrated in the case of steel-making. In a number of processes using a slag, the refractory indirectly plays a part in slag formation due to solution and mechanical introduction. There is no important process used today in which the refractory is used directly as a flux. At one time the linings of converters used for copper mattes were of silica, which combined

TABLE 28. STAGES IN THE TRANSITION OF COALS (Brame)

	Wood	Peat	*Lignite*		*Bituminous*				Carbon-aceous	Anthra-cite
			Brown	Black	1.	2.	3.	4.		
Air-dried										
Moisture - -	20	20	18	15	10	3	1	1	1	1
Volatile matter less moisture -	—	50	47	41	35	34	32	30	11	8
Fixed carbon -	—	27	28	32	45	58	62	64	84	88
Ash - - -	0·5	3	7	12	10	5	5	5	4	3
B.Th.U. per lb. -	6,400	7,700	9,900	10,200	10,700	13,900	14,300	14,400	15,000	15,000
Ash-free dry										
Carbon - -	50	60	67	74	77	84	85·6	87	92	94
Hydrogen - -	6·5	6	5·5	5·4	5	5	5	5·3	4	3
Oxygen - -	43	32	26	19	16	8	5·4	4·7	2	2
Sulphur and nitrogen - -	0·5	2	1·5	1·6	2	3	4	3	2	1
B.Th.U. per lb. -	8,000	10,000	13,200	13,900	13,400	15,100	15,200	15,300	15,800	15,600

Bituminous 1. Lignitous, long-flame steam and house coal.
,, 2. Para-bituminous, hard steam, house and manufacturing coal.
,, 3. Para-bituminous, gas and coking coal.
,, 4. Ortho-bituminous, coking coal.

with the iron oxide, formed in the first part of the blow, to produce the iron silicate slag whereby the iron is removed. This practice was discontinued when a suitable substitute, namely magnesite, was found, because of the disproportionate costs involved. Under arduous conditions, refractories usually need regular replacement.

Brief details of the application of the refractories are given in discussing the production of the various metals.

METALLURGICAL FUELS

Coal. Coal is the basis of most metallurgical fuels. It is well known that coal is the result of the gradual decay and metamorphosis of plant matter over a vast period of time. As the extent of the change or metamorphosis increases, giving the range lignite to anthracite, so does the carbon content increase whereas the hydrogen and oxygen contents decrease ; the **rank** of the coal is said to increase (Table 28).

When coal is burnt, the flame is due in particular to the burning of the volatile combustibles which are driven off by the heat. Flame also results from the burning of carbon monoxide formed by the incomplete combustion of carbon in the fuel. The characteristic slight blue flame of carbon monoxide is to be seen during the burning of anthracite, which contains very little volatile matter. Two important characteristics of coal which clearly affect its utilisation are : (1) the amount of volatile combustible matter evolved, and (2) whether or not the coal fuses and forms a coherent coke on heating (Table 29).

TABLE 29.

CLASSIFICATION SCHEME FOR COAL BASED ON VOLATILE MATTER (Gyngell)

Name	Volatile matter (per cent)	Description
Lignite - -	>45	Non-caking, slacks in air. High moisture
Lignitous Coals -	40–45	Long-flame steam coal, non-caking
Gas Coals - -	32–40	Gas-making coals, strongly caking, open swollen coke.
Coking Coals -	20–32	Coke manufacture, strongly caking, dense hard coke.
Semi-bituminous -	15–20	Short-flame steam coals, caking.
Semi-anthracites -	9–15	Short-flame steam coals, non-caking (Welsh type).
Anthracites -	<9	Very short to no flame, non-caking.

The ash in coal comprises the inorganic mineral matter both finely and coarsely associated with the coal in the ground. It forms the non-combustible residue when the coal is burnt and remains in the coke after carbonisation. Included in the mineral matter are sulphur compounds, especially pyrite, and to a much lesser extent, calcium sulphate ; sulphur is also present in coal as organic compounds with carbon. On carbonising, that is, heating in the absence of air, some of the sulphur passes off as gaseous compounds, but usually more than 80 per cent remains in the coke. When the coal is burnt, a large proportion of the sulphur is converted to sulphur dioxide.

Ash is valueless inert material and, in addition to dilution of the fuel, its presence may create a need for extra flux and heat in certain metallurgical operations. In the iron blast-furnace, for example, the fluxing of the coke ash is an important item. Sulphur is undesirable in metallurgical fuels as it is so easily absorbed by solid and liquid metal, on which it usually has a harmful effect. The amount of coarsely associated mineral matter, including pyrites, in the as-mined coal can be reduced by physical cleaning techniques, reference to which has been made in Chapter 7. Organic sulphur is not usually removed in this way. There is no satisfactory method for removing sulphur from coke. However, sulphur can be removed from gaseous fuels, the best known technique being the removal of hydrogen sulphide by absorption in bog iron ore, $2Fe_2O_3 . 3H_2O$.

Coal can be used in the lump form in reverberatory type furnaces and this was the original fuel for such furnaces ; the coal, high in volatile matter, is burnt on a grate at one end, the flame being drawn across the hearth. However, modern reverberatories are fired with gas, oil or pulverised coal. In the last method of firing, powdered coal is blown into the furnace through suitably designed burners. Almost any coal can be utilised in this way, although that with more than 20 per cent volatile matter, less than 10 per cent ash and not of high coking power is preferred. Pulverised coal fuel gives the flexibility of gas or oil. The quantity of ash formed is a disadvantage, and the cost of grinding is an important factor. Hard pitch can be utilised in a similar manner.

Coke and charcoal. Coke is a more important solid fuel than coal. Its especial applications are in the blast-furnace and foundry. Metallurgical coke is made in special ovens as described below. The other solid fuel of note is charcoal, prepared by the carbonisation of wood. Charcoal is an unimportant metallurgical fuel today, although it is still used in one or two blast-furnaces making special iron. At one time, of course, charcoal was the only fuel used in making iron.

TABLE 30. PRINCIPAL CONSTITUENTS AND CALORIFIC VALUES OF FUEL GASES

Type of gas	Percentage						Heat of combustion —gross calorific power (B.Th.U./cub. ft.)
	CO	CO_2	H_2	CH_4	C_2H_4	N_2	
Blast furnace gas .	20–34	6–18	0·5–6			55–64	80–115
Producer gas . .	16–30	2·5–10	10–19	2–5		50–60	125–165
Water gas (blue) .	35–45	2·5–5	45–53	0·5–3		2–6	250–300
Carburetted water gas	18–40	1–6	28–40	10–25	4–15	2–10	400–700
Coal gas . . .	5–15	0·5–5	42–50	20–42	3–7	2–10	400–600
Coke oven gas . .	5–8	1–3	47–60	25–35	2–6	2–12	390–550
Natural gas . . .	Up to 99 % hydrocarbons, the majority being methane, CH_4						900–1250

Petroleum fuel oil (calorific value about 18,000–19,000 B.Th.U. per lb), and **coal tar** liquid fuels (16,000–17,000 B.Th.U. per lb) are valuable metallurgical fuels with low ash content and giving intense luminous flames. They are flexible and easy to handle. The sulphur content of coal tar fuels is 1 per cent, maximum, but may be considerably higher with petroleum oil, and this may be a disadvantage for certain purposes. Oil fuel is atomised and sprayed into the furnace by steam or air, or is forced under pressure through mechanical atomisers. Oil is used, for example, in crucible and rotary furnaces for melting, and reverberatories for smelting and refining. It is being used increasingly as fuel in open-hearth steel-making furnaces ; in this connection it is also employed to increase the luminosity or heating value of gaseous fuels.

Gaseous fuels. The gaseous fuels used in metallurgy, namely, coal or towns' gas, coke-oven gas, producer gas, water gas and blast furnace gas are derived from coal.

Coal gas is made by the carbonisation of coal high in volatile matter (Table 29) at about 1000° C., in horizontal or vertical retorts, fired with producer gas. The coke is an important by-product, and

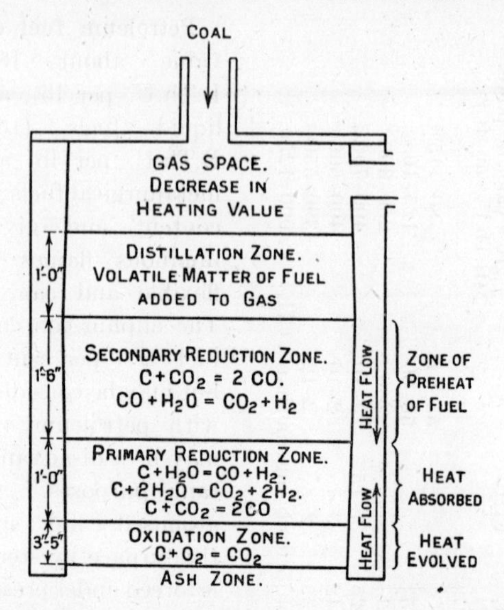

Fig. 202. Reactions in gas producer. If the temperature is too high (in the absence of carbon) there can be a reversal in the gas space of the reaction : $C+CO_2 \rightleftharpoons 2CO$. Using a deep fuel bed is one method of minimising this tendency. From *Fuel*, by J. S. S. Brame and J. G. King. Arnold.

others, such as tar, benzol and ammonia, are removed from the gas before its use. Coal gas is a common fuel for heat-treatment and foundry furnaces.

Coke-oven gas, which is the gas evolved during the production of metallurgical coke, generally has a slightly lower heating value than coal gas ; The gas is used in the steel plant and to augment coal gas supplies for domestic and industrial purposes.

Basically, **producer gas** is made by passing air through an incandescent fuel bed ; but as the overall reaction is exothermic, it is necessary to cool the fuel bed. For this purpose steam is added to the air blast, the steam/carbon reaction being endothermic. In this way the generator can be run continuously and the gas is enriched. Producer gas is an important fuel in the steel industry as well as having non-ferrous applications. The original open-hearth furnaces used producer gas as fuel.

Water gas is essentially a mixture of carbon monoxide and hydrogen formed by blowing steam through an incandescent fuel bed, usually coke or anthracite. In this case the gas is made in short " runs ", alternating with air " blows " to heat up the fuel again.

The blow gases are discarded or utilised in some way, but they are not added to the water gas, which they would dilute. This blue water gas has had some direct metallurgical applications, but the main use is in the carburetted form, that is enriched with oil gas, as substitute towns' gas supply.

Blast-furnace gas is a very lean fuel, a by-product of the iron blast-furnace. Its use is confined to the iron and steel plant ; in certain instances it may be advantageously used for heating the coke-ovens. The cleaning and utilisation are discussed in Chapter 10.

Natural gas, essentially hydrocarbons and largely methane, which is usually associated with petroleum oil, is an important industrial and domestic fuel in oil-producing countries such as America, where it is used in open-hearth steel furnaces and copper matte furnaces, to quote two metallurgical applications. Natural gas has a high calorific value and a low sulphur content.

The composition and heating power of the fuel gases mentioned above are summarised in Table 30 (p.267).

Generation of producer gas. For furnace work, a non- or weakly-caking bituminous coal is generally used as fuel. The hot gas is fed directly via insulated mains to the furnace, enriched with the tar and hydrocarbons from the coal. For use in gas engines the gas is cooled and cleaned of suspended matter. Sometimes hydrogen sulphide is removed from producer gas by treatment with iron oxide.

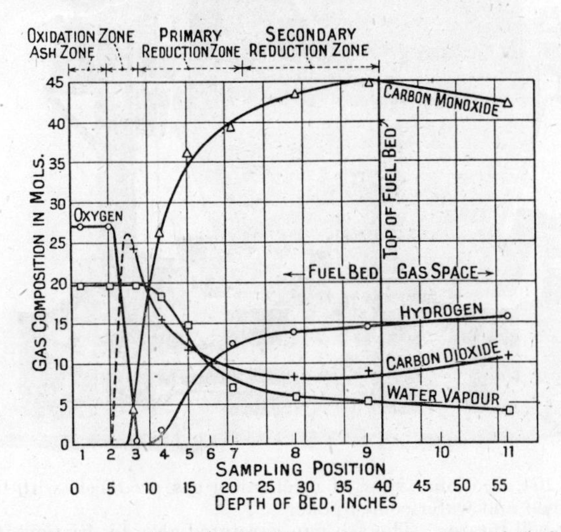

FIG. 203. Composition (mol./100 mol. of nitrogen) of the gas at various levels in the producer. From *Fuel*, by J. S. S. Brame and J. G. King. Arnold.

Coke and anthracite are also used in producers. Usually the fuel is closely sized, of the order of 1 in. Special producers may utilise waste products, such as colliery refuse, wood chippings or sawdust.

The generators are invariably worked continuously, with a mixed blast of air and steam. For furnace heating, the producers are commonly of the pressure type, the blast being forced through, as opposed to the suction kind. The amount of steam in the blast is adjusted to provide a satisfactory working temperature at the fuel bed ; this must be sufficiently above 1000° C. to give efficient gasification for the application in hand and yet not high enough to cause

FIG. 204. Sectional view of mechanical gas producer, with automatic feed and water-cooled poker.

The shell rotates. The ash pan is rotated also, by friction of the ash ; the rotation is stopped periodically in order to loosen the ash and keep it porous. Diameters : 8, 10 and 10·5 ft. inside brickwork. By courtesy of The Wellman Smith Owen Eng., Corp., Ltd.

trouble with clinker formation. It is usually considered that the optimum amount of steam for furnace heating is such that the blast is saturated between 50° and 55° C. The reactions occurring in a producer are represented diagramatically in Figs. 202 and 203; it should be stressed that the zones are not rigidly defined, the diagram showing only the predominating reactions.

A producer-gas generator consists of a vertical steel cylinder lined with firebrick; parts may be water-jacketed, or the whole cylinder may be water-jacketed instead. The fuel is introduced at the top, from which the gas is also drawn off. The fuel bed rests on a grate below which the blast enters; alternatively, and usually with furnace producers, there is really no grate and the bed rests on the ash which is gradually discharged from the bottom through a water seal. The blast inlets project into the ash, which helps to distribute the blast evenly. Most modern large producers are fully automatic (Fig. 204).

Production of metallurgical coke. Most metallurgical coke is manufactured by carbonisation at about 1000° C.–1100° C. in by-product ovens (Fig. 205). An oven consists really of a battery of ten to ninety separate ovens. Each oven is a narrow rectangular box of silica brick, 30–40 ft. long by 6–14 ft. high by 12–22 in. wide. Alternating with the ovens are heating chambers, and below are regenerators. Unlike in the old bee-hive ovens, the gas evolved from the coal during carbonisation is drawn off for use elsewhere. In modern practice, tar, ammonia compounds (as ammonium sulphate), naphthalene, benzol and toluene are recovered from the gas, and it may be purified of hydrogen sulphide before use. A proportion of the gas, about 40 per cent, may be utilised for heating the ovens; alternatively, producer or sometimes blast-furnace gas is used, depending on the conditions at the particular plant. The ovens commonly form part of the iron blast-furnace plant.

The ovens are worked in a certain sequence. They are charged from the top, and at the end of the coking period in a particular oven, which varies with its width from 12 to 24 hours, the doors at each end are opened and the hot coke is pushed out into a truck. The ovens are slightly tapered to facilitate the pushing operation. The hot coke is conveyed to the quenching station where it is quenched with water or inert gas; it is then graded.

The coal used for coking contains less volatile matter than gas-making coal but has stronger caking power (Table 29). The charge is blended with material of weaker coking properties, to suit the oven used and to produce in general a dense, hard and strong coke.

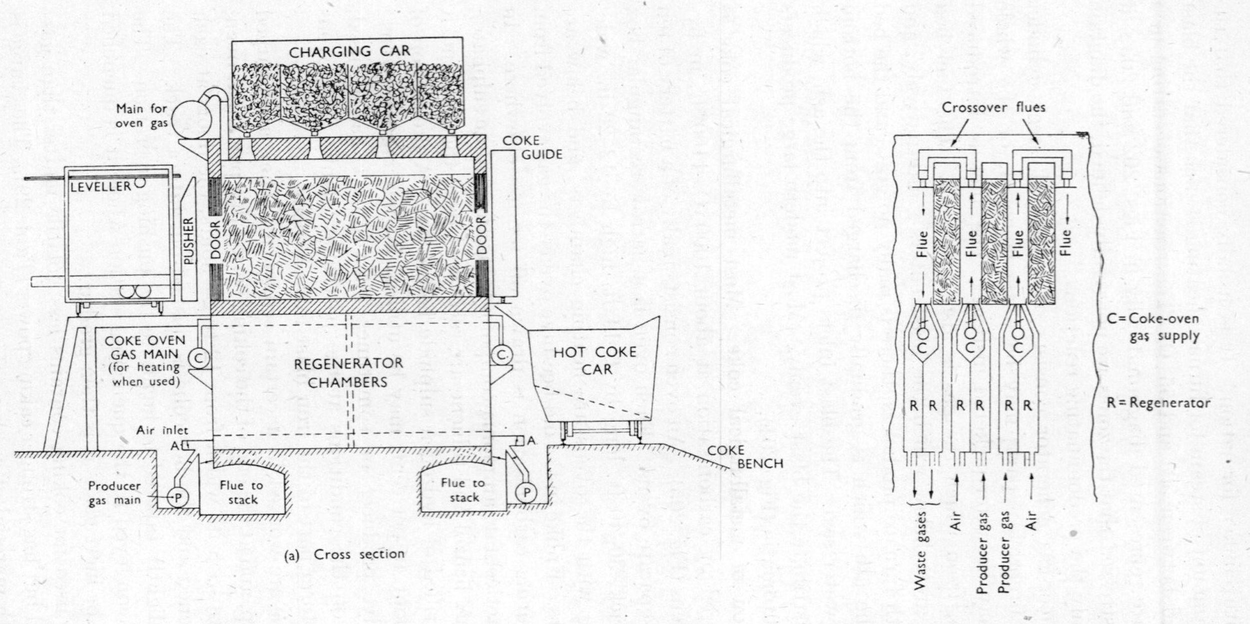

FIG. 205. Diagram of coke oven. When the ovens are fired with coke oven gas, which does not require preheating, all the regenerators are used for preheating the air.

The coal is charged in fine sizes, namely to pass about $\frac{1}{4}$ in. screen; the amount for one oven is of the order of 20 tons.

COPPER

The principal source of copper is sulphide ores; although some is obtained from oxidised and native ores. Important sulphide minerals are chalcocite (Cu_2S), chalcopyrite ($CuFeS_2$) and bornite (Cu_5FeS_4): *see also* Table 15, page 176. There are often associated gold and silver values. In addition, among other sulphides, pyrite is a common associate. Most ores treated contain from just under 1 to several per cent copper.

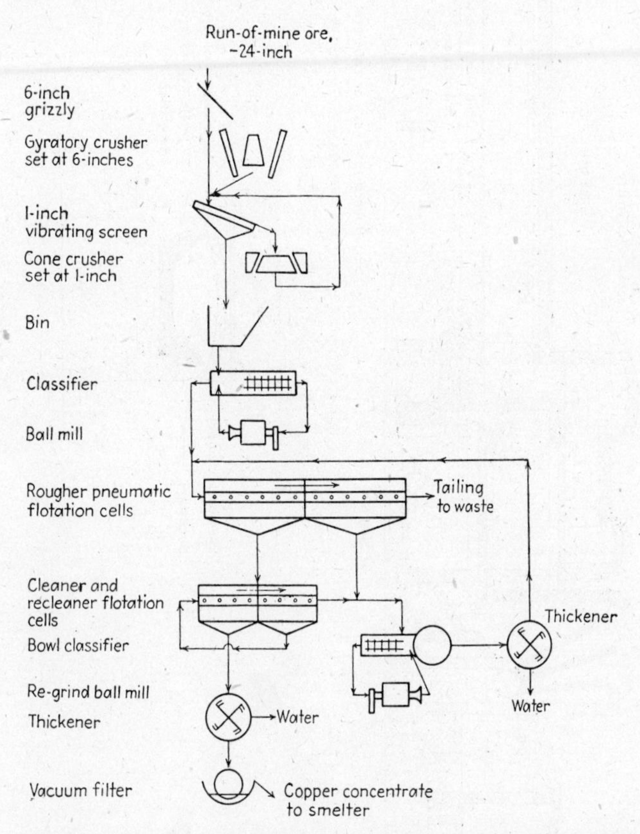

FIG. 206. Flowsheet of flotation concentration plant for copper sulphide ore. Figs. 206, 215 and 226 are from *Principles of Mineral Dressing*, by A. M. Gaudin. McGraw-Hill.

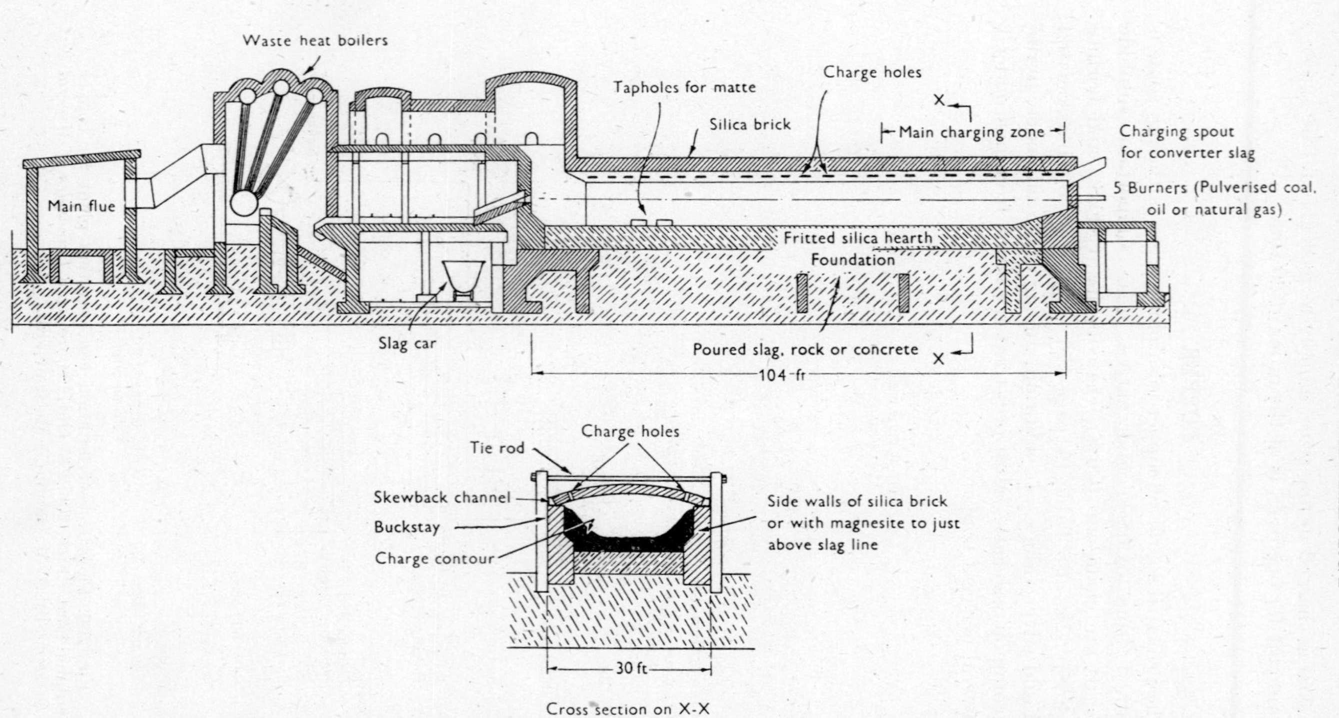

Fig. 207. Reverberatory furnace for matte-smelting copper ores. Small sliding doors are arranged along the sides.

The minimum copper content for pyrometallurgical extraction, which is the usual process, is about 6 per cent; and with this or greater amounts of copper the ores may be directly smelted. With less copper, as is usually the case, concentration is necessary and flotation is the main method (Fig. 206). If the aggregation is suitable, gravity concentration may deal with a coarse fraction. The copper contents of the concentrates range from 5 to 50 per cent and sometimes higher. Recoveries of about 80–97 per cent are made, with the tailings ranging from about 0·4 to 0·05 per cent metal.

The main method for the production of copper from sulphide ore or concentrate involves three principal stages:

(1) *matte-smelting:* concentrating the copper sulphide with some iron sulphide (and the precious metals), and removing waste as slag;

(2) *converting* the matte to crude blister copper;

(3) *refining* the blister copper by fire or electrolytic means.

(1) **Matte-smelting.** Matte-smelting (page 220) is usually carried out in large reverberatory furnaces (Figs. 207 and 208), which are especially suited for fine material as produced by flotation; modern furnaces can treat up to about 1400 tons of ore per twenty-four hours, not counting the converter slag also charged. When powdered coal is used as fuel, the consumption is about 12–18 per cent of the charge. Blast-furnaces and occasionally arc furnaces are also used. Before smelting, the ore may be roasted in multi-hearth roasters to adjust the sulphur content. Flash-smelting (p. 220) has commercial applications.

The reverberatory charge melts down, forming the matte and slag, which flow down towards the flue end of the furnace, separating into layers. Alternatively, there may be a deep molten bath in the furnace. The slag runs off continuously; the matte is tapped off

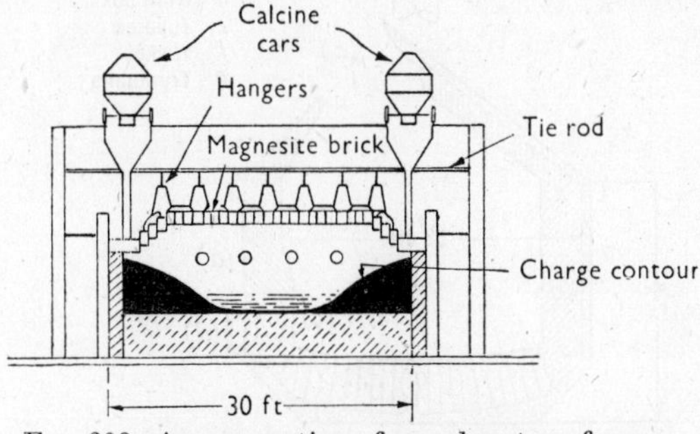

FIG. 208. A cross-section of reverberatory furnace with suspended magnesite roof.

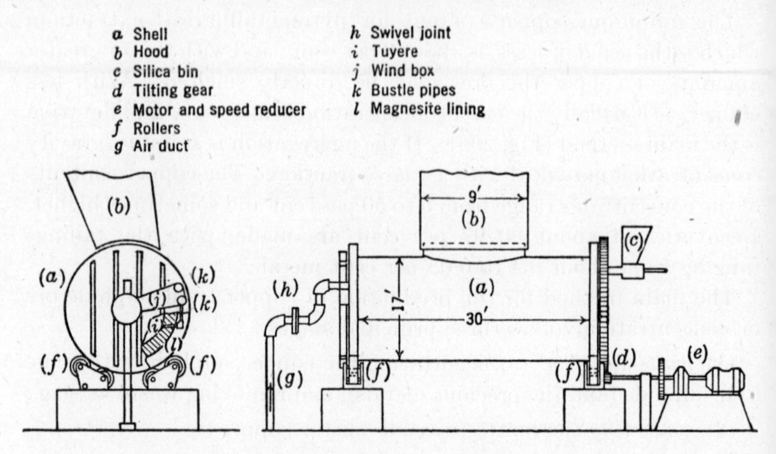

FIG. 209. Peirce-Smith converter. Figs. 209, 210, 213, 214, 224, 227 and 228 are from *Non-Ferrous Production Metallurgy*, by J. L. Bray. Wiley.

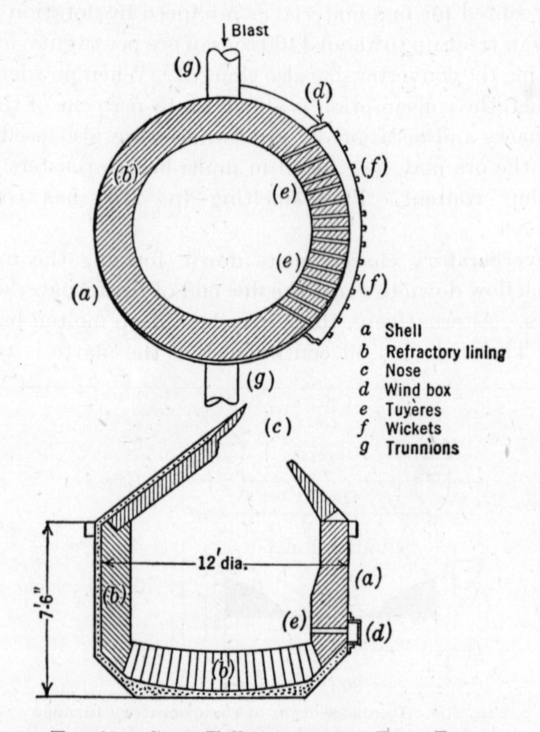

FIG. 210. Great Falls converter. From Bray.

TABLE 31. TYPICAL ANALYSES OF BLISTER COPPER AT DIFFERENT PLANTS

Per cent									oz./ton	
Cu	As	Sb	Pb	Ni	Zn	Fe	S	Se + Te	Ag	Au
[1] 98·4	0·02	0·178	0·001	0·005	0·003	0·13	0·20	not given	111·9	0·295
[1] 98·8	0·10	0·04	0·15	0·05	0·12	0·25	0·17	,,	30·25	0·31
[1] 99·5	0·035	0·015	0·001	0·04	0·002	0·03	0·06	,,	2·50	0·02
				Ni + Co						
[2] 99·2	0·004	0·004	0·005	0·025	0·002	0·025	0·151	0·20	14·0	3·10
[2] 99·2	0·005	0·006	0·013	0·025	0·002	0·044	0·023	0·025	8·50	0·05

[1] Bray. [2] Harloff and Johnson.

to a ladle or matte-car, to be conveyed to the converter as required. Various grades of matte are made, often containing between 30 and 45 per cent copper; Hayward states that the optimum is 40–45 per cent.

(2) **Converting.** Two types of converters are used, the **Peirce-Smith** and the **Great Falls**, both side-blown (Figs. 209 and 210); the former is more favoured, producing about 60–80 tons of copper per operation. The heat evolved by the reactions proceeding (page 221) is sufficient to keep the charge molten during the long time of blowing, of the order of 10 hours. So much heat is generated that often cold scrap is added at stages to cool the charge. Siliceous copper ore can be used as flux for the iron oxide; the slag formed is added to the matte smelting furnace. Generally, the procedure adopted is to blow and slag off the iron, then fill up again with matte, this being continued until the converter is full of copper sulphide ("white-metal"), which is finally blown to copper. There is some elimination of volatile impurities during blowing; the precious metals remain chiefly in the copper. The metal produced is crude, averaging about 99 per cent copper (Table 31); it is cast into fairly large cakes or is sometimes transferred molten to refining. The solidified metal is porous and brittle; it is known as **blister copper** due to the blisters of sulphur dioxide which form.

An interesting point is the removal of bismuth during blowing. Bismuth is a very undesirable element in copper even in small quantities ; it can be removed by electrolysis, but not readily in fire-refining. However, bismuth is volatilised during the iron removal stage of converting, and by using a lower grade of matte, this stage and consequently the elimination of bismuth may be extended.

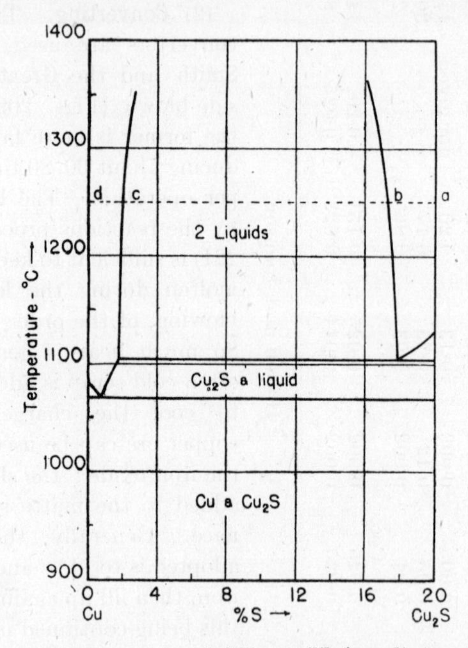

(*a*) Copper-copper sulphide equilibrium diagram.

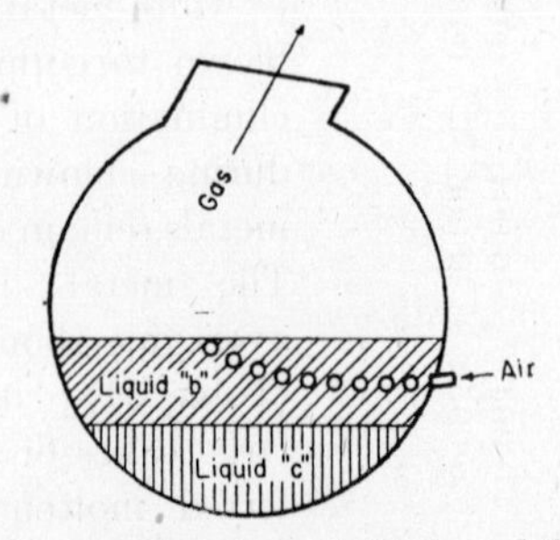

(*b*) Conditions in converter during blowing of the copper sulphide. Finally, when the converter contains only one liquid, " c ", continued blowing reduces the sulphur to " d ".

FIG. 211. Conversion of copper sulphide at 1250° C. From E. A. Peretti, Discussions of the Faraday Soc., No. 4, 181.

This practice has made possible the production of high-grade copper (<0·0025 per cent bismuth) by fire-refining from certain Rhodesian ores, the metal from which would otherwise contain undesirably high amounts of bismuth (0·005–0·01 per cent).

In a recent analysis of copper converting, Peretti has explained the failure of bottom blowing. Taking the white metal as simply copper and sulphur, and referring to the Cu/Cu_2S equilibrium diagram (Fig. 211), at 1250° C. for example, he points out that after some elimination of sulphur two liquids exist. The heavier copper-rich liquid, composition *c*, will settle to the bottom, and continued conversion of the sulphur-rich liquid, composition *b*, in a bottom-blown converter would depend on diffusion (of sulphur he suggests) through the copper-rich liquid. Because of the slowness of the diffusion, heat is not generated sufficiently rapidly to keep the material molten and the tuyères become blocked.

(3) **Refining.** There are two main procedures: (*a*) the blister copper is fire-refined and cast to ingots for working or remelting; (*b*) the blister is given a preliminary fire-refine, cast into anodes, electrolysed, and finally the cathodes are melted, undergoing the fire-refining sequence again, and cast. The latter procedure deals with the majority of the world's copper production.

The factors affecting the choice of refining process are the purity required and that of the blister, and in particular the precious metal content. Precious metals are not recovered in fire-refining, and elimination of certain other elements is poor (Table 33), whereas these elements are separated by electrolytic refining. When reasonable amounts of precious metals are present, their recovery will more than compensate for the increased cost involved by using electrolytic refining. Purity is especially important in copper with respect to the effect on conductivity (Fig. 212). Further, certain impurities, notably bismuth, lead, selenium and tellurium, adversely affect the workability of copper.

Fire-refining of copper. This is carried out largely in reverberatory furnaces of the fixed kind with capacities up to 400 tons, although rotating furnaces are also used. The full operation is arranged in a 24-hour cycle from the start of the charging period to the end of casting (Table 32). Scrap is often included in the charge.

TABLE 32. OPERATIONS IN 24-HOUR CYCLE OF FIRE-REFINING COPPER (Miller)

Charging 1–3 hours.
Melting 8–11 hours.
Oxidising and skimming 3–5 hours.
Poling 2–3 hours.
Casting 4–9 hours.

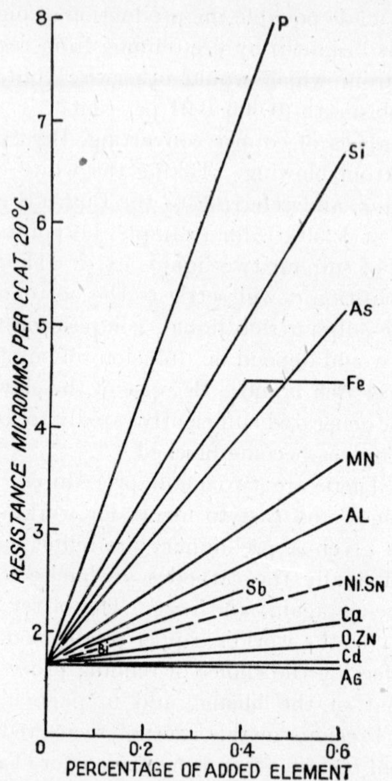

FIG. 212. Effect of various elements on electrical resistivity of copper. From *Metals,* by (Sir) H. Carpenter and J. M. Robertson, Oxford Univ. Press.

The metal is melted down and then oxidised by blowing compressed air through steel pipes inserted in the molten bath. Oxidation is aided by opening the furnace doors and by flapping the surface of the copper with rakes. A certain amount of oxidation also occurs during melting. Some of the impurities are preferentially oxidised and rise out of the copper to form a slag with the flux, generally silica, although lime, nitre and soda ash are also used; there is also some volatilisation of impurities (Table 33). The slag is skimmed off at intervals; the copper content of the slag is high and it is sold as a secondary source or returned to the smelting furnaces. Oxidation is continued until the copper is considerably oxidised, up to about 0·9 per cent oxygen (Fig. 388, p. 507). The end of this stage can be judged by microscopic examination and the appearance of the top surface of a cast sample or of a fractured surface.

TABLE 33. REMOVAL OF IMPURITIES IN FIRE-REFINING COPPER (Miller)

Element	*Observations on Removal*
Sulphur	Eliminated by volatilisation.
Cadmium	Eliminated chiefly by volatilisation.
Zinc	Eliminated partly by volatilisation and partly in slags.
Magnesium	Wholly eliminated in slag.
Aluminium	Wholly eliminated in slag.
Iron	Wholly eliminated in slag.
Tin	Wholly eliminated in soda ash–sodium nitrate slag.
Lead	Tends to be eliminated in slag but cannot be completely eliminated except by excessive slagging with the aid of silica sand.
Arsenic	Wholly eliminated by soda ash and lime slags, otherwise not appreciably reduced.[1]
Antimony	Almost entirely eliminated by soda ash and lime slags, otherwise not perceptibly reduced.[1]
Selenium	Not removed.[2]
Tellurium	Not removed.[2]
Bismuth	Not removed.
Nickel	Not removed.
Cobalt	Not removed.
Silver	Not removed.
Gold	Not removed.

Note 1: Soda ash treatment to remove arsenic and antimony is best carried out after normal slagging; to reduce the harmful effects of soda ash on the furnace refractories lime is added to the slag and it is removed as quickly as possible.

Note 2: Selenium and tellurium can be considerably reduced by the use of fluxes consisting of soda ash, lime and coal (J. B. Nielson); the practical difficulties appertaining to the maintenance of reducing atmospheres are such that removal is not attempted in industry.

When the oxidation is finished, the bath is skimmed and good-grade coke thrown on the surface. The metal is then vigorously deoxidised by " poling " with green tree trunks, which are pushed below the surface. The reducing gases and moisture evolved spray the copper violently in the furnace, which action assists the reduction. It is only practical to reduce the oxygen to about 0·03–0·05 per cent, otherwise the hydrogen content becomes excessive (pp. 379–380), and in this form the copper is cast into ingots, the metal being referred to as **tough-pitch copper** (Table 36). On solidification the hydrogen present and some of the cuprous oxide react yielding steam; sufficient of this is entrapped as bubbles in the metal, mainly in the top central portion, to compensate for the piping, and the casting has a level top surface. With overpoling, the hydrogen content becomes very high and more steam is evolved, causing a raised convex top.

On the other hand, in the heavily oxidised condition, the top surface is depressed because there is little hydrogen to form steam. The tough-pitch condition has been found most satisfactory for working; the holes formed by the steam do not have oxidised surfaces and they are closed and heal up. Tough-pitch copper is not suitable for final castings.

When the copper is to be used for electrical purposes, conductivity tests may be carried out before casting on samples which are hot-rolled and drawn.

For shapes required in large numbers, such as wire-bars for rolling into wire rod, the ingot moulds are arranged on a continuous casting machine (Figs. 267-269, p. 366). The moulds are usually made of tough-pitch copper, dressed with bone-ash wash.

Electrolytic refining. Blister copper is not very suitable for casting directly into anodes, and hence it is usually given preliminary fire-refining as described above. Similar reverberatories are used, although it is stated that in a Rhodesian plant the anode metal is prepared in a 250-ton rotary furnace. Such furnaces are used in a number of plants as "holding" furnaces for blister copper.

The refined blister is cast into anodes, weighing around five hundred pounds, on continuous casting wheels as used for other shapes. Typical anode analyses are given below in Table 34:

TABLE 34. COPPER ANODE ANALYSES

Element	Per cent		
Copper	99·75[1]	99·25[2]	99·41[3]
Bismuth	0·0045	0·003	not given
Cobalt	0·0060	not given	not given
Nickel	0·0154	0·050	0·0293
Iron	0·0050	0·058	0·0065
Arsenic	0·0011	0·060	0·0024
Antimony	0·0002	0·022	0·0023
Selenium	0·0141	0·048	0·264 (Selenium and Tellurium together)
Tellurium	0·0019	0·038	
Lead	not given	0·053	0·0016
Sulphur	not given	0·004	0·0140
Silver	not given	30 oz./ton	17·09 oz./ton
Gold	not given	0·40 oz./ton	8·058 oz./ton
Oxygen	not given	0·100	not given

[1] Friggens and Milligan, typical for Rhodesia Copper Refineries Ltd., Nkana, N. Rhodesia.

Note: This is a very pure copper and electrolytic refining is primarily carried out for bismuth removal, precious metal recovery being a secondary consideration.

[2] Burns, [3] McKnight — American plants.

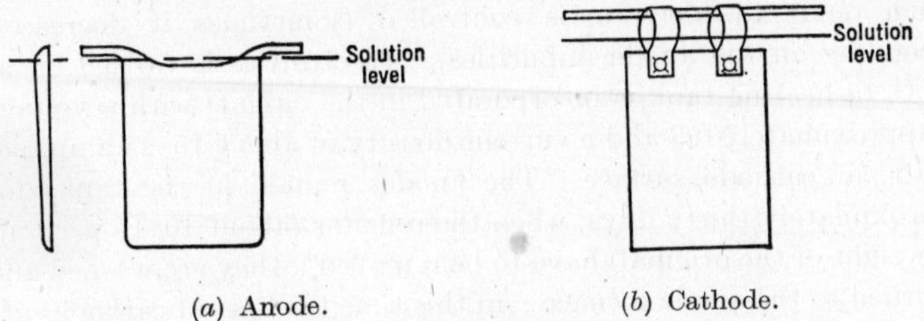

(*a*) Anode. (*b*) Cathode.

FIG. 213. Typical electrode shapes for copper. From Bray.

The most important electrolytic technique for copper is the multiple process, in which the electrodes are arranged in parallel, the thin cathode starting-sheets being of electro-deposited copper (Figs. 213 and 214). The tanks (for example 10 ft. × $3\frac{1}{2}$ ft. × $3\frac{1}{2}$ ft.) are made of concrete or wood and lined with lead containing about 6 per cent antimony. In each tank there are about thirty anodes with one more cathode. The tanks are arranged in groups connected in series to form a unit to suit the generator voltage. The electrolyte is circulated through the tanks at about 3–6 gall./min. by pumping, or by arranging the tanks at different levels. The acid copper sulphate electrolyte contains about 3–4 and 10–15 per cent, respectively, of copper and free sulphuric acid ; regular small additions of glue and hydrochloric acid are made and sufficient sulphuric acid to compensate for that combining with impurities. Portions of the electrolyte are withdrawn at set intervals for purification, so that the overall content of soluble impurities, such as arsenic, nickel and iron, is kept at a reasonable figure ; in the same way the copper content,

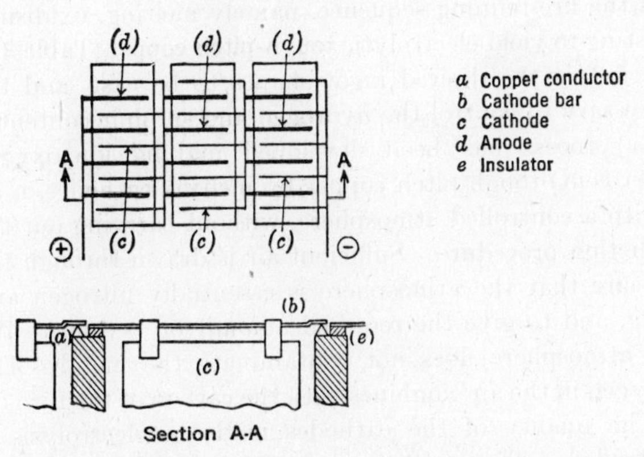

FIG. 214. Electrical connections in multiple process for copper. From Bray.

which tends to increase, is controlled (sometimes it decreases, depending on the anode impurities). Electrolysis is carried on at 50° C. (a heating tank is incorporated in the circuit) with a voltage of approximately 0·3 and a current density of about 15–25 amp. per sq. ft. of cathode surface. The anodes remain in the tanks for approximately thirty days, when the remains (about 10–15 per cent by weight of the original) have to be removed ; they are washed and returned to the anode furnace ; in this time two sets of cathodes are usually made. The anode slimes comprising from a half to a few per cent of the anode weight are periodically removed and worked up principally for the precious metals.

A typical cathode analysis is given in Table 35.

TABLE 35

Element	*Per cent*
Copper	99·9800[1]
Sulphur	0·0003
Iron	0·0009
Bismuth	0·0002
Cobalt	0·0001
Nickel	0·0005
Selenium	0·0006
Tellurium	0·0001
Arsenic	0·0002
Antimony	0·0001

[1] Friggens and Milligan. Figures correspond with those in Table 34, page 282, for the Rhodesia Copper Refineries Ltd., plant at Nkana, N. Rhodesia.

Cathodes may be sold directly for alloying and foundry purposes ; but more generally the washed cathodes undergo final treatment which follows the fire-refining sequence, namely melting, oxidising, poling and casting to yield electrolytic **tough-pitch copper** (Table 36). The melting enables the desired ingot shapes to be cast, and the refining is necessary to control the hydrogen and sulphur contents.

However, a process has been developed making low-oxygen (about 0·01 per cent) tough-pitch copper by melting cathodes in an arc furnace with a controlled atmosphere, without carrying out the oxidation-reduction procedure. Sufficient air is drawn through the furnace to ensure that the atmosphere is essentially nitrogen and carbon dioxide, and to give the required amount of oxygen to the copper ; this atmosphere does not contaminate the metal. The bulk of the oxygen in the air combines with the carbon of the furnace electrodes. The quality of the cathodes made in electrolysis is carefully controlled. The condition of a flowing and regulated atmosphere in melting promotes satisfactory removal of hydrogen and any sulphur present in the metal. The molten metal is led from the furnace to the casting ladle via a sealed launder and pour-hearth, where final adjustments of oxygen-content are made ; oxygen can be increased by admitting air to the launder, and reduced with charcoal or even slight poling in the hearth. The metal in the pouring ladle is covered with charcoal and in the hearth with graphite granules. This process, used at a large Canadian plant, has been described by Waddington (*see also* (3), p. 286).

Ultra-refining of copper may be obtained by vacuum melting and casting.

The bulk of worked copper is tough-pitch, and for most purposes this is satisfactory. The oxygen present, mainly as insoluble cuprous oxide, has little effect on working and mechanical properties, or on the electrical conductivity.

In certain cases the oxygen is undesirable. For example, in hot reducing atmospheres containing hydrogen, " gassing " may occur ; atomic hydrogen diffuses into the hot copper and reacts with the oxide forming steam, which being molecular cannot diffuse. The pressure of the steam may build up sufficiently to rupture the metal, cracking and embrittlement resulting ; the cracks are mainly intercrystalline, due presumably to the grain boundaries being weaker than the bodies at elevated temperatures. In welding

TABLE 36. TYPICAL ANALYSES (PER CENT) OF TOUGH-PITCH COPPER

Element	Electrolytic		High-grade fire-refined
Copper*	99·960[1]	99·94–99·97[2]	99·93
Sulphur	0·0016	0·0020	not given
Oxygen	0·030	0·02–0·05	0·047
Bismuth	0·0002	not given	0·0018
Iron	0·0016	0·0025	0·002
Selenium	0·0006	not given	0·005
Tellurium	0·0001	not given	0·001
Nickel	0·0005	0·0015	0·007
Cobalt	0·0001	not given	not given
Arsenic	0·0002	0·0015	0·001
Antimony	0·0001	0·0015	0·0005
Lead	0·0001	not given	0·0001

[1] Corresponds with ref. 1 in Tables 34 and 35.
[2] Corresponds with ref. 2 in Table 34.
* Standard specifications usually state 99·90 per cent minimum for the electrolytic coppers and also for the high-conductivity grade of fire-refined tough-pitch copper.

tough-pitch copper, severe porosity results due to evolution of steam.

Oxygen-free copper, in which negligible amounts of oxygen are present, may be prepared in the following ways :

(1) By deoxidation of oxygen-bearing copper with elements such as phosphorus having greater affinity for oxygen than has copper. Conductivity is impaired by the small excess of the deoxidant remaining. Thus with phosphorus, the residual is about 0·02–0·06 per cent ; this is in solid solution in the copper and markedly reduces conductivity.

There are numerous elements with considerably greater affinity than copper for oxygen, such as barium, boron, calcium, silicon and lithium, which alloyed with the copper cause less reduction in conductivity than phosphorus (Fig. 212). Various claims are made for their efficiency as deoxidants and apparently some are used in the industry. However, phosphorus in the form of phosphor-copper is extremely efficient and easy to use, and is still the most common ordinary deoxidant for copper, and is almost universal for tin-bronze (or as phosphor-tin in this case).

(2) Electrolytic tough-pitch copper is deoxidised with carbon and cast in an atmosphere of nitrogen and carbon monoxide. Carbon is virtually insoluble in copper.

(3) Cathodes are melted in an induction furnace under a carbon covering in an atmosphere of nitrogen and carbon monoxide, and then cast in the same atmosphere. This is a more recent practice than (2).

(4) Brittle cathodes are made by electrolysis ; these are crushed, washed and dried. The particles are pressed together to a round billet-shape, heated and extruded in a suitable controlled atmosphere ; the product is known as **coalesced copper.**

Methods 2–4 do not impair conductivity. The metal produced by methods (2) and (3) is known as **oxygen-free high-conductivity (O.F.H.C.) copper.**

Pure copper is not favoured for foundry castings, except where electrical or thermal conductivity is important ; an example of its application is for tuyères in the iron blast-furnace. The tough-pitch condition is not satisfactory ; complete deoxidation is necessary. The best practice is to melt the tough-pitch copper under an oxidising flux and deoxidise before casting. Phosphorus is usual for deoxidation, although the other agents mentioned above may be used. Degassing by bubbling nitrogen through the melt for about five minutes leads to sounder castings.

ZINC

The main source of zinc (sometimes referred to as *spelter*) is the sulphide, sphalerite or zinc blende (ZnS) ; sulphides of copper, iron, cadmium and lead are common base associates and in some cases there may be precious metals ; the lead sulphide is often present in worthwhile amounts. Many of the ores fall in the range 2–10 per cent zinc.

There are two main methods of extraction, namely : (1) roasting to oxide, followed by thermal reduction with carbon at about 1100° C., when the metal distils off as a vapour ; and (2) roasting to a mixture of oxide and sulphate, followed by leaching in sulphuric

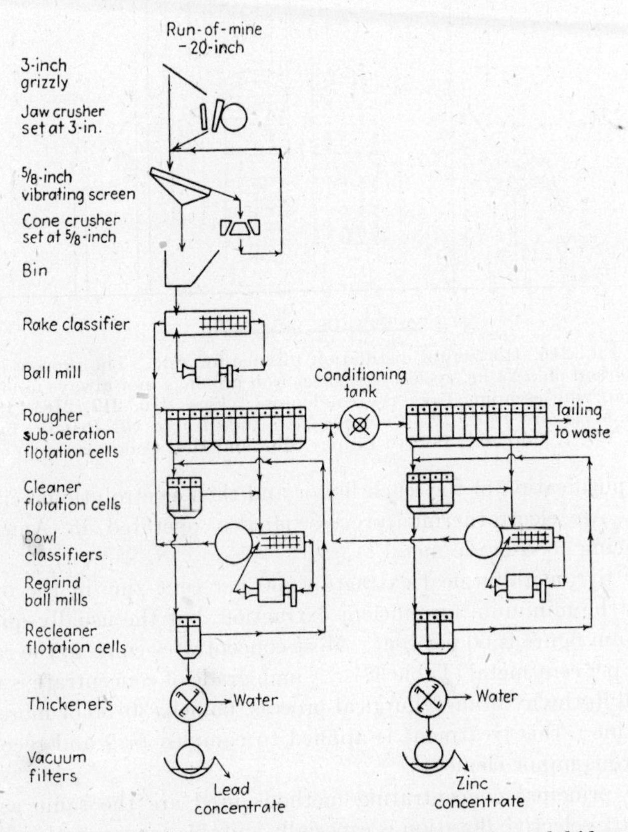

Fig. 215. Flowsheet for the concentration of lead-zinc sulphide ore by selective flotation. From Gaudin.

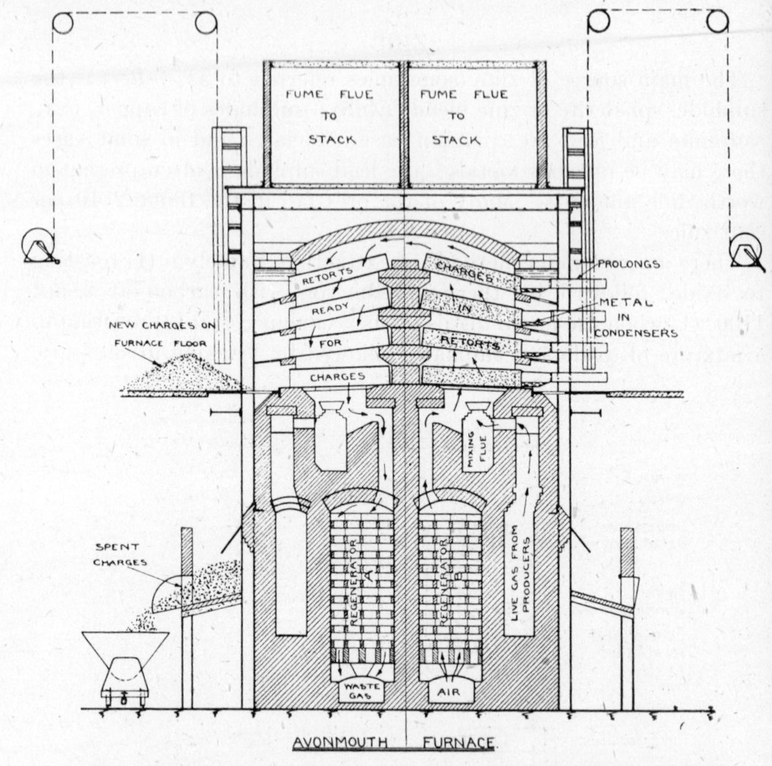

Fig. 216. Horizontal distillation furnace for zinc. The process is worked on a 24-hr. cycle. The sheet-iron prolongs (not always used) trap zinc escaping from the condensers. Figs. 216, 217, 218, 219 and 221 are from *The Zinc Smelting Industry in Gt. Britain*, by S. W. K. Morgan. Fourth Empire Min. and Met. Congress.

acid, purification of the leach liquor and then electrolytic precipitation. An electrothermic process is also operated in America, producing good-grade metal.

For pyrometallurgical extraction, 30 per cent zinc in the ore is about the minimum for efficient extraction, but the usually quoted optimum figure is 60 per cent. Most concentrates come in the range 50–65 per cent metal (Table 37). A high grade of concentrate is used as well in the hydrometallurgical process, namely 30–50 or more per cent zinc ; this treatment is applied to complex ores and recovers numerous minor elements.

The principal concentrating methods used are the same as for copper ; selective flotation is especially suitable for separating other sulphides and for making a separate galena concentrate (Fig. 215).

In addition, sink-and-float has been applied (Fig. 223). Magnetic treatment, although used on zinc minerals, is not employed on ore for metal production ; except in one leaching process, after roasting, a zinc ferrite is removed magnetically for separate treatment.

Distillation processes. These are still the most important method of production.

A special type of multi-hearth roasting furnace may be used for zinc ores, although modern practice is to use the Dwight-Lloyd type of sintering machine. As little sulphur as possible should be left in the ore, as this causes losses in retorting. At the plants in Great Britain five-sixths of the sintering charge is re-cycled sinter.

Two kinds of retorts are used, the old hand-worked intermittent horizontal retorts (Fig. 216 and 217), and the modern continuous

FIG. 217. Inside view showing retorts in position in the horizontal furnace. From Morgan.

The retorts are round or oval in section, about 9 in. internal diameter and 4·5–5·5 ft. long. They are made of fireclay or of silicon carbide and clay. The condensers are also of fireclay.

TABLE 37. TYPICAL COMPOSITIONS (PER CENT) OF ORE AND PRODUCTS AT THE AVONMOUTH PLANT OF THE NATIONAL SMELTING COMPANY

Material	Zn	S	Fe	SiO_2	CaO	Cd	Cu	Pb
Average value of imported concentrates - -	49–58	28–32	3·5–10	0·5–2·1	0·01–0·55	0·10–0·25	0·08–1·0	not given
Approximate composition of sintered concentrate - Zn originally 52% S ,, 30% Fe ,, 8·0% Pb ,, 2·0%	62·5	0·5–0·75	9·5					
Horizontal retort metal -	98·4		0·05			0·1		1·25
Vertical retort metal - -	99·7		0·01			0·05		0·2

vertical retorts (Fig. 218 and 219), both being heated by producer gas, or natural gas for the horizontal retorts when available.

In the horizontal process, the charge consists of roasted (or oxidised) ore mixed with about 40–60 per cent of reducing matter such as anthracite, or a mixture of anthracite with non-coking bituminous coal or coke. In the vertical process, briquettes (4 in. long) are made of the mixture named in Table 38, after thorough grinding and mixing. The briquettes are first coked at about 800° C. before being transferred hot to the retorts

TABLE 38. MIXTURE FOR BRIQUETTES (Morgan)

Sinter	52 per cent
Bituminous (coking) coal	26 per cent
Anthracite	8 per cent
Returned briquette fines	10 per cent
Clay	4 per cent

and a little sulphite lye are used as binders.

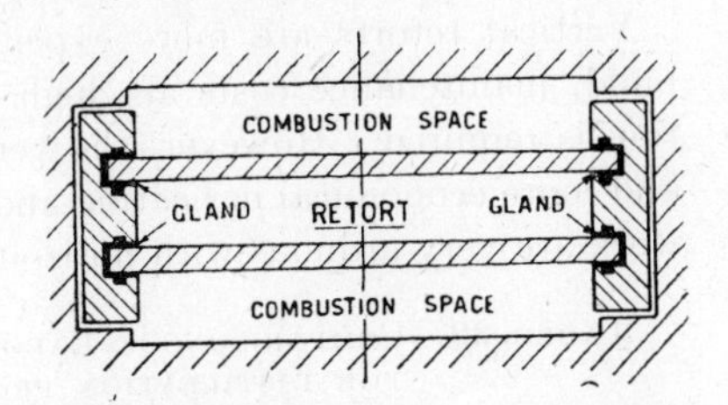

FIG. 218. Horizontal section of vertical retort (made of silicon carbide). Internal dimensions are 7·25 ft. × 1 ft. The retort is 40 ft. high, the lower 28 ft. being heated. From Morgan.

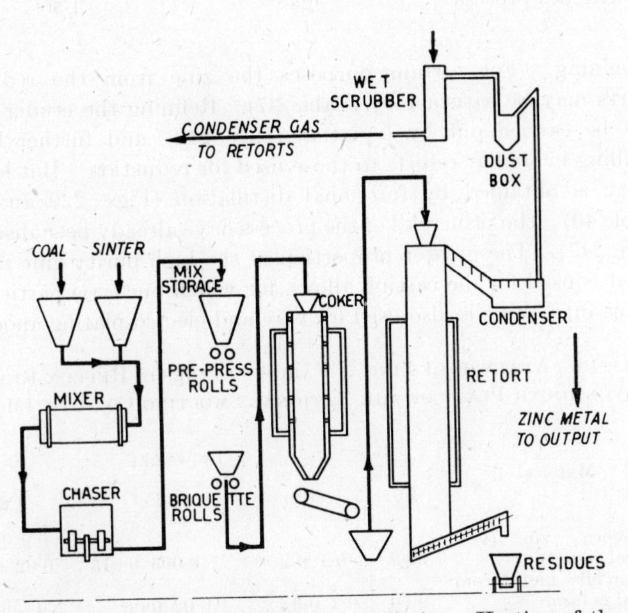

FIG. 219. Flowsheet of vertical retort distillation. Heating of the retort furnace is mainly by producer gas fed direct from the generators, but 20 per cent of the heat is due to the returned condenser gas. The air is preheated by recuperation ; the still hot gases from the latter are then used to coke the briquettes, finally passing to waste-heat boilers. From Morgan.

The material obtained in the prolongs of the horizontal retorts is a dust (known as *blue-powder*) of zinc particles coated with oxide due to oxidation by carbon-monoxide or -dioxide on cooling. Careful control is necessary to minimise this action.

It is stated that the function of the top unheated portion of the vertical retort is to allow some condensation of lead, and to control the carbon dioxide content of the gases.

Vertical retorts are more expensive than horizontal retorts to build, maintenance costs are high and expensive charge preparation is required. However, the vertical process is more consistent and more economical in heating and labour. Further, conditions of work are very arduous with horizontal retorts.

TABLE 39. COMPARISON OF LABOUR AND FUEL REQUIREMENTS FOR DISTILLATION PROCESSES (Morgan)

	Operating man-hours per ton of zinc	Producer coal per ton of zinc
Vertical process -	11	0·64
Horizontal process -	28	1·50

Refining. For certain purposes the zinc from the reduction retorts may be satisfactory (Table 37). Refining the cruder metal may be carried out by liquation (page 242), and further by re-distilling in similar retorts to those used for reduction. But highest purity is obtained by fractional distillation (Figs. 220 and 221) (Table 40); the principles of the process have already been discussed (page 247). The greater proportion of the high-purity zinc so produced is used for die-casting alloys, for which purity is particularly important; some is also used for wire and electro-plating anodes.

TABLE 40. ANALYSIS OF ZINC AT VARIOUS STAGES IN REFLUX REFINING AT AVONMOUTH PLANT OF THE NATIONAL SMELTING CO., LTD. (Morgan)

Material	% by weight			
	Zn	Pb	Fe	Cd
"Severn" zinc (vertical retort) - -	99·7	0·1–0·2	0·005–0·015	0·02–0·08
"Run off" metal from lead column - -	99·0	0·4–0·9	0·02–0·06	Nil
Feed to lead column	99·5	0·15–0·4	0·008–0·03	0·015–0·065
Feed to cadmium column - - -	99·88	<0·003	<0·003	0·03–0·11
"Crown Special" zinc	99·99	0·0005–0·003	0·0005–0·003	0·001–0·003

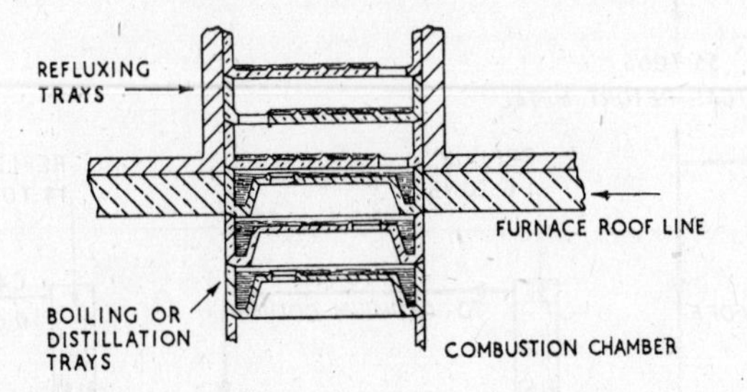

Details of the silicon carbide trays (42 in. × 21 in.) in the column

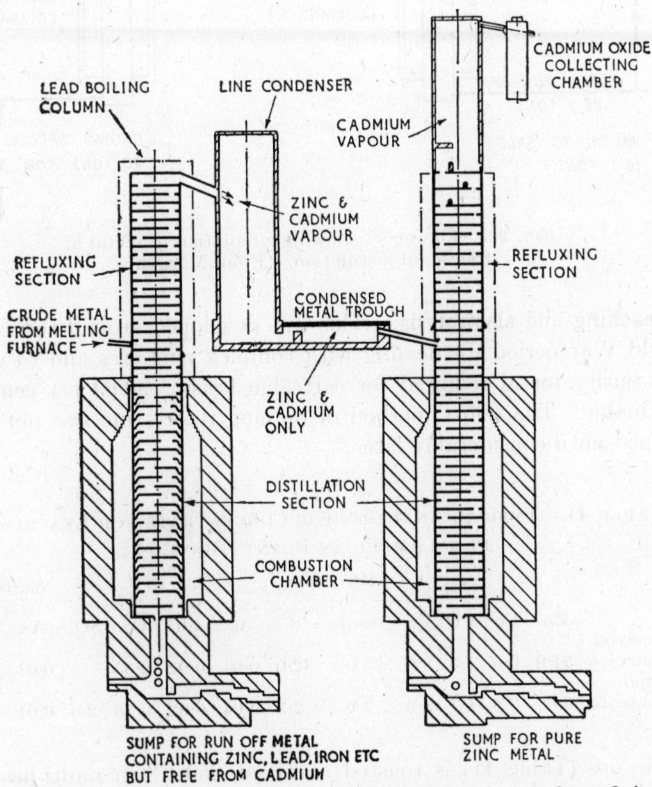

FIG. 220. Diagram of fractional distillation columns for refining zinc (for theoretical details see page 247). Producer gas is used for heating; the air is preheated by recuperation From S. Robson, *The Refining of Non-Ferrous Metals,* Inst. Min. Met., 1950, 337.

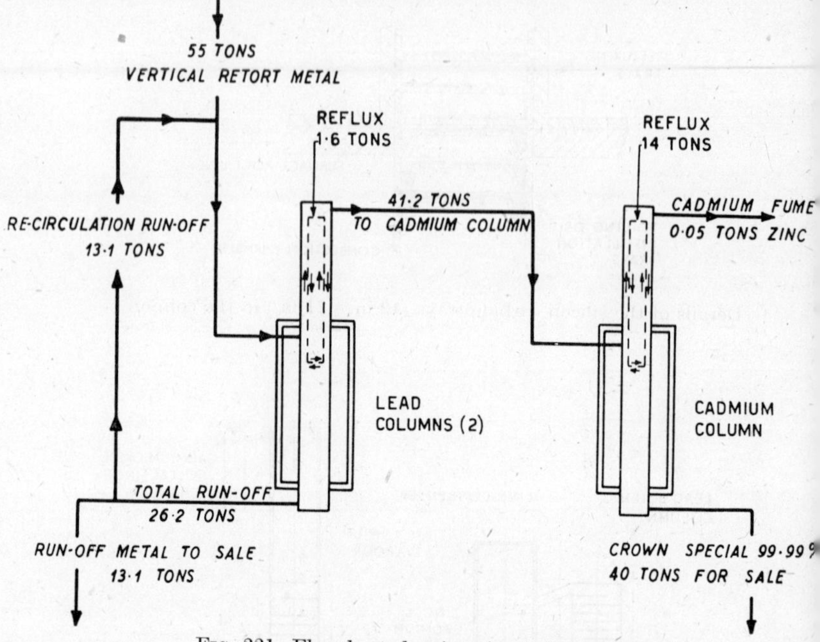

FIG. 221. Flowsheet showing circulation of metal in fractional distillation. From Morgan.

Leaching and electrolysis. This was developed around the First World War period for dealing with complex zinc ores and to give high-purity metal required for cartridge brass; 99·99 per cent is obtainable. The reflux method of refining retort zinc was not developed until considerably later.

TABLE 41. TYPICAL ANALYSES FOR CONCENTRATE FOR LEACHING IN AN AMERICAN PLANT (Bray)

	Percentage										oz./ton	
	Zn	Cu	Pb	Fe	Insol.	S	As	Sb	Cd	SO_4	Au	Ag
As received concentrate	54·0	0·5	1·5	8·0	3·0	32·0	0·04	0·02	0·35		0·01	4·0
Roasted concentrate	60·0	0·5	1·7	8·9	3·6	2·3	0·04	0·02	0·38	2·0	0·01	4·4

The ore (Table 41) is roasted at about 650° C. in multi-hearth furnaces to give a mixture of oxide and a small amount of sulphate to suit the acid requirements of the leaching. High roasting temperatures increase the formation of zinc ferrite ($ZnO . Fe_2O_3$), which is difficult to dissolve. Sintering does not appear to be satisfactory for the ore in the case of leaching; flash roasting has been satisfactorily developed at Trail, B.C.; the output of roasted material and concentration of sulphur dioxide in the gases have been increased by using by-product oxygen to enrich the air to 23 per cent oxygen, and the possibility of using greater enrichment is being considered.

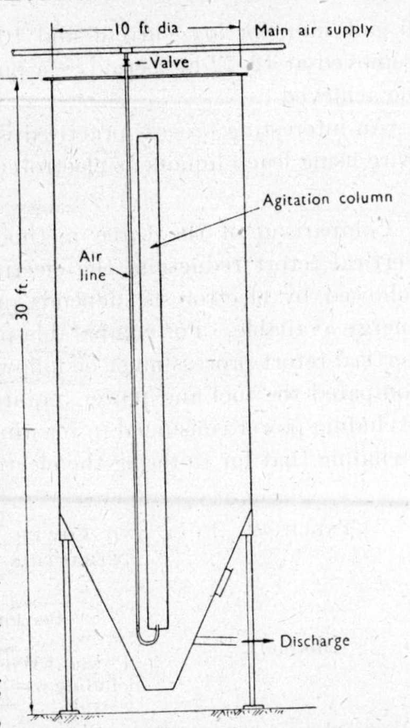

FIG. 222. Pachuca tank for leaching zinc ores.

Leaching with diluted sulphuric acid is carried out in **Pachuca tanks** (Fig. 222). There are various procedures, but they have in common the elimination at some stage of the co-dissolved elements by neutralising the leach liquor with excess ore, giving a zinc oxide separation; and later by precipitation with zinc dust. A very pure electrolyte is necessary for satisfactory electrolysis. The residues and precipitates are worked up for the various elements.

Lead (or lead alloy) anodes are used in the electrolysis, the zinc being deposited on aluminium cathodes from which it can be stripped. The electrodes are arranged in parallel; with the high current density twice as many anodes as cathodes are used, and the anodes are perforated, among other things to allow free circulation. The voltage is about 3·5, and the current densities range from 25 to 100 amp. per sq. ft. of cathode. The zinc and free sulphuric acid in the electrolyte increase with the current density. Using 100 amp. per sq. ft., the free acid is 22–28 per cent; when it has built up to the latter figure, a portion is returned to the leaching plant, being replaced with neutralised leach liquor. The corresponding zinc contents are about 200 and 50 gm./litre, respectively. The electrolyte is heated by the high current and the temperature is kept to about 40° C. by cooling coils; high temperature magnifies the bad effect of impurities in the electrolyte. Typical circulation rates are

6 gall./min. for low current and 10 for high current. The zinc is removed at 12–72 hr. periods ; a purity of over 99·99 per cent can be achieved.

An interesting process practised is the electro-galvanising of steel wire using leach liquors as electrolyte.

Comparison of the three methods of extracting zinc, namely, vertical retort reduction, the electrothermic method and leaching followed by electrolysis, depends on the ore in question and the energy available. For comparable purity with electrolytic zinc, the vertical retort process must be followed by reflux refining. Hey has compared the fuel and power requirements for the three processes, excluding power consumed in roasting and in acid manufacture, but including that for sintering the electro-thermic feed (*see* Table 42).

TABLE 42. FUEL AND POWER REQUIREMENTS FOR ZINC EXTRACTION (Hey)

Method	Per long ton of slab zinc for sale	
	Power (kWh.A.C.) including mechanical	Fuel (tons) for heating and reduction
Vertical retort	190	2·2 Coal and coke (special coal is required)
Electrothermic	3,300	0·8 Coke
Electrolytic	4,150	0·05 Oil (for melting)

Hey points out the difficulty of comparing capital and labour costs, but generalises as follows. From recent estimates for a plant in Australia, it appears that electrolytic and vertical retort plants have similar capital costs ; he says that the cost of an electrothermic plant is likely to be lower. With regard to labour costs, for small plants these are probably highest for the electrolytic process, the difference, however, decreasing with increase in the size of the plant.

LEAD

The principal economic mineral is galena (PbS). Many present-day ores range from about 3 to 10 per cent lead ; but lower grades, even less than 1 per cent, are worked, and there are grades richer than 10 per cent. The ores often contain worthwhile amounts of sphalerite (ZnS); pyrites and copper sulphides, and gold and silver are common associates. The very minimum for thermal extraction is about 10 per cent lead; but actually in modern practice much higher values are demanded. Therefore the ores are usually concentrated.

Concentration methods are similar to those for copper and zinc, namely, flotation, sometimes in conjunction with gravity methods, depending on the ore; flotation is especially useful for separating zinc sulphide (Figs. 215 and 223). Concentrates are often in the range 60–80 per cent lead; recoveries may be as high as 98 per cent.

The main method of extraction consists of smelting with coke (8–13 per cent of charge) and flux in blast-furnaces of rectangular cross-section (Fig. 224), after roasting to oxide. Experiments with oxygen-enriched air blasts in lead blast-furnaces indicate, according to Kirkpatrick, saving in fuel, steadier operation and increased capacity. Roasting is done in Dwight-Lloyd sintering machines, at the same

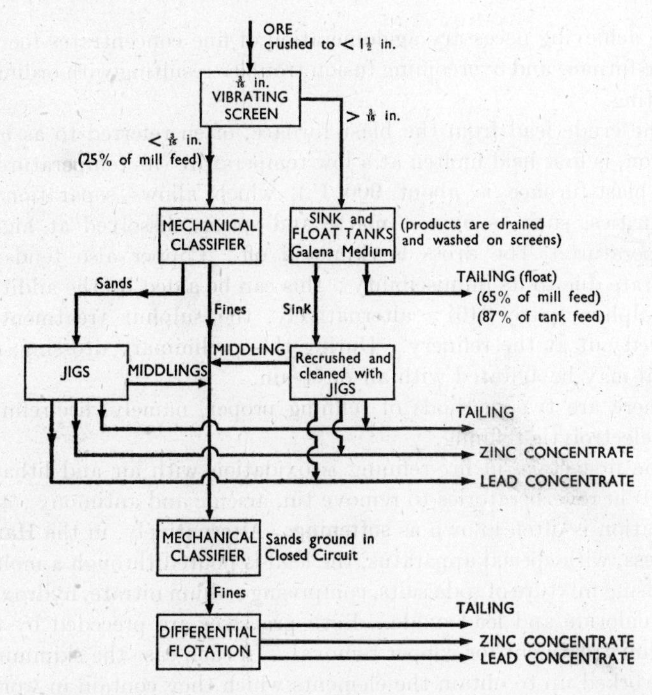

FIG. 223. Flowsheet of concentration plant for lead-zinc sulphide ore utilising jigs and differential flotation, and sink and float for removal of coarse waste.

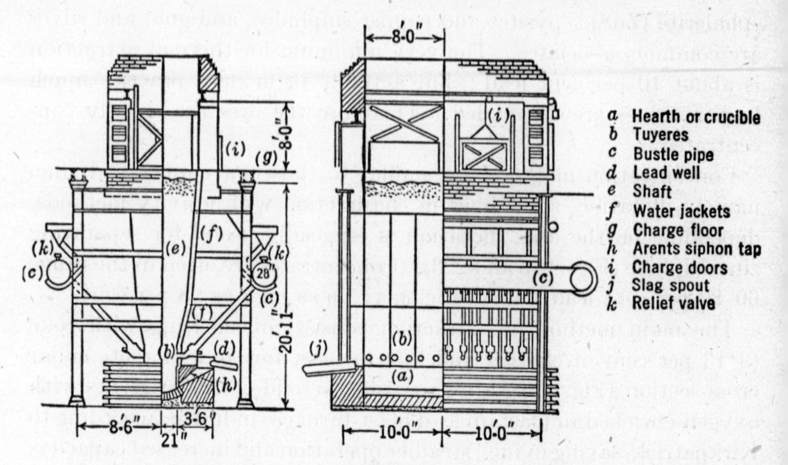

FIG. 224. Blast-furnace for smelting lead ores. Note the siphon method for tapping the lead. From Bray.

time achieving necessary agglomeration of fine concentrates for the blast-furnace and overcoming fusion troubles resulting with ordinary roasting.

The crude lead from the blast furnace, often referred to as **base bullion,** is first held molten at a low temperature (its temperature in the blast-furnace is about 900° C.), which allows separation of impurities, such as oxides, matte and speise, dissolved at higher temperature. The dross is skimmed off. Copper also tends to separate due to its immiscibility ; this can be aided by the addition of sulphur (page 246) ; alternatively, the sulphur treatment is carried out at the refinery. During this preliminary drossing, the metal may be agitated with air or steam.

There are two methods of refining proper, namely, fire-refining and electrolytic refining.

The first stage in fire-refining is oxidation with air and litharge (PbO) in reverberatories to remove tin, arsenic and antimony ; this operation is often known as **softening.** Alternatively, in the **Harris process,** with special apparatus, the lead is poured through a molten oxidising mixture of soda salts, comprising sodium nitrate, hydroxide and chloride and lead oxide. Both processes are preceded by the sulphur treatment for copper removal. In each case the skimmings are worked up to obtain the elements which they contain in worthwhile amounts in a marketable form.

Next, the softened lead is desilverised (gold is removed at the same time) by the **Parkes process.*** As already described, this is a form of liquation; zinc is added to the lead, the melt is cooled and the solid crusts of silver-zinc compound separating are skimmed off. The precious metal and zinc are separated by distillation after treating in a press to remove excess lead withdrawn during skimming. The lead remaining alloyed with the precious metal is removed by the process of **cupellation**, which involves preferential oxidation by an air blast at comparatively high temperature. The insoluble molten litharge formed, which has the power of dissolving other base-metal oxides, is run off from the rich bullion, or is in part absorbed by the shallow refractory hearth on which the operation is conducted. The cupellation principle is utilised in the refining of silver, when lead has to be added to provide sufficient litharge to dissolve the base-oxides. Any other precious metals remain with the silver during cupellation and have then to be "parted" electrolytically or by other means.

In the cupellation assay (page 213), silver and other precious metals are separated from lead by treatment in a muffle furnace on bone-ash dishes, known as **cupels**; all the molten litharge is absorbed by the latter, leaving a bead of precious metals. In this case acid parting is used.

Excess zinc, of the order of 0·5 per cent, remains in the lead after desilverisation, and this is removed by oxidation with steam or air, chlorination or by a vacuum technique (p. 250). The flowsheet of the lead refinery of the Broken Hill Associated Smelters at Port Pirie, South Australia, and analyses of the lead at each stage are given in Fig. 225 and Table 43. At this plant a *continuous* desilverising process is carried on in a special kettle. A layer of molten zinc is maintained on top of the molten lead (there is considerable liquid immiscibility, *see* Fig. 243) which at the bottom is close to its solidification temperature, so that a temperature gradient exists. Lead for refining is introduced through the zinc, and thus displaces desilverised lead from the bottom. The precious metals (and, it should be noted, residual copper) concentrate in the zinc layer which is periodically replaced.

Up to this stage, bismuth is not eliminated, and previously electrolytic refining was necessary when this element was high. However, bismuth can now be separated in fire-refining by a liquation process applied to softened and desilverised lead; it involves the addition of a calcium-magnesium alloy to combine with the bismuth to form a

* It should be noted that the softening in reverberatories is sometimes considered as part of the Parkes process.

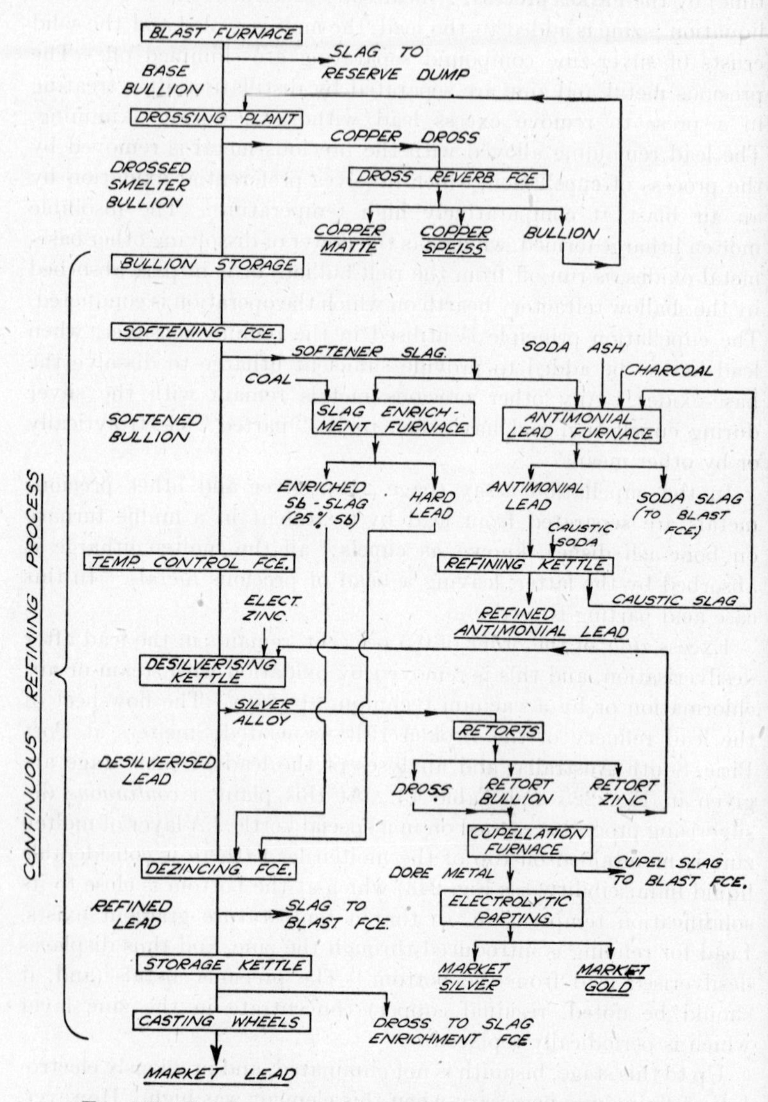

FIG. 225. Flowsheet of lead refinery of Broken Hill Associated Smelters at Port Pirie, South Australia. Note: the bismuth content of the crude lead is sufficiently low, and tin is not present. From F. H. Green, *The Refining of Non-Ferrous Metals*, Inst. Min. and Met., 1950, 283.

TABLE 43. ANALYSIS OF LEAD AT VARIOUS STAGES (Green)

Condition	Zn	Pb	Cu	Fe	As	Sb	Bi	S	Ag	Au
		Per cent							oz./ton	
Average received at refinery from blast-furnaces			1·1	0·2	0·25	0·93	0·002	0·12	46·0	0·04
After drossing and sulphur treatment		98·6	0·004	—	0·13	0·89	0·002	—	46·0	0·04
Lead after softening by oxidation			0·004	—	0·001	0·025	0·002	—	48·0	0·04
Desilverised lead	0·56		0·0005	—	0·001	0·02	0·002	—	0·05	—
Refined lead	0·0002	99·993	0·0004	—	0·0001	0·0037	0·002	—	0·07	—

solid compound which separates. The excess additions can be removed by oxidation or chlorination. Pure bismuth is recovered from the skimmings.

The technique and arrangement in the **Betts electrolytic process** for refining lead are similar to those used for copper. The lead is usually given some preliminary fire-refining, so that the impurities total less than 2 per cent; copper in particular should be low, otherwise it forms a hard insoluble skin on the anodes. The electrolyte is lead fluosilicate ($PbSiF_6$) with free hydrofluosilicic acid (H_2SiF_6), containing 5–10 per cent lead, 8–15 per cent total acid, and 3–5 per cent free acid. Small additions of glue or by-product sulphonates are made to improve the physical nature of the deposit. The temperature of the electrolyte is maintained somewhat above average room temperature; the circulation is at the rate of 3–5 gall. per min. The electrolysing voltage is 0·35–0·55, and the current density 14–18 amp. per sq. ft. of cathode. Arsenic, antimony, bismuth, cadmium, copper and the precious metals are left as slimes, which are worked up. Of the soluble impurities, tin will be deposited with the lead as the two are close in electrochemical behaviour; the tin can be removed by oxidation prior to or after electrolysis. In addition, small amounts of antimony may pass to the cathodes, especially when the current-density and temperature are high; this is also removed by subsequent oxidation. Lead of purity 99·99+ per cent is produced by the process.

TIN

The main economic tin mineral is cassiterite or tinstone (SnO_2). Copper, iron, tungsten and other base metal compounds are often associated with it ; sometimes worthwhile amounts of gold and silver are also present. The primary vein deposits may yield material containing several per cent tin, but that with one per cent and less is worked ; the more important alluvial or placer deposits can be worked (by dredging or hydraulic methods) at very low values indeed : Taggart states that dredging is profitable with tinstone as low as 0·4 lb./cubic yard of gravel.

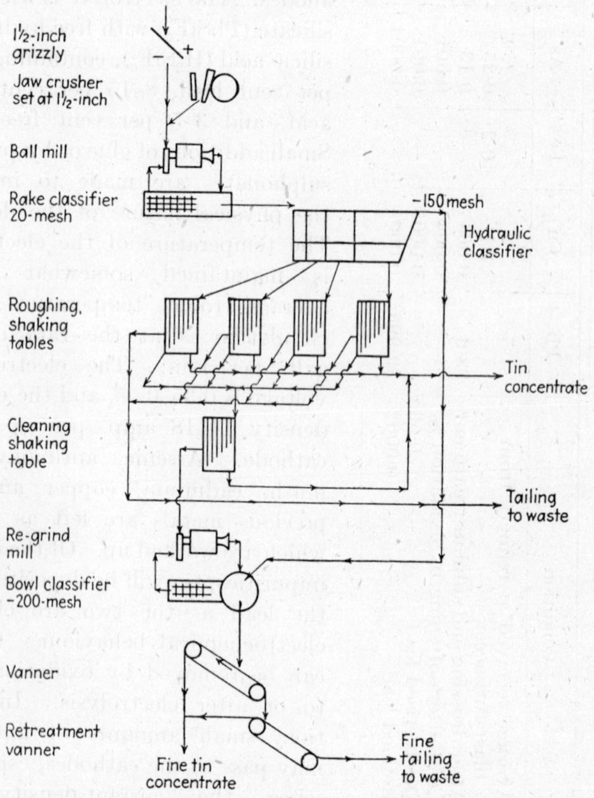

Fig. 226. Flowsheet for gravity concentration of a tin ore. From Gaudin.

The ores are concentrated by gravity methods (Fig. 226); the standard figure for concentrates is 60 per cent tin. Flotation is not yet economical for concentration. Undesirable associated minerals are removed by magnetic separation (iron and iron-tungsten minerals) and flotation (base sulphides and silver). Various other treatments have also been applied for this purpose. Roasting removes sulphur, arsenic and antimony, and converts base sulphides to oxides which can be leached out with acid. Salt added during roasting will cause volatilisation of some elements as chlorides, and will put others in a soluble form suitable for leaching out. In a similar manner, tungsten can be converted to soluble sodium tungstate by roasting with sodium carbonate. Due to conversion of heavy sulphides to the lighter oxides, not so close in density to tinstone, roasting may usefully precede gravity treatment.

The tin concentrates are smelted with charcoal or anthracite coal and fluxes in reverberatory (or blast) furnaces at about 1200° C. There is considerable tendency for tin to enter the slag and for iron to be co-reduced into the metallic tin. Smelting is therefore carried out in two stages. In the first, the reducing conditions and temperature are moderate, so as to minimise co-reduction and obtain a comparatively pure tin; but losses in the slag are high. In the second stage, the slag is resmelted at higher temperatures with a greater proportion of reducing agent and of lime in the slag, in order to recover the tin. The tin obtained is impure and requires considerable refining.

Tin is mainly fire-refined, using liquation and drossing techniques as described in Chapter 8; purity as high as 99·99 per cent tin can be obtained. Electrolytic refining is also possible and has been used. Table 44, taken from one by E. H. Jones, shows the impurities separated by the various refining processes.

TABLE 44. REFINING OF TIN (Jones)

Process	*Impurities removed*
Liquation	iron, arsenic, copper.
Blowing with air or steam	iron, aluminium, zinc, nickel.
Treatment with sulphur	copper.
Treatment with aluminium	antimony, arsenic, copper, nickel.
Electrolysis	lead, antimony, arsenic, copper, bismuth, silver.

NICKEL

The most important source of nickel is the deposits at Sudbury, Ontario, accounting for up to 85 per cent of the world's output, where the nickel occurs mainly as nickel-iron sulphide and also as nickeliferous chalcopyrite. The ore contains copper and nickel each up to a few per cent, with iron of the order of 40 per cent, together with precious metals. There are other sulphide deposits known, but none comparable with those at Sudbury ; the most extensive of the others to date is that at Petsamo, N. Finland, now under Russian control : this has been worked.

At the International Nickel Company's Canadian plant the sulphide ores are prepared by selective flotation to give a copper concentrate and a nickel concentrate (still containing some copper), which are treated separately. Some use is made of hand-picking, and magnetic separation may be employed as well. The ratio of concentration of the nickel is not very great, namely about 3 : 1. The higher-grade ores are smelted direct.

After roasting to adjust the sulphur content, the nickel concentrate is smelted with fluxes (sand and fine quartzite) in reverberatory furnaces to yield a copper-nickel-iron matte and slag, although, flash-smelting (p. 220), already used on the copper concentrate, is proposed. The matte is next treated in converters to remove the iron ; but, as pointed out on page 221, continued blowing cannot be used to remove the copper and obtain metallic nickel.

Some copper-nickel matte (low in precious metals) is roasted to a mixture of oxides and smelted directly to yield a copper-nickel alloy ; but generally the two sulphides are separated, so that pure nickel can be obtained. The most important process for separating the copper-nickel sulphides has been the Orford, now being superseded by a grinding and flotation technique (page 222). The crude nickel sulphide so obtained is ground and washed (if necessary) and roasted to oxide ; the nickel is recovered from the oxide by the **Mond carbonyl process*** (page 224), a process worked in Wales. Alternatively, the oxide is thermally reduced with carbon to crude nickel (about 95 per cent), which is **electrolytically refined,** a process worked in Canada. The metal produced by the Mond process has a purity of about 99·9 per cent nickel ; the electrolytic metal is somewhat less pure : in particular, it contains cobalt of the order of several tenths of a per cent, whereas carbonyl nickel is essentially free from this element (Table 45).

* A process was operated in Germany removing nickel directly from matte under pressure as the carbonyl.

TABLE 45. COMPOSITION (PER CENT) OF COMMERCIAL NICKEL

Metal	Mond Carbonyl process, 1947[1]	Electrolytic	
		International Nickel Company, 1946[1]	Falconbridge, 1953[2]
Nickel	99·92	99·27	99·73
Cobalt	Nil	0·70	0·25
Copper	0·003	0·008	0·01
Iron	0·025	0·02	0·003
Sulphur	0·001	0·002	0·001
Carbon	0·05	—	Nil

[1] By courtesy of S. J. Johnstone. [2] By courtesy of Falconbridge Nikkelverk, Aktieselskap, Kristiansand, S., Norway.

The precious metals concentrated in the matte are recovered during the treatment of the separated copper and nickel portions. According to Hayward, in the Orford process the gold and silver tend to follow the copper, and the platinum metals the nickel. In the latter case the precious metals are obtained from the electrolytic slimes or Mond residues.

In another process applied to Sudbury ores by Falconbridge Nickel Mines Ltd., the ore is concentrated by a combination of hand-picking, magnetic separation and flotation, a separate copper concentrate not being made. A copper-nickel matte is produced from the concentrate by smelting and converting, and this is shipped to Norway where it is ground, roasted and a large amount of the copper leached out with sulphuric acid. The residue is reduced and cast into anodes, the nickel being recovered electrolytically ; the precious metals are obtained from the slimes. At one time copper-nickel mattes were acid-treated for the Mond process.

Nickel-copper-cobalt sulphide ore (low in precious metals) is being mined in N. Manitoba by Sherritt Gordon Mines Ltd. A pressure leaching process (p. 237) has been developed for its treatment, after concentration, and separation of most of the copper by flotation.

Worthwhile silicate deposits of nickel also exist, in which the nickel occurs as garnierite, a complex hydrated silicate of nickel and magnesium. The best known deposit is in New Caledonia, and this was the first major source of nickel, although now far outstripped by the Canadian production. The ore contains about 5 per cent nickel, considerable associated iron, but no copper or precious metals ; it is not concentrated. The ore can be smelted directly, yielding a ferro-nickel. Alternatively, it is smelted with flux and calcium sulphate to give a nickel-iron matte and slag. The iron is removed from the matte in converters. The nickel sulphide remaining is treated in France by grinding, roasting to oxide and thermal reduction.

During the Second World War the Nicaro Nickel Company successfully worked low-grade nickel deposits in Cuba by wet methods (page 210). The deposits consist of oxidised iron ores containing an average of about 0·6 per cent nickel. A nickel carbonate was produced ; this was calcined to oxide and, according to Griffiths, used as such in steel manufacture ; it could of course have been thermally reduced to metal.

ALUMINIUM

Although aluminium is the most abundant metal in the earth's crust and has many desirable attributes, its production tonnage is far behind that of iron. Principally this is due to the fact that many of its occurrences are difficult and expensive to treat. Even the oxide, which is obtainable in fairly pure deposits, is very stable and has to be reduced electrolytically ; although thermal methods have been used to produce aluminium-silicon and aluminium-copper alloys. At present, the almost universal source of aluminium is the ore, **bauxite,** the aluminium-bearing minerals contained therein being hydrated oxides, such as diaspore, $Al_2O_3 . H_2O$, and gibbsite, $Al_2O_3 . 3H_2O$. High-grade deposits have been used containing about 50–60 per cent aluminium oxide ; silica, iron oxide and titanium oxide, which are common associates, are required to be as low as possible (Table 46).

TABLE 46. COMPOSITION OF TYPICAL BAUXITES (Hayward)

Source	Per cent			
	Combined H_2O	SiO_2	Fe_2O_3	Al_2O_3
France -	11–13	20–25	3–5	57–60
Guiana -	29–31	variable	1–3	56–61
U.S.A. -	27–30	low	5–12	56–59

Before electrolytic extraction, a very pure oxide has to be obtained so as not to impair the efficiency of electrolysis or produce an impure metal. Aluminium is a difficult metal to refine on account of its reactive nature : neither fire-refining nor electrolytic refining in aqueous solution is possible. The crude bauxite is cleaned chemically, the most important method being the **Bayer process.** The ore is calcined to dry it and remove organic matter. It is then ground to about 100-mesh and leached in a hot solution of caustic soda under a pressure of 50–70 lb./sq. in. at 150°–160° C. The alumina (Al_2O_3) is dissolved, whereas the other oxides mainly remain as an insoluble "red mud". After separation of the sodium aluminate solution from the mud, it is diluted and slowly cooled and the aluminium is precipitated as hydroxide; precipitation has to be initiated by "seeding" with freshly precipitated fine hydroxide. The hydroxide is separated, washed and dried at around 1000° C. to give almost pure aluminium oxide.

Chemical processes have been developed to obtain pure alumina from low-grade bauxites and clays, but are apparently not economic in present circumstances.

For electrolysis, the aluminium oxide is dissolved in a molten bath of calcium, sodium and aluminium fluorides at about 900° C., and carbon electrodes are used. The cell is lined with carbon, and the molten aluminium produced sinks to the bottom, whence it is regularly removed (Fig. 227). The cell is operated at a voltage of 6–7·5 with a current density of 650–750 amp./sq. ft. of cathode. In practice, about 12 kilowatt hours are used in producing a pound of aluminium. During electrolysis, a crust forms on top of the bath and acts as an insulator. The alumina is preheated on this crust and then fed through a hole made in it. The need for charging is indicated by

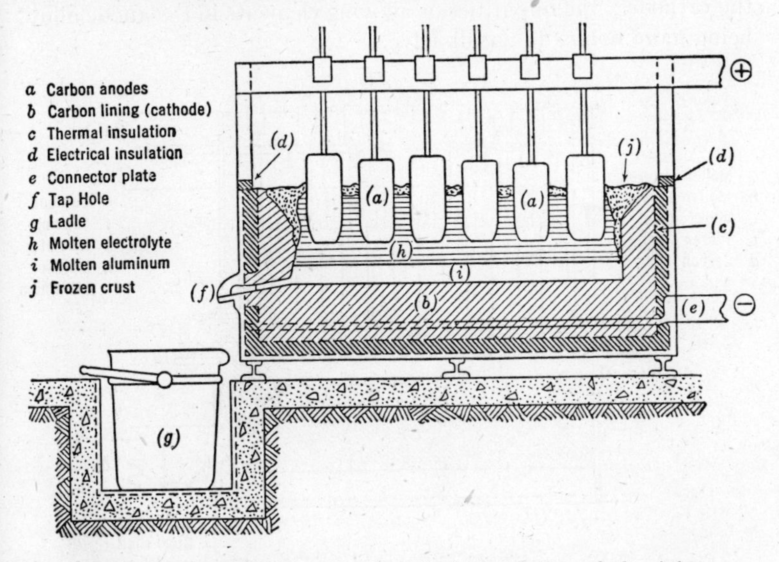

Fig. 227. Cell used for the electrolytic extraction of aluminium. Typical internal dimensions: 8 ft. × 4 ft. × 2 ft. deep. From Bray.

the increased resistance of the bath causing brightening of a shunted lamp, and also by evolution of fluorine. The carbon anodes burn away during electrolysis, the heat supplementing that from the passage of the current through the electrolyte; no external heating of the cell is necessary. As an alternative to pre-shaped and -baked anodes, the **Soderberg** type of continuous self-baking electrode is being used increasingly; in general, the advantages, in addition to continuity of operation, are saving in electrode material and the possibility of enclosing the cell for gas removal.

Aluminium up to about 99·6 per cent purity is normally prepared by direct electrolysis, and up to about 99·85 per cent purity by using very pure oxide and electrodes. By subsequent electrolytic refining using a fused-salt electrolyte, purity of at least 99·99 per cent may be attained. The bulk of aluminium used today is not refined.

The principle of electrolytic refining of aluminium is to use a three-layer molten bath. On the bottom is the crude aluminium alloyed with copper (to about 33 per cent) to increase its density, and with some silicon to reduce the melting point; on top of this is a layer of fused salt electrolyte of lower density; the third layer is the pure refined aluminium. Electrical connections are made to the two metal layers to make them in effect anode and cathode, respectively. On electrolysis, aluminium dissolves at the anode and is deposited at the cathode; the impurities or alloying elements in the anode alloy, being more noble, do not dissolve.

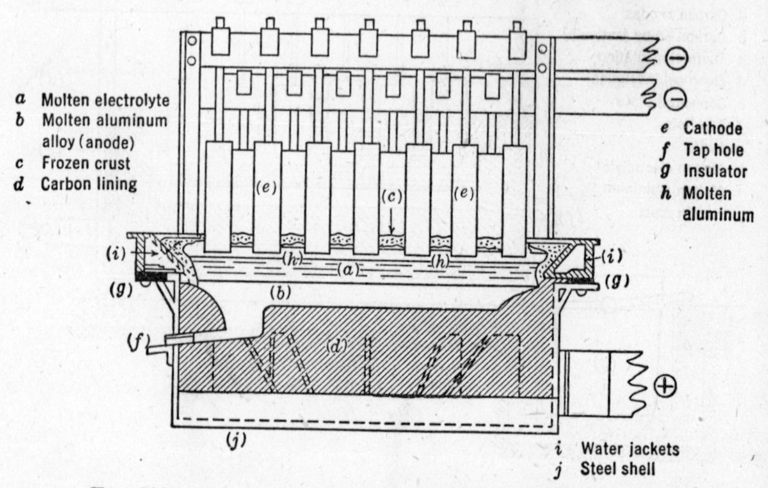

FIG. 228. Hoopes cell for electrolytic refining of aluminium. From Bray.

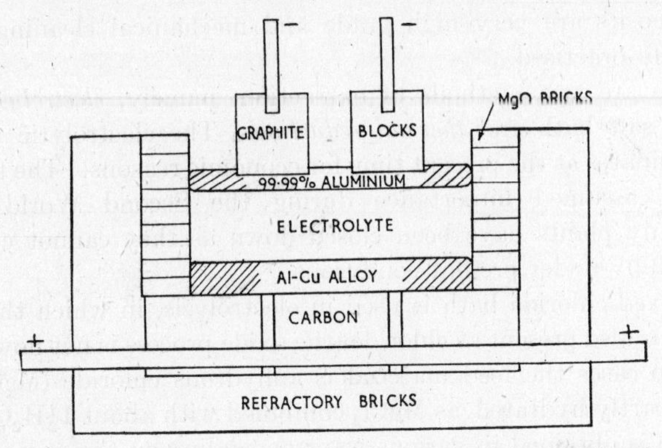

FIG. 229. French process for electrolytic refining of aluminium. The specific gravities of the three layers are respectively, 3·0, 2·7 and 2·3. From J. Waddington, *The Refining of Non-Ferrous Metals*, Inst. Min. Met., 1950, 448.

The first successful application of the technique was by Hoopes; he used a fused-salt mixture of barium, aluminium and sodium fluorides containing dissolved alumina, an operating temperature of 950°–1000° C. being necessary. Hoopes employed a steel cell with a carbon bottom connected to the positive side of the electrical supply; electrical contact was made with the cathode metal by means of several carbon electrodes (Fig. 228). The cell walls were water-jacketed and were lined with a layer of electrolyte which solidified. There are certain difficulties in working, but according to Bray the process is still used.

The Compagnie de Produits Chimiques et Electrométallurgiques Alais, Froges et Carmargue uses a development, which is claimed to be more efficient. An electrolyte consisting of $AlF_3/NaF/BaCl_2$ is used which can be worked at 700°–750° C., and the cell walls are made of magnesite brick with the bottom of carbon (Fig. 229). The composition of the anode alloy is regularly adjusted by addition of aluminium; refined aluminium is drawn off at the top.

MAGNESIUM

Both liquid and solid sources of magnesium are utilised. The former comprise brines from wells and lakes, and sea water. The main solid deposits are those of magnesite ($MgCO_3$), dolomite ($MgCO_3CaCO_3$), brucite ($MgO . H_2O$), and salt deposits, for example, in which the magnesium is present as carnallite ($MgCl_2 . KCl . 6H_2O$);

the deposits are very high grade and mechanical cleaning is not generally practised.

There are two methods of extraction, namely, *electrolysis* of a molten salt bath and *thermal reduction*. The electrolytic method predominates at the present time for economic reasons. The thermal method assumed importance during the Second World War; but many plants have been closed down as they cannot compete successfully under present conditions.

A mixed-chloride bath is used in electrolysis, in which the magnesium is also present as chloride (the oxide process is not now used). In some cases the feed material is anhydrous chloride ($MgCl_2$), in others partly hydrated, as $MgCl_2$ combined with about $1\frac{1}{2}H_2O$. The chloride is obtained in various ways depending on the source being utilised; for example, by crystallisation and drying from brines, or by chemical conversion of the oxide in the form of calcined magnesite, dolomite or the hydroxide obtained from sea water. One method, used in Great Britain, involves heating the oxide with carbon in an atmosphere of chlorine (most of which comes from the electrolytic cell), the reactions being:

$$MgO + C + Cl_2 \rightarrow MgCl_2 + CO$$
$$2MgO + C + 2Cl_2 \rightarrow 2MgCl_2 + CO_2$$

According to Ball, the average power consumption in electrolysis per lb. of metal produced is 9·2 kWh.

Sea water contains about 0·13 per cent magnesium, mainly as chloride and sulphate, and the magnesium is recovered on the large scale in the form of hydroxide which is calcined to the oxide. This oxide can be used for refractory purposes, or for metal production; for electrolytic reduction, the oxide is converted to chloride by one of several methods, an important method being mentioned above. The essential procedure with the sea water involves addition of a calculated amount of lime to precipitate bicarbonates, followed by filtration to remove the calcium carbonate formed and other solid matter. Magnesium hydroxide is then precipitated by addition of regulated amounts of slaked lime in the form of a slurry, according to the reactions:

$$Ca(OH)_2 + MgCl_2 \rightarrow Mg(OH)_2 + CaCl_2$$
$$Ca(OH)_2 + MgSO_4 \rightarrow Mg(OH)_2 + CaSO_4$$

Calcined dolomite is also used in a similar manner as precipitant, its use approximately doubling the yield of magnesia for a given volume of sea water. Teed states that the lime-precipitated material is somewhat purer and is preferable for metal production.

The precipitated magnesium hydroxide is separated and calcined at 1100°–1200° C. to produce so-called reactive caustic magnesia suitable for chlorination. For refractory use, the hydroxide is dead burnt at a minimum temperature of 1650° C.

The thermal reduction processes start with an oxide such as calcined dolomite or magnesite, or that from sea water. Silicon as ferro-silicon is used for reduction of dolomite (Fig. 230 and page 223), and carbon, aluminium (page 232) and calcium carbide were used for the straight oxide. The silicon process operates *in vacuo*, as did the aluminium and carbide processes, enabling lower temperatures to be used. In each case the magnesium is produced as a vapour, which has to be condensed suitably; in the carbon process *shock-cooling* was necessary to prevent reversion on cooling the products (p. 223). Harvey points out that the war-time value of thermal plants lay in the speed with which they could be erected and put into service, and the fact that they did not need direct-current electricity.

Commercially, magnesium is not refined after extraction. Magnesium Elektron, Ltd., state the purity of electrolytic metal to be 99·5–99·9 per cent, depending on the source of materials, and thermally reduced as 99·9 per cent. Magnesium can be refined by sublimation, but this has only been used on small amounts for special purposes.

Ball has stated that electrolytic metal of 99·95 per cent purity can be obtained by special control of the impurities in the electrolyte. Dominion Magnesium Ltd. of Canada are producing 99·95–99·98 per

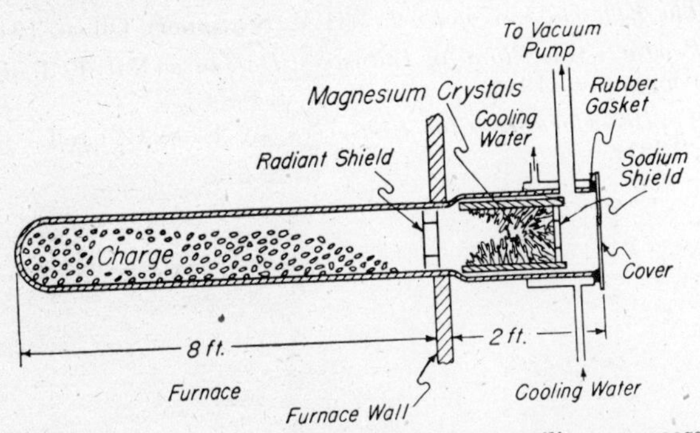

Fig. 230. Retort used in the Pidgeon ferrosilicon process for magnesium. A large number of the steel retorts are arranged in a fuel-fired furnace. The charge is heated to about 1150° C. under a gas pressure of 0·001 in. of mercury. The sodium shield is to condense traces of the sodium impurity, preventing it from entering the vacuum system. From *Magnesium*, by W. H. Gross, Amer. Soc. for Met.

cent magnesium by the Pidgeon thermal process ; the process is also being operated in the United States.

ADDITIONAL READING

1. *An Outline of Metallurgical Practice*, by C. R. Hayward. (Macmillan and Van Nostrand, 3rd edit., 1952).

2. *Non-Ferrous Metallurgy*, by J. L. Bray. (New York, Wiley ; London, Chapman and Hall, 2nd edit., 1947).

3. *Handbook of Non-Ferrous Metallurgy*, by D. M. Liddell (edit.). 2 vols. (2nd edit., McGraw-Hill, 1945).

4. *Metallurgy of Copper*, by J. Newton and C. L. Wilson, (Wiley, 1942).

5. *The Physical Chemistry of Copper Smelting*, by R. W. Ruddle (Inst. Min. and Met., 1953).

6. *The Aluminium Industry*, by J. O. Edwards, F. C. Frary and Z. Jeffries. (McGraw-Hill, 1930).

7. *Trans. Amer. Inst. Min. and Metal. Eng.*, 121, *Lead and Zinc Metallurgy*, (1936).

8. *The Refining of Non-Ferrous Metals*, Symposium (1949). (Institution of Mining and Metallurgy, 1950).

9. Relevant papers presented at the Fourth Empire Mining and Metallurgical Congress, Great Britain, July, 1949 (published at the offices of the Congress, Salisbury Ho., London, E.C. 2). Under headings Session " G " : *Present-Day Trends in Mineral Dressing* ; and Sessions " H " and " I " : *Metallurgy and Metallurgical Industries*.

10. *Refractories*, by F. H. Norton. (2nd edit., McGraw-Hill, 1942).

11. *Fuel—Solid, Liquid and Gaseous*, by J. S. S. Brame and J. G. King. (4th Ed., Arnold, 1935).

12. *The Efficient Use of Fuel*. (H.M. Stationery Office, 1944).

13. *Producer Gas Plant for Industrial Purposes* (Nat. Fed. of Gas Coke Associations, etc., 1942).

14. *Applied Chemistry for Engineers*, by E. S. Gyngell. (2nd edit., Arnold, 1951).

CHAPTER 10

METAL WINNING: IRON- AND STEEL-MAKING

THE predominance of iron in the world of metals is due, apart from its useful properties, to the existence of considerable high-grade deposits of easily reducible oxidised minerals. The main economic minerals are hematite (Fe_2O_3), limonite ($2Fe_2O_3 \cdot 3H_2O$), magnetite (Fe_3O_4) and siderite ($FeCO_3$). Thus the production of iron by far exceeds that of aluminium, although the latter is actually more common in the earth's crust. A number of iron ores, as mined,

TABLE 47. TYPICAL ANALYSES OF PIG IRONS AND CONDITION OF CARBON

Total carbon (%)	Graphitic carbon (%)	Combined carbon (%)	Silicon (%)	Manganese (%)	Sulphur (%)	Phosphorus (%)
3·7	3·50	0·20	2·85	1·31	0·03	0·03
3·22	3·10	0·12	3·13	0·90	0·024	1·61
3·3	3·20	0·10	3·50	0·68	0·05	1·67
3·18	2·80	0·38	2·85	1·38	0·059	1·45
2·97	2·55	0·42	2·67	0·98	0·138*	1·45
3·98	3·53	0·45	2·25	1·0	0·03	0·05
4·0	3·50	0·50	2·75	0·3	0·015	0·03
3·3	2·80	0·50	2·3	1·0	0·05	0·65
3·74	3·18	0·56	2·0	1·0	0·04	0·05
3·9	3·10	0·80	2·0	0·3	0·04	0·05
3·6	2·5	1·1	1·5	0·3	0·08	0·03
3·0	1·8	1·2	1·1	0·65	0·25*	1·4
3·4	2·1	1·3	1·2	0·2	0·11	0·04
3·2	1·4	1·8	0·7	0·3	0·15	0·03
2·40	0·45	1·95	1·20	0·88	0·20*	1·65
2·26	0·15	2·11	0·80	0·45	0·47*	1·41
3·0	0·1	2·9	0·91	0·1	0·3*	0·7
3·0	—	3·0	0·3	0·2	0·20*	0·03
3·25	—	3·25	0·46	0·54	0·1	1·7

* Irons with very high sulphur contents can be used in castings where strength is not critical; they can be used in basic open-hearth steel-making when diluted sufficiently.

TABLE 48. APPLICATIONS OF PIG IRON (Bashforth)

Class	Per cent					Uses
	C	Si	S	P	Mn	
Hematite -	3·0–4·0	2·0–3·0	Max. 0·040	Max. 0·040	0·5–2·0	Acid open-hearth steel manufacture and foundry work.
Bessemer - -	3·5–4·0	2·0–2·5	Max. 0·040	0·040	0·75–1·0	Acid Bessemer steel manufacture and foundry work.
Basic - -	3·0–3·6	0·6–1·0	0·08–0·10	1·2–2·5	1·0–2·5	Basic Bessemer steel manufacture.
Basic - -	2·5–3·5	Max. 1·0	Max. 0·08	1·0–2·0*	1·0–3·0	Basic open hearth steel manufacture.
Foundry - -	3·0–4·0	2·0–3·5	0·080	0·7–1·2	1·0–2·0	General foundry work.

* In American practice the phosphorus contents are lower.

have contained 50 per cent or more iron, and around 20 odd per cent is considered low-grade. Hence, up to the present, comparatively, not a great deal of concentration has been practised, for the ores have been capable of efficient direct smelting. Careful preparation treatments (apart from concentration), such as sintering, have become increasingly common.

Commercial ferrous products. Iron ores are smelted largely in blast-furnaces with coke and a flux, usually limestone. Under the conditions obtaining, a number of other elements are introduced into the iron, mainly from the ore and coke. Thus, notably, up to about 3·5 per cent silicon, 2 per cent phosphorus, and 2 per cent manganese are reduced from their oxides and together with a few per cent of carbon are dissolved in the iron; smaller amounts of sulphur (up to about 0·4 per cent) are also picked up (Tables 47 and 48). The composition of the iron can be controlled to some extent in smelting, but is largely dependent on the raw materials. The metal produced by smelting is known as **pig iron,** the term originating from the fact that it is cast into shapes known as pigs. Pig iron is the almost universal source of all ferrous metals.

Although ordinary pig iron and steels contain appreciable amounts of five elements apart from the iron base, the structures may be interpreted and the properties compared, with certain reservations, on the basis of the binary iron/iron-carbide constitutional diagram (Fig. 231). The microstructures and properties are certainly affected by the manganese, silicon, sulphur and phosphorus contents, and some indication of their effect will be given.

With regard to the phases, α is an extremely dilute solid solution of carbon in body-centred cubic iron, δ is similar; α is known as "ferrite" (Brinell hardness, about 90). The γ-phase is a solid solution based on face-centred cubic iron and is known as "austenite". The carbide is called "cementite" (Brinell hardness, about 800). These phases are discussed in Chapter 3. The dotted line on the diagram at 768° C. represents the temperature at which α changes from ferro- to para-magnetic; that at 210° C. denotes a similar change in the carbide. The eutectoid mixture of the α- and carbide-phases is called "pearlite" (Brinell hardness, 200-450, depending on the fineness of the structure), and the eutectic structure at 4·3 per cent carbon, "ledeburite". These have been mentioned in Chapter 4.

Steel may be taken as containing up to 2·0 per cent carbon, none being present as graphite; with greater amounts of carbon the metal is known as **pig iron** or **cast iron.**

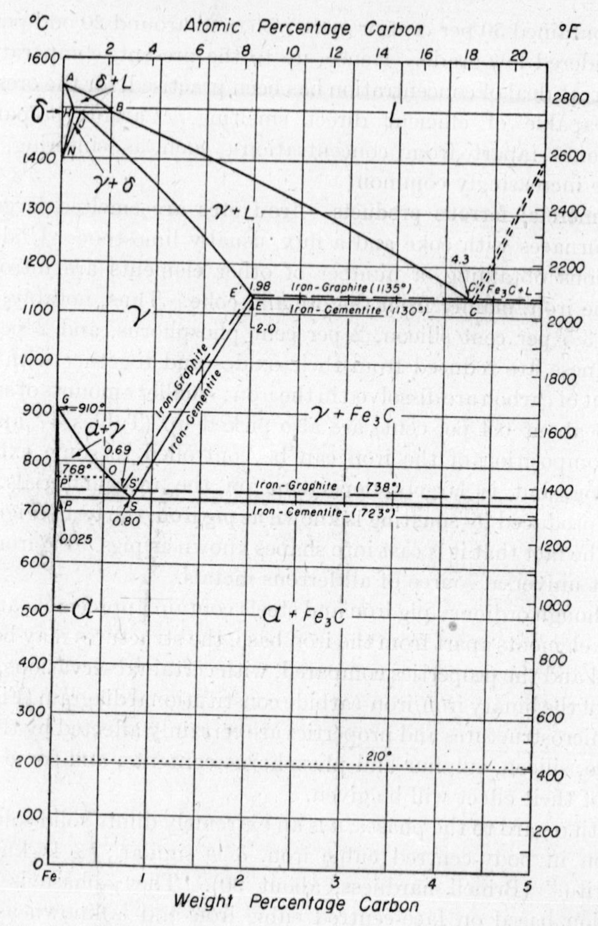

FIG. 231. Equilibrium diagram for iron-carbon system (up to 5 per cent carbon). From *Metals Handbook*, 1948 Edition. American Soc. for Metals.

Steels with less than 0·8 per cent carbon are often referred to as *hypo-eutectoid*, and those with greater amounts of carbon as *hyper-eutectoid*. The terms are used in a similar manner with respect to the eutectic in the range beyond 2 per cent carbon. The arrest temperatures for the solid transformations in hypo-eutectoid steel are referred to as the critical or *A* points. They are numbered in order by subscripts, starting with the eutectoid temperature, and may be further qualified by the letter *c* or *r* for heating and cooling, respectively, as with practical rates of heating and cooling there is noticeable lag in the transformations. Thus Ac_1 is the eutectoid arrest on heating. In hyper-eutectoid steels, there are arrests at the eutectoid and at temperatures corresponding to the line SE in the equilibrium diagram ; the latter arrests may be referred to as Acm.

When the silicon and manganese in cast iron are intentionally higher than the limits given earlier, or greater than about 0·5 and 1·5* per cent respectively in the case of steel, or where elements such as nickel, chromium, tungsten, molybdenum, cobalt and vanadium are added to modify the properties, the materials are referred to as **alloy cast irons** and **alloy steels.** The present account is concerned only with ordinary irons and steels. It must be appreciated that no attempt will be made to offer a complete discussion of the metallography and properties of ferrous alloys, but merely to distinguish briefly their characteristics.

Starting with cast iron : if all the carbon exists as iron carbide (Fig. 232*a* and 233), due to the proportions of this hard and brittle compound, the iron is hard and brittle and difficult to machine (sintered tungsten carbide tools are used). The iron breaks with a fracture of white or silvery appearance and is known as **white cast iron.** On the other

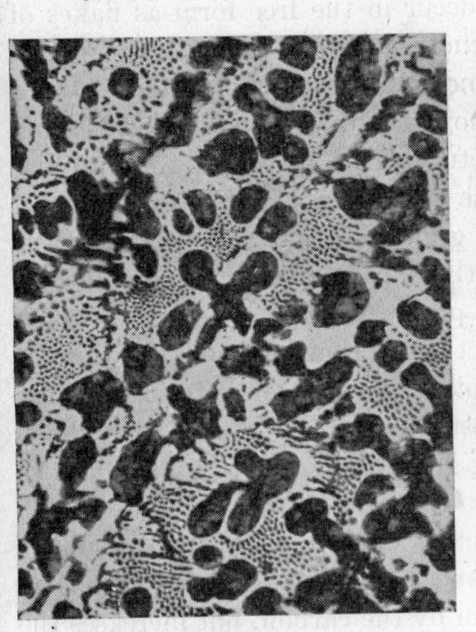

(*a*)

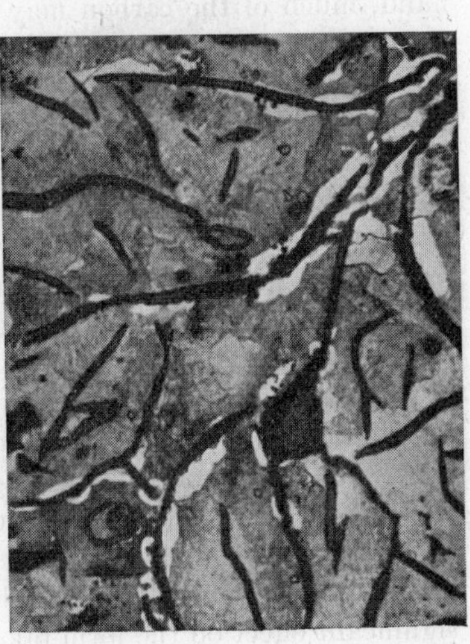

(*b*)

FIG. 232. Microstructures of typical cast irons. ×100.

(*a*) Hypo-eutectic white cast iron. Pearlite (dark) in both dendritic and eutectic form ; carbide (white).

(*b*) Grey cast iron. Flakes of graphite ; pearlite (grey) ; ferrite (white).

* Normally in ordinary steel the silicon and manganese are lower than these upper limits.

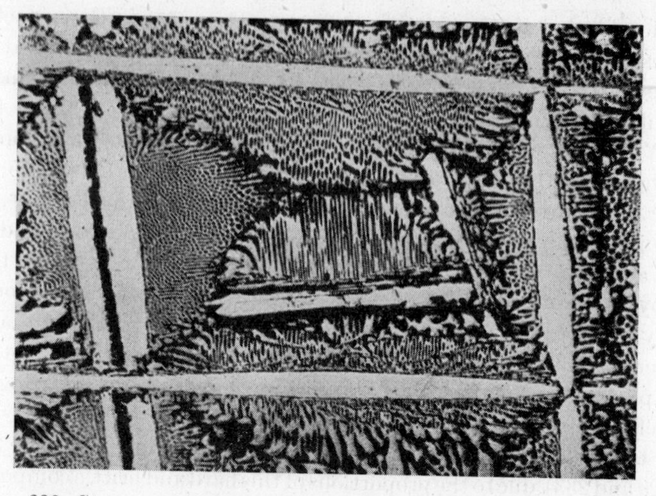

FIG. 233. Structure of hyper-eutectic white iron : primary crystals of Fe_3C in the ledeburite eutectic. ×40. This structure is very rare in ordinary cast iron. From A. M. Portevin, *J. Inst. Met.*, 1923, 29. 239.

hand, much of the carbon may occur in the free form as flakes of graphite, the matrix having a structure similar to steel (Fig. 232*b*). Such iron is softer than white and is machinable ; but it is weak because of the graphite, which, however, does impart good bearing and machining properties. Fracture takes place via the graphite flakes, yielding a dark fracture, the iron being referred to as **grey cast iron**. The shape and size of the graphite can be modified and the mechanical properties consequently improved by certain additions or by special melting and casting procedures.

A number of factors decide whether an iron shall solidify white or grey. If the rate of cooling is rapid, the tendency is to form white, and if slow, grey iron. The most important factor is the silicon content, since silicon has a strong graphitising tendency (Table 47). The direct effect of manganese is to promote the formation of carbide (it has also a desulphurising effect) ; sulphur behaves in a similar manner, but is generally kept as low as possible. Phosphorus has no significant effect on the form taken by the carbon, but increases the fluidity of the metal and thus is usually fairly high in foundry cast irons ; it appears in the micro structure as iron phosphide, Fe_3P. It is suggested that the stable form of carbon in iron is graphite, the carbide being the undercooled metastable form ; and the dotted line in Fig. 231 suggests the constitutional relationship with iron. Further confirmation of this view is the fact that when white iron is heated for a long time between 800° and 950° C. the carbide is converted to graphite. This is actually the basis of the treatment for making **malleable cast iron,** in which the graphite forms in rosette or nodular shape ; consequently the material is much tougher than grey iron with graphite in the flake form. **Mottled cast iron** is intermediate between white and grey, the structure showing a mixture of grey and white zones, and is obtained when border-line conditions prevail.

Cast iron has a certain amount of strength, but little or no plasticity, and is weak or brittle depending upon whether it solidifies grey or white, respectively. Neither form can be worked. However, the iron has good casting properties and is cheaper than steel, and there are numerous applications for which it is suitable. Grey iron is the general foundry material, although white iron has application where hardness and good wear resistance are required : cast iron rolls are frequently made with a chilled white skin ; and white iron is the starting point for malleable iron, which is used considerably. For iron castings there is usually a re-melting stage using pigs from the blast furnace and cast iron and sometimes steel scrap. The iron is then known as **cast iron** ; but it will be seen that there is no significant difference chemically or structurally between pig iron and cast iron.

When better mechanical properties are required than are yielded by cast iron, the extra elements in the iron are regulated to lesser amounts (C, Mn, and Si) or practically eliminated (S and P) by fire-refining to make **steel.** Steel is tougher and stronger than cast iron. It can be worked to improve its properties, which also can be varied considerably by heat treatment. Steel castings (mainly in the range 0·2–0·5 per cent carbon), although more expensive than cast iron, have a number of applications for which they are superior. However, the vast bulk of steel is used in the wrought condition ; the greater proportion by far being mild steel with up to about 0·25 per cent carbon ; the higher-carbon varieties are often heat-treated after working.

TABLE 49. COMPOSITION AND TENSILE TEST RESULTS OF TYPICAL CARBON CAST STEELS

Type	Composition, per cent			U.T.S. tons/in.^{2}	Elongation (per cent)
	Carbon	Manganese	Silicon		
Low carbon	0·09–0·2	0·5–1·0	0·2–0·75	19–32	36–22
Medium carbon	0·2–0·4	0·5–1·0	0·2–0·75	27–36	30–20
High carbon	0·4–0·9	0·5–1·0	0·2–0·75	32–54	26–3

It will be seen from the equilibrium diagram (Fig. 231) that under normal conditions the structure of an alloy with 0·80 per cent carbon consists of a eutectoid mixture of ductile "ferrite" which is essentially pure iron, and the hard iron carbide. With less carbon there is excess ferrite, and with greater, excess iron carbide; the excess usually occurs as a network around the eutectoid, "pearlite" (Fig. 234): in some conditions there is a Widmanstätten structure. With low-carbon alloys, the structure is better described as small zones of pearlite among the ferrite grains; at very low carbon contents, the carbide tends to occur as thin films at the ferrite grain boundaries. The properties of the alloys clearly depend on the amount and distribution of the iron carbide. With increase of this constituent there is increase in hardness and strength, but reduction of ductility; until a network of excess carbide occurs there is always some plasticity, because there is a continuous ferrite matrix in which flow can take place; but beyond the eutectoid composition there is increasing brittleness (Fig. 235 and Tables 49 and 50). Actually, the toughness of hyper-eutectoid steels can be improved by careful working and heat-treatment to disperse the carbide network into separate particles, and this is the usual practice. It will, of course, be appreciated that in general the structure and properties of

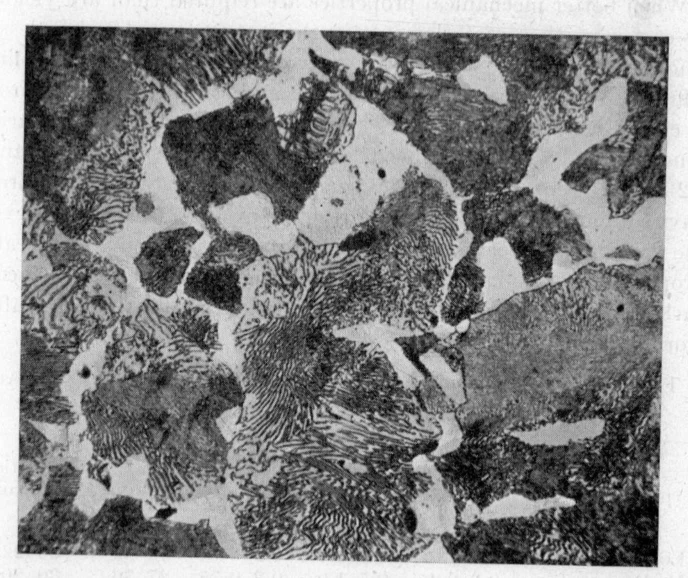

FIG. 234. Microstructure of 0·5 per cent carbon steel, worked and annealed: ferrite (white) and pearlite. ×300.

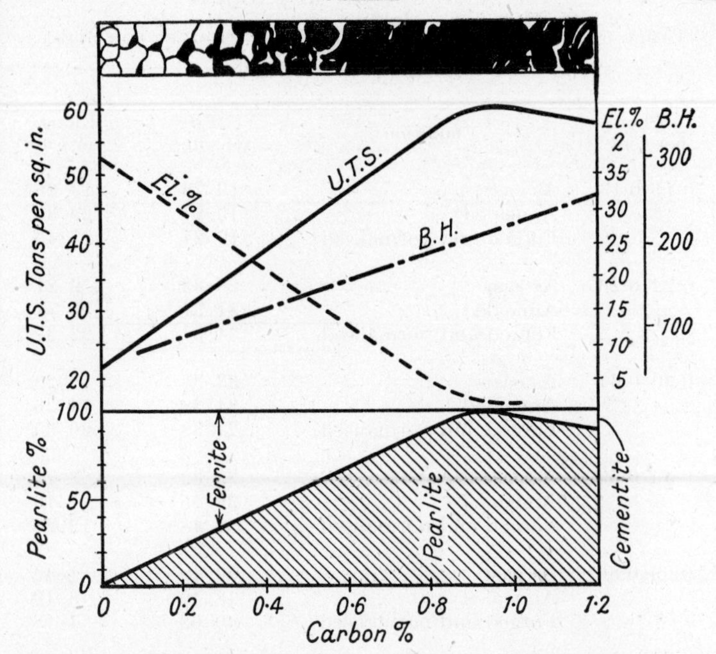

Fig. 235. Variation with carbon content of mechanical properties and microstructure of steel. From E. C. Rollason, *Metallurgy for Engineers*, Arnold.

steel are subject to considerable modification according to the working and heat-treatment carried out (Table 50).

Silicon and manganese both strengthen steel, but the silicon must not be too high or else there is danger of graphitisation; manganese has the reverse tendency, and increases the amount of eutectoid for a given carbon content. Similarly, it should be noted that, in the cast iron range, silicon and phosphorus decrease the carbon content of the eutectic. Sulphur and phosphorus are generally each kept under 0·05 per cent, although the amounts may be considerably higher, as for example in certain free-machining steels. The ultimate effect of those elements in steel is to cause brittleness, especially at hot working temperatures in the case of sulphur. Manganese in sufficient quantity largely counteracts this effect of sulphur.

Ingot iron, or the proprietary "Armco" iron, is made by fire refining as with steel, but the other elements are eliminated so far as possible. **Wrought iron** is also essentially pure iron and is made today by fire-refining pig iron; but in addition, it contains intentionally, small amounts of the refining slag, principally iron silicate.

TABLE 50. COMPARISON OF TENSILE TEST FIGURES FOR STEELS IN DIFFERENT CONDITIONS

Carbon per cent	Condition	U.T.S. tons/in.^{2}	Elong. per cent
0·11–0·13	As cast	19–26	13–25
	Annealed*	19–27	29–35
	Forged and normalised†	19–27	28–46
0·22–0·26	As cast	29–33	9–21
	Annealed	31–37	15–31
	Forged and normalised	24–34	22–39
0·30–0·34	As cast	33–38	10–20
	Annealed	34–38	14–26
	Forged and normalised	27–38	20–35
0·45–0·53	As cast	35–39	3–7
	Annealed	39–45	7–16
	Forged and normalised	32–48	12–28
0·69–0·86	As cast	32–40	1–4
	Annealed	48–49	8–10
	Forged and normalised	40–62	4–18

* Annealing; heating to a moderate temperature in the γ-range and furnace-cooling.

†Normalising: heating to a moderate temperature in the γ-range and cooling in still air at room temperature.

By the working treatment which follows and which forms part of the process, the slag is obtained as a fibrous membrane running through the grains of iron and to which are due certain of the characteristics of the material. For general purposes there is no great call for very high purity iron. For special purposes *electrolytic* and *carbonyl* irons may be used (Table 51).

PIG IRON PRODUCTION

Ore preparation. In order to increase efficiency and with the gradual exhaustion of rich deposits, there has been and is increasing study and use of concentration processes for iron ores. Water-gravity processes, such as washing, jigging and sink-and-float, as well as magnetic concentration, have had commercial application (Figs. 236 and 237).

Certain iron ores may be calcined to drive off carbon dioxide and moisture. There is considerable use of sintering for fines and waste dust, etc., and the crushing of over-size material. As-mined ores may

TABLE 51. TYPICAL ANALYSES OF VARIOUS FORMS OF IRON (TAKEN FROM THE LITERATURE)

Description	Per cent by weight									Notes
	C	Mn	Si	P	S	O	H_2+N_2	N_2	Slag	
"Armco" - -	0·013 0·012	0·019 0·017	0·001 trace	0·003 0·005	0·017 0·025	0·07 not given				
Electrolytic - -	0·0001– 0·08	Trace– 0·01	Trace– 0·008	0·0002– 0·008	0·0001– 0·008	0·06				
Carbonyl - -	0·015 0·0007	Trace *	Trace *	Trace *	Trace *	0·03 $<0·01$				* Unable to identify
Hydrogen treated -	0·0045 0·005	0·002 0·028	0·0002 0·0012	0·001 0·004	0·0015 0·003	0·0005 0·003	$\leqslant 0·001$	0·0001		Electrolytic or carbonyl iron is purified with hydrogen which tends to be comparatively high.
Swedish, Lancashire wrought iron - -	0·03	Trace	0·02	0·052	0·008				0·07– 1·0	Made from low sulphur and low silicon iron.
Staffordshire wrought iron - -	0·02	0·02	0·12	0·228	0·018				ditto	
Wrought iron -	0·08	0·029	0·183	0·115	0·015				2·85	From American source.
Byers No. 1 wrought iron - -	0·08	0·015	0·158	0·062	0·010				1·20	Made by American process described on page 353.

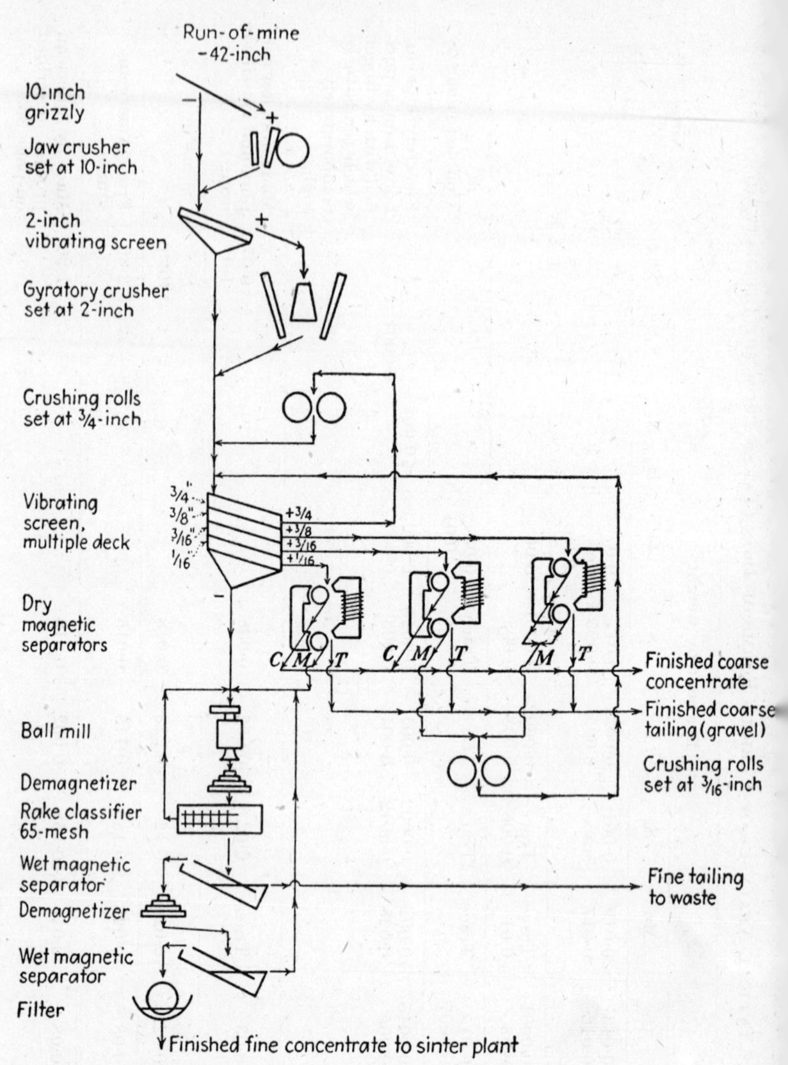

FIG. 236. Flowsheet for concentration of magnetite ore. From A. M. Gaudin, *Principles of Mineral Dressing*, McGraw-Hill.

be fine, or made so during concentration or handling. Sinter-cake is very suitable material for blast-furnace reduction. Another advantage of sintering is the removal of sulphur from associates in the ore. Pre-treatment of iron ores is covered generally by the term " benefication ".

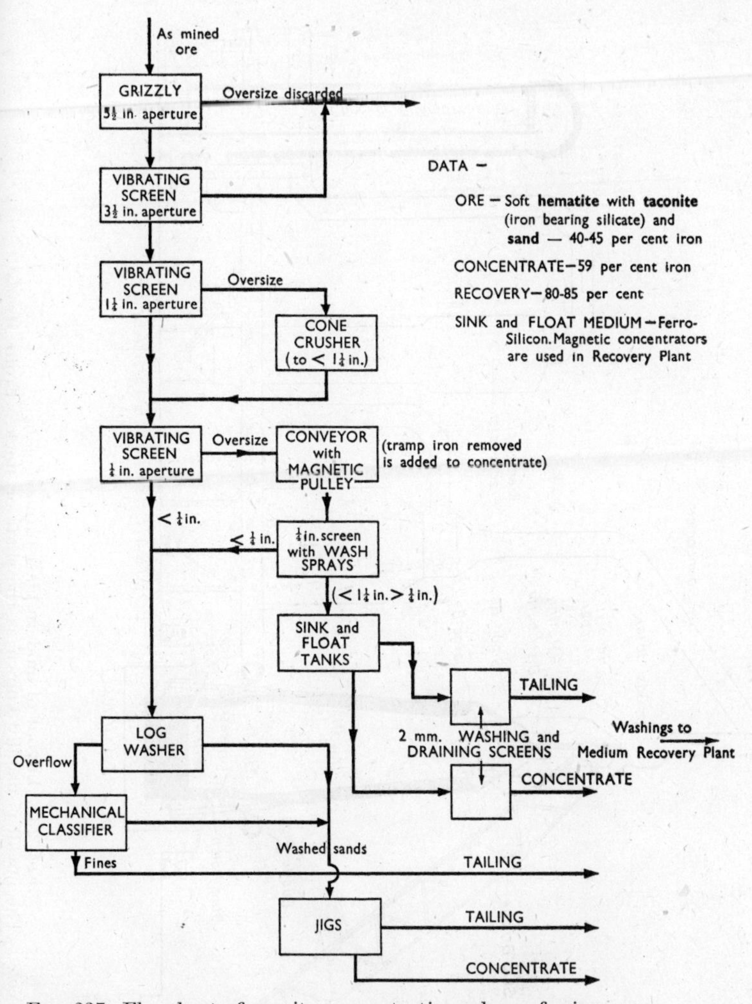

Fig. 237. Flowsheet of gravity concentration scheme for iron ore.

Smelting. Early iron reduction furnaces using charcoal as fuel and reducing agent had no real shafts, consisting merely of holes or hearths in the ground supplied with air by some primitive means such as foot-bellows. As a result, the temperatures created were insufficient to melt the reduced iron, which was produced in a pasty condition. However, due to the low temperatures reached, only a comparatively small amount of impurities was introduced into the metal and a fairly pure workable grade was obtained. It was not

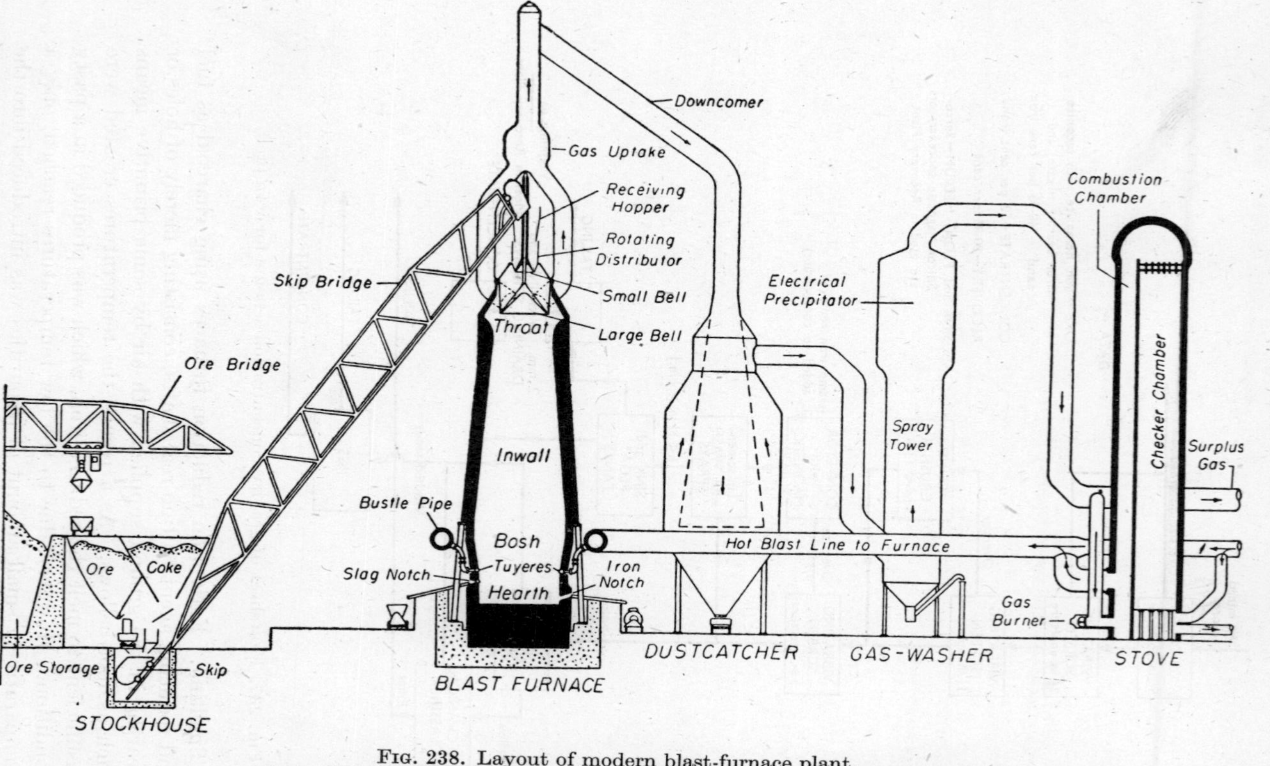

FIG. 238. Layout of modern blast-furnace plant.
Note: The inwall is usually known as the shaft or stack. From *Metals Handbook*, 1948 Edition

possible to separate the iron completely from the slag, and wrought iron was made by working the furnace product.

Shafts were introduced about the fourteenth or fifteenth century in efforts to increase capacities. They created higher temperatures, with consequent production of pig iron.

For many years, efforts have been made to evolve a large-scale direct process for the production of pure iron and steel, in place of the present indirect method. But pig iron smelting remains predominant; although, for example, the Swedish sponge iron process, in which reduction of high-grade ore is carried out in the solid state, carbon monoxide being the effective reducing agent, is operated on a commercial scale. The impure iron produced is made into steel in a separate furnace.

Coke is the usual fuel and reducing agent in the blast-furnace, being first used in the early part of the eighteenth century, although charcoal is still used in a few cases. The amount of coke required depends on the ore and is somewhat under a ton per ton of pig iron produced. The coke used is not the ordinary gas works' variety, but metallurgical coke made in special coke-ovens (p. 271), often at the iron-plant. Among desirable attributes are good strength to resist crushing under the load in the furnace and in handling and charging, suitable degree of porosity, reactivity and size, and low sulphur, phosphorus and ash contents. The advantage of charcoal lies in its purity. Iron ores are commonly siliceous in gangue and usually, therefore, limestone (or sometimes dolomite), which should be as pure as possible, is used as flux; the ash from the coke has to be fluxed as well. The amount of flux clearly depends in particular on the ore. Certain ores are essentially self-fluxing; also calcareous (lime-rich) and siliceous ores may be used to flux each other. Apart from this consideration, a mixture of ores is often used and a portion of metallic scrap as well as scale and iron-rich slag.

In some countries, for example, Switzerland and Scandinavia, where fuel is expensive and electric power available, arc-furnaces are used for iron-smelting; in this case, only sufficient coke for reduction is required. Both shaft type and furnaces similar to those employed in steel-making have been used. However, the bulk of pig iron production in the world is in blast-furnaces operated continuously. The construction and layout of a modern blast-furnace plant is illustrated in Figs. 238 and 239. The hearth diameters of modern furnaces are from 18 ft. to 28 ft., and the number of tuyères ranges from around 8 to 20. The larger furnaces are a little more than 100 ft. high (to the top of the main bell) and with high-grade ores produce

FIG. 239. Modern blast-furnace at Vanderbijl Park, South Africa. This furnace has been producing 1000 short tons of pig iron per day. By courtesy of Ashmore, Benson, Pease & Co.

over 1000 tons of pig iron per day. The refractory lining is fireclay, although there is considerable development in the use of carbon blocks, especially in the hearth.

For even working, the charge should offer uniform resistance to the upward passage of the gases, and this requires careful charging and distribution. In modern furnaces, charging is automatic by skips on to a double-bell arrangement, which minimises loss of gas and pressure. The top hopper and bell are regularly rotated a definite amount to ensure even circumferential distribution. However, there is a general tendency for segregation of coarse material to the centre of the furnace and fine to the outside and this is not prevented. Recently, a modified mechanism, known as compensated charging, has been proposed to overcome the radial segregation, and is being tested. Bucket charging may also be used, but is not very common. A number of furnaces still remain in which barrows are lifted up to the furnace top by hoists, wheeled across a stage and the contents tipped on to the top bell by hand. The order of charging the ore, flux and fuel depends mainly on the size, physical nature and iron content of the ore.

The pig iron is tapped, for example about every six hours, and slag (or " cinder ") more frequently. The iron runs from the furnace through sand channels into sand **pig beds** (Fig. 240) ; a skimmer is arranged to separate slag coming off with the metal towards the end of the tap. In modern continuous pig casting machines the pigs are cast in metal moulds arranged on an endless conveyor.

In integrated iron and steel plants, the iron is usually stored molten in mixer furnaces with capacities up to and exceeding 1000 tons and in which fluctuations in composition are smoothed out. Mixers may be worked actively, when some refining is carried out. Steel foundries are separate from the iron plant and their raw material is solid pigs and steel scrap.

The slag is dumped or utilised for some purpose. Blast-furnace slags are used as ballast, road-making materials, in cements and for bricks. The possibility of using the slags as basic addition to oppose soil acidity has been quoted ; the ferrous slags generally employed as fertilisers are those rich in phosphorus from basic steel-making processes. An interesting application is the manufacture of slag wool (used for thermal insulation) by disintegrating molten slag with steam jets. Certain slags may disintegrate due to constitutional transformations accompanied by volume changes. Unstable slags may be stabilised by treating when molten with a limited amount of water, forming " foamed slag ".

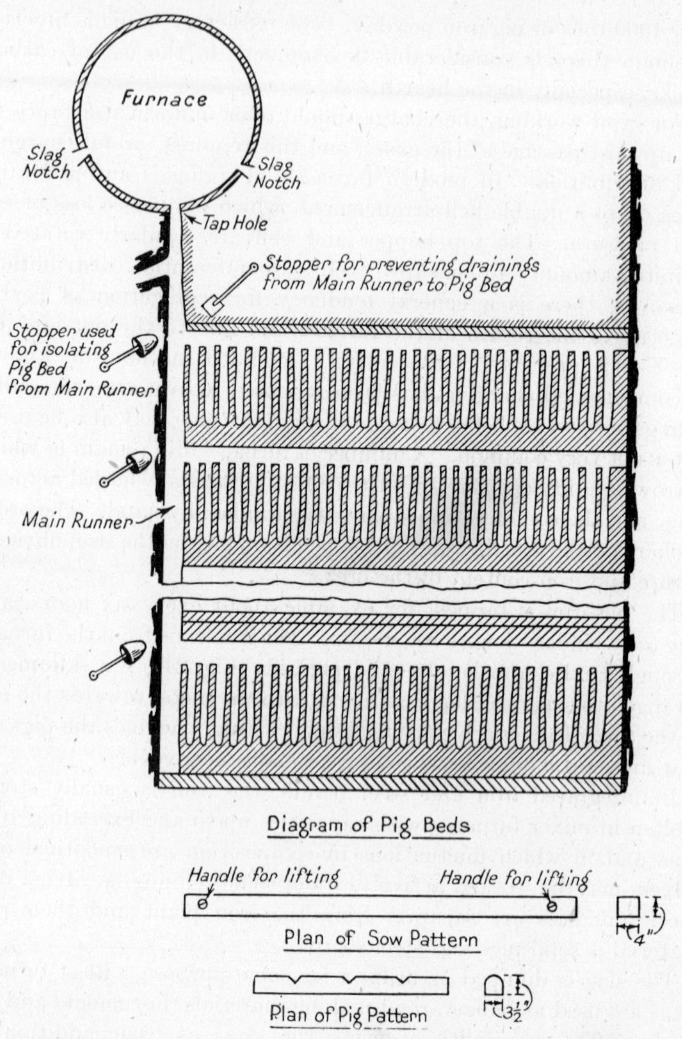

FIG. 240. Layout of pig bed. FIGS. 240, 241 and 242 are from G. R. Bashforth, *The Manufacture of Iron and Steel*, Chapman & Hall.

Blast-furnace gas. Up to about half the heating value of the coke charged to a blast-furnace remains in the gas passing off at the top. The gas is a lean mixture of essentially carbon monoxide, carbon dioxide and nitrogen, with a heating value of about a sixth of that of towns' gas. For highest economic efficiency it is essential that the blast-furnace gas be utilised. About 40 per cent of the total bulk is used for preheating the air blast and for power requirements on the furnace, for example, for the blowing engines. The excess is utilised for various purposes ; for example, it may be burnt to produce steam which is used in turbo-generators ; employed directly as fuel in gas engines driving generators ; or used in various furnaces such as steel-ingot heating furnaces, or after enrichment with other fuels, in the open hearth-furnaces. For furnace work, blast-furnace gas needs preheating as well as the air.

Before utilisation, the gas must be cleaned of its dust content, which otherwise chokes and corrodes the chequer brickwork of hot-blast stoves, clogs furnace valves and is clearly undesirable in gas engines. The blast-furnaces are generally equipped with primary dust catchers of some kind, in which the speed of the gas is reduced and the direction of flow changed, allowing dust to settle out (Fig. 238). Further cleaning is carried out by washing the dust out as a sludge, by dry filtration through cloth, by electrostatic precipitation or by a combination of these. In electrostatic precipitation the gas is passed through an electrical field of the order of 10,000 volts per in. The field is maintained between earthed steel tubes or plates, and wires or chains from which project points ; the positive electrodes hang between the steel plates or inside the tubes. The dust particles become charged, repelled from the positive and attracted to the negative electrodes. Periodically the gas flow is diverted, the current switched off and the negative electrodes knocked to ensure that all the dust has dropped off. In the wet type operating on moist gas from a washer, the dust is removed as a thin sludge flowing down the collector. The dust from the various cleaners may be incorporated in the sintering charge. Similar cleaning plant is used in non-ferrous plants, the main aim being to recover valuable fume and dust and to remove objectionable constituents before outlet into the atmosphere ; sulphur gases, which would also be objectionable, are used in sulphuric acid manufacture.

The air blast for the iron furnace is usually preheated in the range 550°–850° C. in stoves of various kinds, although a few furnaces are worked with cold blast. The preheating results in a saving in heat in the furnace, and enables higher temperatures to be reached. In the heating stoves (Fig. 238), blast-furnace gas is burnt for a time to heat up chequer brickwork ; then the burning is stopped, and air passed through in the reverse direction to be heated up. Each furnace has several such stoves working in sequence ; it is advantageous if some method of temperature equalisation can be applied. Thermal advantages also arise from drying the air blast, and both silica-gel and refrigeration have been applied, but drying is not usually carried out. Calculations and experiments show that reduced fuel consumption and increased production are to be expected from enriching the air blast with oxygen ; for a given proportion of coke the temperature at the tuyères would be increased.

A modern development, used in several American furnaces, is to operate the furnace with high gas pressure at the top, namely about 8–12 lb. per sq. in., instead of the usual value of about 2 lb. per sq. in. This enables the production rate to be increased by increasing the air blowing-rate ; the blowing pressure at the tuyères is raised from 12–15 to 20–25 lb. per sq. in. The high top pressure keeps down the rate of upward flow of the gases, the density being increased ; and thus ensures sufficient time of contact with the charge ; at the same time it opposes dust losses and " hanging " of the charge in the furnace, which would otherwise result. Alternatively, it has been suggested that lower coke consumption may be obtained from the modification. High top pressure has been tried in Scotland recently, but so far no conclusive results have been obtained.

Chemistry of pig iron manufacture. Heat is liberated around the tuyères where the coke is burnt to carbon dioxide, reduction to carbon monoxide following. Reduction of the iron oxides takes place largely in the solid state as the charge is descending in the stack, the main reducing agent being the carbon monoxide in the ascending gases. The nitrogen in the blast is essentially inactive from a chemical aspect, but is important in transferring heat from the combustion zone to the descending charge. Thus in normal furnaces a limit to the benefits of oxygen enrichment of the blast would be reached when the nitrogen content was so lowered that the top of the furnace became colder than about 100° C. and thus useless (the usual temperature is about 200–300° C.). Use of oxygen with advantage beyond this limit would probably mean a low shaft-less furnace and modified practice.

It should be noted that not all the coke charged reaches the tuyères ; some is used up earlier by direct reduction of iron oxide. In addition, an appreciable *solution-loss* occurs as the coke is descending by reduction of carbon dioxide in the gas stream to monoxide.

Melting of slag and metal commences in the bosh, where reduction of iron oxide is completed. Some reduction of other constituents of the charge occurs, especially in the hottest parts, the elements produced dissolving in the iron. Carbon is dissolved by both solid and liquid iron. Finally, molten slag and metal collect in the hearth.

The principal constituents of blast-furnace slags are aluminium oxide, calcium oxide and silica. There may be some magnesium oxide, depending on the ore and whether dolomite is used for fluxing. Generally, the slag has a $\frac{CaO+MgO}{SiO_2}$ ratio of the order of 1·4 with aluminium oxide between 10–20 per cent, although 15–18 per cent is often considered preferable.

The temperature reached by the slag collecting in the hearth depends mainly on its free-running temperature. It also depends to a lesser extent on the temperature of the combustion zone and the extent of the melting zone (through which the slag passes), which are increased by increasing the proportion of coke and the temperature of the blast. The free-running temperature of the slag is raised by increasing the lime content, although too much lime causes the slag to become unworkable. Increase in the lime creates a need for more heat, but the effect of raising the temperature in the combustion zone for a given slag composition is to increase the working rate rather than the slag temperature. The temperature of the iron is raised by any factors which increase the temperature of the combustion zone or slag.

A few per cent of *carbon* is always dissolved in the iron ; the final amount is affected by the temperature of the iron, its time of contact with the coke in the hearth and the amount of other elements present. Any possibility of control is outweighed by other considerations.

Essentially all the *phosphorus* in the charge is reduced and enters the iron.

Of the *manganese*, under average working 50–75 per cent of that in the charge may be reduced and dissolved in the iron. Increase of lime in the charge tends to increase the amount of manganese reduced. The manganese oxide acts as a base and combines with silica, but lime being a stronger base will displace it to be reduced. Further, the reduction of manganese oxide is endothermic and therefore is increased by rise in temperature.

Some *silicon* is also reduced and goes into the iron ; the amount is increased by rise in temperature, but increase in the lime counteracts this by fixing the silica in more stable combination.

About 90 per cent of the *sulphur* in the furnace enters via the coke, and several per cent of the total amount is found in the pig iron ; an important factor therefore in controlling sulphur is to use as pure coke as possible. It appears that a greater amount of sulphur than the final value is dissolved in the iron in its passage through the furnace, reaching a maximum at the tuyère level. Subsequent desulphurisation by the slag occurs at the main slag/metal interface and during passage of the iron globules through the slag layer.

Sulphur is taken to be dissolved in the molten iron as iron sulphide (FeS), although in fact the exact condition is uncertain. The presence of manganese tends to cause formation of insoluble manganese sulphide (MnS), or possibly (FeMn)S.

Sulphur in the form of ferrous sulphide is taken into the slag as calcium sulphide according to the reaction :

$$FeS + CaO + C \rightarrow CaS + Fe + CO \quad \text{.....................(1)}$$

which is a sum of :

$$FeS + CaO \rightarrow FeO + CaS \quad \text{.......................(1}a\text{)}$$

and

$$FeO + C \rightarrow Fe + CO \quad \text{..........................(1}b\text{)}$$

The reducing conditions in the blast-furnace favour the progress of (1*b*)and thus that of (1*a*) by removing the iron oxide. The insoluble manganese sulphide, on coming into contact with the slag, also reacts with the lime to form calcium sulphide :

$$MnS + CaO \rightarrow MnO + CaS.$$

For the reactions to proceed there must be available lime, and increase of the lime content of the slag, therefore, favours desulphurisation ; as does rise in temperature because of increased fluidity and diffusion, and because the formation of calcium sulphide is endothermic. The larger the volume of the slag the more sulphur is dissolved, and this is an important factor in desulphurisation.

It is also possible to desulphurise pig iron in the ladle on tapping from the blast-furnace by treatment with sodium carbonate (sometimes a high proportion of lime and fluorspar may be incorporated) according to the following reaction :

$$FeS \text{ (or } MnS) + Na_2CO_3 \rightarrow Na_2S + CO_2 + FeO \text{ (or } MnO)$$

If this process is used, the blast-furnace can be operated with more acid slag than otherwise.

STEEL-MAKING

Steel is made from pig iron by fire-refining treatments of an oxidising nature. In each case a slag is produced and two types of processes are distinguished, namely, *acid* and *basic*, depending on whether the slag is predominantly siliceous (acid) or high in lime (basic). Hence the furnace lining in contact with the slag is made of siliceous material, or basic material (such as dolomite or magnesite) according to the nature of the slag. The type of process operated depends on the raw material (Table 48). If sufficiently low in sulphur and phosphorus, the acid process is used and the slag is required to retain only the silica and manganese oxide produced by preferential oxidation from the iron ; the sulphur and phosphorus contents of the charge have actually to be lower than required, because of concentration during the process. In both processes the carbon is eliminated as carbon monoxide. The basic process is used where in addition phosphorus elimination is required ; it is also able to remove sulphur. The additional refining is achieved by using slags high in lime, which will be free to react with and retain the phosphorus as calcium phosphate* after its oxidation, and will combine with and dissolve sulphur, according to the following reactions :

$$2P + 5FeO + nCaO \rightarrow n(CaO) . P_2O_5 + 5Fe \text{ (heat evolved)}$$

$$FeS + CaO + C \rightarrow CaS + Fe + CO \text{ (heat absorbed)}$$

It will be seen that whereas removal of phosphorus requires oxidising conditions, best desulphurising is obtained with reducing conditions, which can only be realised in electric arc furnace practice. It should be noted also that desulphurising is favoured by high temperatures, but dephosphorising, being exothermic, is better suited by lower temperatures. In the basic process, the silicon in the charge should be low, as otherwise extra lime is needed to neutralise it after oxidation. Both acid and basic processes are operated in the open-hearth furnace, the Bessemer converter and the electric arc furnace ; but the greatest amount of steel is made by basic open-hearth practice.

Bessemer converter process. In the **Bessemer converter process** (Figs. 241-43), the oxidation is carried out by blowing air through the molten pig iron, which is charged in this condition at about 1210°–1250° C. by ladle from mixer or cupola. Under these conditions of oxidation, the other elements are eliminated substantially in order of their affinity for oxygen at the prevailing temperatures, that is silicon and manganese first, followed by the carbon and lastly, during the so-called " after-blow " (in the basic process), the phosphorus. No external heating is used, the oxidation of the metalloids, especially silicon in the acid process, and phosphorus and manganese in the basic process, supplies the heat necessary both to keep the iron molten and raise the temperature as purification proceeds and the melting point of the metal consequently rises. The composition of the iron used in the process is thus governed partly by the heat requirements (Table 48).

* Such slags are utilised as fertilisers, when sufficiently rich in soluble phosphorus.

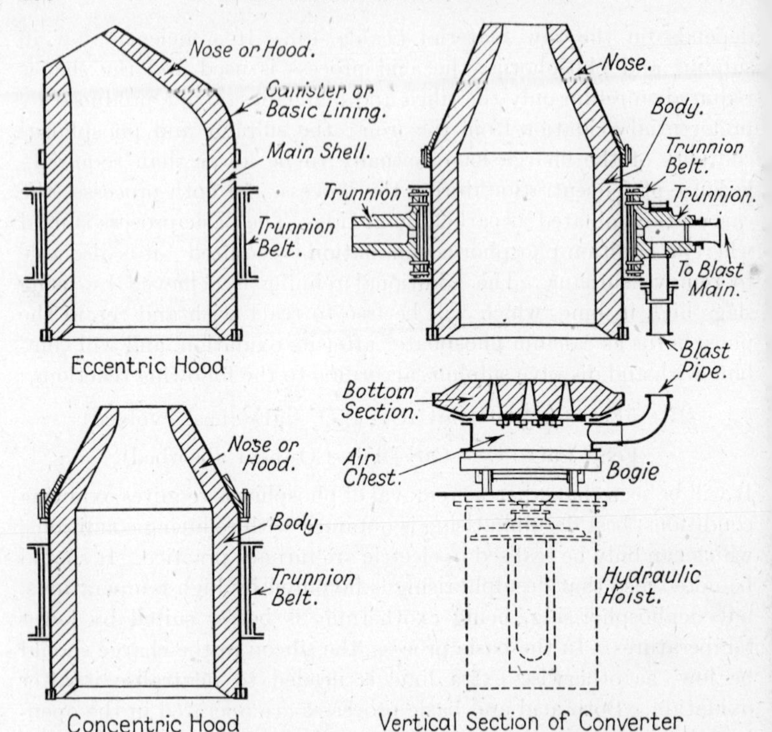

Fig. 241. Details of Bessemer converter. From Bashforth. Capacities range from 5 to 30 tons, although larger, up to 60 tons, are used in Germany.

Usually at some stage during the blow, steel scrap (up to about 15 per cent of the charge) is added to cool the metal. On the other hand, if the temperature is too low, ferrosilicon can be added, or the converter turned down so that some of the blast blows across the surface, quickly generating heat.

The refining sequence can be followed by the appearance of the flame at the mouth of the converter ; the end-point of the blow in the basic process is confirmed by the appearance of a spoon sample of the metal. In America, where only the acid process is used, a photo-electric method has been developed to follow the progress of the blow ; experiments have been made in Great Britain, but the technique is not utilised in normal practice. Spectroscopic techniques have also been investigated. The whole refining operation is very rapidly completed, taking time of the order of 20 minutes. Thus a 25-ton converter, for example, has a very considerable daily output.

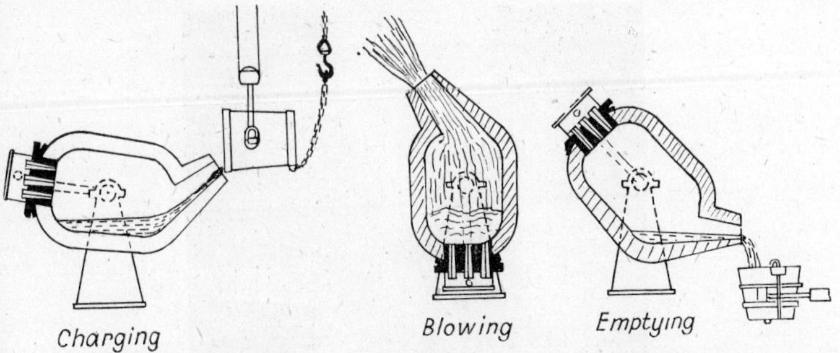

FIG. 242. Operation of Bessemer converter. From Bashforth.

In the acid Bessemer process, the slag is composed of the oxidation products silica and manganese oxide, together with some iron oxide and a certain amount of the refractory lining. In the basic process, burnt lime (about 300 lb. per ton of iron) is added to make the basic slag.

There are only three Bessemer plants in Britain producing steel ingots ; two use the basic process and the other the acid.

The Bessemer process results in removal of the metalloids to very low contents and some oxidation of the iron, producing essentially an impure iron. Therefore, after converting, the composition is adjusted and the melt deoxidised by appropriate additions. In Swedish practice, which employs the acid process, the metal is blown down to the required composition ; the bath is sampled and tested for carbon during blowing. The steel has a high reputation for quality.

It has been generally considered that Bessemer steel was likely to be inconsistent in properties because of the difficulty of control. However, the Bessemer Sub-Committee of the British Iron and Steel Research Association reported in 1949 that the thorough and regular control of the present-day Bessemer practice results in a regular output of high quality steel.

Bessemer steel differs from open-hearth steel of the same carbon content in several respects and the differences govern its application. It has better machining qualities and, it is claimed, welding qualities, higher tensile strength, higher degree of work-hardening, but a greater tendency to embrittlement due to strain-ageing and quench-ageing. The differences have been attributed to the higher phosphorus and nitrogen contents of Bessemer steel, and to the generally higher degree of oxidation in manufacture. It seems that all these factors play their part, and are not necessarily the only factors involved.

FIG. 243. Bessemer converter during blowing. By courtesy of the British Iron & Steel Federation.

In one of the British basic works, low-nitrogen Bessemer steel is produced by careful temperature control, so that the final figure is between 1580° and 1600°C ; the temperature of each blow is taken by immersion thermo-couple. As well as temperature, the pressure of the blast, its nitrogen content and the time of contact with the metal are important factors affecting the nitrogen content of the final steel.

In the other British basic plant, low-nitrogen steel is made, as required, by using a shallower bath of metal in the converter, resulting in a lower blast pressure and shorter time of contact with the metal, and by adding iron oxide in the form of ore or mill-scale. The oxide has a cooling effect, so that the usual scrap steel additions are not made. By this modification the usual nitrogen content of about 0·015 per cent is approximately halved and at the same time the phosphorus content is considerably lowered ; a typical nitrogen content of open-hearth steel is 0·005 per cent. It is stated that the steel produced approaches open-hearth steel in properties. The final position will probably be that the differing characteristics of Bessemer steel will be controlled to suit the application.

Oxygen enrichment of the blast should also lower the nitrogen content of the steel. It is claimed that other advantages should arise from oxygen enrichment in the converter. A number of trials have been made, especially on the Continent, and favourable results are reported; this procedure has been used for a number of years at a basic plant in Bavaria. Oxygen has also been used successfully, diluted with carbon dioxide (or steam) to reduce the reaction temperature at the tuyères, in the dephosphorising stage of the basic process when nitrogen absorption is high.

For foundry work, small acid converters are used, generally of a modified side-blown type known as the **Tropenas.** The blast does not pass through the metal, but across the surface of the bath (thus high nitrogen does not result), giving more heating because the carbon monoxide is burnt to dioxide. A slag layer rich in iron oxide is produced, from which oxygen is transferred to the metal. The charge for the converters is melted in cupolas; it consists of steel scrap and pig iron. Carbon is picked up in the cupola; the silicon content (for heating) is adjusted by ferrosilicon additions to the cupola charge, or before or during the blow in the converter. The cupola metal may be desulphurised by soda ash treatment. In the Stock side-blown converter, solid pig iron is charged and melted with oil burners introduced through the tuyères, before being blown to steel.

Oxygen enrichment has been applied in Britain to side-blown converter practice on the commercial scale; the blast contains 30 per cent oxygen by volume compared with the 21 per cent in air. The advantages are a shorter time of blowing, and hotter metal, or reduction in the amount of pig iron or ferrosilicon necessary. Against this, of course, as with every application of oxygen, must be offset the cost of oxygen. It has been suggested that a basic side-blown process (with oxygen enrichment) might be developed for the large-scale production of ingots.

The use of oxygen directly in metal winning has been restricted hitherto by the cost of production. In spite of recent developments, the cost remains relatively high; but further improvements concurrent with increased use are to be expected. It must be stressed that oxygen is not a fuel. The advantages of enrichment lie in the decrease in the amount of inert ballast, the nitrogen. Thus in heating processes, the fraction of the energy of the fuel available above the working temperature is increased. In the case of direct use in refining, the process is speeded up and this may also cause a useful rise in temperature. In general, with higher temperatures and sometimes more violent reaction refractory wear is likely to be increased.

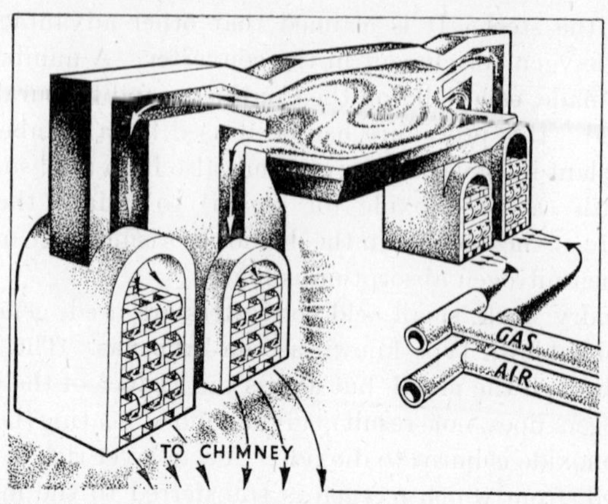

FIG. 244. Principle of open-hearth furnace. The reversals in the regenerators are made every 10–20 minutes. By courtesy of the British Iron & Steel Federation.

Open-hearth practice. Considerable proportions of steel scrap are usually incorporated in the charge for the open-hearth furnace; the process originated with an all-pig charge, but various proportions have been used, including all steel scrap, depending on supplies; however, the majority of operations is with the proportion of pig in the range 25–75 per cent. The furnace may be regarded as a special form of reverberatory. The charge is contained in a relatively shallow hearth, and heating is by means of a gas, oil, tar or combination flame burning across the top, alternately from each end, employing the regenerative principle for preheating the air and lower-grade gases (such as producer) when used (Figs. 244–46 and 248–51).

In the *acid process* the working hearth is made of silica sand sintered into place; the *basic hearth* is made of mixtures of calcined magnesite or dolomite and the basic slag.

The temperature of working in the open-hearth furnace is limited by the maximum safe working temperature of the silica roof, which up to the present is almost universal in basic as well as acid furnaces. This temperature is about 1660° C., and thus the speed of melting is restricted; as the minimum tapping temperature of many grades of steel is in the range 1590–1620° C., it does not leave much latitude. Basic roofs made of mixtures of chromite and magnesite have been developed and used in some cases. These have higher working temperatures, although they are more expensive and heavier than silica and have certain disadvantages in use.

The use of oxygen in the open-hearth furnace offers a means of increasing the production rate. The main improvement with respect to combustion lies in shortening the melting time, especially when large amounts of steel scrap are used, by using oxygen to raise the flame temperature when the rate of heat input is not sufficiently rapid to bring the roof temperature to the limit. Considerable full-scale work is going on in America with liquid fuel furnaces, the oxygen being injected with the fuel. It might also be advantageous to use oxygen to control the flame at later stages in the process.

The open-hearth furnaces usually have considerably larger capacities than converters, but the time of operation is much longer, varying according to the amount of refining that has to be carried out from about 6 to 20 hours. Basic furnaces range in capacity from 10 to 400 tons* ; the larger sizes in particular are of the tilting type. Acid furnaces are usually fixed and smaller, namely up to about

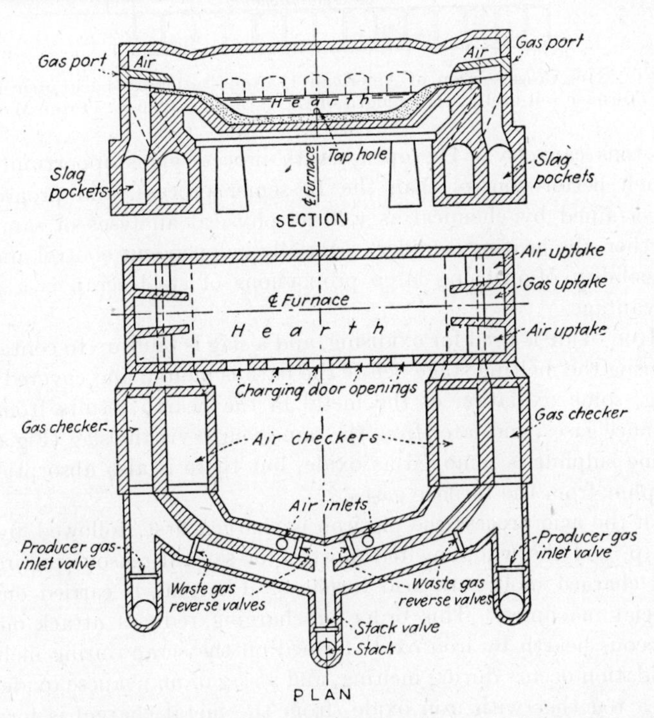

FIG. 245. Open-hearth furnace fired with producer gas. FIGS. 245 and 246 are from H. K. Work, *Basic Open Hearth Steelmaking*, American Inst. Min. Met. Eng.

* A 550-ton furnace is in operation in America.

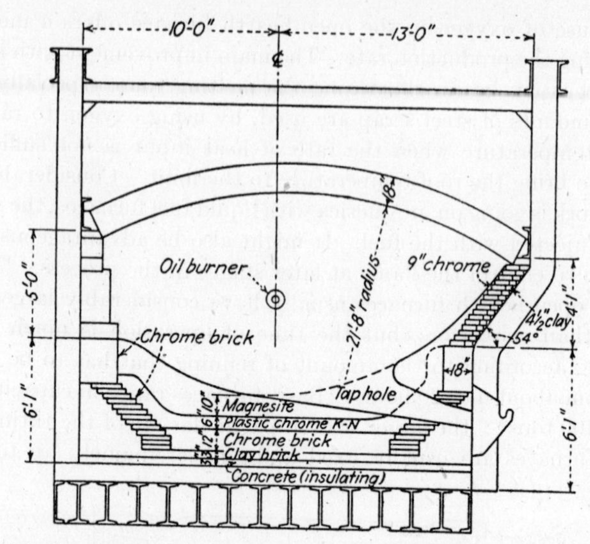

FIG. 246. Cross-section of American 175-ton stationary basic open-hearth furnace (oil-fired). The length of the furnace is 82·5 ft. From Work.

80 tons capacity. The open-hearth process gives opportunity for much better control than the Bessemer process, and progress is ascertained by chemical as well as physical analyses of samples; further, the heating is under essentially independent control and the possibility of utilising large proportions of steel scrap is a great advantage.

Iron oxide is used for oxidising, and a slag is built up to contain it. During the melting stage before the bath is molten and covered with slag, some oxidation of the metal in the hearth results from the furnace gases, and later from the same source via the slag (Fig. 247). Some sulphur is removed as oxide, but there is also absorption of sulphur from the furnace gases.

In the **acid process** the pig iron is charged first, followed by the scrap, and the whole melted down; for several reasons pig iron is not charged molten to acid furnaces. Charging is carried out by special machines. This order of charging reduces attack on the siliceous hearth by iron oxide formed on the scrap during melting. Oxidation occurs during melting, and a slag of manganese oxide and silica together with iron oxide (from the metal charge) is formed. After melting, iron ore (Fe_2O_3) or mill-scale (Fe_3O_4) (a purer form of iron oxide) is added to continue and complete the oxidation; additions of lime are also made to control the slag (Table 52).

TABLE 52. TYPICAL CHANGES IN METAL AND SLAG COMPOSITION IN ACID OPEN-HEARTH PROCESS (Dawtry, Hatfield and Wright)

	When completely melted	1 hr. after melting	2 hr. after melting	3 hr. after melting	4 hr. after melting	5 hr. after melting	6 hr. after melting before adding finishings
				Metal			
Carbon %	1·30	1·18	1·04	0·70	0·48	0·32	0·26
Silicon %	0·55	0·48	0·08	0·06	0·07	0·07	0·07
Manganese %	0·24	0·20	0·06	0·08	0·09	0·08	0·07
Oxygen %	0·004	0·004	0·008	0·012	0·015	0·016	0·018
				Slag			
Silica (SiO_2) %	48·00	48·00	54·0	58·0	58·0	59·5	59·5
Iron oxide (FeO) %	27·00	27·00	18·0	12·0	11·0	11·2	11·0
Manganese oxide (MnO) %	15·00	14·50	12·0	11·5	11·0	11·0	10·5
Lime (CaO) %	0·50	0·50	6·0	12·0	13·0	13·5	13·8

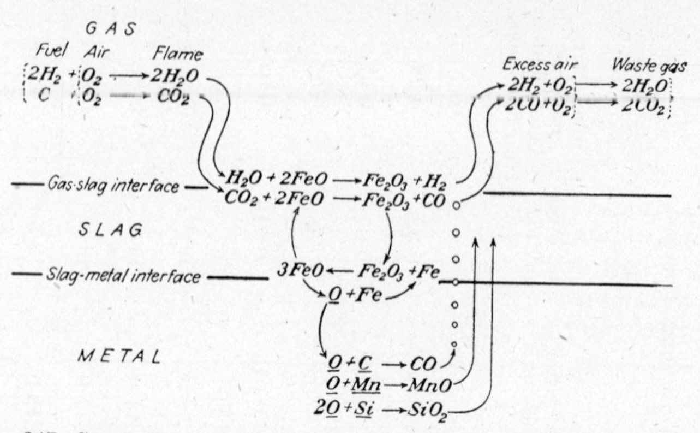

Fig. 247. Suggested mechanism of oxidation in open-hearth process. From F. M. Washburn, *Basic Open Hearth Steelmaking*. American Inst. Min. Met. Eng.

The **basic process** is the more important, and the following indicates typical procedure for a charge of steel scrap with about fifty per cent or more hot metal (pig), in a fixed furnace, although a number of variations in detail are possible. The hearth, after the previous charge has been tapped, is fettled or repaired with raw or burnt dolomite. Limestone is charged first, followed by ore, steel scrap and then any solid pig iron or old ingot moulds. Limestone will not harm a basic hearth, although it is sometimes preferred to charge

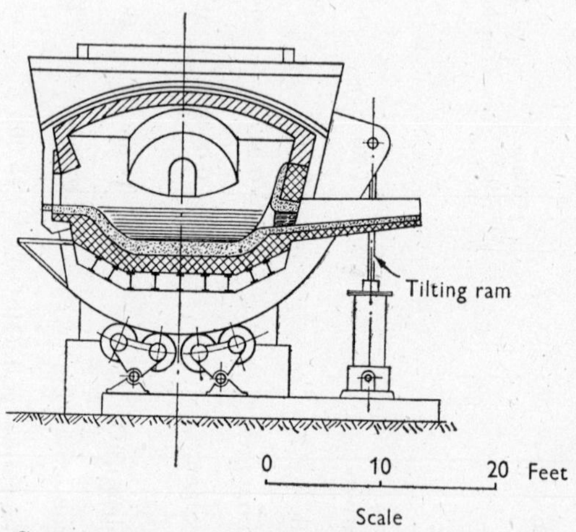

Fig. 248. Cross-section of a British 250-ton tilting basic open-hearth furnace (producer gas fired).

some steel scrap first ; pig should not be charged directly on to a basic hearth. The heat, which has been partly on during charging, is then put on full. With large amounts and especially of light scrap, this material may be charged in stages.

When the temperature has reached at least about 1200° C, and the charge is beginning to melt, the molten pig iron is poured in from a ladle via a chute. The iron oxide in the furnace (ore and that formed on the scrap) reacts with the metalloids in the pig, although at first the reactions should not be too vigorous. As heating continues,

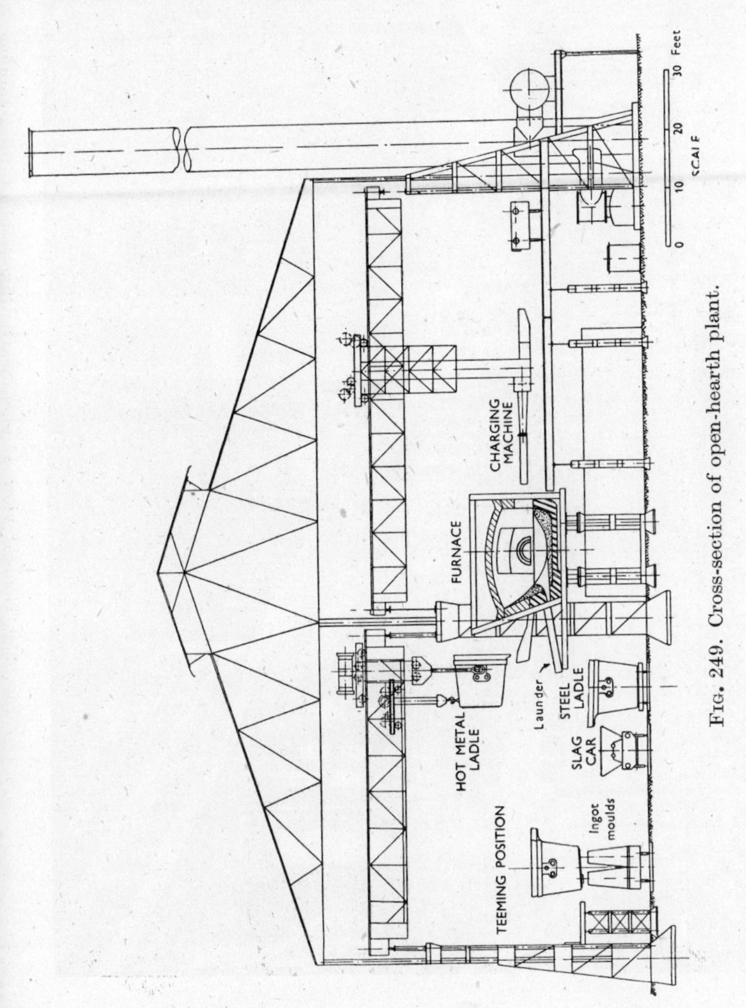

FIG. 249. Cross-section of open-hearth plant.

Fig. 250. General view of open-hearth (fixed) plant from tapping side

Fig. 251. Open-hearth plant from charging side. By courtesy of the Wellman Smith Owen Eng. Corp. Ltd.

reaction in the furnace does become more vigorous, and considerable amounts of carbon monoxide are evolved from the oxidation of the carbon, causing foaming of the slag, which may be sufficient for some to be run off through the slag notch. This can be useful, for some phosphate and silica will be removed in the slag without a great loss of lime, which in the main should still be at the bottom of the furnace. The practice of running off slag at this stage is followed with high proportions of hot metal in the charge which result in a high slag volume.

As the temperature in the furnace increases, calcination of the limestone commences, although on adding the hot metal the main gas evolved is carbon monoxide, producing what is known as the "ore boil". Later, with the higher temperatures, and as the ore boil subsides, there is rapid evolution of carbon dioxide, the "lime boil" occurs and the lime starts coming to the surface. Some oxidation results from this carbon dioxide.

These boiling actions and that later, when the bath is fully molten and oxidation of the carbon is continuing, are valuable in purging the metal of hydrogen and nitrogen. Further, the agitation promotes better contact between metal and slag, thus speeding up refining and improving heat transfer.

TABLE 53. ANALYSES OF METAL AND SLAG AND LOG SHEET IN FIXED BASIC OPEN-HEARTH PROCESS (Lintern and Hacking)
[60-ton furnace, fired with producer gas]

	When melted (*a*)	2 hours after melting (*b*)	¾ hour after (*b*) (*c*)	Finished steel (*d*)
Per cent		*Metal*		
Carbon	1·10	0·61	0·540	0·56
Silicon	—	—	—	0·103
Sulphur	0·042	0·038	0·031	0·034
Phosphorus	0·380	0·045	0·035	0·035
Manganese	—	0·23	0·30	0·57
		Slag		
Silica (SiO_2)	19·4	14·0	11·8	—
Ferrous oxide (FeO)	3·33	5·76	9·42	—
Ferric oxide (Fe_2O_3)	2·13	3·71	2·00	—
Alumina (Al_2O_3)	1·22	1·31	1·37	—
Manganous oxide (MnO)	8·74	6·82	5·95	—
Lime (CaO)	50·5	52·2	53·9	—
Magnesia (MgO)	5·07	5·21	6·70	—
Phosphorus pentoxide (P_2O_5)	8·60	9·73	7·33	—
Sulphur	0·19	0·27	0·38	—

TABLE 53—*continued*

		tons	cwt.	tons	cwt.
p.m.					
9.00	Finished fettling.				
	1st run of scrap charged - - - - -			9	6
9.50	2nd run of scrap charged - - - - -			10	18
11.00	Partly burnt lime charged -	2	8		
	3rd run of scrap charged - - - - -			6	8
a.m.					
12.30	4th run of scrap charged - - - - -			8	0
1.40	Broken moulds charged (cast iron) - - -			6	0
2.45	Mixer metal charged (C 3·0%/Si 0·56%/ S 0·028%/ P 1·6%/Mn 1·2%) - - - - - - -			18	5
	Total metallic charge - - - - -			58	17
3.50	2 cwt. fluospar fed.				
4.55	2 cwt. fluorspar fed.				
5.30	Clear melted. Slag and metal samples taken—see analysis (*a*).				
5.50	10 cwt. burnt lime fed.				
	6 cwt. mill scale fed.				
6.20	6 cwt. mill scale fed.				
	2 cwt. fluorspar fed.				
6.35	10 cwt. burnt lime fed.				
	6 cwt. mill scale fed.				
7.00	6 cwt. mill scale fed.				
7.25	Slag and metal samples taken—see analysis (*b*).				
7.27	First slag off.				
7.35	1 cwt. mill scale fed.				
7.45	4 cwt. Spiegel and 10 cwt. burnt lime fed.				
7.55	5 cwt. burnt lime fed.				
8.05	3 cwt. burnt lime fed.				
8.15	Slag and metal samples taken—see analysis (*c*).				
8.20	10 cwt. burnt lime fed.				
8.25	6 cwt. burnt lime fed.				
8.30	Tapped.				

Finishing materials	cwt.	qu.
Ferro-manganese - - -	0	2
Silico-manganese - - -	4	2
45% ferro-silicon - - -	1	0

Wt. of steel tapped, 56 tons 4 cwt.
Ingots cast, 24 and 20 cwt. scrap end.
Final analysis (pit sample) – see (*d*)

Note : At this plant, ore additions with the metallic charge are arranged to give a carbon figure at melt-out of 0·60% higher than the final. No ore or scale was needed in this particular case.

It should be appreciated that the characteristics of the " heat " are modified by the composition of the charge and method of working. Thus with low proportions of hot metal and no ore in the initial charge, the vigour of the oxide/metalloid reaction is greatly reduced. Further, if burnt lime is charged instead of limestone, there is no lime boil.

Eventually, when the lime has properly joined the slag, the charge is completely molten. By this time the silicon will have been practically eliminated as well as a good proportion of the carbon, phosphorus and manganese. Thereafter, additions of ore and limestone or burnt lime are made to reduce the carbon and phosphorus to the required amount and dissolve as much sulphur as possible; it is usual for residual manganese of the order, for example, of 0·2 per cent to remain during refining. Fluorspar may be added to thin the slag; an advantage is that higher lime may be carried with satisfactory fluidity, thus promoting better desulphurisation; but fluorspar impairs the usefulness of the slag as a fertiliser. It is usually arranged that the carbon content when the charge is melted down is about 0·5 per cent higher than required in the finished steel. The bath is best worked so that the carbon is just below the required figure at the end of refining. The carbon in deoxidant and alloy additions will then bring it up to that required. Sometimes it is necessary to add carbon as anthracite or coke in the ladle on tapping, although, in general, procedure involving large additions in this way is not favoured. In certain circumstances the carbon content is raised by additions of pig iron to the furnace. Typical procedure and analyses at various stages can be followed in detail in Tables 53-55.

The rate of carbon elimination from the liquid bath is increased by blowing in oxygen or air through steel pipes or "lances", due to the increased agitation and rate of oxygen supply, although the resulting splashing is harmful to the refractories. In some cases the value of the oxygen lance lies in quickly raising the bath temperature. The oxygen lance is having considerable full-scale use in America.

In tilting furnaces, slags can be poured off as required and all or part of the steel can be cast at one time.

As the metal in the open-hearth usually retains appreciable amounts of metalloids, it is not as oxidised as the metal in the Bessemer process at the end of refining and thus needs less deoxidation. Further, in the acid open-hearth process, by controlling the final slag to a low iron oxide content, by virtue of the partition the oxygen content of the metal in contact may be minimised.

The usual finishing additions for steel, used in appropriate combinations, are ferro-manganese (about 80 per cent Mn; 5–7 per cent C; 0·5–1 per cent Si); spiegel (about 16–20 per cent Mn; 5–6 per cent C; 1 per cent Si), ferro-silicon (various grades); and

TABLE 54. WORKING OF A TYPICAL CHARGE IN 100-TON BASIC FURNACE (FIXED: COKE-OVEN GAS-FIRED) USING HIGH PROPORTION OF HOT METAL (Geary)

p.m.
11.25 Charge tapped.
12.00 Tap hole closed.

a.m.
12.25 Fettling finished.
12.25 Charging started.
12.35 10 tons 11 cwt. scrap charged.
1.15 6 tons 8 cwt. limestone and 26 tons Swedish ore charged.
1.30 11 tons 13 cwt. pig iron charged.
2.10 44 tons 10 cwt. mixer metal.
2.40 40 tons 0 cwt. mixer metal; analysis: C 3·65%, Si 1·25%, S 0·044%, P 1·23%.
3.15 3 tons slag off.
5.00 6 tons slag off.
6.05 42 cwt. burnt lime.
6.30 30 cwt. ore, 28 cwt. lime.
6.43 Sample: C 1·73%, S 0·043%, P 0·26%.
6.55 30 cwt. ore, 28 cwt. lime.
7.30 30 cwt. ore, 14 cwt. lime.
8.30 3 cwt. spar, 5 cwt. scale.
9.00 3 tons slag off.

a.m.
9.07 Sample: C 0·65%, S 0·04%, P 0·03%.
9.30 14 cwt. lime.
10·03 Sample: C 0·65%, P 0·03%
10.15 14 cwt. lime.
10.38 Sample: C 0·62%.
10.40 Slag sample: Fe 6·0%.
10.45 14 cwt. lime.
11.00 7 cwt. lime.
11.10 7 cwt. lime.
11.12 Sample: C 0·55%, P 0·028%, Mn 0·07%.
11.25 Sample: C 0·54%, Mn 0·06%.
11.37 Sample: C 0·53%.
11.45 Tapped.

Some ferro alloys are added to the bath, the final adjustment of the carbon, manganese and silicon being made in the ladle.

Weight of ingots, 105 tons 10 cwt.
Final analysis (pit sample)
C 0·62 / Si 0·13 / S 0·033 / P 0·035 / Mn 0·77%.

TABLE 55. WORKING OF TYPICAL BASIC CHARGE IN 80-TON FIXED FURNACE (FIRED WITH MIXED COKE-OVEN AND PRODUCER GAS) (Drewery)

a.m.
7.00 Furnace tapped.
7.15 Bottom dried up.
7.20 Tap-hole closed. Fettling.
7.55 Warming bottom.
8.00 Commenced charging.
8.15 9 tons scrap charged.
9.00 9 tons of ore and 5 tons of limestone charged followed by further 19 tons scrap and 2 tons pig iron.
10.45 53 tons mixer metal charged (C 3·80%; Si 0·47%; S 0·039%; P 1·22%; Mn 0·85%
11.00 Slagging.
11.30 About 3 tons of slag off.

p.m.
1.25 Sample drawn and judged.
1.30 20 cwt. Swedish ore fed.
2.10 Sample: C 0·70%; S 0·051%.
2.15 20 cwt. Swedish ore.
2.30 40 cwt. burnt lime, 8 cwt. fluorspar charged.

p.m.
3.00 Sample: C 0·35%; S 0·044%; P 0·25%.
3.05 29 cwt. scale charged.
3.10 Slagging, 1 ton run off.
3.25 Sample: C 0·26%; Mn, 0·14%; P 0·05%.
3.26 20 cwt. burnt lime charged.
3.46 Sample: C 0·19%; P 0·04%.
3.50 Tapped.

Pit Sample Analysis: C 0·21%; Si 0·034%; S 0·0317%; P 0·036%; Mn 0·46%.
Weight of ingots, 80 tons 12 cwt.

Typical finishing additions are:

ferro-manganese	0·15	cwt./ton of steel
ferro-silicon	0·03	
silicon-manganese	0·01	

About half the ferro-manganese is added to bath; remainder of finishings introduced in ladle.

silico-manganese (for example, Mn 65–70/Si 17–20/C 1·5) ; and also aluminium, which is an extremely stringent deoxidant. These materials are added in the furnace or to the steel in the ladle. With basic practice, care has to be exercised in the addition of finishers in the presence of slag, as there is a danger of reducing phosphorus back into the metal. However, in the basic open-hearth process, wherever possible some deoxidation is carried out in the furnace, as this allows for better separation of deoxidation products ; other additions are then made in the ladle. In basic converter practice the bulk of the slag is poured off first and additions made in converter or ladle. Aluminium is not added to the furnace but in the ladle, although sometimes part may be added in the ingot moulds. The efficiency of various elements for the deoxidation of steel may be compared by reference to Fig. 185, page 229.

When making alloy steels in the open-hearth furnace, the extra elements, usually in alloy form, are added at the end of the heat, due to their high affinity for oxygen. Nickel, copper and molybdenum have less affinity for oxygen than iron and may be added earlier, even during charging ; they can be charged in the form of steel scrap. The steels made in the converter are usually plain carbon, but when extra alloying additions are required they can be made at the end of the blow.

Steel for castings, and high-carbon and most alloy steel ingots, require thorough deoxidation or **killing**. But low-carbon steel ingots for rolling, especially with less than 0·15 per cent carbon, may be only partly deoxidised, giving rise to controlled gas evolution on solidification due to reaction between the remaining iron oxide and the carbon generating carbon monoxide, some of which is retained in the steel as porosity. This produces the type of steel known as **rimming steel** (p. 376). The great majority of steel is cast into ingots for working (pp. 368-68).

The **arc-furnace** (Fig. 252) uses a steel charge comprising scrap steel, or molten steel made in some other process, for finishing. The furnace is used for making high-grade carbon steels and in particular alloy steels. The basic type offers the greatest scope. Higher temperatures are independently possible in the arc furnace and thus more basic slags can be used ; there is no fuel combustion to produce contamination, and especially advantageous is the fact that both oxidising and reducing conditions can be achieved. The latter is utilised in various ways to minimise loss of oxidisable elements such as chromium in alloy steel practice when considerable alloy steel scrap is incorporated in the charge.

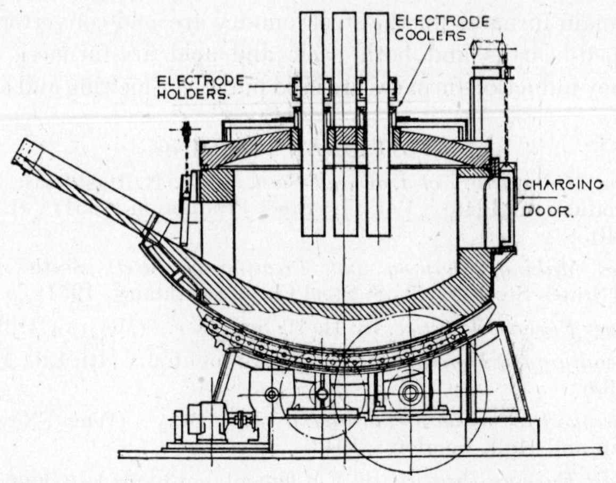

Fig. 252. Electric-arc steel furnace. From A. G. Robiette, *Electric Melting Practice*, Griffin. The arcs are struck between the three carbon electrodes via the charge. In Britain, the largest furnaces have about 35 tons capacity, but in America capacities range up to at least 100 tons. Normally the furnaces are circular in plan, but the 100-ton units may be elliptical (with six electrodes).

In one common procedure in the arc furnace, a basic oxidising slag is built up during melting, removing in particular carbon and phosphorus ; this can be taken off and a reducing slag containing lime, fluorspar, silica, carbon and/or ferrosilicon made up, giving a very high degree of desulphurisation and good deoxidation ; additions of the required ferro-alloys are made during this stage, or sometimes to the ladle.

A modern development in arc-furnace practice is the use of an oxygen lance for injecting high-pressure oxygen into the bath, during the oxidation period. This removes carbon more rapidly than by ore alone ; during lancing, the arc is not needed for heating. The use of the oxygen lance has special advantages in the manufacture of stainless steel.

"Armco" iron is made in the open-hearth furnace. Wrought iron is made by melting pig iron and oxidising with iron oxide in a **puddling furnace**, which is of reverberatory type, with an inner lining of iron oxide. The temperature is such that the purified iron is obtained in the pasty state. It is withdrawn from the furnace containing and coated with entrapped slag and thoroughly worked, during which some of the slag is removed. In an American process (Aston or Aston-Byer), iron is blown in converters and poured into a bath of slag maintained at such a temperature that the iron forms a pasty lump, which is withdrawn and worked.

The main furnaces for the steel foundry are acid converters, small acid open-hearths and both basic and acid arc-furnaces. High-frequency induction furnaces are used purely for melting and alloying.

ADDITIONAL READING

1. *The Manufacture of Iron and Steel*, by G. R. Bashforth. Vol. I. Iron Production (1948). Vol. II. Steel Production (1951). (Chapman and Hall).

2. *The Making, Shaping and Treating of Steel*, Sixth Edition. (United States Steel Co. U.S. Steel Corp. Subsidiary, 1951).

3. *Blast Furnace Practice*, by R. H. Sweetser. (McGraw-Hill, 1938.)

4. *Metallurgy of Iron and Steel*, by B. Stoughton. (4th Ed., McGraw-Hill, 1934).

5. *Ferrous Production Metallurgy*, by J. L. Bray. (Wiley, New York : Chapman and Hall, London : 1942).

6. *Blast Furnace Practice*, by F. Clements. (3 vols.). (Benn, 1929).

7. *Symposium on Steelmaking*, (Acid and Basic Open-Hearth Practice). Special Report No. 22 (Iron and Steel Inst., 1938).

8. *Basic Open Hearth Steelmaking*. Seeley W. Mudd Series. Physical Chemistry of Steelmaking Committee (American Inst. of Min. and Met. Eng., 1944).

9. *Report on The Bessemer Process*. Special Report No. 42. (Iron and Steel Inst., 1949).

10. References to papers on Thermodynamics of Ferrous Processes are given at the end of Chapter 8.

11. *The Use of the Oxygen Lance in British Electric Furnace Practice*, by T. H. Harris, W. H. Everard, and D. J. O. Brandt, J. Iron and Steel Inst., 165, 399, (1950).

12. *Refractories*. by F. H. Norton. (McGraw-Hill, 1942).

13. *Steelplant Refractories*, by J. H. Chesters. (United Steel Companies Ltd., 1944).

14. *The Instrumentation of Open-Hearth Furnaces*, British Iron and Steel Res. Assoc. (Allen and Unwin, 1951).

The following are recommended for the physical and engineering metallurgy of iron and steel.

15. *Metallurgy for Engineers*, by E. C. Rollason. (2nd Edit., Arnold, 1949).

16. *Metals*, Vol. II, by (Sir) H. Carpenter and J. M. Robertson. (Oxf. Univ. Press, 1939).

17. *Steels in Modern Industry*, W. E. Benbow (editor). (Iliffe, 1951).

18. *Engineering Steels*, by L. Aitchison and W. I. Pumphrey. (Macdonald and Evans, 1953).

CHAPTER 11

METAL MELTING, ALLOYING AND CASTING IN PRACTICE

Melting. Steel castings and ingots for working are generally cast directly from the refining furnace in which the steel is made. In certain cases there may be a separate melting and alloying stage. In the cast iron foundry, the pigs cast at the blast furnace are re-melted and any extra alloying carried out. Pure copper ingots for working are cast directly from the refining furnace. With copper for castings and other non-ferrous metals, usually the refined metal is cast into notched bar ingots (Fig. 253) or sometimes slabs, of suitable sizes. These ingots are remelted, alloyed as required and cast into final shapes or ingots for working. Clean scrap of known composition is often incorporated at the melting stage. The various procedures are due partly to metallurgical factors and partly to the structure of the industry.

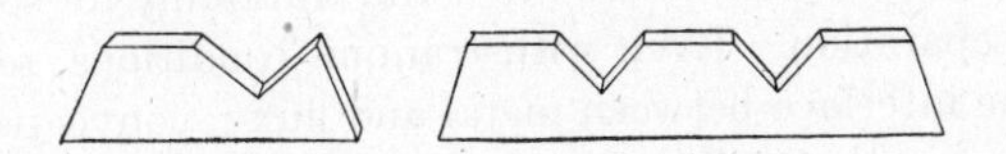

FIG. 253. Notched bar ingots (copper).

Although melting implies an inert process, in fact reactions with the atmosphere and even the crucible are often involved, and various precautions become necessary. Impurities may also be introduced with the metal as mechanically entrapped slag or electrolyte, surface moisture, corrosion products, grease and oil ; or in combination with the metal, such as oxygen in fire-refined copper or hydrogen in electrolytic copper. Further, fluxes may be a source of impurities ; and impurities may be accidentally picked up in various ways. Apart from careful preparation of the material, operational control and choice of crucible material, the measures adopted to obtain pure and sound metal may be considered under two headings, namely, *flux treatment* and *metal/gas considerations*.

Flux treatment. Fluxes are added to the charge to combine with insoluble impurities and form a slag, to form a protective cover on the molten metal, or to provide reducing or oxidising conditions. Often more than one of these functions are fulfilled.

Charcoal is a solid flux used as a protection from oxidation, but frequently fluxes are used in the molten condition. Mixtures of several compounds may be employed to give a low melting-point and fluid flux. Care should be taken that the fluxes are not excessively reactive with the crucible materials. Important practical examples of cleaning fluxes are silicates, borates, chlorides and fluorides, lime and soda ash. It is practicable to use more expensive materials than in extraction, where large quantities are necessary. A siliceous flux will remove and hold oxides, as will borax; lime and soda ash will remove sulphides and dissolved sulphur (this may also be removed by metals with greater affinity for it). Some fluxes do not combine with insoluble impurities, but function by wetting or coating them. Manganese or copper oxide is used as an oxidising flux, especially for copper and its alloys; generally the oxide is mixed with sand and glass to make a fusible mixture.

Active fluxes may be stirred into the molten metal to ensure good contact, or the flux may be placed in the bottom of the crucible before the metal is charged. Better contact could be obtained by thorough agitation as in certain refining processes, but this is not generally done in melting practice. After any stirring of metal and flux, the melt should be allowed to stand tranquilly for some time to allow full separation. Even with tranquil conditions, reaction will occur at the interface between metal and flux; convection currents and diffusion in the underlying metal will enable this to continue.

Alloying. In non-ferrous winning practice elementary metals are usually produced, and **non-ferrous alloys** are made at the melting stage. The alloying technique depends on a number of factors, such as the proportions of the various metals, their relative melting and boiling points, mutual solubilities, reactive natures, and the form in which they are most easily obtained.

Thus in the case of tin and lead, or copper and nickel, the two metals are satisfactorily melted together. Small amounts of high melting-point metals such as copper or manganese are added to molten aluminium in the form of solid hardeners, namely Al 50/Cu 50 and Al 75/Mn 25, respectively; these have lower melting points and dissolve more easily than the elements. Iron is most conveniently added to brass as an iron-zinc alloy. By using such hardeners, in addition to ready solution, oxidation losses during the actual alloying are minimised. Reactive elements are also usually added in the form of alloys to avoid unpleasant reactions and associated losses in alloying, as well as making storage more convenient. Hence phosphorus is added to molten copper and its alloys as solid phosphor-copper containing, for example, 15 per cent phosphorus ; in making phosphor-bronze, an alloy of phosphorus and tin may be used instead. Deoxidising additions are frequently made in the alloy form, as for example with phosphorus as above, or calcium to copper as a 50–50 Ca/Cu alloy.

In those cases where a volatile metal has to be alloyed with a high melting-point metal, the latter predominating, the volatile metal is added as late as possible. The same also applies when the metal in lesser proportion is readily oxidised. Thus in making brass from virgin metals, the copper is melted first and the solid zinc added just before casting ; even so, a small allowance has to be made for volatilisation. Similar considerations arise in alloying cadmium with copper. Tin and aluminium bronzes are made by adding solid tin or aluminium to molten copper after it has been deoxidised with phosphorus, and silicon or manganese, respectively ; deoxidation is not necessary in making brass. On the other hand, if the volatile (or readily oxidised) metal predominates, it is melted first and the other added, often as a hardener ; or the two metals may be melted together. Care must be taken that the higher melting-point metal is fully dissolved.

Usually it is satisfactory to make solid alloying additions to the molten predominating metal, because (*a*) the molten metal may be given suitable superheating, (*b*) alloying often lowers the melting point or range, and (*c*) heat may be evolved on solution. Heat losses are reduced by pre-heating the solid addition ; this also removes any moisture.

Thorough stirring is necessary to ensure uniform mixing in alloying. An up and down motion should also be used especially if there is marked difference in density between the metals ; aluminium bronze provides a notable example of this.

Ordinary cast iron and plain carbon steel are produced directly as such. In making **alloy cast irons**, the extra elements are added at the melting stage. Many **alloy steels** are produced by making the necessary additions during the steelmaking, although in some cases there may be a separate alloying stage. Additions of nickel and copper are made in the elementary form ; but other elements, such as silicon, manganese, chromium, tungsten, molybdenum and vanadium are usually added as ferro-alloys (that is, alloyed with iron and containing carbon as well), which are easy to obtain directly by smelting. Alloy additions in steel practice may also be made in the form of alloy steel scrap containing sufficient of the desired elements. Aluminium for deoxidation is added in the elementary form or as an iron-aluminium alloy ; silicon and manganese for this purpose are used as ferro-alloys as above.

Occasionally alloying additions are made in the form of a compound, which is reduced in the molten metal. Thus sodium may be added to aluminium-silicon alloys as sodium fluoride, and molybdenum to steel as calcium molybdate, and chromium and tungsten to steel as oxides in arc-furnace practice.

Melting furnaces. Crucible melting is widely used in the non-ferrous industry, and is suitable for small melts of steel and cast iron. The crucibles, with capacities usually up to a few hundred pounds, are heated in gas-, oil- or coke-fired furnaces (Fig. 254). For larger sizes the crucible is fixed in the furnace, which tilts for pouring (Fig. 255). The crucibles are made of fireclay, or more usually of graphite

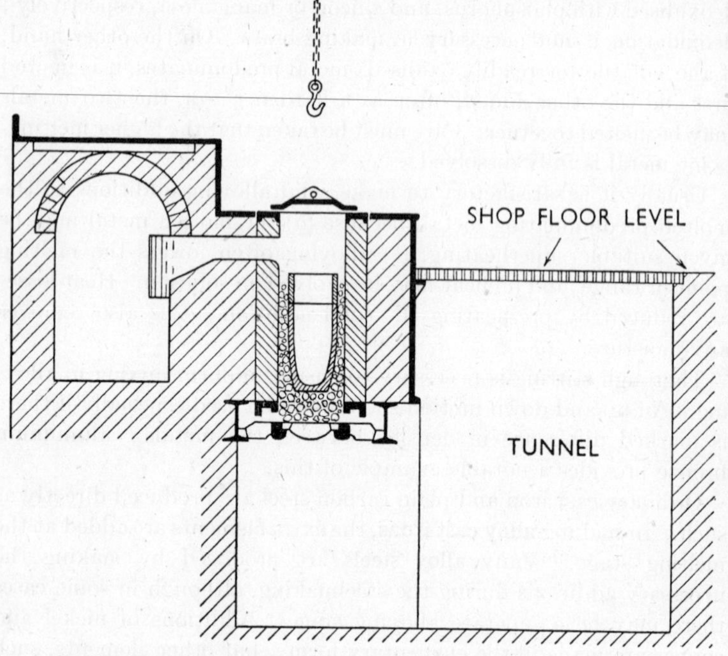

FIG. 254. Natural-draught, coke-fired crucible furnace. A forced air draught supplied by a fan is now often used. From N. I. Bond-Williams, Symposium No. 6. Inst. Metals.

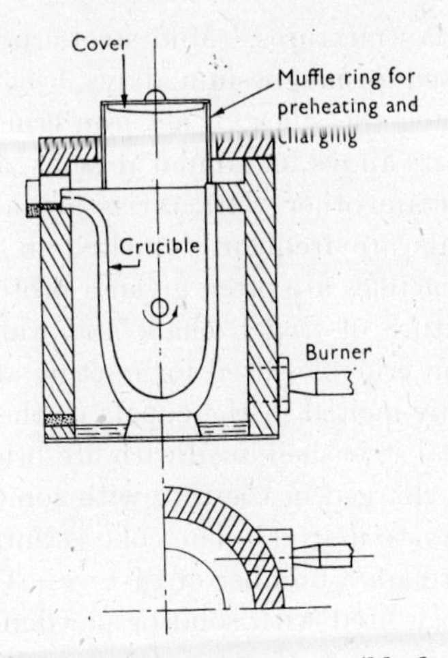

FIG. 255. Gas-fired tilting crucible furnace.

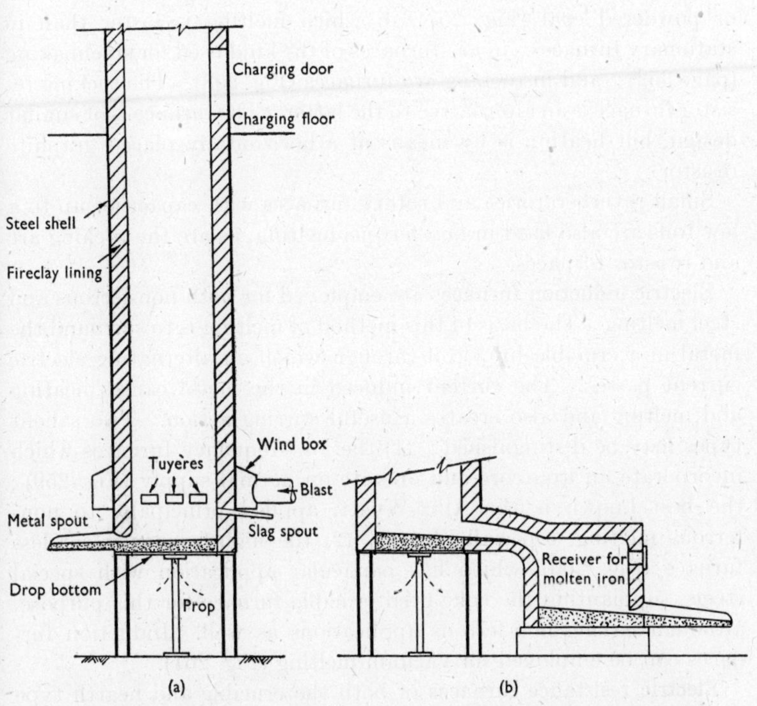

FIG. 256. Cupola for melting cast iron. Dimensions : inside dia. 3–7 ft. ; melting-rate 5–25 tons of iron per hour. Height, from drop bottom to bottom of charging door, 14–25 ft.

or plumbago and clay mixtures. Mild steel crucibles (welded from sheet or cast) are used for magnesium alloys, because the magnesium attacks clay, reducing the silica. Cast iron crucibles are also used for aluminium and its alloys for similar reasons, although plumbago or graphite and certain other refractories are also suitable. Low melting-point metals are frequently melted in steel or cast iron crucibles. Metal crucibles are often given a protective non-metallic wash; thus a mixture of french chalk and water glass is recommended for cast iron crucibles used for melting aluminium.

Cast iron is usually melted in the **cupola** or the **air furnace.** The cupola is a cylindrical steel shell lined with fire-brick (Fig. 256). The metal and coke are charged in the top, with some limestone to flux the ash and other waste matter. The coke is burnt by air blown in near the bottom through a number of tuyères. The air furnace is a form of reverberatory fired with solid or powdered coal or oil, and typically has a capacity of 15 tons. Cast iron is also melted in rotating furnaces (up to about 10 tons capacity) fired with oil, gas or powdered coal (Fig. 257), in which melting is faster than in stationary furnaces; in arc-furnaces of the kind used for steelmaking (page 352); and in rocking arc furnaces (Fig. 258). The rocking resistor furnace is an alternative to the latter. The furnace is of similar design, but heating is by means of a horizontally placed graphite resistor.

Small reverberatories and rotary furnaces with capacities up to a few tons are also used in non-ferrous melting, as are the rocking arc and resistor furnaces.

Electric induction furnaces are employed for both non-ferrous and steel melting. The basis of this method of melting is to surround the metal in a crucible by a coil through which an alternating electric current passes. The current induced in the metal causes heating and melting and also creates a useful stirring action. Two salient types may be distinguished: (1) the low-frequency furnaces which incorporate an iron core and operate on normal supply (Fig. 259); the best known is the Ajax-Wyatt, applied principally to non-ferrous melting, especially brass; (2) the high-frequency coreless furnace (Fig. 260), which has particular application with special steels, supplanting the coke-fired crucible furnace for this purpose, although having non-ferrous applications as well. Induction furnaces can be employed for vacuum melting (Fig. 261).

Electric resistance furnaces of both the crucible and hearth type are manufactured for non-ferrous melting, especially for the lower melting-point metals.

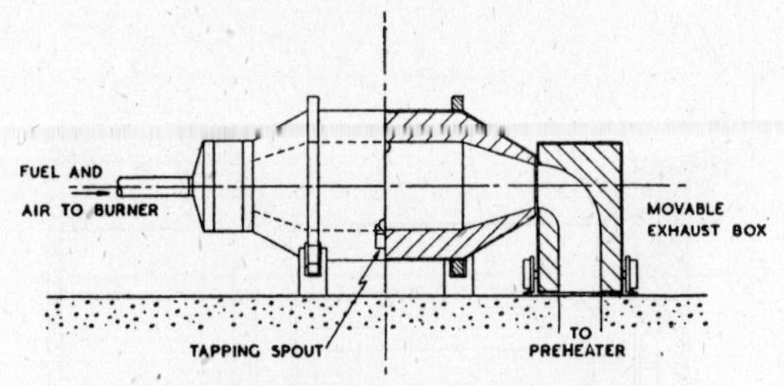

FIG. 257. Rotary melting furnace.
By courtesy of the Inst. Brit. Foundrymen.

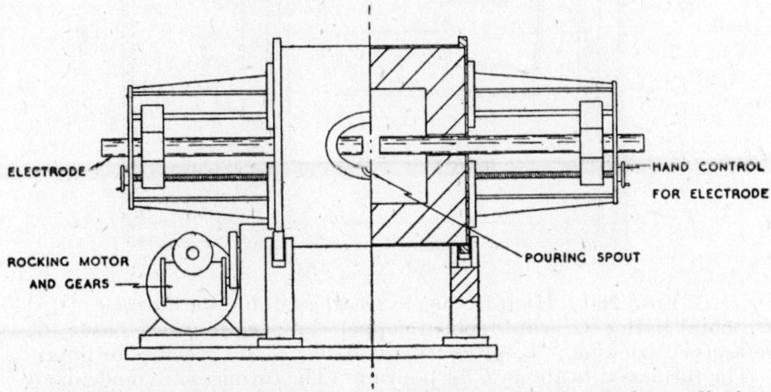

FIG. 258. Indirect rocking arc furnace. Heating is by radiation from the arc. During operation the furnace is rocked about its horizontal axis to improve heat transfer. Capacities are up to about 2 tons. By courtesy of the Inst. Brit. Foundrymen.

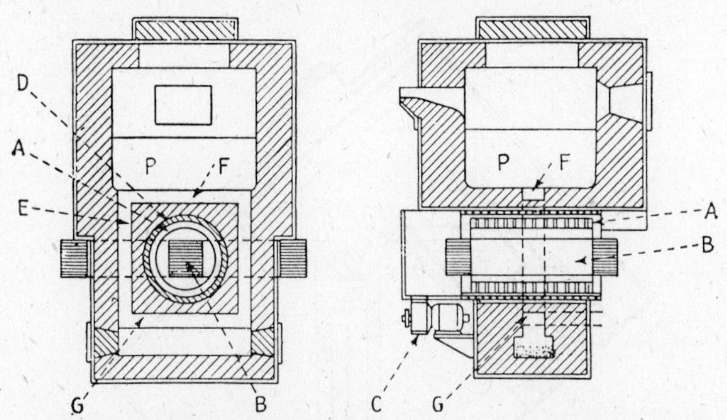

FIG. 259. Low-frequency induction furnace. *A*, primary coil ; B, core ; *C*, blower for cooling windings and core ; *D*, insulation ; *EFG*, melting channel acting as secondary loop of transformer circuit ; *P*, hearth containing main charge. Common metal capacities are 600 lb., 1200 lb., and about 1 ton, and the furnace is tilted for pouring. The secondary channel has to be kept full of molten metal between charges. From *Handbook of Non-Ferrous Metallurgy*. McGraw-Hill.

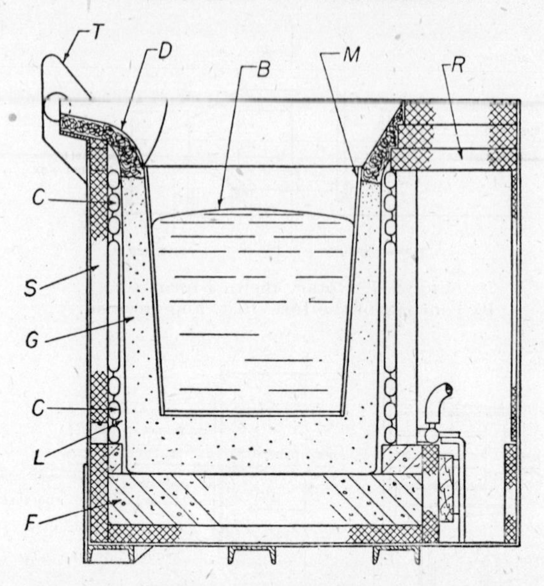

FIG. 260. High-frequency coreless induction furnace
B, metal bath ; *C*, water-cooled copper coil ; *F*, firebrick base ; *G*, refractory packing ; *L*, protective coil liner ; *M*, crucible or liner.
The furnace tilts about *T* for pouring. The furnaces are made in all sizes up to about 10 tons capacity. Figs. 260, 261 and 270 are from *Metals Handbook*, 1948 Edition, Amer. Soc. for Metals.

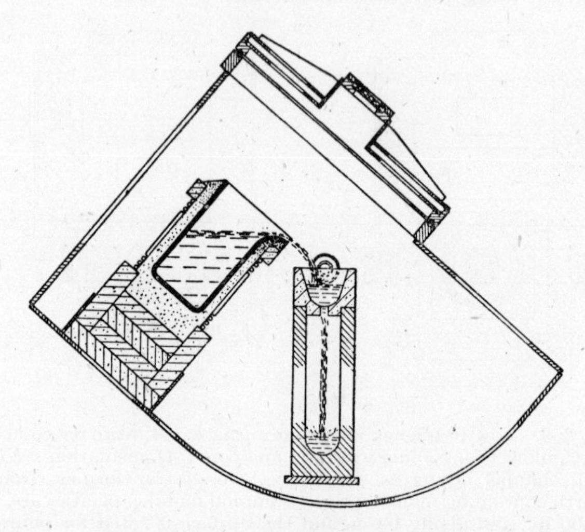

FIG. 261. Arrangement for vacuum melting and casting with induction furnace. From *Metals Handbook*.

In the separate crucible furnaces the crucible is removed for casting. In the other furnaces described above, the metal may be poured directly into ingot moulds, which can conveniently be brought under the pouring spout; but, especially for castings, the metal is transferred to the mould via a ladle of some sort.

Production of ingots for working. The ingots are usually circular in cross-section, or square or rectangular with rounded corners; in some cases special shapes may be used (Figs. 262 and 263). The size of ingots for working depends on a number of factors, such as the size and shape required in the wrought metal, the working process, and the general quantity demand for the metal. Ingots of the common steels are usually several tons in weight or even considerably more when large objects are required; ingots of special steels, for example tool steels, are much smaller, and may be of the order of one or several hundred pounds. Non-ferrous ingots are generally less than 1 ton in weight, and many are less than ½ ton. A steel ingot approxi-

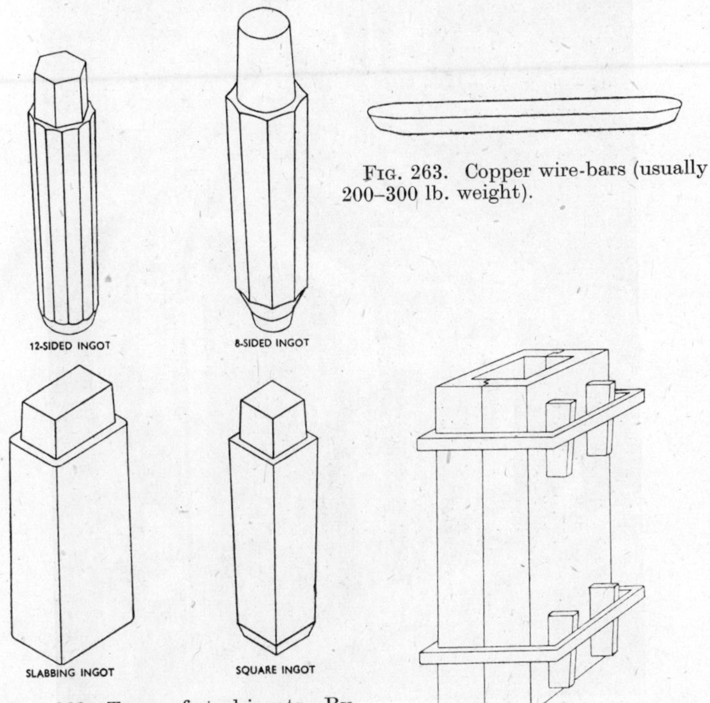

Fig. 263. Copper wire-bars (usually 200–300 lb. weight).

Fig. 262. Types of steel ingots. By courtesy of United Steel Companies, Ltd.

Fig. 264. Split-type ingot mould.

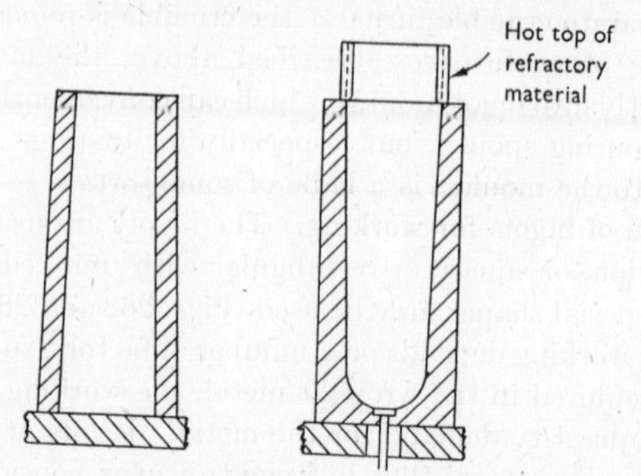

FIG. 265. Common ingot moulds for steel.

FIG. 266. Junker water-cooled mould opened for removal of ingot. The actual mould is of copper plate ($\frac{1}{4}$–$\frac{3}{4}$ in. thick). Note the tundish for distributing the pouring stream. By courtesy of the Copper Development Association.

mately 2 ft. square by about 6 ft. long weighs between 4 and 5 tons ; a brass slab about 3 in. thick by $1\frac{1}{2}$ ft. by $2\frac{1}{2}$ ft. weighs of the order of 1,000 lb.

The ingot moulds for steel are usually made of grey cast iron ; both cast iron and copper are used considerably for the non-ferrous metals: copper itself is usually cast into copper moulds. Metal moulds give good surfaces, and rapid cooling of the metal ; their thickness should be sufficient to ensure that the inner surface does not reach too high a temperature, else sticking may occur. Dressings, such as soot, graphitic grease, tar, pitch, aluminium, whitewash and lime or bone ash washes are applied in a suitable manner to the mould surface for its protection, to reduce sticking and to improve the ingot surface. Volatile dressings may be used to fill the mould with reducing gases. By preventing too early solidification, dressings reduce the formation of a rippled surface.

Slabs of certain non-ferrous metals for rolling may be cast into flat open moulds. Apart from these and copper wire-bars, ingot moulds are comparatively narrow and made in two parts, which are hinged or held together by clamps or rings and wedges (Fig. 264); this construction facilitates "stripping", that is, removal of the solidified ingot. Alternatively, the mould body is in one piece with tapered inside walls (Fig. 265). For non-ferrous metals, water-cooled moulds have been developed ; an important example is the Junker, used particularly for copper and nickel and their alloys (Fig. 266): note also the moulds used on the machine employed for rapid casting of copper ingots (Fig. 269). Ingot moulds usually stand vertically and are filled from the *top* (Figs. 267–271). *Bottom* or *uphill pouring* (Fig. 272) is used for steel where a good surface is required ; this has little or no application commercially with non-ferrous metals. For these metals, when very smooth and tranquil conditions of pouring are required, as with aluminium bronze to prevent the enfolding of the tenacious oxide skin, the **Durville process** is used (Fig. 273). In a simpler method used for aluminium alloys, a rotary mould is used and the metal poured down the side from the crucible (Fig. 274); various other means have also been devised. Turbulence during top-pouring is also reduced by using a tundish giving several pouring streams.

A number of processes for **continuous casting** for some of the common non-ferrous metals have been developed (Fig. 275). Simple rounds and slabs are produced mainly for working ; the method has also been applied to hollow shapes. More recently it has been applied to steel. There is also an ingenious development typified by the

FIG. 267. Casting copper wire-bars on Walker mechanical casting wheel, from reverberatory refining furnace. The moulds are of solid copper. After pouring, cooling by water sprays is applied. When the mould has travelled about half a revolution of the wheel, it is rotated to dislodge the wire-bars into a water tank. The mould is then dressed by spraying with a bone-ash suspension, and rotated to the horizontal position as it moves round to the pouring ladle again. From H. J. Miller, *The Refining of Non-Ferrous Metals*, Inst. Min. and Met.

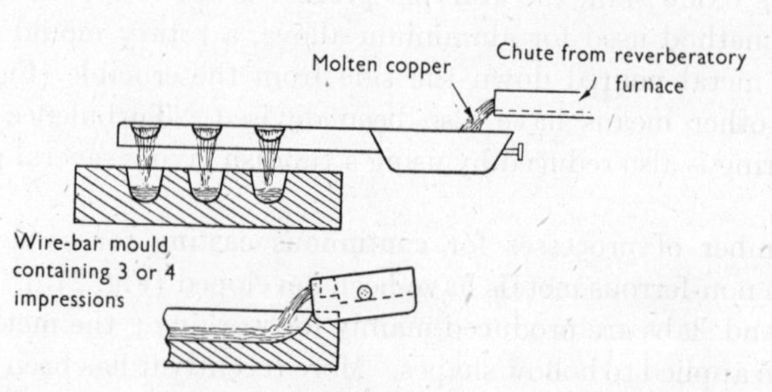

FIG. 268. Method of pouring in casting copper wire-bars.

FIG. 269. Casting copper cakes (vertically) in water-cooled copper moulds on Walker casting wheel. By courtesy of the Copper Development Association.

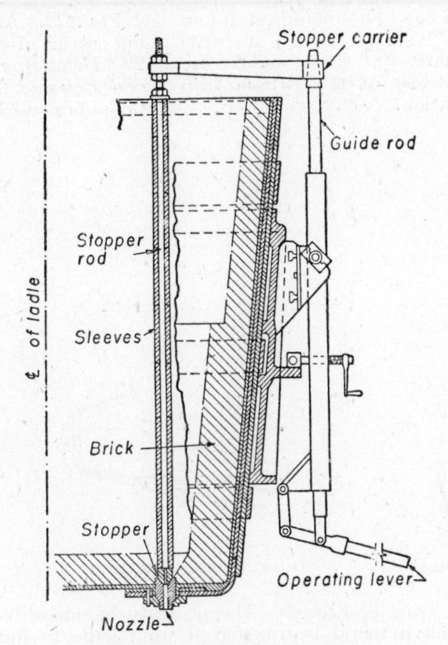

FIG. 270. Bottom-pour ladle for steel. From *Metals Handbook.*

FIG. 271. Teeming steel ingots from double-nozzle ladle. The moulds stand on bogies and the ladle is moved over the moulds; alternatively, the moulds are moved. By courtesy of the British Iron and Steel Federation.

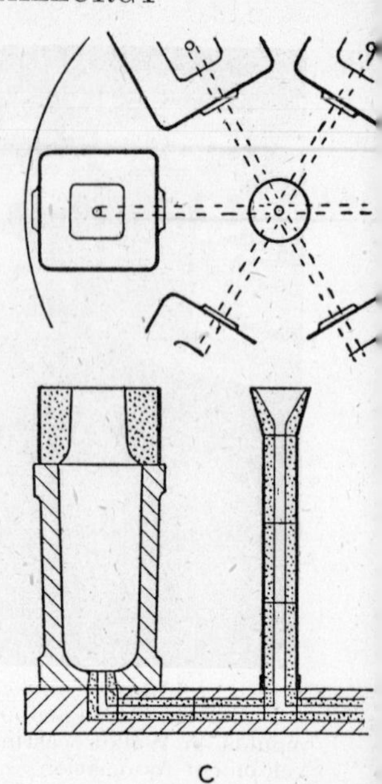

FIG .272. Arrangement for up hill casting of steel ingots. Fron *The Metallurgy of Deep Drawin and Pressing*, by J. D. Jevons Chapman and Hall.

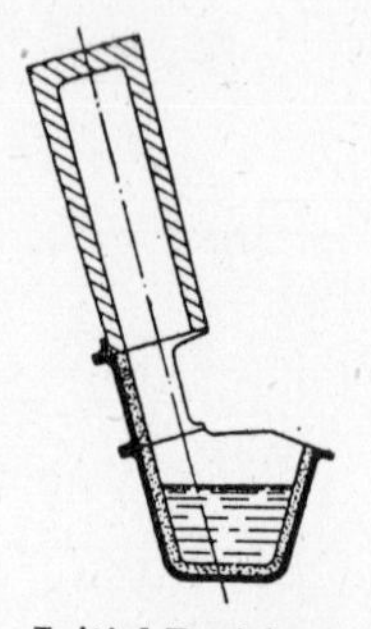

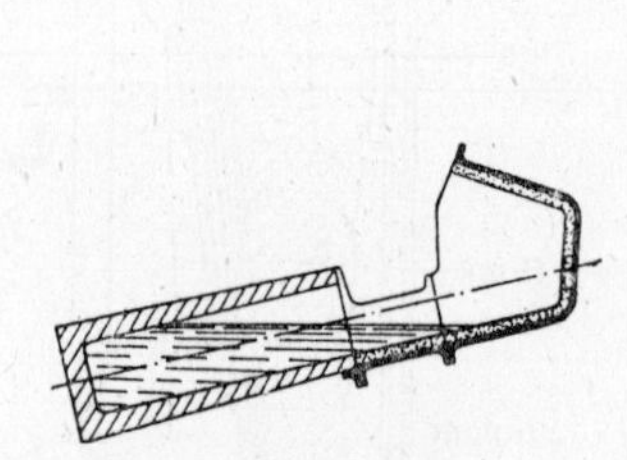

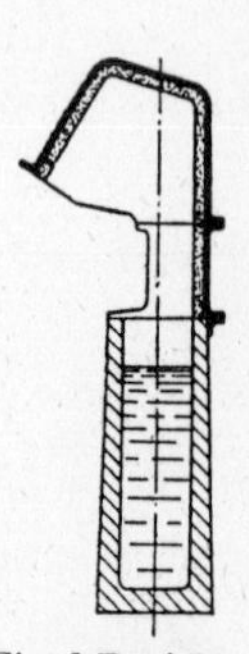

Initial Position Intermediate Position Final Position

FIG. 273. Durville Process. The apparatus is smoothly rotated so that the molten metal is transferred from ladle to ingot mould. From *The Casting of Brass Ingots*, by R. Genders and G. L. Bailey. Brit. Non-Ferrous Met. Res. Assoc.

Hazelett process, in which molten metal is continuously cast between rolls and directly rolled to strip (Fig. 276). In spite of many difficulties a satisfactory product has been made with several metals.

Non-ferrous ingots for working are sometimes known as **billets**. In the case of steel, this term is applied to metal which has had some preliminary working (normally about $1\frac{1}{2}$–5 in. square in section), and which forms the starting material for a subsequent working operation.

When ingots are to be hot worked, it is usual practice with non-ferrous metals to allow them to cool, and then reheat for working. This may be done with steel, but frequently the hot ingots are transferred to soaking pit fur-

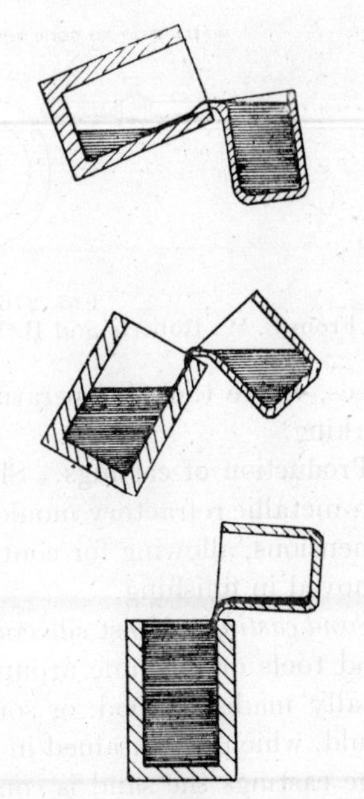

Fig. 274. Tilting of mould to reduce turbulence during pouring. From E. Scheuer, *J. Inst. Metals* 1949, 76, 113.

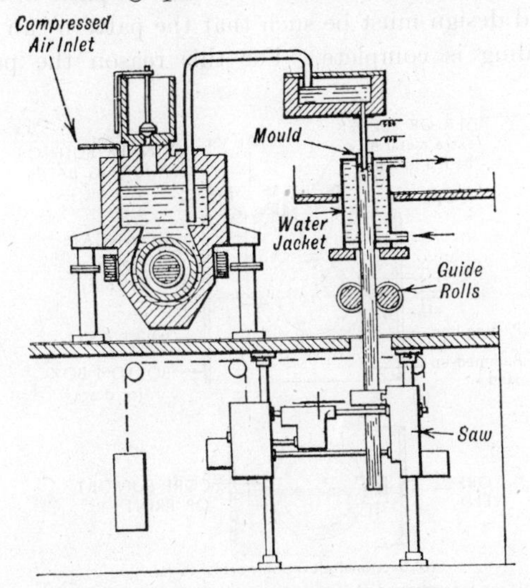

Fig. 275. Principle of continuous casting machine. By courtesy of *The Engineer*.

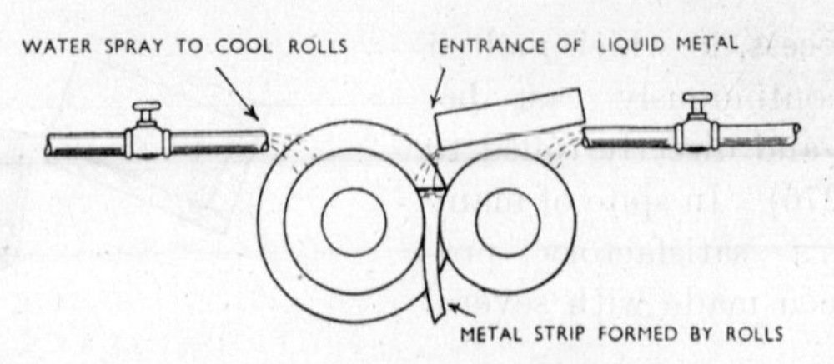

Fig. 276. Hazelett process.
From C. W. Roberts and B. Walters, Symposium No. 9. Inst. Metals

naces, where their temperature is adjusted and equalised, prior to working.

Production of castings. Shaped castings are made in metallic or non-metallic refractory moulds, which are as close as possible to final dimensions, allowing for contraction and the amount of metal to be removed in finishing.

Sand casting. Moist siliceous sand bonded with clay is rammed by hand tools or machine around a well-formed and accurate **pattern** usually made of wood, or sometimes metal or a plastic, to give the mould, which is contained in a metal moulding box (Fig. 277). For large castings the sand is contained in pits in the floor or by brick walls braced with metal. Simple, large and uniform shapes are swept out of the sand with a suitably shaped *strickle board.* The molten metal finds its way by gravity into all parts of the moulds.

The mould design must be such that the pattern can be removed when moulding is complete. For this reason the patterns and

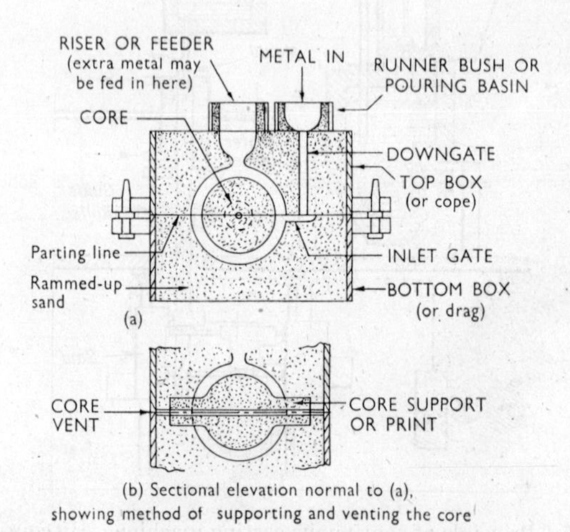

Fig. 277. Arrangement for sand casting a hollow sphere.

moulds are made in a number of parts. **Metal chills** may be included in the sand moulds to hasten the cooling and refine the structure of the metal in certain parts of the casting ; hollow places in the castings are made by the use of **sand cores,** which are shaped from sand bonded with linseed oil (or other materials) and then baked. The cores are made of such strength that they break up easily when the solidified metal contracts. The design of the channels or **runners** through which the metal enters the mould, and the **risers** or feeding heads, which are to ensure the mould being filled and shrinkage being compensated, and through which air and gases escape as well as through vents, are among a number of factors which must be observed in making a satisfactory mould. The moulds can be used once only, as the sand surface becomes spoiled ; further, the mould is at least partly destroyed in removing the casting.

Other additions may be made to the sand or applied as surface dressing for various reasons. Thus sawdust or straw may be added to improve the porosity, carbon to improve the metal surface and reduce the tendency for the sand to burn on, and inhibitors such as sulphur and boric acid to prevent the reaction of magnesium with the moisture in the sand. The moulds are sometimes used with the sand in the moist or " green " condition, or they may be dried throughout (which is desirable if any reaction between metal and moisture is likely) or skin-dried before use. Large moulds are generally dried where possible, because they are stronger in this condition. Gases, and steam evolved from the moisture in the sand during casting, also escape through the pores in the sand.

Sand casting is applicable to practically all the common metals and is especially suitable for the production of small quantities, for tooling costs are negligible, although patterns are expensive. Sand casting is particularly useful because of the wide range of sizes of the product that is possible ; further, it is the only casting process suitable for the production of large objects such as lathe and other machine bases and frames, large propellers, and rolls for various purposes. Sand castings are cleaned up by shot or sand blasting, tumbling, grinding and cutting ; this is followed by the necessary machining. As with other casting processes, there need be little scrap, for feeding heads, risers and the like may be returned to the melting furnace.

Die casting. This involves the casting of shapes into metal moulds known as **dies.** The dies are made of steel or cast iron, and are filled by gravity, or under pressures up to about 10 tons/in.^{2} Die castings have superior surfaces and better dimensional accuracy than sand castings. Final machining and similar operations are minimised or even unnecessary, and the rate of production is high. However, the first cost of the dies is very considerable; this is due to their shaping rather than the intrinsic cost of the material. Pressure die casting is faster and more automatic than the gravity method, but the machines are very much more expensive. Die casting, particularly under pressure, is thus only feasible when large numbers of the same casting are required. It is applicable to most non-ferrous metals and more recently to cast iron. It is not practicable to make large shapes by die casting; sizes are limited usually to several pounds, but very small ones are possible.

Centrifugal casting. This may be considered as a special form of die casting by which hollow cylindrical shapes in particular may be conveniently produced. The mould rotates (up to about 1200 r.p.m.) and the molten metal is fed inside and distributed around the mould by the centrifugal action (Fig. 278); rotation continues until solidification is complete. An advantage of centrifugal casting, apart from being well adapted for circular shapes, is that it produces a sounder and more uniform casting than static means, due to the essentially uni-directional solidification. The mould is usually of steel or cast iron, although non-metallic linings may be used; it is rotated in a horizontal or vertical plane.

Not only is centrifugal casting suitable for drums, tubes and shafting, but also for wheels and gear blanks. Composite castings may be made; thus steel may be lined with bronze, and wheels made with one metal for the rim and another for the inside. Perhaps the best-known example of centrifugal casting is the production of cast iron pipes for water, sewage, and gas mains. Centrifugal means are also used for filling the moulds in other forms of casting, the

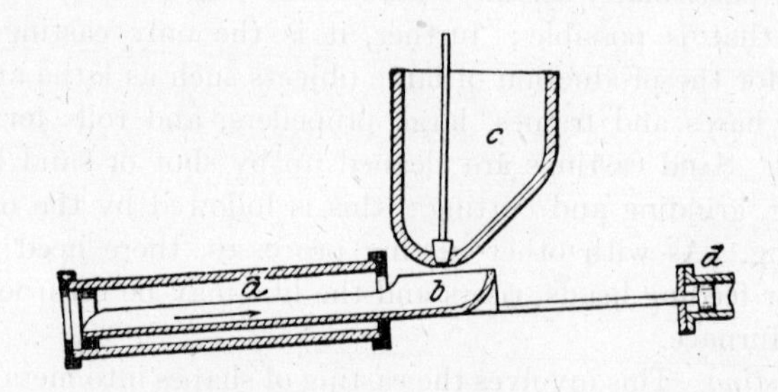

FIG. 278. Principle of centrifugal casting. The pouring spout, *b*, is withdrawn gradually along the inside of the rotating mould, *a*, by the piston, *d*. After Geiger, from *The Principles of Physical Metallurgy*, by G. E. Doan and E. M. Mahla. McGraw-Hill.

mould being placed at the periphery of a horizontal turntable ; thus casting is under centrifugal pressure. This technique has been used for casting steel and other high melting-point alloys in refractory (non-metallic) moulds, and for filling the moulds in the investment process.

Precision casting : investment or lost wax process. Precision casting utilises non-metallic mould material and is particularly useful where only a small number of parts of intricate shape is required having good dimensional accuracy and surface finish without high initial outlay. In addition, the technique is especially advantageous for high melting-point metals and those difficult to machine and work. It is most suitable for small castings up to about a pound in weight, although somewhat larger are possible. The process has been used for many years by dentists and statue makers ; its application in other fields is more recent.

The essentials of the process are as follow. A pattern of the desired shape is carefully made in any suitable easily machinable metal. An impression of the pattern is made in Wood's or similar metal by a simple casting operation. Wood's metal is a low melting-point (about 70° C.) alloy containing the following metals in parts by weight : Bi 7–8/Pb 4/Sn 2/Cd 1–3. The impression has very clean and accurate surfaces if the surface of the pattern is good. The impression is filled with molten wax, which is allowed to solidify and then removed. Thus a wax pattern similar to the original is obtained, and around this the investment is cast. There are a number of investment mixtures, but many are composed of fine silica and some bonding material ; they are made as wet pastes. The investment casting is allowed to set, and then the whole is heated for several hours at 500–700° C., when the wax volatilises leaving a firm, hard and accurate refractory mould. Alternatively, frozen mercury or moulded plastic patterns may be used which are melted out. Allowances are made for the expansion and contraction of all the materials used, including the metal cast, to ensure close final dimensions. The moulds are filled by gravity, pressure, or centrifugal means, and are only used once.

The procedure may be simplified if the shape desired is not complicated, when the die for the wax pattern can be directly machined in steel, brass, aluminium or zinc. For complex shapes a positive pattern as described earlier is usually easier to machine than a negative impression.

Shell-moulding process. A notable development in the manufacture of accurate castings of good surface finish is the shell-moulding process. A thin mould is made around a metal pattern from a mixture of sand

and 6–8 per cent resin, which is then cured. The process appears to be applicable to most common metals, except, at present, ordinary steel.

Slush casting. This technique is used for making hollow ornamental castings in zinc, lead and tin-base alloys. The molten alloy is poured into a metal mould ; when a solid shell of sufficient thickness has formed, the remaining liquid is poured out.

SOLIDIFICATION: (1) GAS-METAL PHENOMENA

Origin of gases. Gases mainly originate by solution in some form in the metal from the air or furnace atmosphere, although, for example, electro-deposited copper already contains hydrogen. On cooling and solidification the gases are evolved, or retained in solid solution and/or as compounds in the metal. At the melting stage the metal may already contain gaseous impurities and is prone to absorb more. The aim in melting is, therefore, to eliminate the gases present and prevent the absorption of others.

Further, during the actual casting operation, gases may be picked up in some way. Thus air or other gas in the mould may be entrapped or the metal may absorb oxygen during pouring, or there may be reaction with mould dressings or moisture in sand moulds. Due precautions have to be taken to minimise these occurrences.

The usual constituents of the atmospheres with which molten metals are in contact are hydrogen, oxygen, nitrogen, carbon dioxide, carbon monoxide, water vapour, sulphur dioxide and hydrocarbons. Moisture on the metal and combined with the fluxes as well as gases from oil or grease on the charge will supplement those due to fuel combustion and to the air.

Of the elementary gases, hydrogen especially dissolves appreciably in a number of common metals when molten, in particular copper, nickel, aluminium, magnesium and iron. Hydrogen solubility is altered, often being decreased, by alloying additions, although the solubility is usually still pronounced ; but in the case of brass the zinc apparently keeps the metal almost free of hydrogen and will remove it substantially from molten copper. In addition the aluminium oxide skin formed on aluminium and alloys containing aluminium gives mechanical protection against absorption. Oxygen dissolves considerably in molten silver and other precious metals, copper, iron and nickel ; but not in aluminium, magnesium, zinc, tin or lead, a stable oxide forming which is not appreciably soluble in the metal. Similarly, in numerous cases alloying additions form insoluble oxides and act as deoxidants for the metals, which in the elementary form dissolve oxygen. Nitrogen is virtually insoluble in many common non-ferrous metals, but dissolves in iron and, for example, chromium, manganese and molybdenum. It is likely that elementary gases are in solution in the atomic state, dissociating at the metal surface.

Compound gases are insoluble in molten (or solid) metals, although they may be decomposed by reaction at the metal surface, after which the products dissolve ;

$$H_2O + 2Cu \rightleftharpoons Cu_2O + 2H \quad \text{......(1)}$$

(both oxide and hydrogen dissolve)

$$6Cu + SO_2 \rightleftharpoons 2Cu_2O + Cu_2S \quad \text{......(2)}$$

(sulphide dissolves as well as the oxide)

$$3H_2O + 2Al \rightleftharpoons Al_2O_3 + 6H \quad \text{......(3)}$$

(hydrogen dissolves, the oxide is insoluble)

$$H_2O + Mg \rightleftharpoons MgO + 2H \quad \text{......(4)}$$

(hydrogen dissolves, the oxide is insoluble)

Hydrocarbons may also dissociate to yield soluble products. Hydrogen absorption by molten metals has been shown to be more rapid and pronounced from the decomposition of water vapour by reaction with the metal than from the dissociation of molecular hydrogen, which requires more energy.

Gas evolution on solidification of the common metals occurs mainly as a result of the marked decrease in solubility of hydrogen (Figs. 279 and 280), and the formation of compound gases when reactions such as (1) and (2) above proceed from right to left, or $FeO + C \rightleftharpoons Fe + CO$ in incompletely deoxidised steel ; similar reactions may occur in nickel and nickel alloys. Oxygen is only evolved on solidification of the noble metals. Thus with silver there is copious evolution of dissolved oxygen (giving rise to "spitting" in the cupellation assay) ; an oxide of silver is formed, but easily dissociates ; it remains in the metal if sufficient pressure is applied.

Allen has pointed out that the behaviour of gases and metals may be generalised by reference to the position of the metals in the electro-chemical series. Thus with the noble metals, troubles arise from the evolution of oxygen due to the instability of the oxides. With copper, iron, nickel and cobalt, which form moderately stable oxides, gas evolution is principally due to reaction of the oxide with a non-metallic impurity having a gaseous oxide, such as hydrogen,

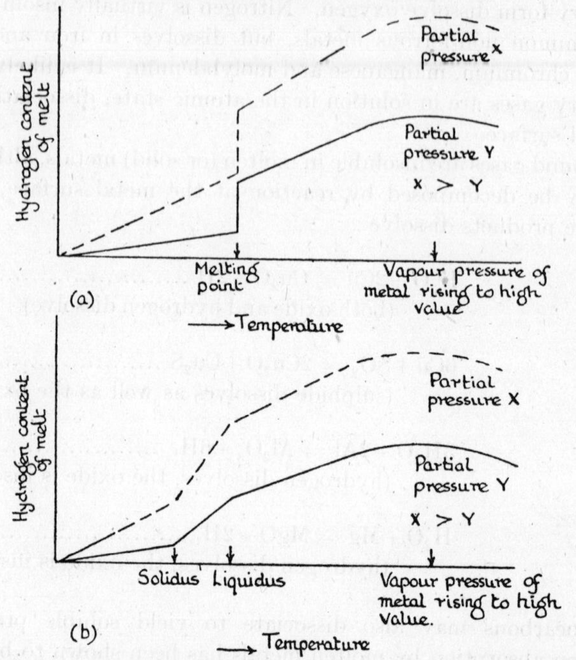

FIG. 279. Hydrogen solubility-temperature curves for (*a*) pure metals and eutectics, etc., and (*b*) alloys freezing over a range of temperature. Figs. 279 and 287 are from *Shrinkage and Gas Effects in the Casting of Non-Ferrous Metals and Alloys*, by W. A. Baker. Brit. Non-Ferrous Met. Res. Assoc.

carbon or sulphur. Finally, in the very base metals such as aluminium and magnesium, where the oxide is very stable, gas evolution is due to hydrogen. It should be noted, however, that gas troubles are not generally encountered in casting lead, tin, zinc and their alloys.

Much of the gas evolved during cooling in the liquid state may escape as bubbles or by diffusing to the surface. During solidification also, part at least of the gas escapes ; but some bubbles are likely to be entrapped as rounded holes of various sizes or of interdendritic shape and position depending on the metal, the conditions of solidification and the stage when formed. With very fast cooling, some gas may be retained in enforced solution. The gases or their reactants tend to concentrate by diffusion into the last of the liquid. In tough-pitch copper and rimming steel ingots, gas holes are concentrated towards the upper part of the ingot and usefully counteract the piping tendency (Fig. 281).

Gas porosity causes weakness and unsoundness in castings and is therefore undesirable, although it is less harmful in the form of small isolated holes. Provided they are not oxidised and not too near the surface, gas holes may be healed up in working if the metal can be pressure-welded easily, such as occurs regularly with tough-pitch copper and rimming steel, for example. Cavities near the surface (due both to evolved gas and entrapped mould gases) are likely to become opened up during working, become oxidised and fail to weld up, thus forming surface oxide laminations, sometimes known as spills. These defects in fabricated metal also originate in other ways such as from surface folds on the ingot surface arising from pouring too cold. Blisters originating from entrapped gas may develop on worked material at various stages.

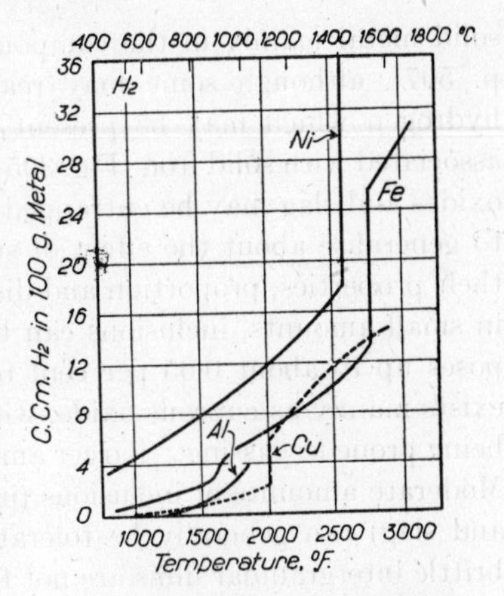

FIG. 280. Hydrogen solubility in various metals, when in contact with a hydrogen atmosphere at 1 atmosphere pressure. The volume dissolved is given as that which would be occupied at N.T.P. From *Practical Metallurgy*, by G. Sachs and K. R. Van Horn. Amer. Soc. for Metals.

Apart from the precious metals, dissolved oxygen is retained in the

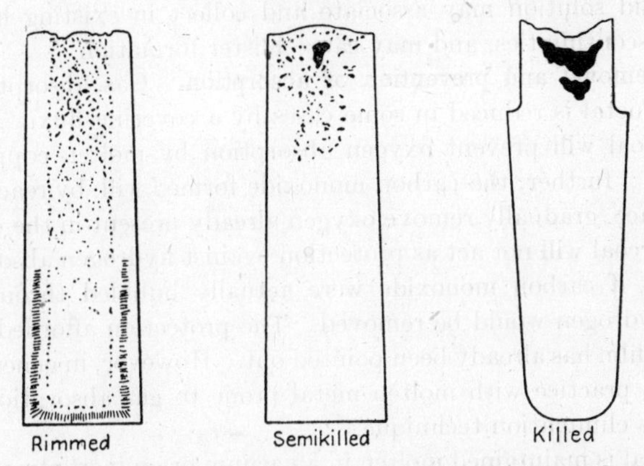

FIG. 281. Types of steel ingot (sectioned). The rimmed steel is porous due to the evolution of carbon monoxide. This occurs because of incomplete deoxidation, the residual iron oxide reacting with the carbon on cooling. Killed steel is completely deoxidised. From G. Soler, *Basic Open Hearth Steelmaking*. Amer. Inst. Min. Met. Eng.

solid metal mainly in the compound form (Figs. 388, 396 and 400 p. 507), although some may react with any carbon, sulphur or hydrogen which may be present. Nitrogen also stays intimately associated with solid iron (Fig. 395, p. 512). In many cases insoluble oxides and slag may be entrapped in the solid metal. It is difficult to generalise about the effect of such inclusions, which depends on their properties, proportion and distribution. In a number of cases, in small amounts, inclusions can be tolerated. Thus for most purposes up to about 0·05 per cent oxygen is left in copper, where it exists mainly as cuprous oxide, with little serious effect, apart from being prone to gassing. Larger amounts of oxygen cause brittleness. Moderate amounts of inclusions (in particular deoxidation products and slag) can generally be tolerated in the softer steels, provided brittle intergranular films are not formed. In fact a definite characteristic of wrought iron is the incorporation of membranes of slag; and improved machinability is obtained in some metals by the presence of well-distributed weak particles. However, it is generally agreed that inclusions should be eliminated as far as possible in the harder varieties of steel, such as tool steel.

Primary solubility of gases in solid metals in some cases is without harm. On the other hand hydrogen may be responsible for cracking in steels under certain conditions and causes brittleness. Precipitation due to decrease in solubility may create noticeable effects. Thus strain ageing in steel has been attributed to the precipitation of oxides, hydrides and nitrides. A gas rejected in the atomic form from solid solution may associate and collect in existing holes or other discontinuities, and may cause blister formation.

Gas removal and prevention of absorption. Gas absorption by molten metal is reduced in some cases by a covering flux. A layer of charcoal will prevent oxygen absorption by molten copper, for example; further, the carbon monoxide formed will, by reaction at the surface, gradually remove oxygen already present in the copper. But charcoal will not act as protection against hydrogen absorption, although if carbon monoxide were actually bubbled through the metal hydrogen would be removed. The protection afforded by an alumina film has already been pointed out. However, in general, the soundest practice with molten metal prone to gas absorption is to use a gas elimination technique.

If metal is maintained molten in a **vacuum** or an **inert atmosphere,** the dissolved gas will usually diffuse out until its pressure or partial pressure in the atmosphere balances its internal pressure in the metal. If the gas is continuously removed, the melt will be completely degassed. This procedure is applied commercially in a number of special cases.

Similar results to the above can often be more easily obtained in practice by **scavenging treatments,** that is by bubbling an inert gas through the molten metal. The dissolved gas diffuses into the bubbles, again until its partial pressure in the bubble balances that in the metal. Thus hydrogen is removed from copper and its alloys by scavenging with nitrogen or dry air. Aluminium and its alloys are degassed of hydrogen by nitrogen, chlorine, mixtures of nitrogen and chlorine, or volatile chlorides such as titanium tetrachloride and boron trichloride. Only the nitrogen is inert ; the value of the others, it is stated, is that they will remove any oxide coating of the bubbles which might prevent diffusion of the dissolved gas. For the same reason an active flux may be used with an inert gas. These considerations apply to other alloys containing aluminium, such as aluminium bronze. Chlorine can also be used to degas magnesium alloys. The removal of hydrogen from brass is due to a scavenging action by the zinc vapour which evolves continuously ; cadmium also exerts this effect in copper. Further, the high vapour pressure of the zinc in brass prevents the entry of hydrogen.

It is accepted that in open-hearth steel-making the "boil" gases, carbon-monoxide and -dioxide, exert a similar scavenging effect for dissolved hydrogen and nitrogen. Thus the nitrogen content of open-hearth steel is lower than that of ordinary Bessemer steel (p. 338).

Oxidation-reduction degassing. In the case of compound gas formation, when the oxygen solubility is high, the other reactant may be removed considerably from the molten metal in the form of the compound gas by thorough oxidation, which forces the reaction in the necessary direction. The dissolved oxygen is then removed at as late a stage as possible with a suitable deoxidant. Thus hydrogen (and sulphur and carbon) can be brought to a low figure in copper and certain of its alloys by an oxidising flux containing copper or manganese oxide. The reaction $2Cu + H_2O \rightleftharpoons Cu_2O + 2H$ is forced from right to left, eliminating the hydrogen in steam (Fig. 282). The metal is then deoxidised with phosphorus or some other element prior to casting. A similar principle is utilised in fire-refining copper. Reaction gas unsoundness can also be prevented in certain nickel alloys by oxidation-reduction treatment. It is considered also that hydrogen is eliminated from molten steel when oxidising conditions prevail in the refining process, as well as by the scavenging action of the boil gases.

Deoxidation itself will prevent evolution of reaction gas, although

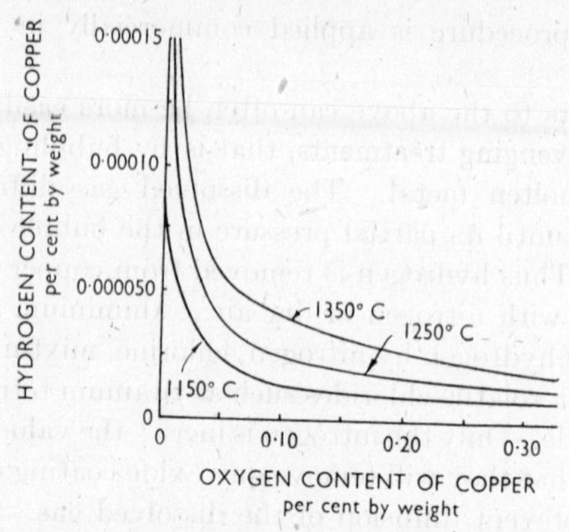

FIG. 282. Relation between hydrogen and oxygen contents of molten copper. After N. P. Allen and T. Hewitt.

the element remaining, even if not a gas, may be undesirable in other ways. When hydrogen is the remaining reactant, its evolution as such after deoxidation may cause unsoundness, thus necessitating its removal with nitrogen for example. But, it has been pointed out that as hydrogen it may escape more readily than in steam during solidification, for hydrogen in comparison can diffuse easily.

The water vapour reaction with aluminium or magnesium does not lead to evolution of water vapour on solidification, nor can hydrogen be removed by oxidation because of the insolubility and great stability of the oxide. Similarly, oxidation does not remove hydrogen from copper melts containing appreciable amounts of elements having greater affinity for oxygen, such as phosphorus, silicon and aluminium, for stable insoluble oxides are formed. In these cases, a scavenging treatment with a suitable gas is necessary.

It should be stressed that the degassing techniques described in the foregoing are no guarantee against subsequent re-entry of gas. However, the time interval before pouring is usually short, the combustion in the furnace will generally have ceased, and the metal may be protected by its own oxide skin or a covering layer of flux; further, gas entering with the charge will have been removed.

Apart from oxygen, gases are not generally removed by the formation of an insoluble compound. It is claimed, however, that lithium will remove hydrogen from copper as a hydride as well as deoxidising, and that aluminium, titanium and zirconium in excess of deoxidation requirements will remove nitrogen from steel or fix it in an inactive form.

Deoxidation. This is effected by adding an element with a greater affinity for oxygen. Notable examples are phosphorus for copper, gunmetal and bronze ; silicon, manganese and aluminium for steel ; magnesium deoxidises nickel as well as removing sulphur. The deoxidant is often added in the form of an alloy with the metal being deoxidised. Normally the amount of deoxidant added is such that a small excess remains in the metal, 0·02–0·05 per cent phosphorus being typical for copper. The excess may be undesirable in some respects, for example in reducing the conductivity of copper, although in bronzes phosphorus is frequently employed as an alloying component as well as for deoxidation. Excess of deoxidant is useful in counteracting oxidation during casting, or evolution of reaction gas due to small residual amounts of oxygen and other reactant concentrating in the last part of the metal to solidify. Insoluble oxides (formed by impurities or alloying elements) which do not separate freely are likely to be entrapped in the solid metal. This can be prevented by the use of deoxidants forming easily separating products. Thus stannic oxide does not readily separate from bronzes, but its formation is prevented or it may be removed by using phosphorus.

Deoxidation is not necessary for aluminium, magnesium, lead, tin or zinc, or for many alloys containing these metals. In addition, cast iron does not need deoxidation.

Other methods. Varous methods of eliminating gas unsoundness aim at full escape of the gas on solidification. Presolidification has been used to remove hydrogen from aluminium and magnesium. The melt is stirred as it is allowed to cool and solidify slowly in the crucible to give good opportunity for escape of the hydrogen. The metal is then quickly remelted and finally cast. The method does not find much favour in practice because of the extra time and cost.

Directional solidification, such as is obtained in ingots, allows escape of the evolved gases. The best condition is that of unidirectional growth from the bottom of the mould upwards ; this is approached in continuous and centrifugal casting methods, and by applying water cooling to the bottom of a mould arranged with walls that lose heat slowly. Apart from special methods, improvement can be obtained in ordinary top-poured ingot practice by pouring slowly almost in layers.

Oxidation in casting is combatted by filling the mould with reducing gases from volatile mould dressings, pouring through a gas flame, and, as already pointed out, by excess of deoxidant. To protect magnesium, the surface of the metal and the pouring stream are dusted with sulphur to give a sulphur dioxide atmosphere, which is not harmful for magnesium.

The entrapping, among the growing crystals, of gas or air in the mould is especially likely to arise with turbulent pouring. With castings, good mould design and careful pouring should overcome the tendency. In ingot practice, the simple open-top mould design facilitates escape of such gas, and tranquil pouring can be obtained by uphill methods or the Durville process. Turbulence is also reduced by slow pouring, or by the use of a tundish (Fig. 266), which distributes the main pouring stream into a number of smaller ones. A high pouring temperature and unidirectional solidification favour freedom from mechanically entrapped gases.

(2) GRAIN-ARRANGEMENT : MACROSTRUCTURE

In practice, the grain arrangement is affected by numerous factors such as (*a*) the mould material and the dressing, (*b*) the mould temperature, (*c*) the pouring temperature of the metal relative to its melting point and the mould temperature, (*d*) the size of the casting, (*e*) the conditions of pouring, and (*f*) constitution of the metal. Inherent or added nuclei may also have marked effect on the structure.

Assume that conditions of casting are such that the mould is completely filled and the metal becomes tranquil before solidification begins (in practice this will not usually be so with metal moulds). With chill-casting in metal moulds cooling is initially very rapid, and commonly a surface layer of metal is quickly chilled below the freezing point, forming very small equi-axial *chill grains*. If the section of the casting is very thin, drastic chilling may be effective throughout the section. With large sections the chill grains only

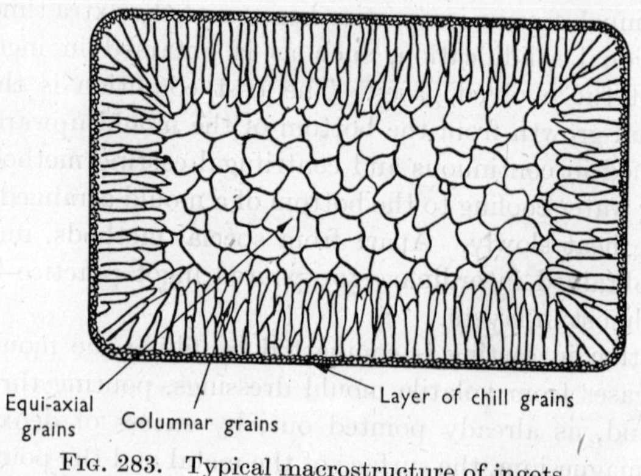

FIG. 283. Typical macrostructure of ingots

extend a small distance, and a temperature gradient is set up in the molten metal. Under these conditions *columnar grains* form, growing in towards the centre from the sides and bottom of the mould (Fig. 283). Because a temperature gradient exists and general cooling is proceeding, the metal will solidify in thin layers. In the case of pure metals and alloys solidifying at a constant temperature, the demarcation between solid and liquid is fairly sharp; but with alloys solidifying over a range of temperature, there will be a semi-solid zone, the thickness depending on the freezing range and the steepness of the temperature gradient. Under both conditions no new nuclei are formed, and the existing grains extend normal to the mould face, lateral growth being restricted by mutual contact. However, in some cases with alloys which solidify selectively, slowness of diffusion may cause the liquid adjacent to the growing crystals to be so enriched in one metal or impurities that the melting point becomes lower than that of the liquid of initial composition farther in, and from which new crystals start (Fig. 284). Thus columnar growth may be stopped and comparatively small equi-axial crystals form.

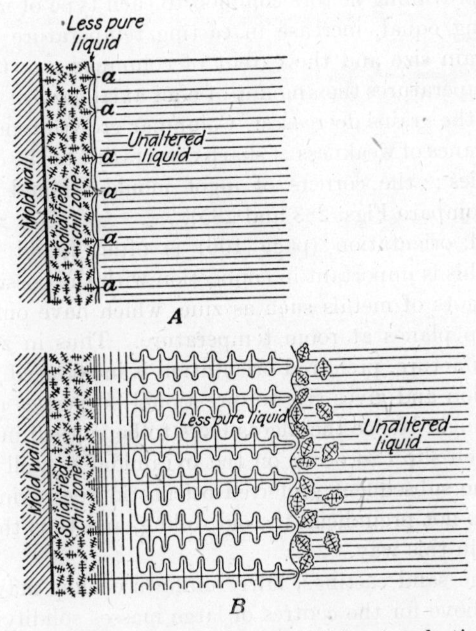

FIG. 284. Stopping of columnar growth due to selective crystallisation. Figs. 284 and 289 are from J. W. Halley, *Basic Open Hearth Steelmaking*. Amer. Inst. Min. Met. Eng.

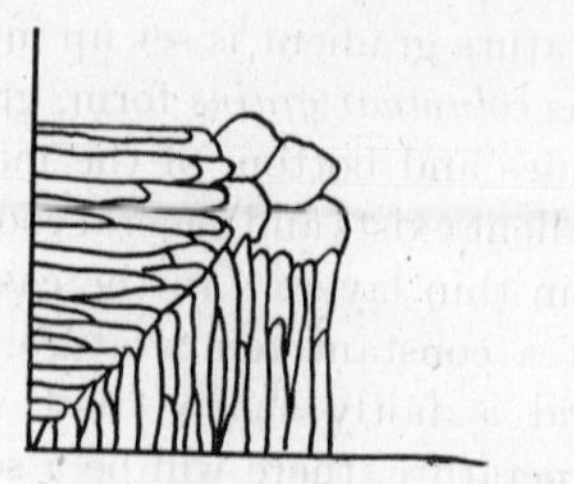

Fig. 285. Effect of sharp corner on columnar crystallisation.

Columnar grains may extend right into the centre of the casting; but in comparatively large sections the metal in the centre may reach a fairly uniform temperature and then, well-lagged by the solidified metal, the mould walls and the air gap resulting from contraction of the solid metal away from the mould surface, this metal will cool gradually to produce large equi-axial (commonly called "equi-axed") grains (Fig. 283). The cooling need not be absolutely uniform, but the temperature gradient will not be sufficient to prevent growth from centres in advance of the existing crystals.

The speed of solidification and extent of the chilling action (including chill and columnar grain-formation) are to some extent greater with copper than with cast iron moulds, and increase with water cooling. However, the differences are reduced because the air gap, mould dressing and conductivity of the shell of solidified metal are prevailing factors common to each type of mould. Other things being equal, increase in casting temperature increases the average grain size and the extent of columnar growth: with low casting temperatures the amount of equi-axial growth increases and the size of the grains decreases. Columnar growth tends to produce diagonal planes of weakness at sharp corners due to the concentration of impurities; the corners of ingot moulds should therefore be rounded (compare Figs. 283 and 285).

Preferred orientation (page 106) is often found in columnar growth. This is important in connection with the possibility of cold working ingots of metals such as zinc, which have only one set of possible slip planes at room temperature. Thus in zinc slabs for sheet manufacture, preferred orientation is introduced by columnar crystallisation and gives rise to directional properties unfavourable to cold rolling. Hence the ingots have to be worked initially above 100° C., when slip can occur on the pyramidal as well as the basal planes. The subsequent preferred orientation occurring on recrystallisation is not prejudicial to cold rolling, and thus the sheets can be finished in this way.

With large sand castings, fairly uniform cooling may obtain—as described above for the centres of large masses solidifying in metal moulds—resulting in large equi-axial grains which become larger towards the centre as cooling becomes slower. In smaller sections the mould may produce sufficient temperature gradient for the formation of columnar grains. In both chill and sand casting, the structure will clearly vary with the size of the section.

Turbulence in the molten metal during solidification may considerably affect the grain arrangement, especially in preventing columnar growth and reducing the grain size. This is because the turbulence tends to keep the temperature uniform, wash solid particles off the advancing solid and distribute them in the liquid where they may act as nuclei. When metals are cast near their freezing point, the agitation also tends to prevent undercooling, promoting the formation of nuclei.

In top-poured ingots, in particular, solidification usually begins around the bottom of the mould soon after pouring is started, and with a single pouring stream the penetration of the fresh metal continues to be very deep, the metal flowing outwards and upwards from the bottom. It will be appreciated that for a specific initial temperature of the molten metal a faster pouring rate increases the turbulence, but with a slow rate the metal is longer getting into the mould and will be at a lower temperature before agitation ceases. As already mentioned, apart from special methods of casting, turbulence is reduced in top pouring by distributing the main stream into several smaller ones by means of a tundish. Splashing, which is especially likely at the beginning of top pouring, must be avoided, as the splashed metal may stick to the mould surface and not ultimately blend with the main body of metal (especially if the pouring temperature is low), thus forming a surface defect.

Turbulence is also caused by gas evolution from the solidifying metal or from volatile mould dressings. Thus, for example, although columnar grains are usually formed in killed steel ingots, these are absent in rimming steel. It has also been shown with brass ingots that the gases from a volatile dressing will inhibit columnar growth.

(3) EFFECTS OF CONTRACTION

In most metals the irregular or statistical close-packing of the atoms in the liquid state is not so close as the regular crystallised structures. Thus during solidification metals contract in volume, in addition to the normal liquid or solid contraction (Fig. 286). It is interesting to note that there is a slight expansion when bismuth and antimony solidify, as also occurs with water. The expansion can be explained by the fact that the two metals in question have an "open" crystalline structure, which is less closely packed than that of

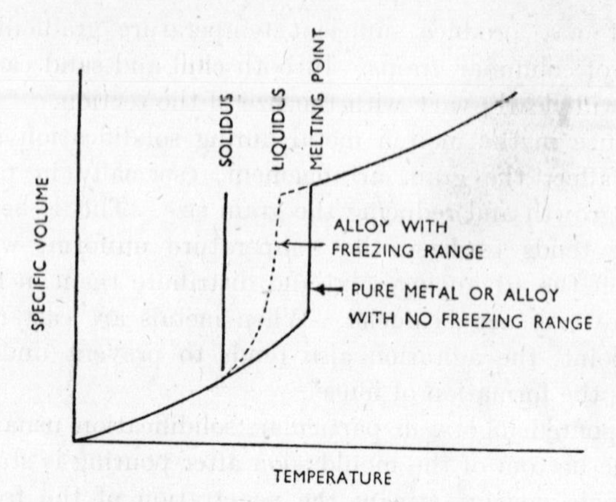

FIG. 286. General form of volume-temperature curves for pure metals and alloys. The volume change on solidification is in the range of 3–7 per cent. From G. L. Bailey and W. A. Baker, Symposium No. 6. Inst. Metals.

the liquid. This would be due to the partly homopolar bonding which exists in these metals. Silicon, which is almost completely bound by homopolar bonds in the solid state, also expands on solidification.

A parallel to the above is obtained in polymorphic transformations in solid metals. Apart from the steady contraction on cooling or expansion on heating, a marked expansion or contraction occurs at the transformation temperature, depending on whether there is

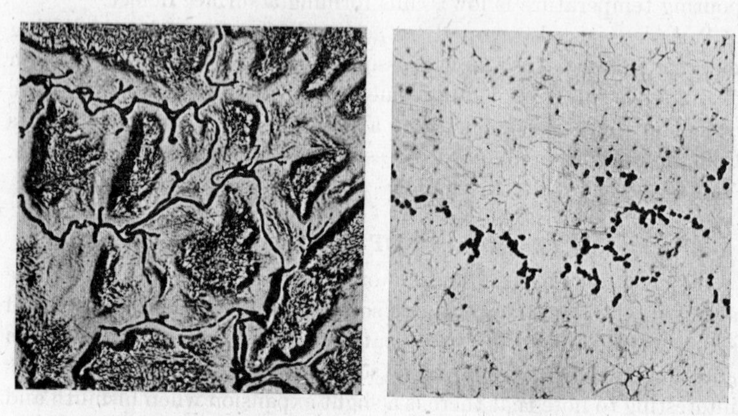

(*a*) Interdendritic fissures in tin bronze.

(*b*) Porosity in magnesium alloy

FIG. 287. Micro-effects of shrinkage. From Baker.

change from a closely packed to a less closely packed structure or vice versa.

The liquid to solid contraction is an important cause of unsoundness in cast metal, for unless extra metal is supplied to the growing crystals, shrinkage cavities or fissures will be formed between them (Fig. 287). Although the shell forming first does contract, this does not markedly compensate for the considerable liquid-to-solid shrinkage that has still to occur.

In ingot practice where this skin shrinkage is noticeable, cracking may occur and the molten metal may leak or " bleed " through the cracks, producing an objectionable defect. The cracking may be due to uneven movement away from the mould face, expansion due to the rise in temperature caused by the air gap formed, or the pressure of the head of molten metal inside on the unsupported skin. Steel ingots are poured very rapidly, but the rate has to be limited so that a skin, of sufficient thickness to withstand the ferrostatic pressure, forms concurrently. Faster pouring rates can be used with corrugated moulds than for those with plane faces because the skin thickens more rapidly on account of the greater cooling area.

When solidification is directional, as in ingots, where it proceeds inwards from sides and bottom and the chilling action of the mould is effective, compensation for shrinkage occurs at the advancing solid face. For pure metals and alloys freezing at constant temperature, the liquid/solid boundary is fairly sharp, and adequate compensation should be obtained. Unless extra metal is added, a depression or **primary pipe** results at the heat centre, the central top portion (Fig. 288*a*) ; a crust may form over the pipe. In alloys solidifying over a range of temperature, there is an advancing pasty region which increases with the freezing range and reduction of temperature gradient. In this region zones of lower freezing-point liquid may become isolated ; on solidification, there will not be sufficient metal to fill the spaces, and shrinkage cavities will be formed. When the chilling action of the mould and directional

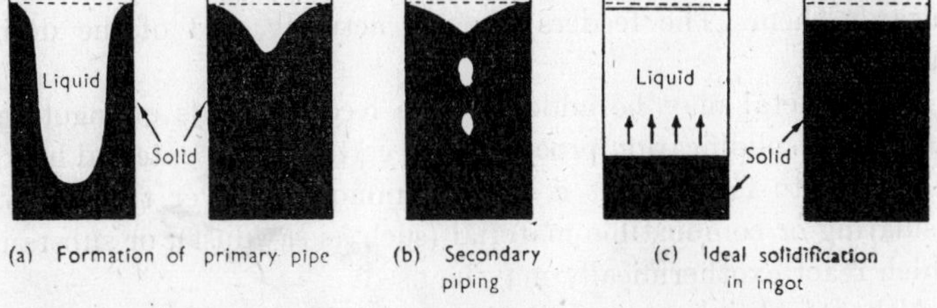

FIG. 288. Macro-shrinkage effects in solidification.

solidification cease, the remaining metal solidifies from random centres and feeding of compensating metal may not be so satisfactory.

It will be seen that the optimum conditions for freedom from shrinkage are therefore a high temperature gradient and directional solidification such that the advancing cup-shaped solid face is kept as shallow as possible to reduce the likelihood of opposite sides bridging and forming a **secondary pipe** (Fig. 288*b*). By pouring slowly shallowness is encouraged, because time is allowed for considerable solidification at the bottom before it starts at the top ; and combined with a high pouring temperature, freedom from entrapped gas porosity and surface folds will be encouraged. The ideal would be unidirectional solidification (Fig. 288*c*).

Small shrinkage cavities can be tolerated in ingots except near the surface, as they will heal up on working. The primary pipe in ingots is cut off before working or at an early stage in working, for as the surfaces are exposed to the air healing is unlikely. With killed steel ingots usually a "hot top" of refractory material is used (Figs. 265 and 281), which acts as a reservoir for feeding the ingot, the pipe eventually occurring in this portion, which is discarded. Occasionally external heating may be applied to the head. In tough-pitch copper the evolution of steam replaces the pipe with a region of closed gas holes, which heal up on working. There is a similar occurrence with rimming steel (Fig. 281) ; this permits the use of "big end down" moulds which are easier to strip, and give greater yield. Such moulds are not suitable for killed steel due to the greater tendency for secondary pipe formation due to bridging.

When solidification is more uniform, as in large sand castings, the top will act as a feeding reservoir. Provided the interdendritic spaces do not become isolated, the feeding metal will be drawn down (it will be appreciated that, if gas enters shrinkage cavities, feeding will be opposed). In castings of complicated and varying section, feeding clearly becomes more difficult. Shrinkage is combatted by the provision of adequate feeders arranged as far as possible so that solidification proceeds from the remotest part of the casting towards them. The feeders are not actually part of the desired shape.

Extra metal may be added to the feeding heads of ingots and castings as solidification proceeds. In certain cases external heating is applied to feeders ; it is quite common to cover the top with insulating or combustible material (such as sawdust), or substances which react exothermically may be used.

Although shrinkage porosity is undesirable in castings, small and isolated shrinkage cavities are of course less harmful than larger or connected ones to the general properties and soundness of a casting.

For certain bronzes a process has been developed in which a small amount of hydrogen, generated by reaction between the metal and the moist sand of the mould, is utilised to disperse long shrinkage channels. Apart from the pipe, depressions due to shrinkage may also be formed on other parts of the surface.

Due to differential contraction, or the restraint of contraction by the mould during or after solidification, stress of sufficient magnitude to cause **hot tearing** in the metal may be set up. Tearing is most likely to occur in the solidification interval, when small amounts of a low melting-point phase or aggregate are present.

Internal stresses due to the effects of contraction may be left in metals ; they may be largely removed by annealing, that is, heating to moderate temperatures in the solid state, followed by slow cooling.

(4) SEGREGATION IN CAST METAL

Frequently cast metal is heterogeneous due to disproportionate concentration, or segregation, in certain parts both of principal constituents and of impurities. Insoluble impurities will collect in the last parts of the casting to solidify, which, if cooling is uniform, will be between the dendrite arms and at grain boundaries. Cored solidification will also produce what may be called *micro-heterogenity* or *micro-segregation* ; similarly, this term may be applied to aggregates of two or more phases. But the average distribution of the constituents may be quite uniform, and analyses from different parts of the metal will be the same. However, in practice, it is often found that pronounced concentration of impurities or constituents, that is, *macro-heterogenity* or *macro-segregation*, occurs in certain parts of the casting. This is generally implied by the term segregation as applied to cast metal.

As the usual form of solidification is from the mould walls inwards, in alloys the liquid solidifying in the centre towards the top may become enriched in one metal (or soluble impurity) due to selective crystallisation. Similarly, there is a tendency for insoluble impurities and constituents forming at a later stage to be concentrated in the centre of the casting. This is known as **normal segregation**.

On the other hand, a high concentration of later solidifying composition may be found at or near the outside of the casting, and is referred to as **inverse segregation**. An extreme case is " tin sweat " in bronze, in which a tin-rich layer, which may also contain high phosphorus and lead, if present, exudes at the surface.

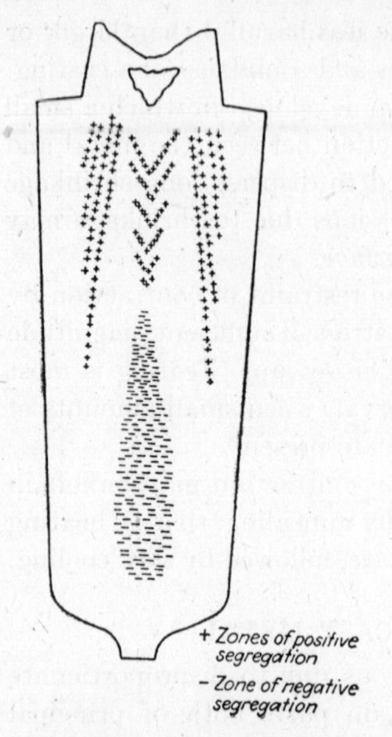

FIG. 289. Segregation in killed steel ingot. The central and outer regions of positive segregation are often referred to as the V and Λ segregates, respectively. The degree of segregation of the principal constituent elements is in the following order: sulphur, (phosphorus, carbon), silicon, manganese. From J. W. Halley.

A particular form of inverse segregation occurs in steel (Fig. 289). Both forms of segregation may develop in the same alloy under different conditions of solidification.

Many explanations have been offered for inverse segregation, some of them very ingenious. Three main theories are: (1) owing to the contraction of the solidified outer shell, pressure is exerted on the still molten metal inside and forces it through interdendritic channels to or towards the surface; (2) the gas evolved during solidification (this tends to become concentrated in the last of the liquid) creates a pressure, which has the same effect as (1); (3) molten metal from the centre of the casting is "sucked", because of shrinkage, into the interstices of the dendrites growing inwards.

It appears that different mechanisms or combinations may obtain in different instances, and that not all factors are covered by the above. The effect of gas seems to prevail in the case of tin sweat in bronze, for the application of the oxidising flux-degassing treatment to melting has been shown to prevent the exudation. Generally, the following conditions lead to inverse segregation; (*a*) a high thermal gradient between outside and centre of the casting; (*b*) a wide freezing range in the metal.

Difference in density between the constituents of solidifying metal gives rise to **gravity segregation.** The first crystals to form, when not linked up with one another and if fairly different in density from the liquid, may sink, or rise towards the top, especially if the cooling is slow. Thus, in lead-antimony and tin-antimony alloys, there is considerable tendency for gravity segregation of the less dense primary antimony-rich cuboids. The gravity settling of purer crystals (forming freely when columnar growth has ceased) has been suggested to account for the zone of negative segregation in killed steel ingots (Fig. 289).

If there is liquid immiscibility, then it is extremely difficult to avoid segregation in the liquid state.

ADDITIONAL READING

1. *Electric Melting Practice*, by A. G. Robiette. (Griffin, 1935). *See also* ref. 26, Chapter 12.

2. *Modern Foundry Practice*, E. D. Howard (Edit.) (Odhams Press).

3. *A Manual of Foundry Practice*, by J. Laing and R. T. Rolfe. (2nd Ed. Chapman and Hall, 1938).

4. *Foundry Practice*, by W. H. Salmon and E. N. Simons. (Pitman, 1951).

5. *Non-Ferrous Foundry Practice*, by J. Laing and R. T. Rolfe. (Chapman and Hall, 1940).

6. *Non-Ferrous Castings*, by R. F. Hudson. (Chapman and Hall, 1948).

7. *Metallurgy of Steel Castings*, by C. W. Briggs. (McGraw-Hill, 1946).

8. *The Solidification of Castings*, by R. W. Ruddle. Monograph and Report Series, No. 7. (Institute of Metals, 1950).

9. *Practical Metallurgy*, by G. Sachs and K. R. Van Horn. (American Soc. for Metals, 1940).

10. *Modern Billet Casting, with Special Reference to the Solidification Process*, by E. Scheuer. *J. Inst. Metals*, 76, 103 (1949).

11. *Basic Open Hearth Steel Making*. Chapter IX, *Moulds and Pouring Practice*, by H. J. Sweeney. Chapter X, *Ingot Structure and Segregation*, by J. W. Halley. (Amer. Inst. Min. Met. Eng., 1944).

12. *Casting of Brass Ingots*, by R. Genders and G. L. Bailey. Research Monograph No. 3. (British Non-Ferrous Metals Research Association. 1934).

13. *Symposium on Metallurgical Aspects of Non-Ferrous Metal Melting and Casting of Ingots for Working*. Monograph and Report Series No. 6. (Institute of Metals, 1949).

14. *The Casting of Non-Ferrous Ingots*, by L. Aitchison and V. Kondic, (Macdonald and Evans, 1953).

15. *Symposium on the Control of Quality in the Production of Wrought Non-Ferrous Metals and Alloys. I. The Control of Quality in Melting and Casting. J. Inst. Metals*, 81, 329, (1952–53).

16. *Metals*, by (Sir) H. Carpenter and J. M. Robertson, Vol. I. (Oxford Univ. Press, 1939).

17. *Shrinkage and Gas Effects in the Casting of Non-Ferrous Metals and Alloys*, by W. A. Baker. (British Non-Ferrous Metals Research Association, 1944).

18. *The Solidification of Metals and Alloys*. (Amer. Inst. Min. Met. Eng., 1951).

19. *Inverse Segregation : A Review*, by N. B. Vaughan. *J. Inst. Metals*, 61, 35 (1937).

CHAPTER 12

MECHANICAL WORKING AND OTHER SHAPING AND TREATING PROCESSES

Mechanical working. Mechanical working performs two functions, namely, it shapes the metal, and refines the structure, giving general improvement in mechanical properties. The processes include those of rolling, forging, pressing, stamping, drawing and extruding. A large quantity of any specific shape must generally be required to justify its essentially complete production by mechanical working ; otherwise where possible the shape will be machined out or constructed from standard wrought stock.

The improvement in properties that results from hot working or cold working and annealing is due to the refinement of the structure, the closing up of gas or shrinkage holes provided they have not become oxidised, the homogenising, and the dispersal of networks and films of weak insoluble impurities. In the production of a finished shape in wrought metal, the size of the initial cast metal and the arrangement of the operations must be such that thorough working throughout is given by the reductions in section then required. Thus with small drop forgings or stampings, in which the whole of the shaping is in one short stage, rolled or extruded material is generally used as stock. The actual reductions in shaping would not alone be sufficient if made directly on cast metal. For several reasons metal that is worked largely in one direction usually has directional properties (p. 464).

The top portion of ingots for working is often *cropped* or *scalped off*, or machined away, before or after some preliminary working, thus removing the portion containing the primary pipe and some of the normally segregated impurities. This is generally the case with steel, and also brass for example ; but zinc slabs and usually copper wire-bars are rolled directly (sometimes the tops of wire-bars may be machined). Surface defects on the ingots may also be removed before or after some working, by chipping or burning out, or by machining or scraping. For special purposes, ingots may be machined all over before working. The ideal ingot should be sound and of uniform composition and structure, having moderate grain size with a good surface. These conditions are met with to varying extents in practice.

In modern practice, ingots are generally broken down hot, unless the metal becomes brittle or weak (**hot shortness**), for less power is required, and larger and faster reduction can be made than by cold working with intermediate annealing. Considerable cold reduction of steels, for example, would be impracticable. Initial cold working is not possible with zinc ingots because of preferred orientation effects, as discussed on page 384. If cold breaking down is carried out, a number of intermediate anneals is usually necessary. Some non-ferrous metals are cold-rolled in this way and the ingots are generally smaller than those in corresponding metals which are hot worked. Typical hot-working and annealing temperatures are given in Tables 56 and 57. One or more reheatings may be necessary in hot working.

TABLE 56. TYPICAL HOT-WORKING TEMPERATURES

Plain carbon steel	Maximum initial temperature ranges from 1300° C. for 0·1 per cent carbon steel to 1050° C. for 1·5 per cent carbon steel (900° and 725° C. are approximate lower limits, respectively).
Low-alloy steels	Initial temperature about 25°–50° C. lower than for plain carbon steel of of same carbon content.
High-speed steel and stainless steel } High-alloy steels	Range 1200°–1000° C.
Nickel	Range 1250°–900° C.
Monel (approx. 2 pts. Ni/1 pt Cu with small percentages of Mn and Fe)	Range 1175°–1040° C.
Inconel (approx. 76% Ni/15% Cr balance mainly Fe)	Range 1250°–1000° C.
Copper	Range 900°–650° C.
Brasses	Range 850°–650° C.
Aluminium and its alloys	Range 500°–350° C.
Magnesium alloys	Range 450°–250° C.
Zinc	Range +170°–110° C.
Zinc alloys	Range 300°–200° C.
Lead and alloys	up to about 250° C.

TABLE 57. TYPICAL ANNEALING (SOFTENING) TEMPERATURES
(Compare with Recrystallisation Temperatures, Table 8 p. 107)

Metal	Temperature	Metal	Temperature
Mild steel	550°–650° C.	Copper	350°–650° C.
Nickel	700°–900° C.	Brass	450°–700° C.
Monel	750°–950° C.	Aluminium and alloys	350°–425° C.
Inconel	850°–1050° C.	Magnesium alloys	about 350° C.

Some processes, for example rolling, are suitable for either hot- or cold-working. On the other hand, some are specifically for working of one kind ; thus extrusion is a hot-working process, and deep drawing and pressing are cold-working. Wrought shapes may be produced completely by hot-working, one or more processes being involved ; whereas cold-working processes are mainly for shaping or finishing, starting with wrought stock (intermediate annealing may be necessary). The final hot-working or annealing temperature is important in determining the final grain size ; intermediate temperatures may also be important, as in the production of sheet for pressing and deep drawing.

Cold-working gives a much superior surface finish to hot-working, and better dimensional accuracy ; it is also useful for varying the final properties of the metal. Prior to cold-working, hot-worked metal has to be pickled in acid to remove the scale. This is necessary after annealing treatments as well, unless the heating is carried out in controlled atmospheres which are inert to the metal.

The working processes are essentially the same for various metals, differing only in detail. It will be appreciated that with most processes there is considerable auxiliary equipment, such as roller tables for conveyance, hot or cold saws and shears, and levelling and straightening machines. Details of such equipment are not generally given in the following account.

Rolling. The section of the metal is changed and reduced by passing it between metal rollers revolving in opposite directions (Figs. 290 and 291). Compressive forces are involved and an in-

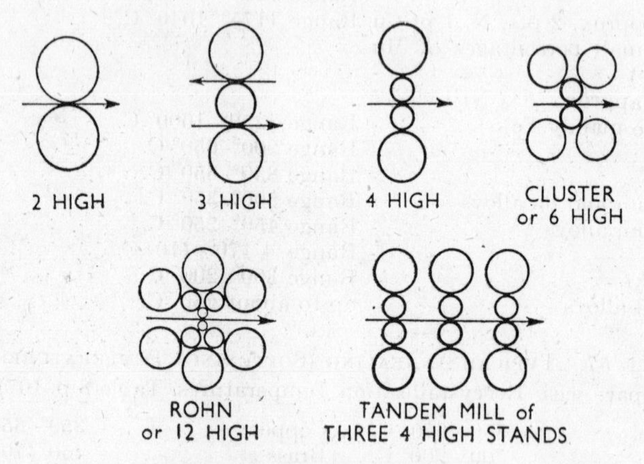

FIG. 290. Types of rolling mills.
From C. E. Davies and L. R. Underwood, *Met. Ind.*, 1944, 64, 306.

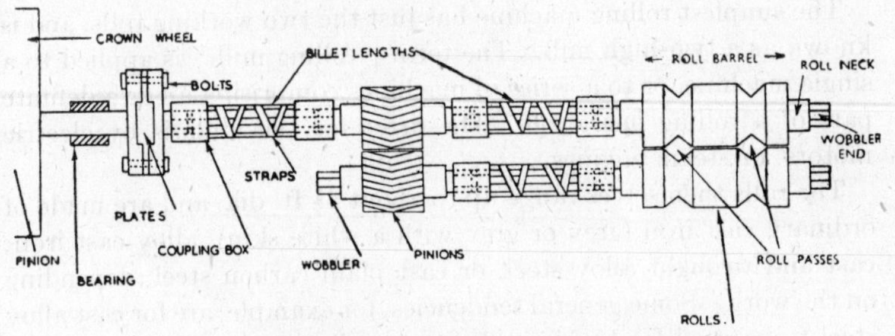

FIG. 291. Drive arrangement for two-high rolling mill.
By courtesy of United Steel Companies, Ltd.

crease in length is obtained as a result of the reduction in section, the metal leaving the rolls faster than it enters. If flat sheet is to be produced, plain rolls are used ; if sections are required, the rolls are grooved appropriately (Fig. 292). Rolling is a hot- or a cold-working process for steel and non-ferrous metals. It is the most usual method for breaking down ingots, as well as being a finishing process producing sheet, various sections, for example, rounds, hexagons, rails and girders, and in a special form, tubes. However, non-ferrous tubes and many sections are commonly produced by extrusion.

With materials that are very tender in the cast state, such as some aluminium and magnesium alloys, a little preworking by a less severe process, such as extrusion or hydraulic pressing, may be given to the ingots prior to rolling.

FIG. 292. Pair of roughing rolls for joists.
By courtesy of The British Rollmakers Corporation Ltd.

The simplest rolling machine has just the two working rolls, and is known as a **two-high mill.** The term " rolling mill " is applied to a single machine, or to a series of machines comprising all or a definite part of a rolling operation. The drive for the mills is by electric motors, or steam engines.

The rolls themselves range up to about 4½ ft. dia. and are made of ordinary cast iron (grey or grey with a white skin), alloy cast iron, cast and wrought alloy steel, or cast plain carbon steel, depending on the work. Some general tendencies, for example, are for cast alloy steel to be used for breaking down as well as many other purposes, white cast iron for intermediate and finishing work, and forged alloy steel for cold-rolling flat material. A special development is the production of composite cast iron rolls with an alloy iron skin and ordinary grey iron core. Small sintered tungsten carbide rolls have been used for flat cold-rolling.

The grooves in rolls for making sections are known as **passes.** This term is also used to denote one journey of the metal through any rolls, plain or grooved. There is a practical limit to the amount of reduction that can be made in any one pass ; it may be up to about fifty per cent reduction in cross-sectional area, but average figures are nearer ten to twenty-five per cent. Considerable reduction is necessary to ensure thorough working of cast metal, and in the production of a section such as a rail the final shape must be reached in easy stages. Thus the production of rolled metal usually requires a considerable number of passes. Where a variety of sections is produced, the usual aim is to standardise as much of the preliminary roughing work as possible.

In some cases, as with flat products, a number of passes may be made between the same rolls by reducing their distance apart after each pass ; with sections, different passes are arranged side by side. However, for the complete operation, at least two or three " stands " or sets of rolls are required. The different rolls in an operation may often be arbitrarily classed as roughing, intermediate and finishing.

In steel parlance, the first mill used on ingots is often known as a **cogging mill or blooming mill** (Fig. 293) and the products as blooms, around 5 in.–9 in. square or rectangles of about the same size ; on further reduction they are referred to as billets, about 1½ in.–5 in. square, and the mill producing them as a **billet mill.** Slabs for sheet are rolled from ingots in **slabbing mills.**

Generally, there is no lubrication between metal and rolls in hot-rolling, although the rolls are usually cooled with water sprays, or water-soluble oils. Sometimes lubricants are used for non-ferrous

FIG. 293. Cogging of steel ingot in two-high mill.

The ingot is rolled backwards and forwards and regularly turned through 90°. The short collars control the spreading action, and for the same purpose the surface of the rolls is slightly convex, except usually in the first and last grooves. Considerable work is done in each groove by varying the distance apart of the rolls between passes. By courtesy of Colvilles Ltd.

metals, and they may be needed to counteract the effect of the cooling water on the metal. Various lubricants are used in cold-rolling.

Types of rolling mills. So far, only the two-high mill has been mentioned ; in its simplest form the rolls only revolve one way, and for return of the work to be given another pass, the metal must be lifted back over the top, or carried round to the front again. Alternatively, the work passes on to another mill, as in continuous rolling. An improvement is the reversing two-high mill, in which the rolls are made to reverse ; the work can then be passed backwards and forwards. Another type of machine is the **three high-mill** (Fig. 290), in which the metal can be passed through the bottom rolls, and back again through the top pair.

For the rolling of sheet and strip in comparatively long lengths, the use of small working rolls reduces the power required ; however, these are not usually strong enough in themselves and must be supported by backing-up rolls, which are as large as practical. The simplest form of this arrangement is the **four-high mill**; in addition, there are six high and various cluster mills (Fig. 290). Different claims are made for the various types, but generally the four-high mills are preferred because of their simplicity; yet they possess the main advantages of backed-up mills. The mills may be reversing mills or not, depending on their use. By making the middle roll in the three-high mill relatively small (Lauth mill), part of the advantages of backed mills may be obtained.

Another kind of mill is the **Universal mill**, in which, in addition to two horizontal rolls, there is a pair of vertical rolls, which work on the edges of the metal. Universal mills are especially suitable for the production of thick plates and I beams (Fig. 294).

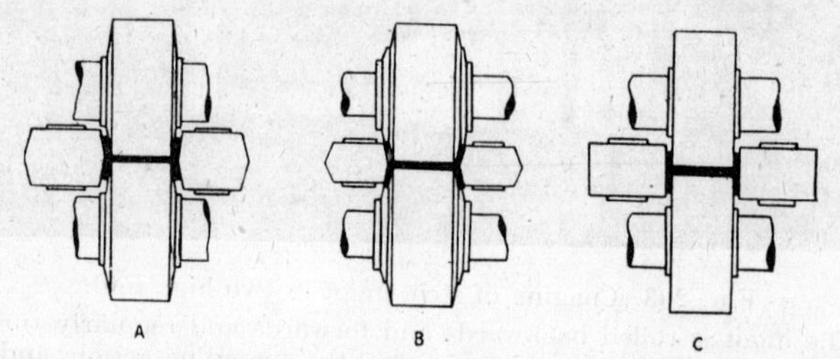

FIG. 294. Universal mill. *A* and *B*, roughing stands; *C*, finishing stands. By courtesy of United Steel Companies Ltd.

Generally, the rolling process is intermittent, the rolls being arranged one after the other (that is in tandem), end-on, or some other combination. In the rolling of thin rounds in long lengths, the metal may be looped through a number of mills arranged end-on. For mass production continuous rolling is practised; a series or " train " of rolls is arranged in tandem, but fairly close together. Each set of rolls has a fixed opening, and revolves faster than the preceding set to compensate for the increase in length from each reduction. The metal passes continuously through the mills, being in a number at the same time. Continuous rolling is used in the production of billets (that is, bar for further shaping), and for flat products. There must be a large and generally continual demand for the section being produced in order to justify the high initial cost of continuous rolling installations, for only one pass is made in each stand of rolls and thus many more are required than with the intermittent techniques, although they may be quite short.

The actual speed of the rolling operation depends on the layout of the mill, whether it is hand or mechanically served, and on the con-

FIG. 295. Hot-rolling of steel bars.
By courtesy of English Steel Corporation Ltd.

dition and sensitivity of the metal. Exit speeds of up to $3\frac{1}{2}$ thousand feet per minute have been used on continuous strip mills, but for general purposes speeds are much lower than this, of the order of one to several hundred feet per minute. Cast metal is likely to be " tender ", and therefore initial rolling in particular is fairly slow and not too severe in reduction.

Rolling of sections. For this purpose, two-high reversing and three-high mills are common (Figs. 292 and 295). Universal and non-reversing two-high mills may also be used. The bulk of section rolling is done hot. The difference between " open " and " closed " passes should be appreciated (Fig. 296). Fins tend to be produced with open passes, but greater reductions can be made than with closed passes. The latter are more accurate but weaken the rolls, because of the deeper grooves necessary in the roll body. Generally, breaking down is carried out in open passes, and certain shaping and particularly finishing operations in closed passes.

When a section is reduced, much of the reduction goes into elongation of length, but some sideways spread is also produced. Section reduction can only be made by vertical compression, and the width of the pass must be greater than the width of the metal entering to allow for the spread, especially in closed passes ; in an open pass,

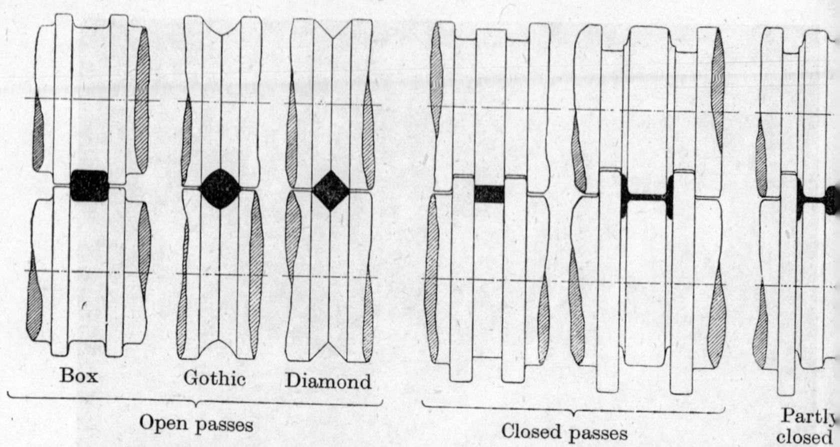

FIG. 296. Types of passes. From *The Metallurgy of Steel*, Vol. II, by F. W. Harbord and J. W. Hall. Griffin.

overfilling may be compensated by fin formation. Thus frequently between passes the section is turned through 90°, so that all-round reduction is made. The turning of the piece may also be caused by the disposition of the passes in the roll, or to remove a fin formed in a previous pass. However, if a fin is such that it cannot be rolled down properly into the body of the section, it is likely to fold over, resulting in a surface defect sometimes known as a lap ; similar defects in rolled metal also often originate from surface defects in the ingots.

For most sections, especially with steel where large ingots are used, the early passes are similar, individual characteristics being developed later. In the very early passes the surface of the rolls is often "ragged" or corrugated to increase their bite ; the ragging must not be such as to mark the ultimate shape. Typical pass sequences for wire-rod and rails are shown in Figs. 297 and 298.

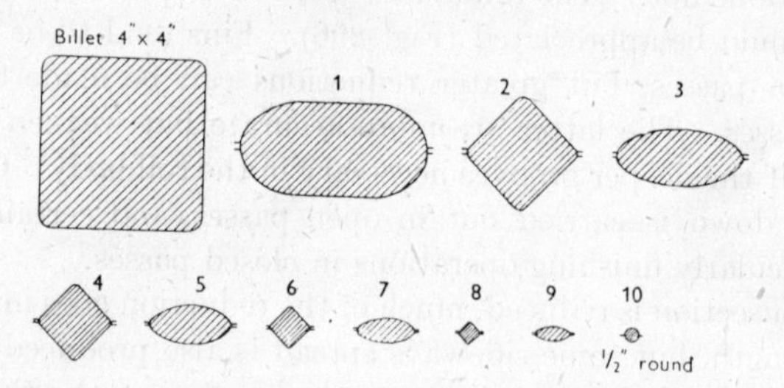

FIG. 297. Passes for rolling wire-rod from steel billets. The diamond and oval sequence enables rapid reduction to be obtained. Similar pass sequence is used for non-ferrous metals.

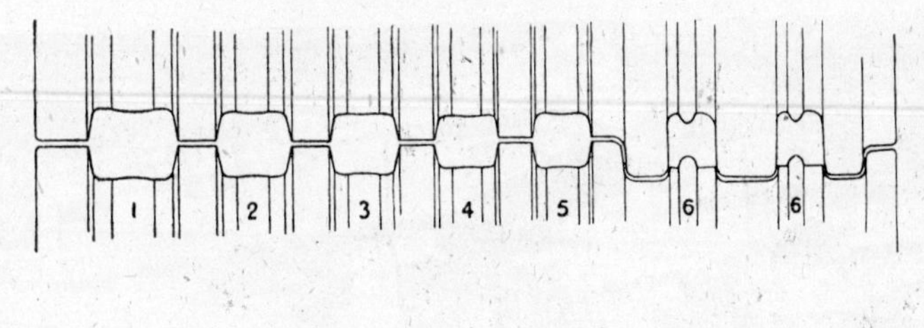

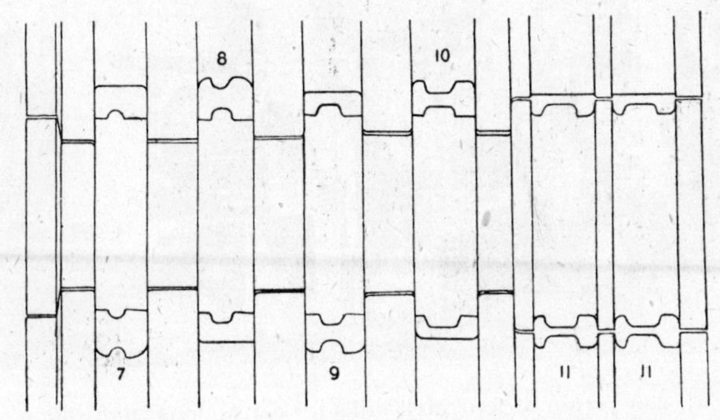

FIG. 298. Roughing and finishing stands for rolling bullhead rails from blooms. By courtesy of United Steel Companies Ltd.

Rolling flat products. Flat products comprise plate, sheet, strip and foil. It is not possible to define rigidly these products, as there is no hard and fast terminology. As given, they are in order of decreasing thickness, apart from sheet and strip, which may be distinguished on width basis, sheet being the wider. On the other hand, the terms may indicate difference in manufacture, in that strip is produced continuously in long lengths and rolled in one direction, whereas sheet may be cross-rolled or pack-rolled. The bulk of the rolling is done hot where possible ; if good surfaces and close dimensions are required, finishing is done cold. However, certain non-ferrous metals in some cases are not hot-rolled at any stage but rolled cold with intermediate annealing ; in such cases the ingots are usually thinner than the corresponding ones for hot working.

The ingots for flat products are often cast in the form of slabs ; but for steel, when the final product is not wide, a standard ingot may be used for both flat material and sections. Practically every kind of mill is used for flat material : Universal mills are useful for rolling the edges of plates and for edging slabs during breakdown. Apart from the backed-up mills, rolling is usually on the intermittent plan. Sometimes, as with cold-rolling zinc, a number of sheets are rolled together in a **pack.** Four-high mills are used especially in con-

FIG. 299. Train of four-high mills for continuous cold rolling. By courtesy of W. H. A. Robertson and Co., Ltd.

tinuous rolling of flat material, four to six, for example, in tandem, comprising a typical finishing train. Provided the metal is thin enough, it is handled in coils, and a number are welded together in continuous rolling. Power reelers are used to coil up the metal as it leaves the rolls ; similar reelers are situated at the back end (Fig. 299). The power reelers are also used to apply tension to the metal as it is rolled, this being beneficial. In some cases only one mill is used, and the metal is reeled backwards and forwards. In one design using tension, the Steckel mill, for cold-rolling, the rolls are not driven (Fig. 300).

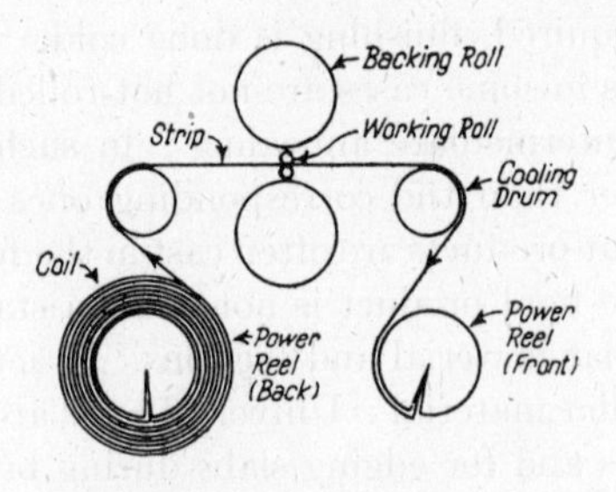

FIG. 300. Principle of the Steckel mill. From *Practical Metallurgy*, by G. Sachs and K. R. Van Horn, Amer. Soc. for Metals.

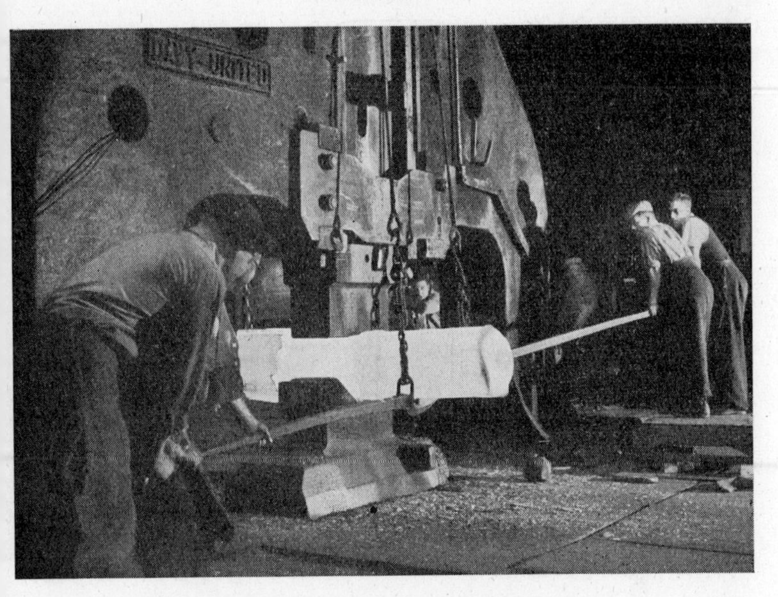

Fig. 301. Forging with 6-ton steam hammer.
By courtesy of English Steel Corporation Ltd.

FORGING

Forging is largely a hot-working process ; the shaping force may be a sudden blow struck by drop hammer, steam hammer, or mechanical or pneumatic forging machine (Figs. 301, 302 and 308) ; whereas in press-forging the metal is squeezed steadily in hydraulic presses (Figs. 303 and 304). Forging is carried out between open- or

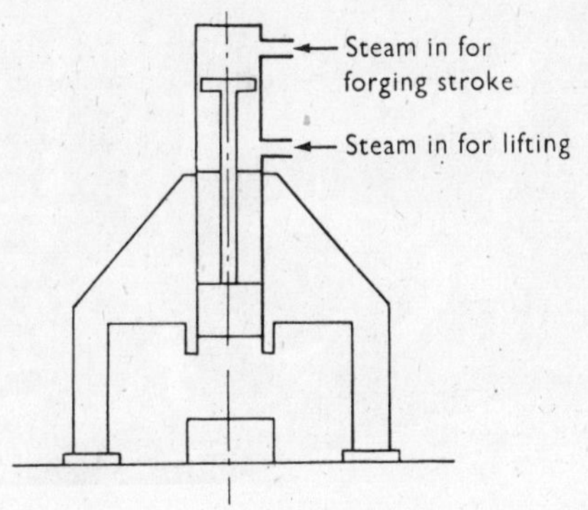

Fig. 302. Principle of double-acting steam hammer. Steam action supplements that of gravity on the hammer.

Fig. 303. Diagram of hydraulic press. The main cylinders (1–3 are used) are actuated by high-pressure water, and the lifting cylinders by steam or water. Capacities of such presses are up to 15000 tons (total force). Figs. 303, 305 and 306 are from R. Liston, *J. West Scot. Iron and Steel Inst.*, 1943–44, 51, 112.

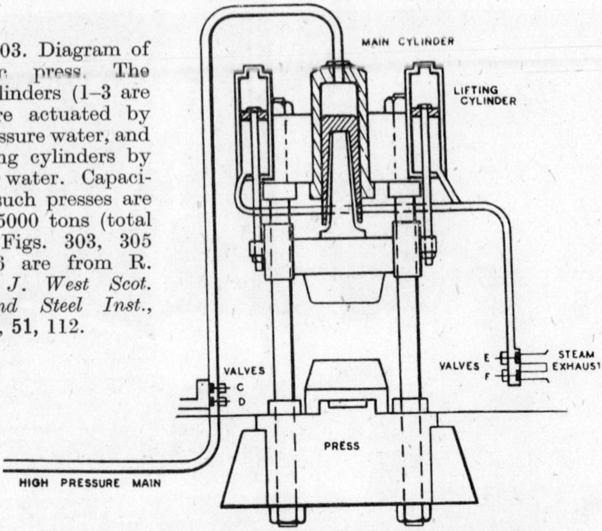

MAIN CYLINDER
LIFTING CYLINDER
VALVES
C
D
VALVES
E
F
STEAM
EXHAUST
PRESS
HIGH PRESSURE MAIN

Fig. 304. Press-forging of pressure vessel.
By courtesy of English Steel Corporation Ltd.

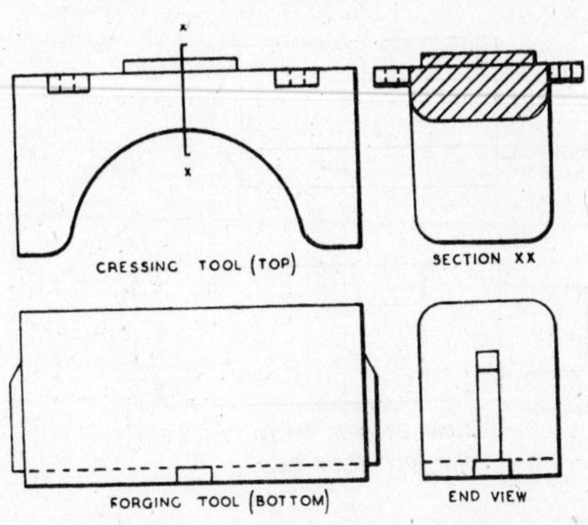

Fig. 305. Tools used on hydraulic press. For each type, the other tool of the pair is similar. The cressing tools are used in operation D, Fig. 307 (and see also Fig. 304) to lengthen the hollow forging, while the top forging tool is used for expanding the diameter, operation C, Fig. 307. From Liston.

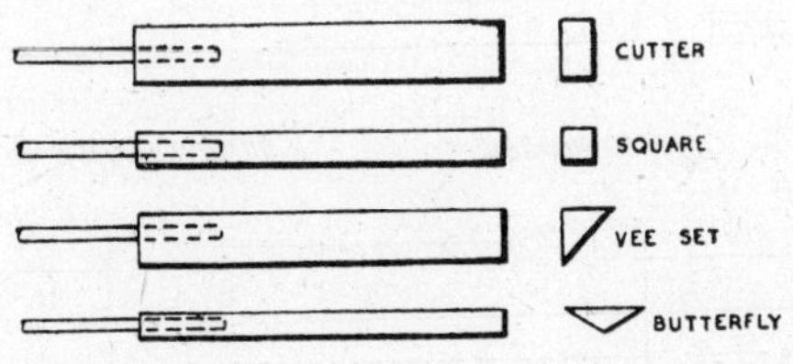

Fig. 306. Hand forging tools. From Liston.

closed-dies. Forging in open-dies is similar to the original process of hand forging ; the metal is not completely surrounded by the dies or tools, which are attached to the press or hammer. There are several forms of tools having different action ; in addition, there are various hand tools used to localise the applied force ; hollow shapes are worked on mandrels after boring or punching out (Figs. 301 and 304–307). Open-die forging is used for producing wrought stock from ingots ; closer control is possible, although the process is more expensive and slower than rolling. It is also used for the manufacture of objects which in the main cannot be made by other working processes because of their shape or size, such as chains, propellers, aeroplane undercarriage parts, rolls, pressure vessels, wheels and tyres. Hydraulic presses are used for large and moderate sized work, and drop hammers for moderate and small sizes.

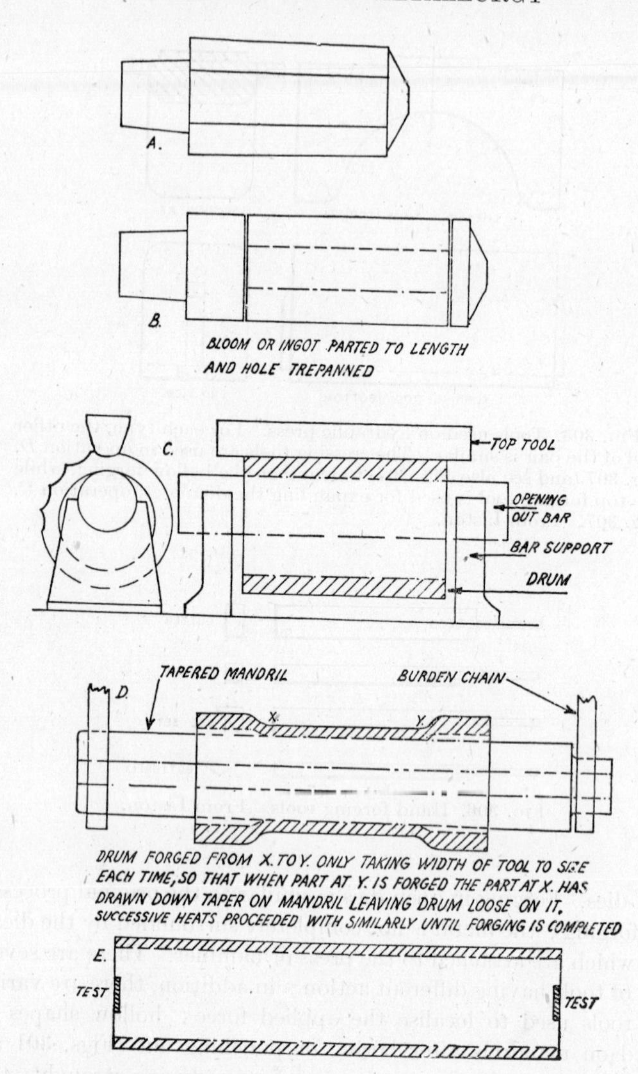

Fig. 307. Stages in the manufacture of steel boiler drum by press-forging. For small drums the initial hole may be punched out under the press. From *Metals*, Vol. I, by (Sir) H. Carpenter and J. M. Robertson. Oxford Univ. Press.

Forging in the hydraulic press is less severe on the metal than rolling (hence the pre-pressing of some tender materials before rolling) and is more likely to close and heal up holes in cast metal, provided surfaces are clean. Hammer forging is more severe than either pressing or rolling ; it is less likely to close up holes, and its effects tend to be more superficial, as much of the energy of the blow is dissipated at the surface of the metal, although the latter point does not arise as long as proper reduction is eventually made. A decided advantage of the hydraulic press over the drop hammer is the absence of shock and its effect on the machine, foundations and local buildings.

With forging in closed-dies, the die is made in two parts ; one part is attached to the anvil, and the other to the hammer or moving part of the press. A piece of hot metal predetermined to overfill slightly the die shape is placed in the bottom die, and the top die is forced against it, thereby causing the metal to take the internal shape of

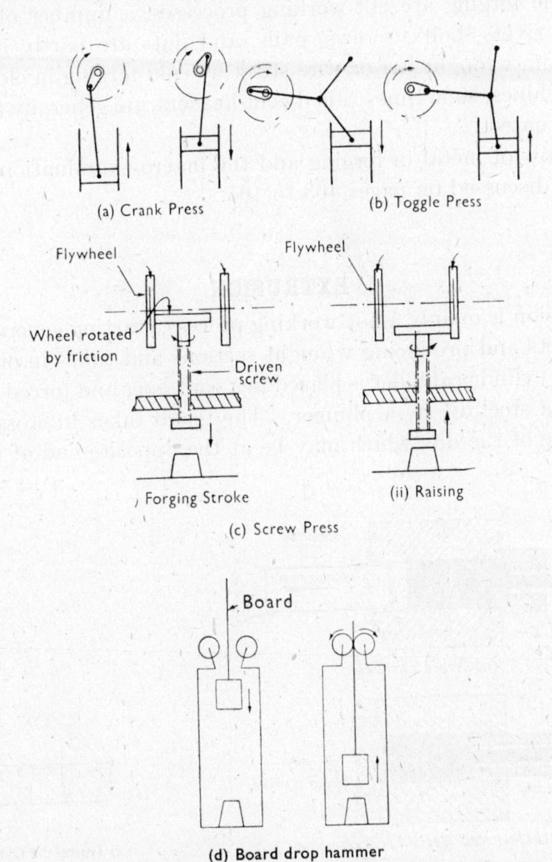

Fig. 308. Machines used in the manufacture of closed-die forgings. Another kind of drop hammer uses a belt for raising the hammer.

the die space. The overfill forms a " flash " where the die parts meet, and acts as a protective cushion. The operation may involve one or more stages. Closed-die forging is used for the rapid production of large numbers of fairly small parts such as internal combustion engine parts and small tools, usually from rolled or extruded stock, and which cannot be worked in other ways. Drop hammers and the pneumatic and various mechanical forging machines are generally employed (Fig. 308), although hydraulic presses may be used. Forgings produced in closed-dies are generally known as **drop forgings** (although strictly this term is limited to those made with drop hammers) or **stampings.**

Cold forging. Although open-die forging and the majority of closed-die forging are hot-working processes, a number of objects, such as rivets, bolts, screws, nails, and nuts are partly or wholly made from wrought bar or wire stock by cold forging in closed-dies. The machines, sometimes called **cold-headers,** are generally mechanically actuated.

The flow of metal in forging and the macro-examination of forgings are discussed on pages 463 to 465.

EXTRUSION

Extrusion is mainly a hot-working process, starting generally with cast billets and producing wrought sections and tubes in one stage. A heated cylindrical billet is placed in a container and forced out of it through a steel die by a plunger. The metal takes in cross-section the shape of the die, which may be at the opposite end of the con-

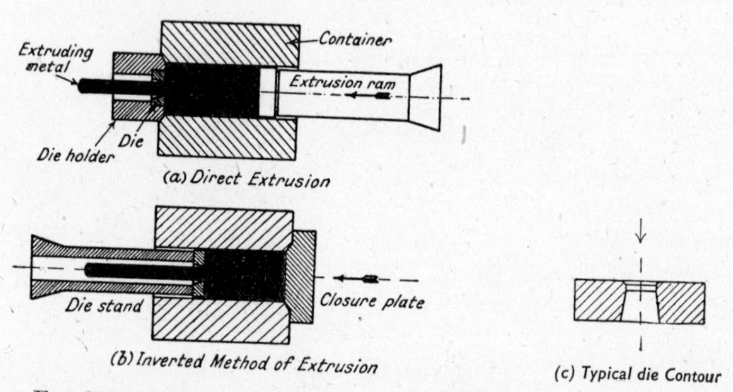

FIG. 309. Methods of extrusion. Figs. 309, 311 and 319 are from *Extrusion of Metals*, by C. E. Pearson. Chapman and Hall.

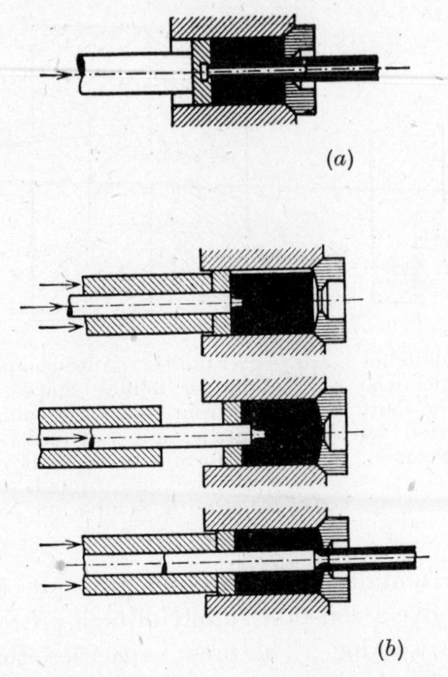

FIG. 310. Extrusion of tubes. Figs. 310, 314, 332–334 are from *Practical Metallurgy*, by G. Sachs and K. R. Van Horn. Amer. Soc. for Metals.

(*a*) From hollow billet—the mandrel moves through the die with the tube, but at a slower rate.

(*b*) A solid billet is first pierced by the mandrel. In this example, the mandrel does not move during the extrusion of the tube, but often it does move as in (*a*).

tainer to the plunger or in the plunger itself, the arrangements being known, respectively, as **direct** and **inverted extrusion** (Fig. 309); in some cases there may be several dies. In the direct process, the billet moves relatively to the container, whereas it does not in inverted extrusion. For making tubes, a steel mandrel or round bar is arranged in a circular die space, and during extrusion the metal flows through the annular space so formed. Hollow billets are used for tubes, or solid billets are first pierced in the extrusion operation (Fig. 310). Bridge dies have been used for lead (Fig. 311); although apparently they are not favoured due to bad welding of the lead after passing around the supporting arms for the mandrel. Recently, this procedure has been applied to the production of small tubes and hollow shapes from solid billets in certain aluminium alloys (Fig. 312); its use has been mentioned in connection with copper also. In such cases, pressure-welding of the metal is involved.

The extrusion machines are generally hydraulic presses arranged

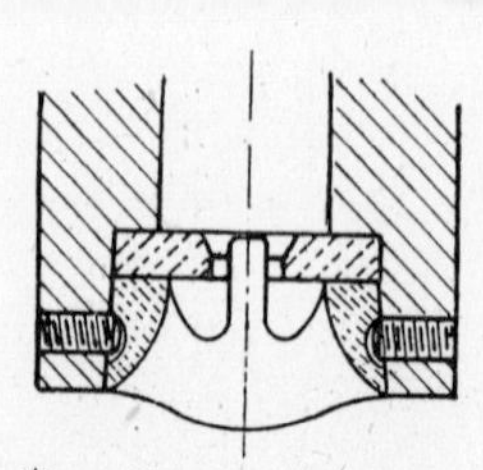

FIG. 311. Bridge die for lead pipe, arranged in the end of the ram. The short mandrel is supported by four arms. From Pearson.

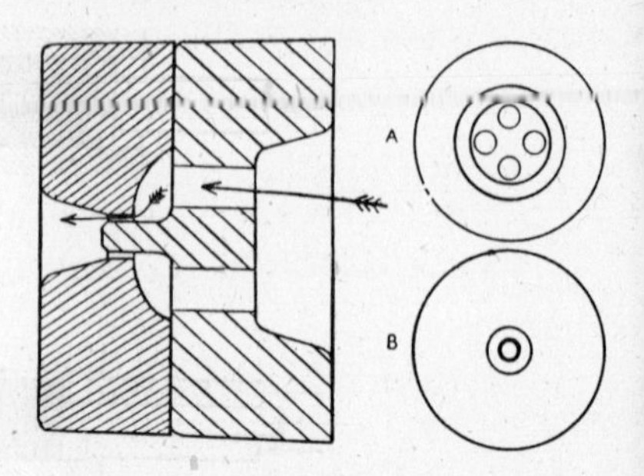

FIG. 312. Ante-chamber or port-hole die for hollow shapes. *A*, back view; *B*, front view. The solid billet is extruded into a number of rods (*A*) which weld up to form a tube as they pass round the mandrel and through the die (*B*). From C. Smith, Symposium No. 9. Inst. Metals.

vertically or horizontally (Figs. 313 and 315), provided with accumulators which give a constant supply of high-pressure water, thus ensuring smooth working. The press capacities, that is, the total force they are capable of exerting, range from about 500 tons for lead to about 6000 tons (container bore 20 in.) for large sections in aluminium alloys. For copper and its alloys, capacities up to 7500 tons (container bore 10 in.) have been used; but the usual pressures are not greater than 2500 tons. Mechanical presses have some limited application; in addition they are used in special processes, such as the impact extrusion of collapsible tubes. Special heat-resisting tool steels are used for dies, mandrels and container linings, particularly for high-temperature work. In a number of cases the containers are heated. For lubrication between metal and tools a graphite grease is common; tallow is used for lead.

Extrusion is a very important process for the fabrication of sections and tubes in the common non-ferrous metals and alloys; with the more plastic materials, such as 60/40 brass, a variety of complex sections is possible. Although very limited, extrusion has some application with steel, for example, in the production of stainless steel tubes. In general comparison with rolling, the advantages of extrusion are that the section may be produced in a very short time in one stage, although the process is not severe on the metal. The process is versatile and suitable for small quantities, since change in section is achieved by change of die; with rolling, however, expensive changes of rolls may be necessary. Further, extrusion is capable of producing sections impossible with rolling operations;

FIG. 313. Charging copper alloy billet into horizontal extrusion press. From N. Swindells, *Met. Ind.*, 1949, **74**, 359.

relatively complex sections and also re-entrant angles can be formed by extrusion. Sizes are to some extent restricted because of the high press capacities required for sufficient reduction. The bulk of extruded material is less than about 6 in. diameter, although this may be considerably exceeded. With aluminium alloys, structural sections in sizes within a 16 in. diameter circle and tubes up to 12 in. diameter can be made. Against extrusion it must be said that characteristic defects may arise in the metal, and it is doubtful whether working is so thorough as in rolling.

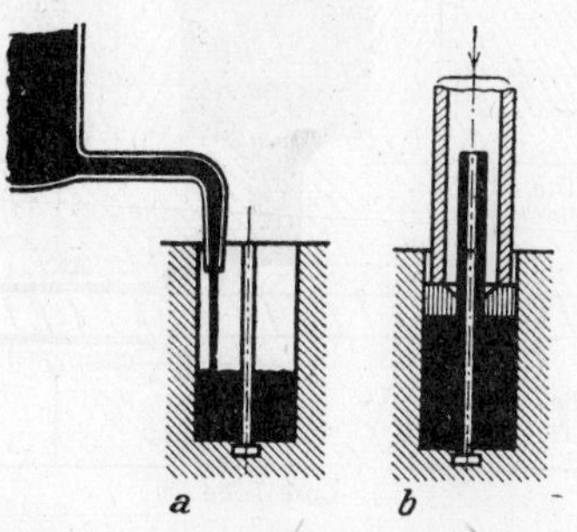

FIG. 314. Extrusion of lead pipe. (*a*) casting the lead; (*b*) extruding. The lead is extruded at a temperature of about 250° C., in order to decrease the pressure required and to increase the speed of operation. From Sachs and Van Horn.

Pure and alloy lead pipe and cable-sheathing are made by extrusion. Vertical presses employing the inverted technique are used for pipe (Fig. 314). Cable-sheathing is manufactured by direct extrusion in vertical presses (Fig. 315). The practice for lead differs from that for other metals in that pre-cast billets are not commonly used, and in normal practice the molten lead is cast directly into the container ; a typical amount is 500 lb. The lead being cast around the mandrel, it is not necessary to arrange for piercing. In the horizontal continuous lead cable-sheathing presses, such as the Henley and the Pirelli, the direct extrusion principle is used ; the solid lead out of contact with air is forced into the container and out via the die by a screw mechanism. Solid sections such as lead and solder wire are also made by extrusion ; resin-cored solder is made similarly to cable-sheathing.

The other non-ferrous metals are extruded mainly by the direct process and largely in horizontal presses (Fig. 313). Vertical presses are also used, especially for small tubes in brass ; the difficulty with them is the room required for disposal of the extrude, although several advantages are claimed.

A defect peculiar to extruded metal and arising from the mode of

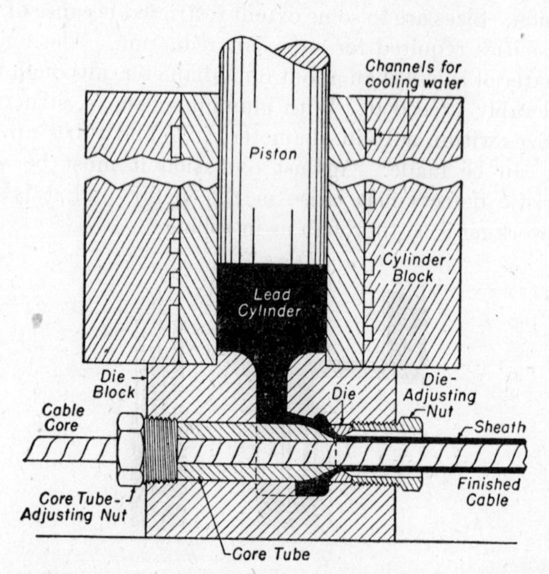

FIG. 315. Vertical press for lead sheathing of cable. Operation is intermittent due to the need to replenish the lead. The lead sheath grips the cable and draws it through the press. From Metals Handbook, 1948 Edit. Amer. Soc. for Metals.

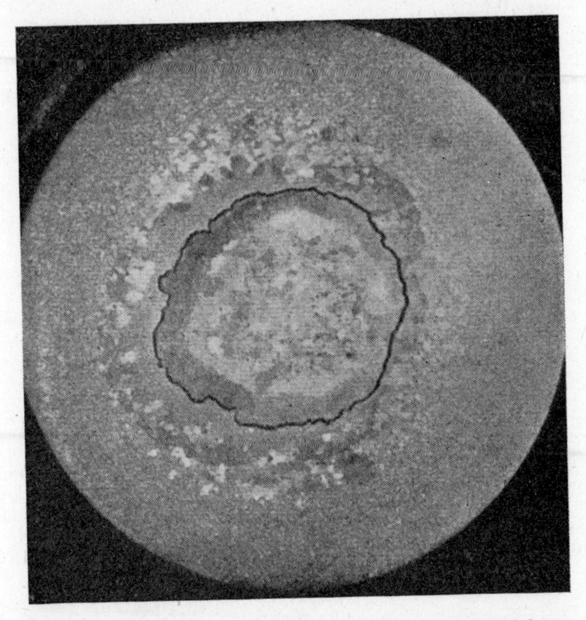

FIG. 316. Annular extrusion defect in direct-extruded brass rod, resulting in a loose core, ×1·5. From R. J. Redding, *J. Inst. Metals*, 1921, 26, 246.

deformation is the presence of a more or less ring of what is essentially oxide running through it (Fig. 316). It is known as the (**annular**) **extrusion defect** or as **piping**. In metals other than lead and its alloys, the defect originates in the skin or surface of the billet, which becomes dirty and oxidised in casting, reheating and actually during extrusion, and eventually enters the extrude (Fig. 317). The shape and presence of the defect is modified by the form of extrusion used, the die contours, the number of dies and their position, the temperature of the billet and the container, and the effectiveness of the lubricant. In practice, because of the incidence of this defect, a certain portion of the billet is left unextruded and scrapped, or the latter part of the extrude may be scrapped.

An important method of minimising the defect consists of making the pressure disc (follower plate or dummy block) used between the billet and the plunger slightly smaller than the bore of the container. Consequently during extrusion the outer skin is sheared off and left in the container as a "skull" usually about $\frac{1}{16}$–$\frac{1}{8}$ in. in thickness. Some improvement may result from machining the billet

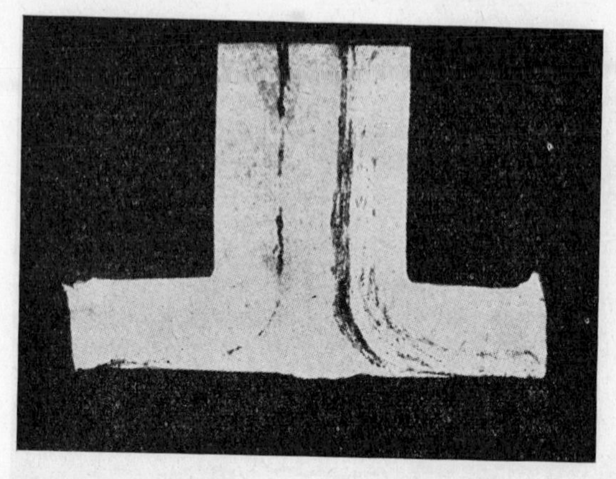

FIG. 317. Scrap end of brass extrusion billet from direct process showing formation of the extrusion defect (2/5 actual size). Due to the method of deformation and friction effects between the metal and press container, the colder outer region of the billet and especially the oxidised skin flow into the extrude from the ram end, following a a funnel-shaped path. From R. Genders, *J. Inst. Metals*, 1921, 26, 257.

after casting and before reheating; and reheating in a non-oxidising atmosphere would also help.

A similar defect is found in lead products, although it arises in a somewhat different way due to the different technique. Thus with lead there is a certain amount of the metal left unextruded each time, and the fresh metal is poured in on top; after several charges, a number of oxide laminations may be present at successive oxidised interfaces, and at some stage these may be extruded into the products. In addition, radial oxide defects may be found in lead pipe and sheathing where the metal has parted, become oxidised and welded up in passing around the mandrel or mandrel support. A number of methods of reducing the incidence of oxide with lead have been evolved. In some cases, as in the continuous cable-sheathing press, all operations are carried out in a non-oxidising atmosphere, including melting and casting.

Another disadvantage of the extrusion process is the unevenness of working along the length of the extrude. It will be apparent that the portion leaving the die first undergoes comparatively little deformation, the amount increasing as the operation proceeds. Further, in aluminium alloys, for example, due to the mode of deformation, the grain size may vary considerably across the section of the extrude. As in rolling, working at a falling temperature results in structural differences along the length of product. Uneven grain size may also be obtained in lead pipe, arising from the coiling after extrusion. If the pipe is coiled while too hot, critical conditions of deformation and temperature may be sufficient to produce unduly large grains in the areas affected, namely in diametrically opposite regions (Fig. 318). The defect is sometimes known as **zoning,** and in service cracks have been found to develop in the coarse zone.

(*a*) Satisfactory structure.

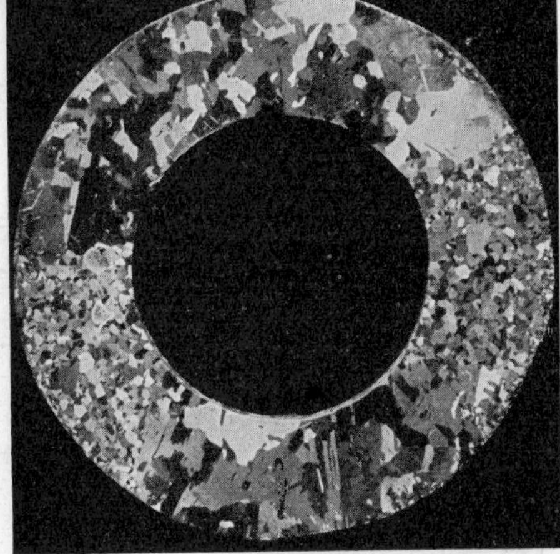

(*b*) Zoned structure.

FIG. 318. Structures in extruded lead pipe. ×3.
Note: The normal structure of worked, unalloyed lead is considerably coarser than that of other metals.
From *The Mechanical Properties of Lead in Relation to Behaviour in Service,* by G. L. Bailey, Brit. Non-Ferrous Metals Res. Assoc.

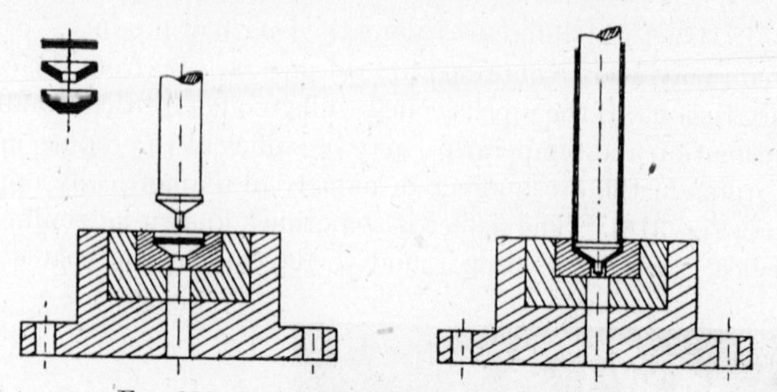

FIG. 319. Impact extrusion. From Pearson.

The remedy is to cool the pipe sufficiently before coiling, or to use an alloy lead which is not prone to the effect.

Some metals, especially a number of light alloys, are very sensitive to the speed of deformation in extrusion. If too fast, a roughened or cracked product results. Thus in practice speeds of extrusion vary considerably ; for example, the speed of brass leaving the die may be 500 ft./min., whereas for duralumin it is only 10 ft./min.

Impact extrusion. There are a number of other special processes in which the flow of the metal is essentially one of extrusion ; wrought stock is used and working may be cold. Among these various techniques one worthy of mention, because of the familiarity of its products, is the impact extrusion at room temperature of

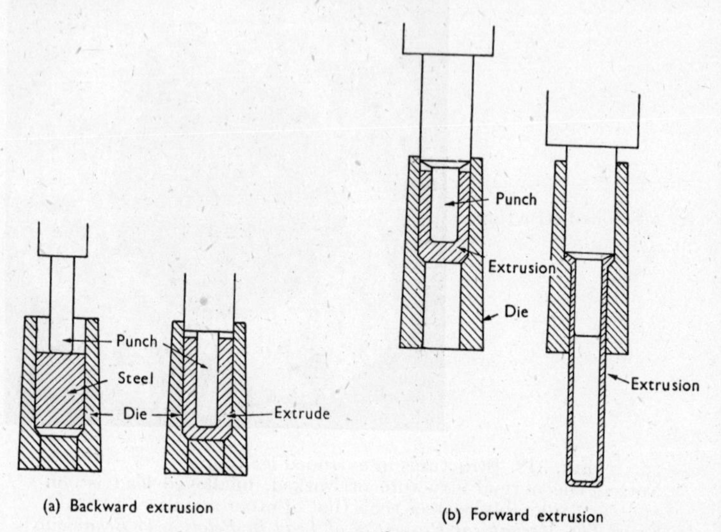

FIG. 320. Cold extrusion of steel.

collapsible tubes in lead, tin, tin-coated lead, zinc and aluminium. A pointed punch descends swiftly on to a disc-shaped blank (cut from rolled sheet) arranged in a die, causing the metal to flow upwards and around the punch (Fig. 319). Zinc battery cans and similar shapes in other metals are also produced in this way. The short tubes made by impact extrusion are in sizes up to about 5 in. in diameter.

Recently, cold extrusion has been successfully applied to steel, using both " forward " and " backward " techniques (Fig. 320); these techniques can also be combined. The steel is given a phosphate coating to act as a base for the lubricant. The principle shown in Fig. 320*b* is similar to the established *Hooker Impact Process* for cold extrusion into tubes of ductile metals, such as copper, 70/30 brass and aluminium.

TUBE-MAKING

Seamless tubular shapes can be made by centrifugal casting or even by electroforming; but the most desirable properties are generally found in wrought tubes. Originally, working methods of tube-manufacture commenced with statically-cast hollow blanks, or billets were drilled or machined out. However, in many cases modern processes start with a solid ingot or billet. Most non-ferrous tubes are made by *extrusion*, when piercing and shaping can be combined, although some of the following processes described for steel are also applicable.

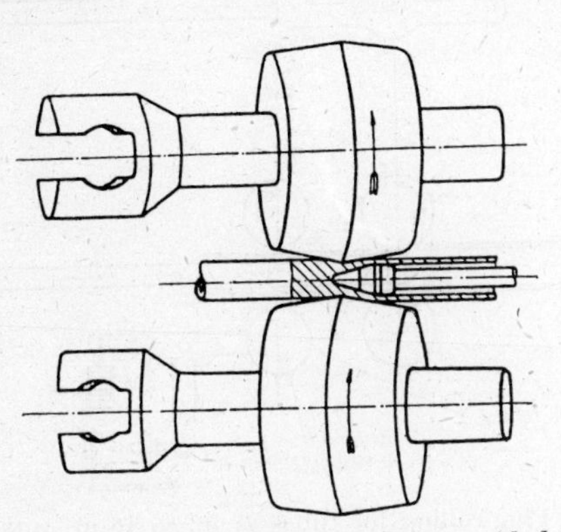

FIG. 321. Rotary-piercing. The hot billet is guided between the rolls, which grip and spin it at high speed. The action tends to open up a hole in the centre which is formed out by the plug. Figs. 321, 323, and 327 are from E. C. Wright and S. Findlater, *J. Iron and Steel Inst.*, 1938, **138**, 109.

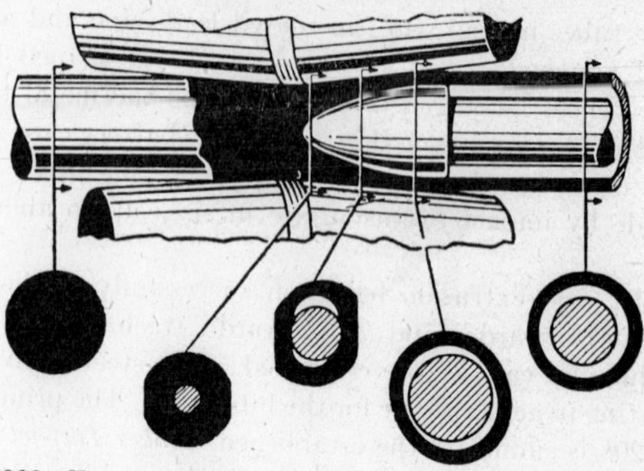

FIG. 322. Changes occurring in cross-sectional area of metal during rotary-piercing. Figs. 322, 324, 326, 329 and 330 are from J. W. Jenkin, *Metallurgia*, 1945, 33, 3.

Extrusion may be used for tubes of special steels, such as stainless steel, but ordinary steel tubes are made by other methods involving usually a separate *piercing* stage, followed by further shaping and

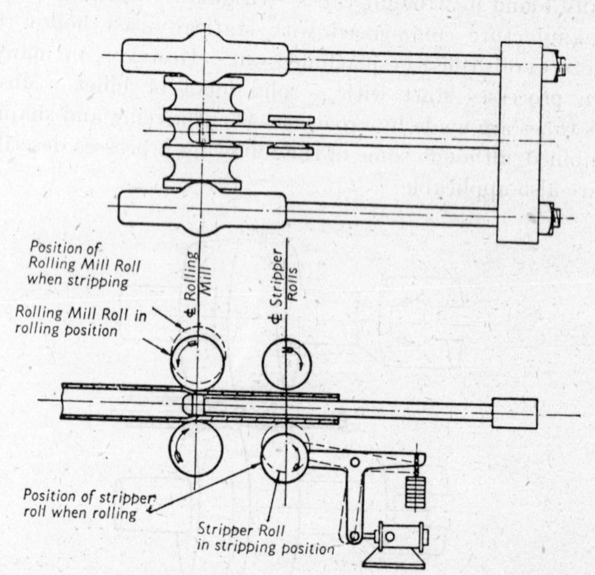

FIG. 323. Plug-rolling for tubes $2\frac{1}{4}$ in. to 16 in. outside diameter. The hot blank is rolled in the grooved rolls over a plug. This gives reduction in wall thickness and outside diameter. The stripper rolls are used to return the tube to the entry side again. Two passes are usual, the tube being rotated 90° between them. From Wright and Findlater.

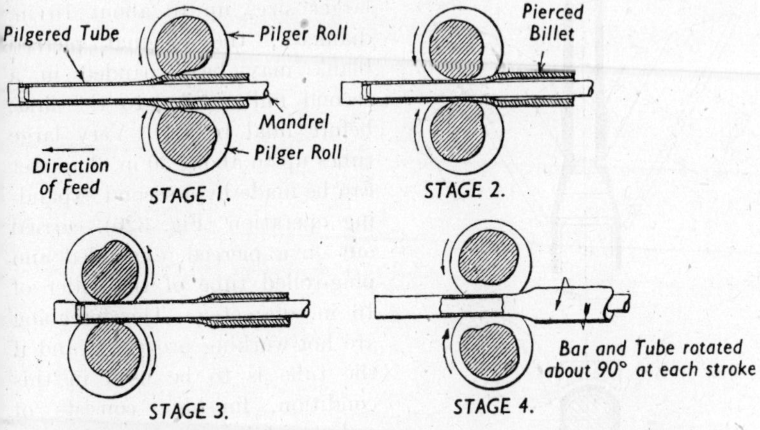

FIG. 324. Diagram showing the step-by-step method of rolling in the Pilger process. This can be applied to the production of tubes of 2–18 in. outside diameter. From Jenkin.

elongation. **Rotary-piercing** (Figs. 321 and 322) is an important method, the rough-pierced blank being improved, sized and elongated by **plug-rolling** over a mandrel between grooved rolls (Fig. 323) in America, or in a **Pilger-mill** (Figs. 324 and 325) in Britain and Germany ; both processes are carried out hot. For the

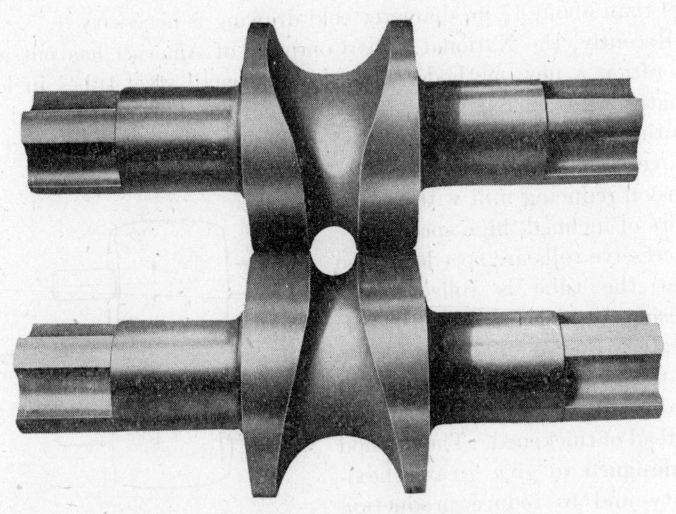

FIG. 325. Pair of Pilger rolls.
By courtesy of the British Rollmakers Corporation Ltd.

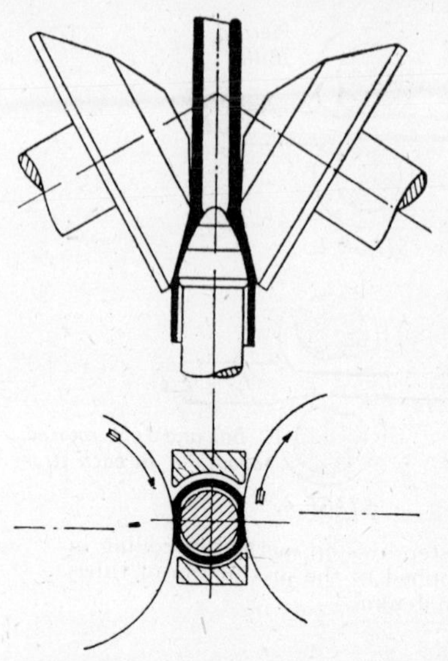
FIG. 326. Rotary expanding mill. From Jenkin.

larger sizes up to about 16 in. diameter, the original pierced blank may be expanded in a second mill similar to the first, before final rolling. Very large tubes up to about 30 in. diameter can be made by a second expanding operation (Fig. 326), carried out on a pierced, expanded and plug-rolled tube of the order of 16 in. diameter. The foregoing are hot-working processes, and if the tube is to be used in this condition, finishing consists of *reeling* while still hot, that is, light cross-rolling on a mandrel (Fig. 327) which rounds up and burnishes the tube; and is followed if necessary by a sizing pass or two in sizing rolls.

Steel tubes smaller than about 3 in. diameter are made from larger ones by rolling down hot in a **reducing-mill**, which consists of a series of grooved rolling mills arranged at 90° to each other and at 45° to the vertical. For sizes less than about $1\frac{1}{4}$ in. diameter cold-drawing is necessary.

Recently, the National Tube Company of America has put into operation a new method for hot rolling small steel tubes in long lengths after piercing. Plug-rolling and reeling are replaced by continuous rolling on a mandrel through eight mills inclined as above. This is followed by a tension-reducing mill with twelve pairs of inclined, high-speed rolls. Successive rolls are speeded up so that the tube is rolled under tension, which makes possible greater reduction in diameter than by the ordinary reducing mill and enables the walls to be thinned instead of thickened. The method is designed to give greater flexibility and to reduce production costs.

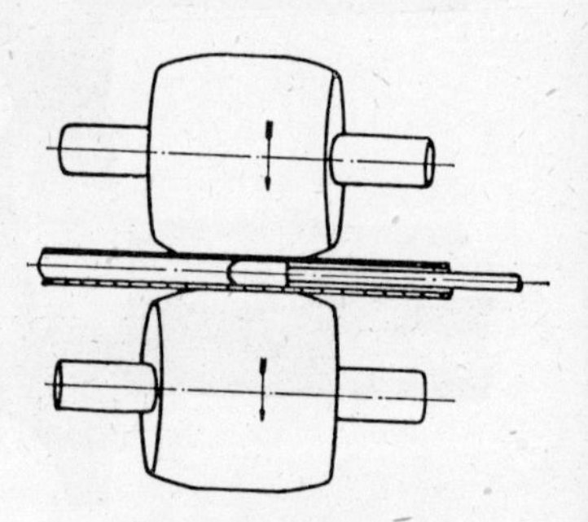
FIG. 327. Reeling. From Wright and Findlater.

Hot-worked steel tubes are also produced by the **push bench** method, and the **cupping process.** In the former, a punch is forced into a square-rolled billet (with rounded corners) placed in a cylindrical die, whence a rough tube blank is produced. The end of a long mandrel is inserted in the blank, which is then pushed through a series of reducing dies (Figs. 328 and 329). The tube is finished by reeling, which enables the mandrel to be removed ; the closed end is then cut off. In the cupping process, a disc is first punched from sheet ; this is next made into a cup and gradually worked into a tube, one end of which is closed (Fig. 330). The process is used for making certain storage cylinders ; the other end may be closed up by a separate operation.

If either non-ferrous or steel tubes are required with good surfaces, accurate shape and close tolerances, they are finished by *cold-drawing.* Cold-drawing is also employed to make very small tubes ; steel hypodermic needles are made in this way, for example. Thinner-walled tubes can be made by cold-drawing. Before drawing,

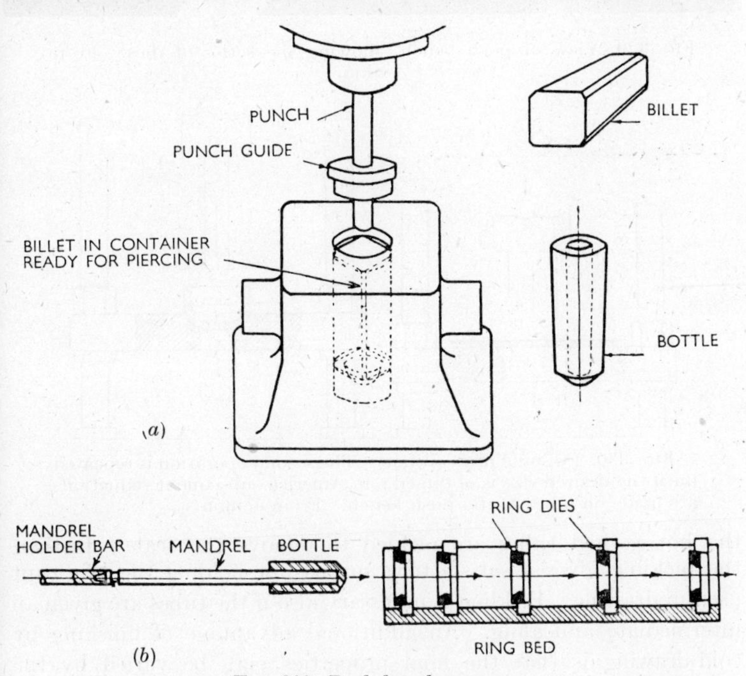

FIG. 328. Push bench process.

(*a*) Punching ; (*b*) reducing on push bench. Produces tubes 3 in.–8 in. outside diameter. From *The Manufacture of Seamless Tubes*, by G. Evans. Witherby.

Fig. 329. View of push bench, showing the series of dies. From Jenkin.

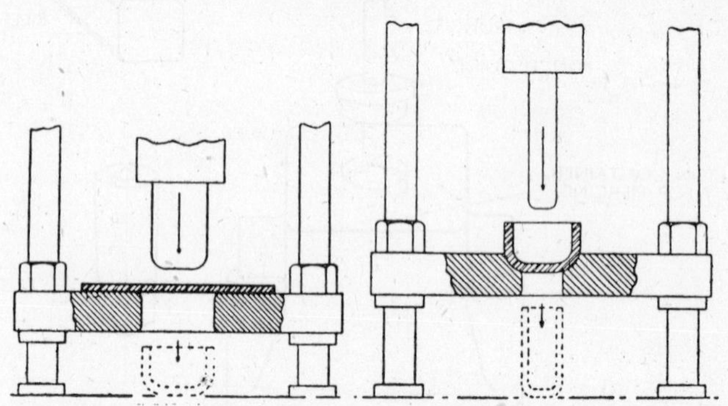

Fig. 330. Cupping process (hot). The second operation is repeated until the desired size is obtained; in America subsequent reductions are made on a horizontal push bench. From Jenkin.

the hot-worked tubes are pickled to remove the scale; further, the pickling gives a satisfactory surface for holding the lubricant used in drawing. Pickling is necessary also if the tubes are given an intermediate annealing. An additional advantage of finishing by cold-drawing is that the final properties may be varied by the amounts of residual cold work. Tubes may also be finished cold on the Pilger principle.

For some purposes, tubes made by *welding* (or brazing) bent-up sheet or strip are satisfactory. There is essentially no limit to the size that may be made in this way, and there is a variety of techniques.

DRAWING

Drawing, in the main, is a cold-working process and is much used for finishing tubes and sections. Wire is made by drawing from hot-rolled, or occasionally with non-ferrous metals extruded, rod, about $\frac{1}{4}$ in. in diameter. Small tubes are also made from larger ones by drawing. In the latter two cases, considerable total reductions may be made in the production of fine sizes. In some cases change of section is made by stages in drawing. As pointed out in the section on tube-making, hot-worked material is pickled before drawing, and after intermediate annealings.

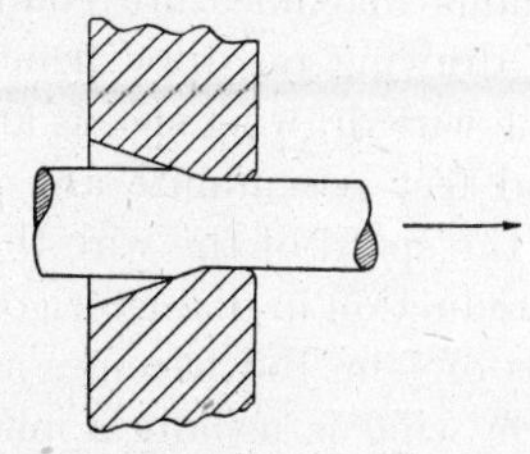

FIG. 331. Principle of drawing.

In the drawing process the metal is reduced in section by pulling through a die (Fig. 331); one end of the metal must be pointed to get it through the die initially. The dies are made of steel (which may be chromium-plated) or white cast iron; tungsten carbide is being increasingly used for moderate sizes; and fine wire is drawn through diamond dies. Thick sections and tubes are drawn on draw benches (Fig. 332); the lengths handled may go up to about 60–70 ft., but lengths of between 20 ft. and 30 ft. are usual. Tubes are drawn with or without mandrels (Fig. 333). Suitably small sizes of metal are coiled during drawing (Fig. 334).

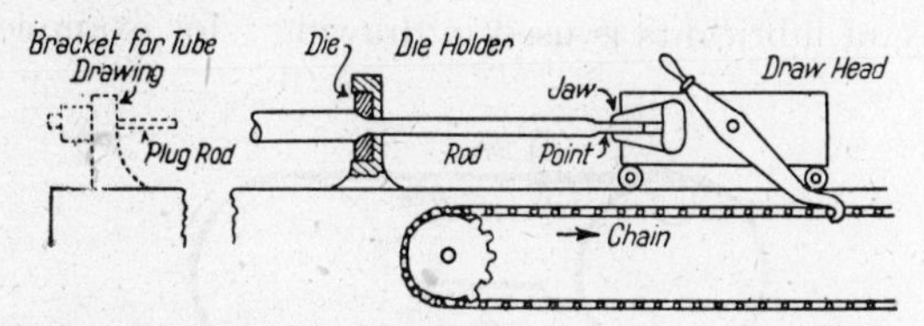

FIG. 332. Draw bench. When the draw head reaches the end of the bench, the drawn length is cut off and the draw head is returned to repeat the operation until the original length is used up. From Sachs and Van Horn.

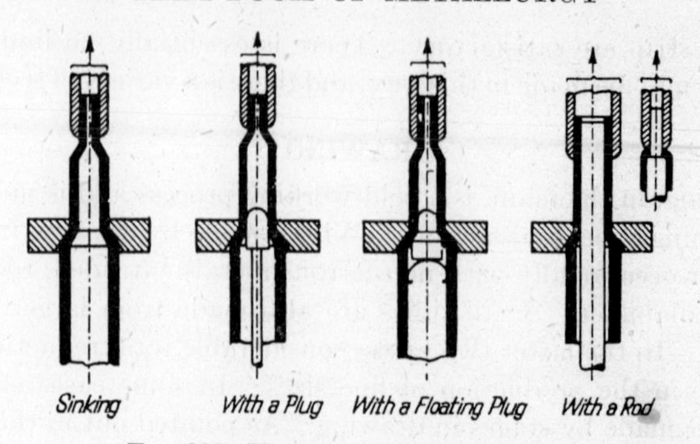

FIG. 333. Methods of drawing tubes.
From Sachs and Van Horn.

Multiple die continuous machines are commonly used for thin wires. The speeds of drawing on draw benches are up to about 250 ft. per minute ; fine wire drawing speeds are greater, and values up to several thousand feet per minute are common. With continuous wire drawing, the speed of the wire through successive dies must increase, for the reduction in diameter goes into length ; thus, for example, 440 yards of $\frac{1}{4}$ in. rod becomes about 14,000 yards at 0·044 in. diameter. Drawing is usually applied to shapes smaller than about 10 in., although this may be considerably exceeded. The drawing of tubes down to about 0·01 in. outside diameter is standard, and even smaller sizes are reported. With normal methods wire at least as small as 0·002 in. diameter is drawn ; the smallest wire die in use in Britain is reported to be 0·00028 in. in diameter. It should noted that the drawing force must not be such that the breaking stress of the reduced metal is exceeded. Lead cannot be drawn, lead " wire " being extruded. The reductions made in drawing per pass or draw are generally less than 50 per cent reduction in cross-sectional area. An example in copper wire drawing is the reduction of $\frac{1}{4}$ in. rod to 0·052 in. by continous practice using ten dies.

A variety of lubricants is used in drawing ; for example, grease,

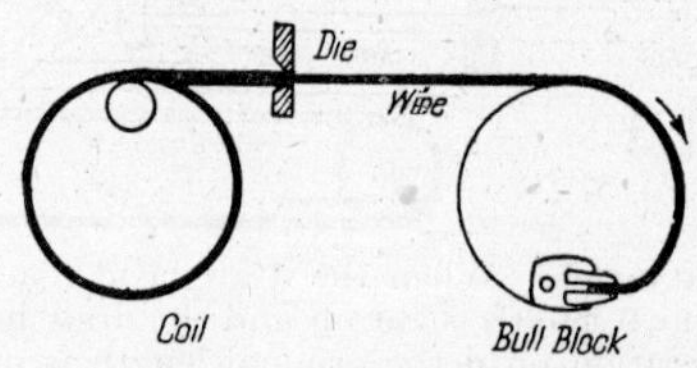

FIG. 334. Wire drawing. From Sachs and Van Horn.

tallow, oils, soap solution, water-soluble oils. Continuous wire drawing is often done with the assembly immersed in a tank of the lubricant, such as soap solution or water-soluble oil ; a liquid made by the fermentation of rye flour in water may be used for steel. In the case of steel, a pickled or rusted surface or a phosphate coating is found a very satisfactory base for the lubricant ; a layer of lime dried on the metal after neutralising the pickling solution may serve the same purpose. Steel may be coated with another metal such as copper or lead to act as a form of lubricant.

In a number of cases, defects in drawn material originate earlier. However, cracking may be caused by excessive drawing speeds or bad die design, and scratches may arise from the dies or dirty lubricants.

COLD PRESSING AND DEEP DRAWING

These processes are associated cold-working processes producing shapes from sheet stock ; typical products are motor-car bodies, lamp containers and reflectors, fire extinguisher bodies, bullet envelopes, cartridge cases and cylinders of various kinds. The operations range from making a suitable impression in one stage, to cupping followed by a number of re-drawings (Figs. 335–338). It will be seen that working occurs with or without change in wall diameter. There are no strict definitions of " pressing ", " drawing " or " deep-drawing ".

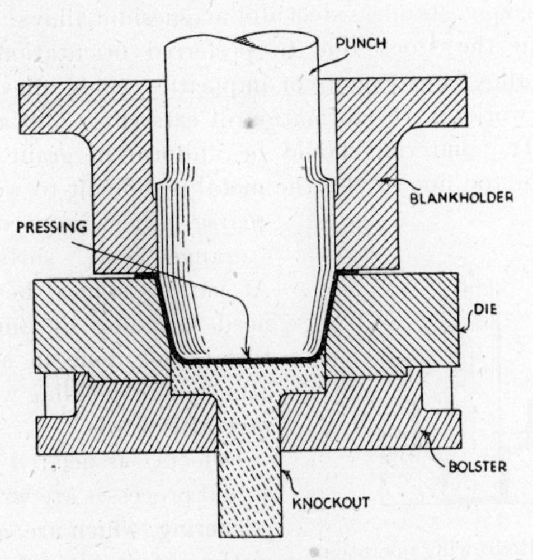

FIG. 335. Simple pressing operation.
By courtesy of the Aluminium Development Association.

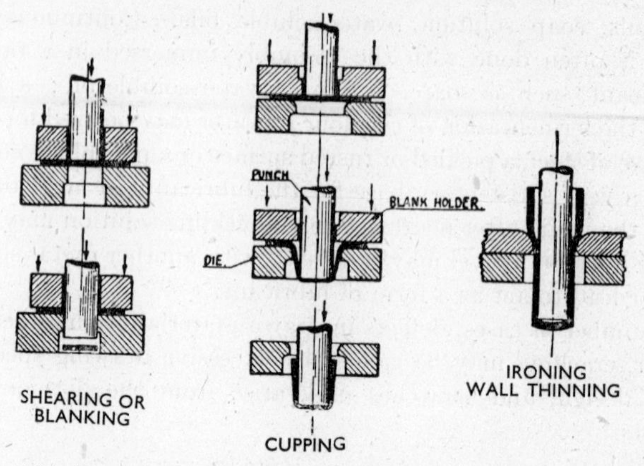

FIG. 336. Typical deep drawing operations. After R. S. Hutton, from *Metals*, Vol. II., by (Sir) H. Carpenter and J. M. Robertson. Oxf. Univ. Press.

Working is carried out in hydraulic, pneumatic, or mechanical presses. Steel forming-tools are used, and some use is made of sintered tungsten carbide. In addition, particularly for light alloy pressings, tools of zinc alloy, lead-antimony alloy, plastic, wood, and rubber are used.

Pressings are made in a variety of materials, such as mild steel, copper, brass, nickel silver, aluminium and its alloys, nickel, copper-nickel alloys, zinc, stainless steel and magnesium alloys. Directional properties in the stock due to preferred orientation, elongated particles of alloy constituents or impurities, cause uneven deformation during working, the formation of **ears** (Fig. 339) and possibly cracking. The material should be uniform in grain size, which should not be too fine or else the metal is difficult to work ; or too coarse, otherwise a roughened or " orange peel " surface results. At various stages the metal may need softening by annealing ; if this is not done in a controlled atmosphere, pickling will be necessary afterwards.

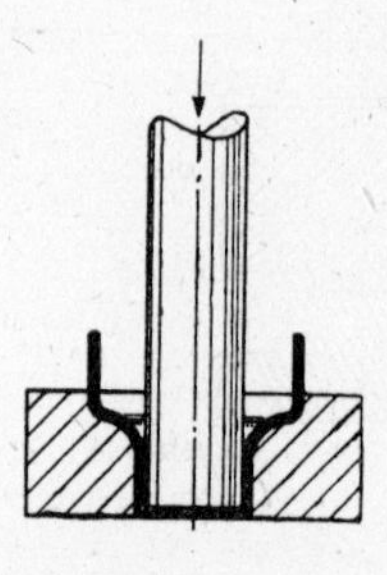

FIG. 337. Redrawing operation. By courtesy of the Copper Development Association.

Defects associated with the actual processes are **wrinkling** and **puckering**, which are corrugations in the unformed part of the sheet and in the formed part, respec-

Fig. 338. Pressing of brass headlamp reflectors.
By courtesy of the Copper Development Association.

tively ; they can be overcome by careful control of tool design and conditions of pressing. **Scoring** of the drawn part may be due to rough tools, or grit in the lubricant, on the work or from the surroundings. **Fouling** arises from the seizing of metal and tools, and is caused by lubrication failure arising from a low film strength of the lubricant, badly polished tools, too high a speed or too great a pressure of working, for example.

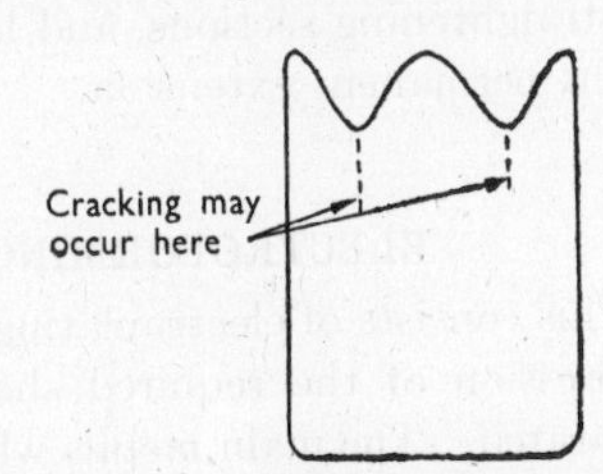

Fig. 339. Drawn cup with " ears ".

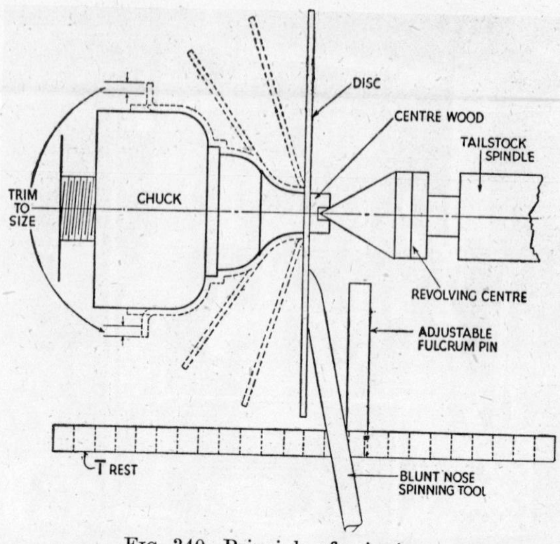

FIG. 340. Principle of spinning.
By courtesy of the Aluminium Development Association.

Spinning. This is a cold-working process by which round and complicated shapes are made from circular blanks by rotating them in a lathe, and forming and shaping with blunt steel or hardwood tools. The disc is forced around a metal or wooden chuck of the shape desired (Fig. 340). The tools are held by hand or in some cases arranged on the lathe. A considerable variety of shapes up to quite large sizes may be made by spinning. Typical products are large reflectors, radial engine cowlings and domestic hollow-ware. Spinning is particularly applicable to the production of a small number of parts, and for experimental work ; it is sometimes used to finish pressings and to carry out complex further shaping on them.

Stretch-forming is also a cold-working process in which sheet is shaped by stretching around a former. The principle is also utilised in straightening sections, and levelling sheet by giving the material slight permanent extension.

ELECTROFORMING OR ELECTROTYPING

This consists of electroplating metal on to a die having a negative impression of the required shape ; the die and deposit are then separated. The main metals which can be deposited in this way are iron, copper, nickel, and chromium. The dies may be made from low melting-point alloys, or from wax which is given a coating of graphite to produce a conducting surface ; separation is effected by melting the die. Another method is to make the die from a metal, such as aluminium, magnesium or zinc, which may be chemically dissolved from the formed part. In the foregoing cases, the die is generally made from a master pattern. The most accurate method involves the production of a steel die by machining and grinding, and which is removed by pressure from the deposit ; parting compounds are used to facilitate this.

The electroforming process has restricted use in comparison with the main shaping processes ; its great advantage is that it is capable of producing intricate shapes with good surfaces and to close dimensions, requiring no further treatment. An example is the production of a computator cam for calculating machines. The process has been in use for a considerable time, for example, in the printing trades and the production of gramophone records, and was further developed during the Second World War. At present the maximum thickness which it is practical to make is quoted at about half an inch. Seamless tubes may be deposited on a rotating cathode, and another useful application is the deposition of bearing alloys on to their steel shells. Electrodeposition also has considerable use in the building up of worn parts.

POWDER METALLURGY

In this process, fine metallic powder is agglomerated to form stock, or usually finally shaped, parts. The main process consists of cold pressing followed by heating. Shaping and initial adhesion of the particles are obtained by pressing the powders at room temperature between steel dies in mechanical or hydraulic presses ; pressures up to about 50 tons per sq. in. are used. Bonding is definitely attained by cold pressing, but the resulting compacts are weak. Final cohesion is caused by heating the compacts in non-oxidising atmospheres for times varying from ten minutes to a few hours, depending on the material. The temperature is well below the melting point in the case of pure metals, but with alloys the melting point of one constituent is often exceeded. Considerable contraction in volume and increase in density result from the heating; this may cause distortion of the compact, necessitating subsequent sizing in a press, during which a little working of the metal may occur. Due allowance is made for the shrinkage in the initial dimensions When stock is being produced, as in tungsten metal-

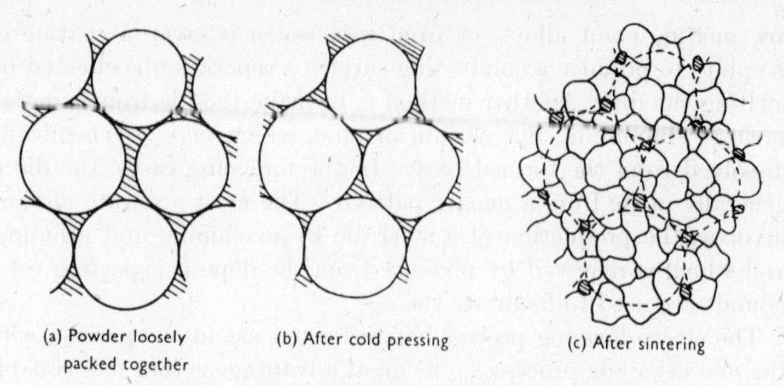

FIG. 341. Stages in powder metallurgy operation.

lurgy, hot-working follows pressing and sintering. The pressing and heating stages may be combined by hot pressing, when lower pressures are required and denser compacts are obtained. Commercial development of hot pressing is held up by practical difficulties. The whole operation of producing finished compacts may be referred to as **sintering,** and the metal as sintered. On the other hand, the term sintering may be reserved for the heating operation.

It is apparent that a cold-pressed compact will contain many pores. The adhesion obtained by cold pressing will be due to some form of residual surface forces. The enhanced bonding resulting from heating is brought about by recrystallisation and crystal growth across the cold-worked interfaces ; this can often be confirmed by microscopic examination (Fig. 341). In addition, where alloys are concerned, diffusion is important, and when the temperature is higher than the melting point of one constituent, this gives a form of fusion welding between the particles. The reduction of porosity brought about by sintering is due in some way to the atomic movement and migration that take place. When partial fusion occurs, this is important in filling the pores. The porosity is not completely removed merely by heating. In some cases the fine-pored condition is a desired and utilised characteristic. Sounder compacts are produced by hot pressing, which may approach a hot-working operation.

The preparation of the metal powders is an important aspect of powder metallurgy ; the particle size is of the order of 1/200 in. Among the methods used are non-coherent electro-deposition from aqueous or fused salt electrolytes, mechanical comminution, granulation of molten metal with water, " atomisation " of molten metal with steam or air, reduction of oxides and other compounds, decomposition and deposition from a gas, as nickel and iron from their volatile carbonyls. Each method gives a powder the particles of which are of characteristic shape. Thus electrolytic powders may be dendritic, comminuted flattened, and carbonyl iron spherical. Powders produced by other means may be reduced further by mechanical milling. Sometimes the powders are annealed in a non-oxidising atmosphere to remove gases from them.

Applications. Applications of this technique are numerous and varied, although small on a tonnage basis when compared with the main fabrication processes. Examples are given below.

(1) The manufacture of small parts in iron and steel, bronze, brass and some aluminium alloys.

(2) In the production of **high melting-point metals,** such as tungsten and molybdenum in the elementary form, because it is impracticable usually to melt the metal. In the case of tungsten, for example, pure tungstic oxide is prepared from the ore and then reduced to a tungsten powder at about 1200° C. The powder is cold-pressed to a bar and sintered, hot working following sintering. Powder metallurgy technique is also used in one method of preparing oxygen-free copper.

(3) An important high-temperature application of powder metallurgy is in the manufacture of **hard-metal cutting** and **working tools,** in which hard high melting-point carbides such as those of tungsten, titanium, boron, tantalum and molybdenum are incorporated, tungsten carbide being most used. Although very hard, the carbides are brittle and would be unsuitable on their own for most purposes, apart from the difficulties of production, although castings have been made. For this reason a tougher metal such as cobalt (or nickel) is incorporated with the carbide. In the manufacture of the tools, cobalt and carbide powders are mixed together, pressed and sintered (hot-pressing has been applied with carbon dies and electric resistance heating). The final sintering temperature is such that the cobalt fuses. The ultimate structure consists of carbide particles well dispersed and embedded in a cobalt-rich matrix. Some shapes are made by machining from a block, which has been pressed and presintered at about 700°–800° C.; in this form it is possible to shape the material by workshop methods before final sintering.

In addition to cutting tools, the **cemented carbides** are used for punches and pressing tools, small rolls for cold rolling strip, drawing dies and high-speed bearings in machine tools.

(4) A characteristic of the powder metallurgy technique, namely,

the fine *porosity* in the metal, is utilised in bearings and filters, and in making metal burners and parts of light weight. Burners and filters, for example, can be made in iron or nickel. The most outstanding example is the **porous bronze bearings** ("Oilite Bronze"). Copper and tin powders in the right proportions are mixed, cold pressed to the shape required, and sintered at a temperature well above the melting point of tin. A small percentage of graphite may be added as well as volatile materials to accentuate the inherent porosity of the product. The resulting porous bronze will behave like a solid sponge, and soak up considerable quantities of oil. During service, this oil is fed to the bearing surface, the oil being filtered as it passes through the metal. The use of such bearings is particularly advantageous in inaccessible positions.

(5) Copper-tungsten, copper-molybdenum, silver-molybdenum and silver-tungsten alloys are used for **electrical contact materials.** Apart from melting point considerations, these pairs of metals are immiscible in the liquid state, and have considerable differences in specific gravity; hence there are many difficulties in casting them. The powder metallurgy process has been used satisfactorily, although it has been found better to carry out a semi-powder metallurgy procedure. Thus in the case of the copper-tungsten alloys, a porous tungsten sinter is made, which is then dipped in molten copper, when the copper is soaked up and fills the pores in the tungsten. A similar technique has been used in America to produce a high-strength steel impregnated with copper or with a copper-base alloy ("Sinteel G"); the compact is claimed to be free from porosity.

(6) Production of **permanent magnet alloys.**

(7) Other interesting applications include the manufacture of bimetallic strips, commutor segments, ink blotters, dental bridges, name plates and plaques.

(8) **Non-metallic and semi-metallic applications.** Cutting tools may also be made from sintered alumina, using iron oxide as a bond; this material has other possibilities, for example, as facing for gas turbine blades and in wire-drawing dies. The combination of refractory oxides and metals by powder metallurgy offers many attractive possibilities for high-temperature work. Metals may be incorporated with plastics to increase the strength of the latter. Magnets for certain purposes are made of a mixture of ferrous powder and plastic material. The nature of the compacts gives certain magnetic advantages over fully metallic magnets; further, they are much lighter. Grinding wheels may be made incorporating steel and diamond powder. Two other interesting applications are copper-

graphite brush materials for electric motors and a copper-asbestos compact for clutch- and brake-lining material.

It will be seen from the above that in addition to the production of small parts, in which it is in competition with other processes, powder metallurgy has its own particular fields. The advantages of powder metallurgy for small parts are good dimensional accuracy and finish, often requiring no further treatment ; high production rates can be maintained. Further, scrap losses are negligible, although this must be considered in conjunction with the cost of the powders, which is considerably higher than bar or ingot stock. However, it is claimed that the latter point may be more than offset by the fact that there is no scrap loss in the process. On the other hand, tooling and machine costs are relatively high, so the process is most economical for large numbers of parts. There are certain limitations on the shapes that may be pressed, imposed by die design and the poor flowing power of the powders normal to the pressing direction, and the process is limited generally to small sizes. The section should not be so thin as to make the compacts too fragile in the cold-pressed state. The largest size made so far by powder metallurgy has been quoted as 3 in. thick by an area of 8 sq. in., but it is also reported that pieces of sintered carbide may be supplied up to 24 in. in diameter.

WELDING, BRAZING AND SOLDERING

It may be advantageous in a number of cases to make certain objects by joining a number of component parts together, or certain parts may need attachment after bulk fabrication. For these purposes welding, brazing and soldering may be used ; they are also useful for repair.

Fusion welding. In fusion welding, the parts to be joined are held together and the interface melted ; whereupon the two parts blend. On cooling, solidification occurs and the parts are held together by a zone of cast metal ; extra metal is often added to the weld zone (Fig, 342). More than one run may be made with thick material, especially steel.

Heating for fusion welding is supplied by oxy-acetylene or similar torch flames, by an electric arc struck between two carbon or tungsten electrodes, or between the work and one electrode ; or, a rod of filler metal may be used as one electrode with the work as the other. An atmosphere of helium or argon, respectively, is maintained around the arc in the helium or argon arc processes using tungsten electrodes. In the atomic hydrogen process the heat is due to that

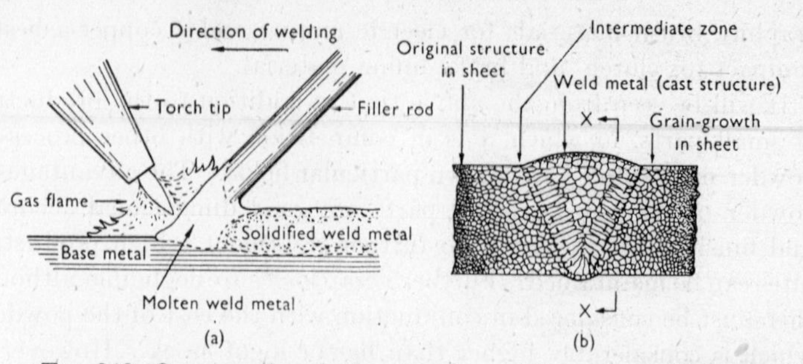

FIG. 342. Oxy-acetylene fusion welding. (*a*) Operation. (*b*) Structure in weld zone. Diagram (*a*) is an approximate section on *XX* (*b*) during welding.

evolved in the change from atomic to molecular hydrogen as well as that from burning the hydrogen ; initial dissociation of the hydrogen is obtained by passing the gas through an arc maintained between two tungsten electrodes. The " Thermit " principle is also employed in fusion welding of ferrous metals. Electrical resistance heating is used in spot welding (Figs. 343 and 344), and its various modifications, namely projection, seam, stitch and butt welding.

Frequently, in fusion processes other than resistance welding, fluxes are used to dissolve any oxide or other foreign matter on the surfaces to be welded and form an easily separating fluid slag. The slag may serve as a protective cover. In arc welding the flux may be required to protect and stabilise the arc. The fluxes are applied in various ways ; for example, they may be applied first to the metal as paste or powder, or fed in during welding ; consumable metallic arc electrodes may be coated with flux. As many of the fluxes are

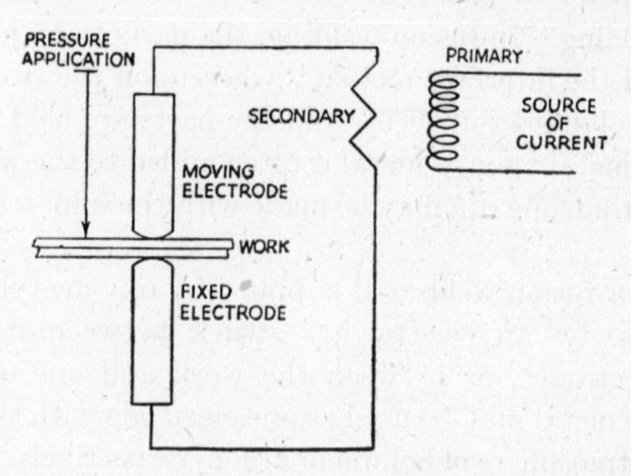

FIG. 343. Resistance (spot) welding. The electrodes are of copper with hard tips. By courtesy of The Aluminium Development Association.

corrosive, thorough washing of the work after welding is necessary. Common ingredients of welding fluxes for non-ferrous metals are borax and halide salts of sodium, potassium and lithium. The constituents of electrode coatings for steel include ferro-alloys, various oxides, silicates, fluorspar and organic matter such as wood-meal. No fluxes are required in the helium or argon arc processes, as the inert gas protects the metal from contamination.

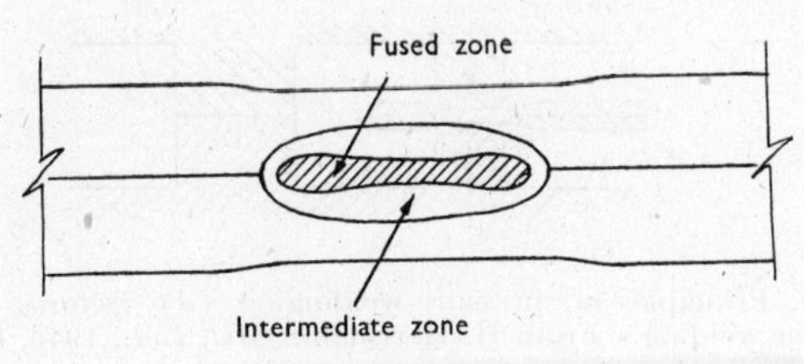

FIG. 344. Resistance weld.

Fusion weld areas may be hammered after welding to improve their properties. Welded parts may be stress-relieved by annealing or in the case of steel the properties are improved by normalising. In multi-run arc welds in steel the structure of underlying weld metal is refined by the heating from subsequent layers.

Pressure-welding. This process is typified by the blacksmith's method of welding wrought iron and mild steel. The operation is carried out at a high temperature in the solid state, there being no fusion. The metal parts are hammered and firmly held together; recrystallisation occurs at the interface, the crystals growing across the junction. Sand and borax are used as fluxes. The same principles are involved in the manufacture of lap- and butt-welded steel tubes, in the closing and healing up of porosity in ingots during working, and in the more refined modern method of pressure-welding (Fig. 345). The latter has been applied particularly to aluminium and the light alloys, although silver, copper, brasses, tin-bronzes and copper-nickel alloys have been shown to be capable of being pressure-welded. Undoubtedly in some cases recrystallisation or crystal growth takes place across the interface during the pressure-welding of non-ferrous metals, but Tylecote points out that there are many cases where this does not seem to have occurred. It is possible to make welds at room temperature. The cold pressure-welding of aluminium has been applied in the commercial production of aluminium-sheathed electric cables. An advantage of pressure-welding is the absence of a cast structure. The metal surfaces should be clean

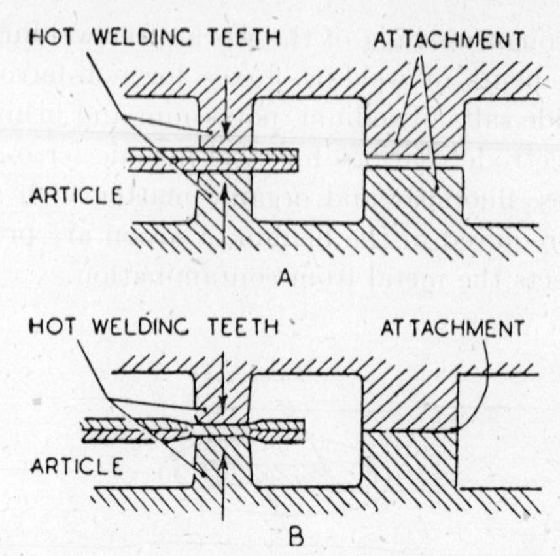

FIG. 345. Principle of pressure-welding. (*A*) Before welding; (*B*) after welding. From H. Herrmann, *Met. Ind.*, 1946, 68, 143.

and may be prepared by mechanical methods such as scratch brushing or by pickling.

Defects in welding take the form of misalignment, improper fusion in the case of fusion welds, cracks, entrapped slag, flux, oxide or gas, or weakness associated with the heating of parts adjacent to the weld zone.

Brazing. In brazing the basis metal is not melted and the bonding metal has a lower melting point; for example, copper and brass are used for steel. Brass is also used for suitable non-ferrous metals. Various combinations of copper, zinc and silver, sometimes with cadmium or phosphorus, are extensively used for ferrous and non-ferrous metals; the alloys are often known as *silver solders* (Table 58). For brazing aluminium alloys, lower melting-point aluminium alloys are used.

TABLE 58. EXAMPLES OF SILVER SOLDERS

	Ag	Cu	Zn	Cd	P	Flowing point
	10	50	40	—	—	849° C.
	20	45	35	—	—	808° C.
	40	40	20	—	—	790° C.
	70	20	10	—	—	740° C.
" Sil-fos "	15	80	—	—	5	704° C.
" Easy-flo "	50	15·5	16·5	18	—	635° C.

Fluxes of similar composition to those for fusion welding are used in brazing. All manner of heating devices are employed for melting the brazing metal, including furnace brazing, in which the brazing metal as wire, sheet or powder together with flux is placed at the proposed joint, and then the whole object heated in a furnace, or it may be immersed in a suitable bath of molten salt. In one method, steel is furnace-brazed with copper in a special atmosphere rich in hydrogen, generally no flux being necessary.

Soldering. For soldering, comparatively low melting-point alloys are used, namely those of lead and tin, or with the addition of other metals such as antimony, bismuth, cadmium and silver (Table 7, p. 90). Fluxes include zinc chloride or mixtures of zinc and ammonium chlorides in solid form, and "killed spirits" (hydrochloric acid to which zinc has been added until action ceases). Resin, tallow and olive oil are non-corrosive but mild in action. The same variety of heating methods is used for soldering as for brazing. The classical method is of course with the copper "soldering iron".

The defects in brazed and soldered joints, apart from misalignment, are failure of jointing metal to "wet" the basis metal, and gas holes and inclusions of foreign material.

It is a workable explanation that bonding in soldering and brazing is effected by the formation of an alloy layer between the bonding and basis metal (Fig. 346), and undoubtedly this does form in many cases, the amount increasing with time and temperature. However, bonding can occur with little or no alloying; thus molten lead will wet and adhere to solid copper (in a hydrogen atmosphere). Further, in spray-coating, good adhesion is obtained under conditions that scarcely permit any alloying. In brazing and soldering, the ability of the molten metal to penetrate crevices, that is the capillary action, is often of utmost importance.

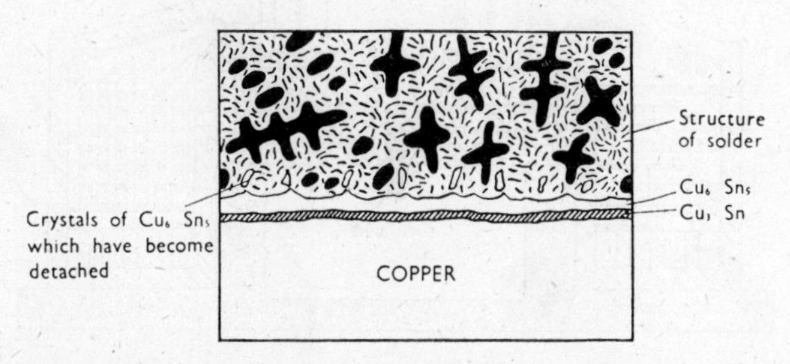

Fig. 346. Sketch showing microstructure when solder is applied to copper; layers of Cu_3Sn and Cu_6Sn_5 are formed.

HEAT-TREATMENT OF METALS

Various thermal treatments are applied to solid metal, such as heating for hot-working, heating to and controlled cooling from a suitable temperature to modify the structure and properties, annealing cold-worked metal to bring about recrystallisation and softening, to remove internal stress, and in sintering and various surface treatments. It is not within the scope of this book to detail these treatments, or the wide variety of furnaces used, which utilise heating by coal, oil or gas, electric resistance and even by currents induced in the metal, and include baths of molten salts in which the work is immersed. However, the principles of a few examples are illustrated in Figs. 347–356.

With immersion heating, the metal is to a large extent protected. But in other types of furnaces the metal is in contact with air, or the products of combustion, and scaling generally occurs ; further, with steel the atmosphere may be carburising or decarburising according to the reactions :

$$Fe_3C + CO_2 \rightleftharpoons 3Fe + 2CO \quad \ldots\ldots\ldots\ldots(1)$$

$$Fe_3C + 2H_2 \rightleftharpoons 3Fe + CH_4 \quad \ldots\ldots\ldots\ldots(2)$$

Nascent hydrogen produced by the decomposition of water vapour appears to be necessary for (2) to proceed.

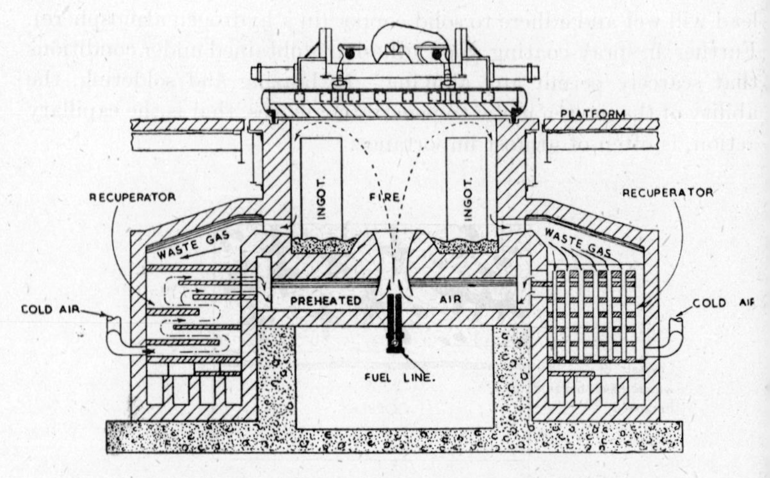

FIG. 347. Recuperative soaking pit furnace for steel ingots. By courtesy of The United Steel Companies Ltd.

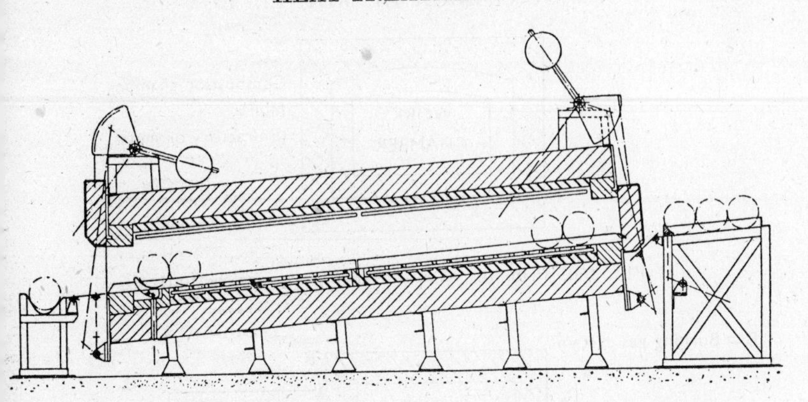

FIG. 348. Billet preheating furnace with gravity feed, suitable, for example, for copper alloys for extrusion. The furnace is fired with gas or oil. From Pearson.

For these reasons heat-treatment in appropriate cases may be carried out in **controlled atmospheres.** The work is contained in a muffle or chamber heated by electric resistors, or if by combustible

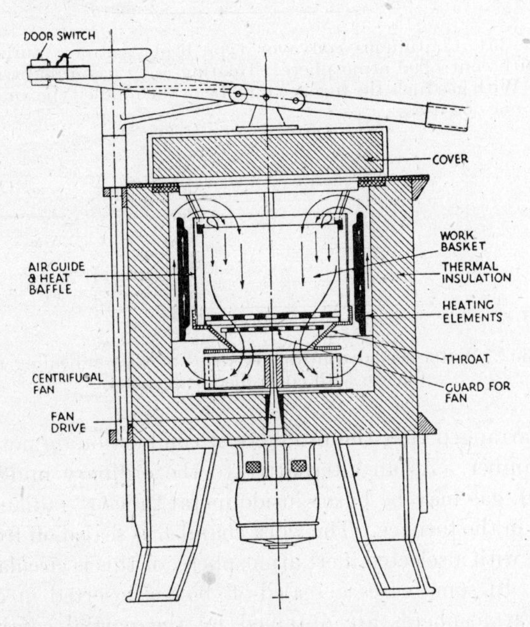

FIG. 349. Electric forced-air circulation furnace used for heating aluminium alloys for working or for heat-treatment. By courtesy of The Aluminium Development Association.

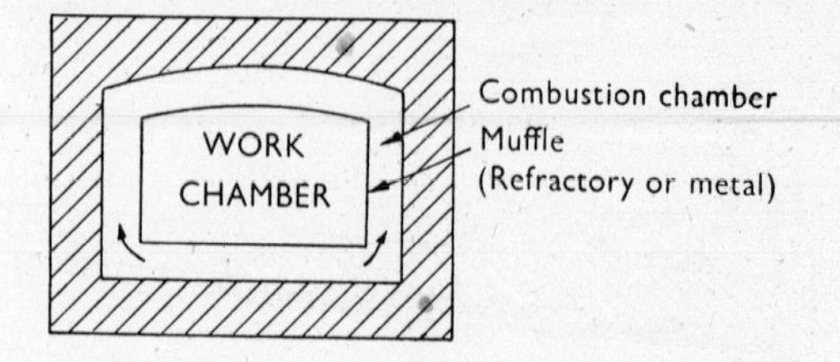

FIG. 350. Principle of muffle furnace (cross-section).

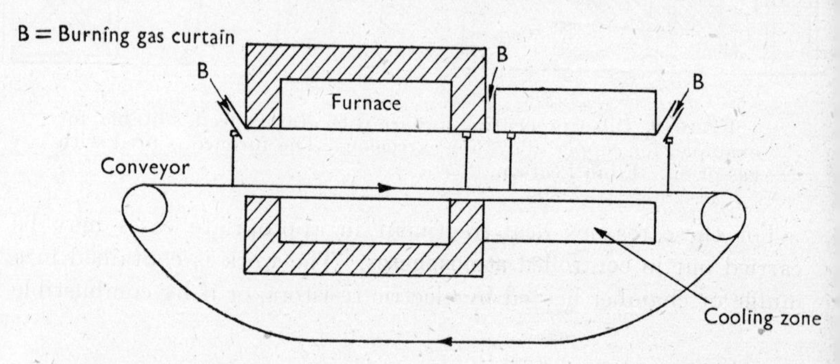

FIG. 351. Continuous conveyor type heat-treatment furnace for use with controlled atmosphere. Heating is by gas or electric resistors. With gas fuels the furnace may be of the muffle type, or radiant tubes may be used.

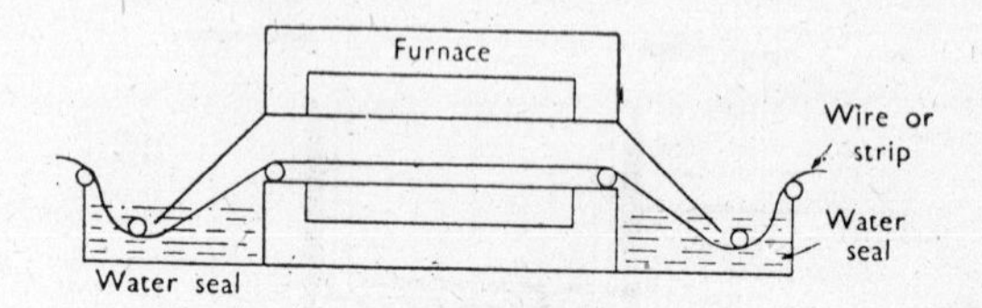

FIG. 352. Water-sealed continuous strip- or wire-annealing furnace for use with controlled atmosphere.

fuels, so arranged that the products of combustion do not enter the work chamber. As an alternative to the ordinary muffle furnace (Fig. 350), gas may be burnt inside metal tubes (" radiant tubes ") arranged in the furnace. The work chamber is sealed off from the air and filled with a selected inert atmosphere, or this is circulated (Figs. 351–53). In some cases a sealed-off box is inserted in a furnace. Suitable atmospheres are obtained by the partial combustion of various fuel gases followed by the removal of the moisture. Cracked ammonia can also be used ; this is also best partly burnt and dried.

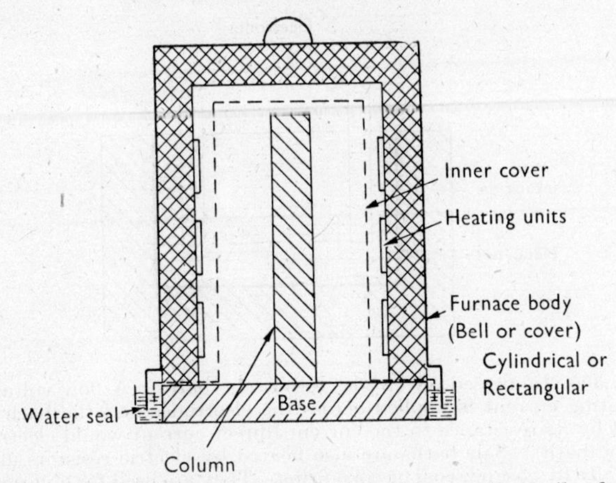

FIG. 353. Bell furnace used especially for annealing coils of wire or strip in steel or non-ferrous metals, often in controlled atmospheres; the column is used to support the coils. The rectangular-shaped furnace, without a column, can be used for sheet or bars. One bell or cover can be employed for several bases; the inner cover protects the charge during the cooling period. Heating is by electric resistors or radiant tubes.

The use of controlled atmospheres is especially applied to softening cold-worked metal (also known as "bright-annealing"), and hardening and tempering steel; in the latter case it is more important to prevent decarburisation than scaling. It is obvious that in heating for hot working there is no point in preventing scale formation. Sintering in the powder metallurgy technique is also carried out in a controlled non-oxidising atmosphere.

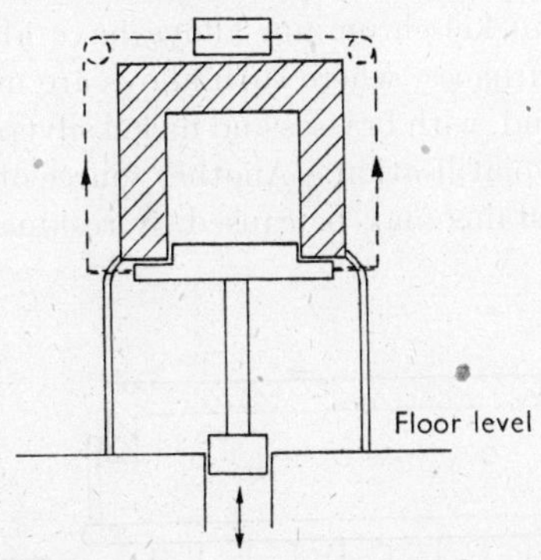

FIG. 354. Electrically heated elevator furnace for various heat-treatments of ferrous and non-ferrous alloys. The base is loaded at floor level and then raised by mechanism from underneath or from above.

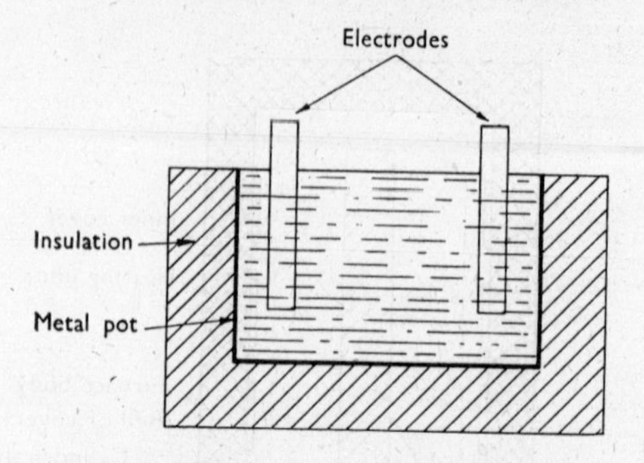

FIG. 355. Immersed electrode fused-salt bath. A low-voltage alternating current is applied across the electrodes and the bath is heated by its resistance to the current (direct current would electrolyse the bath). Salt baths are also heated by electric resistors and externally by gas, oil, coal or coke firing. They are used for a variety of heating operations on ferrous and non-ferrous materials.

With furnaces in which products of combustion come into contact with the metal, some control can be exerted by burning with a deficit of air, so that a reducing atmosphere is obtained, providing this does not too adversely affect thermal efficiency.

Certain precautions have to be observed in the composition of the controlled atmosphere. For example, with tough-pitch copper the atmosphere must not be such as to cause "gassing" (p. 285). Sulphur is especially harmful to nickel and its alloys, causing embrittlement; and it may result in staining with other metals. Nitrogen is undesirable for nickel-chromium alloys and these are oxidised by carbon dioxide and water vapour. The harmful effects of sulphur and nitrogen on nickel-chromium alloys have also to be borne in mind in electric furnaces, where such alloys are used as resistors.

On the other hand, with brasses and nickel silvers, care is necessary to minimise zinc volatilisation. Another source of trouble in bright-annealing is that stains may be caused by residual lubricant on the metal.

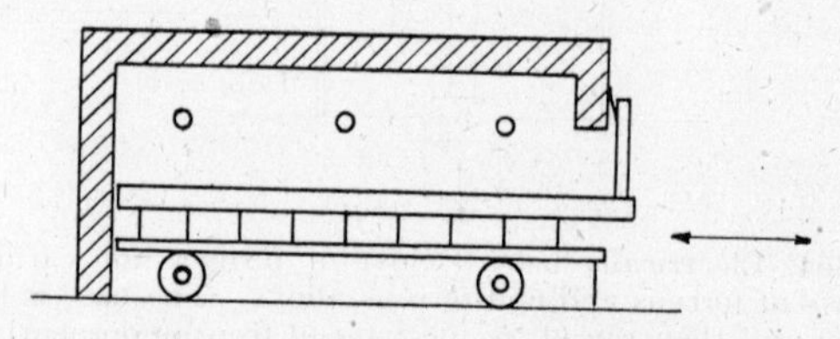

FIG. 356. Principle of bogie furnace, for heavy work.

APPLICATION OF PROTECTIVE COATINGS TO METALS

Frequently metal is protected against corrosion by the application of a coating with a greater resistance. Both metallic and non-metallic coatings are employed.

Metallic coatings. The application of metallic coatings by **electro-deposition** is well known (some use is made of electrochemical replacement). The fundamental principles of such processes have already been discussed in Chapter 8.

In **cladding**, the basis metal is sandwiched between pieces of the coating metal, and then the composite is rolled to produce so-called " clad " metal, usually in the form of sheet. Examples are " Alclad ", which is duralumin, an aluminium alloy, coated with pure aluminium ; " Niclad ", nickel-coated steel ; and tin-coated lead.

With the **hot-dipping** technique, the metal is dipped into a bath of the molten coating metal and then withdrawn. The surfaces of the basis metal should be clean, and a flux is used in the process. An alloy layer is formed between the two metals (Fig. 357). Common examples are the " galvanising " (zinc-coating) of steel, tinning of steel and copper, and the coating of steel with lead or solder (" terne-plate ").

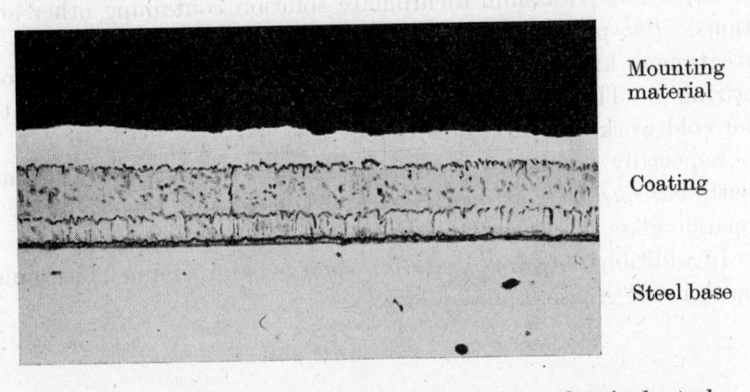

FIG. 357. Microstructure of zinc coating on galvanised steel. ×450. Three iron-zinc compound layers can be seen, and the outer layer is zinc or zinc-rich solid solution. By courtesy of The British Non-Ferrous Metals Research Assoc.

The coating metal can be melted and **sprayed** in fine particles by compressed air on to the work, the surface of which must be clean and roughened, for example, by sand or shot blasting. Spraying has considerable advantage in its flexibility and portability ; thus it can be applied in the field to bridges, pylons, storage tanks and similar structures. Common spraying metals are zinc and aluminium, although the process is widely applicable.

In another technique the basis metal is heated in a powder of the coating metal (at a temperature below its melting-point), which *diffuses* in to form the coating. Commercial examples, applied to iron and steel, are " sherardising " (zinc), " calorising " (aluminium) and " chomising " (chromium).

Non-metallic coatings. These are in general only recommended as a base for painting. A familiar example is the " blueing " of steel in which by heating in air or fused potassium nitrate a protective coating of *oxide* is produced. The " anodic oxidation " or **anodising** of aluminium and certain of its alloys intensifies with nascent oxygen the protective oxide-skin that is normally present. The article is made the anode in an electrolytic cell with fairly strong sulphuric acid (15–20 per cent or 70 per cent), dilute chromic acid (3 per cent) or dilute oxalic acid (3–8 per cent) as electrolyte. The cathodes are of carbon, lead or stainless steel. Direct or alternating current is used with voltages generally up to about 60, although this may be exceeded. For decorative effects the coating may be coloured by impregnating it with dyes. *Oxide* or *chromate* coatings are produced on magnesium alloys and zinc and its alloys by treatment in hot potassium dichromate solution containing other additions. *Phosphate* coatings are applied to steel, for example, by the treatments known as " Coslettizing ", " Parkerizing " and " Bonderizing ". The phosphate also forms a useful base for lubrication for cold-working operations such as wire drawing.

Especially for domestic purposes, steel and cast iron are coated with *vitreous* or *porcelain enamel*. The coating is essentially an opaque glass fused on at red heat.

In addition, of course, materials such as paint, enamel, bituminous matter and grease are used.

ADDITIONAL READING

1. *Practical Metallurgy*, by G. Sachs and K. R. Van Horn. (American Soc. for Metals, 1940).

2. *Metals*, by (Sir) H. Carpenter and J. M. Robertson. (Oxford Univ. Press, 1939).

3. *Metals Handbook*, 1948 Edition. (American Soc. for Metals).

4. *The Making, Shaping and Treating of Steel*. (6th edition. United States Steel Co., United States Steel Corp. Subsidiary, 1951).

5. *Roll Pass Design*, by W. Trinks. Vol. I, 2nd Edit., 1933. Vol. II, 2nd Edit., 1934. (Penton Pub. Co.).

6. *Non-Ferrous Rolling Practice.* (Amer. Inst. Min. and Met. Eng., Inst. Metals Div. Symposium Series, Vol. 2, 1948).

7. *Elements of Rolling Practice.* (United Steel Co. Ltd., 1949).

8. *Plastic Working of Metals and Power Press Operation*, by E. V. Crane (Wiley, 1932).

9. *Extrusion of Metals*, by C. E. Pearson. (Chapman and Hall, 1944).

10. *Manufacture of Seamless Tubes*, by G. Evans. (Witherby, 1934).

11. *Technology of Light Metals*, by A. Von Zeerleder (translated by A. J. Field). (Elsevier. Cleaver-Hume, 1949).

12. *Technology of Magnesium and its Alloys*, by A. Beck. (F. A. Hughes and Co., Ltd., 1943).

13. *The Metallurgy of Deep Drawing and Pressing*, by J. D. Jevons. (Chapman and Hall, 1945).

14. *The Hot Working of Non-Ferrous Metals and Alloys.* Symposium. Monograph and Report Series No. 9. (Inst. of Metals, 1951).

15. *The Cold Working of Non-Ferrous Metals and Alloys.* Symposium. Monograph and Report Series No. 12. (Inst. of Metals, 1952).

16. Various Information Bulletins on Fabrication and Treatment of Aluminium and its Alloys, published by the Aluminium Development Association.

17. Bulletins issued by the Copper Development Association.

18. *Principles of Electroplating and Electroforming (Electrotyping)*, by W. Blum and G. B. Hogaboom. (McGraw-Hill, 1949).

19. *Powder Metallurgy*, by P. Schwarzkopf. (Macmillan, 1947).

20. *Powder Metallurgy*, by W. D. Jones. (Arnold, 1937).

21. Symposium on Powder Metallurgy. (Special Report No. 38. Iron and Steel Inst., 1947).

22. *Modern Assembly Processes. Their Development and Control*, by J. L. Miller. (2nd Edit., Chapman and Hall. 1946).

23. *The Welding of Non-Ferrous Metals*, by E. G. West. (Chapman and Hall, 1951).

24. *The Joining of Metals.* (Institution of Metallurgists, 1952).

25. *Industrial Furnaces*, by W. Trinks. Vol. I, 4th Edit., 1951. Vol. II, 2nd Edit., 1942. (New York, Wiley. London, Chapman and Hall).

26. *Induction Heating*, by N. R. Stansel. (McGraw-Hill, 1949).

27. *The Heating of Steel*, by M. H. Mawhinney. (Rheinhold, 1945).

28. *Equipment for the Thermal Treatment of Non-Ferrous Metals.* Symposium. Monograph and Report Series No. 14. (Inst. of Metals, 1952).

29. *Controlled Atmospheres for the Heat Treatment of Metals*, by I. Jenkins. (Chapman and Hall, 1946).

30. *Protective Films on Metals*, by E. S. Hedges. (2nd Edit., Chapman and Hall, 1937).

31. *Protective Coatings for Metals*, by J. W. Gailer and E. J. Vaughan. (Griffin, 1950).

32. *Tinplate*, by W. E. Hoare and E. S. Hedges. (Arnold, 1945).

33. *Galvanizing* (*Hot-Dip*), by H. Bablik (translated by C. A. Bentley). (3rd Edit., E. and F. N. Spon, 1950).

34. *Metal Spraying and Sprayed Metal*, by W. E. Ballard. (3rd Edit., Griffin, 1948).

CHAPTER 13

TESTING METALS

TESTS are carried out on metals for a variety of purposes among which are the following :

(*a*) to assess fundamental properties ;

(*b*) to find a suitable metal for a specific purpose (*development testing*) ;

(*c*) to determine data (especially stress) for design ;

(*d*) to assess workability ;

(*e*) to determine or check chemical composition ;

(*f*) to check that preparation and treatment have been satisfactory, with regard both to the presence of flaws and the general condition (*acceptance testing*) ;

(*g*) to study the incidence of flaws and improve manufacturing techniques.

Development tests. These involve comparison of behaviour under the conditions of service or conditions fairly close to them. Such tests include corrosion tests, in which specimens are compared under service environments, or conditions approximating to them in the laboratory ; in addition, creep, fatigue, stress-corrosion and corrosion-fatigue tests at room temperature, and creep and fatigue tests at elevated temperatures. Generally, specimens of simple shape are used. The results obtained may be sufficient for direct application, but on the other hand subsequent pilot or even full-scale tests may be necessary. The foregoing are essentially long-time tests involving possibly many years to obtain conclusive results. It is apparent that short-time tests are desirable, and these have been developed in some cases. However, short-time tests are only satisfactory when properly correlated with long-time tests.

Acceptance tests. Once suitable material has been found by development and service tests, or as the result of general experience, a specification is drawn up of test results with which fresh batches must conform, as well as being essentially sound ; in addition, a certain range of chemical composition will be specified, together with tolerances of impurities. This procedure ensures that satisfactory metal is obtained in each case. The testing entailed may be referred to as **acceptance testing**. Apart from chemical analysis, mechanical testing in the form of tensile, hardness, and notched-bar impact tests at room temperature are the commonest form of acceptance testing; these tests check the general condition and preparation, and may also indicate the presence of flaws. Direct tests for flaws, such as radiographic and magnetic methods, are not always used in acceptance work. It should be appreciated that the main use of mechanical testing for acceptance purposes is indirect, in the sense that the results do not directly indicate behaviour in service. There may be no direct or known connection between the characteristics determined in the acceptance test and those required in service.

In certain cases other tests may be used; for example, measurement of electrical conductivity, magnetic properties, and microscopic and X-ray examination of the structure. An interesting application of the use of electrical conductivity measurements at an intermediate stage is in the fire-refining of copper for electrical purposes. Before tapping, to ensure that conductivity is correct, a small sample is cast and rolled, and conductivity measurements are made. If metal is susceptible to special forms of weakness in certain conditions, extra tests will have to be made to ensure that the necessary precautions have been taken in manufacture to avoid susceptibility. The number of tests used for acceptance depends on the metal, the shaping process, and the stringency and conditions of service.

Acceptance tests may be carried out on essentially finished articles, or on stock which is to be fabricated further by metallurgical or engineering methods. The scheme of testing depends to a considerable extent on whether the test is destructive or not, but also on the form of the metal. In the case of non-destructive testing, such as radiography, there may be one hundred per cent inspection (that is, every article is examined); alternatively, samples may be taken and examined at intervals, and the results interpreted statistically. When the test is destructive, for example the tensile test, for examination of stock, specimens may be cut off every so often. When parts in the form of forgings or castings are being tested by destructive means, samples may be taken from a batch and specimens cut out; or the objects may be especially prepared with extra portions which can be cut off for testing. In the latter case it must not be implied that the samples are typical of the condition of the whole, which is unlikely. For this reason it is equally or more satisfactory in many cases, where a destructive test is required on each article, to prepare separate specimens which undergo the same treatment as the objects. Thus for castings, separate test bars are cast at the same time. It will be appreciated that the possibility of using attached or separate specimens only applies when the test determines some physical property or characteristic of the metal. When testing for flaws, or in the study of the actual shaping operation, it is clear that the shaped articles must be tested.

MECHANICAL TESTING

Mechanical tests are usually carried out at room temperature, but for investigation work and for assessing workability, useful results are obtained by performing the tests at elevated temperatures. In mechanical testing, determinations are made of certain aspects of the behaviour of metals under stress, that is, associated with their mechanical properties. The most common forms are the tensile, hardness, and notched-bar impact tests.

Tensile test. Some features of the tensile test have already been discussed (p. 116); this section will be confined to discussing the observations made in standard testing, with a brief description of the methods and machines used in their determination.

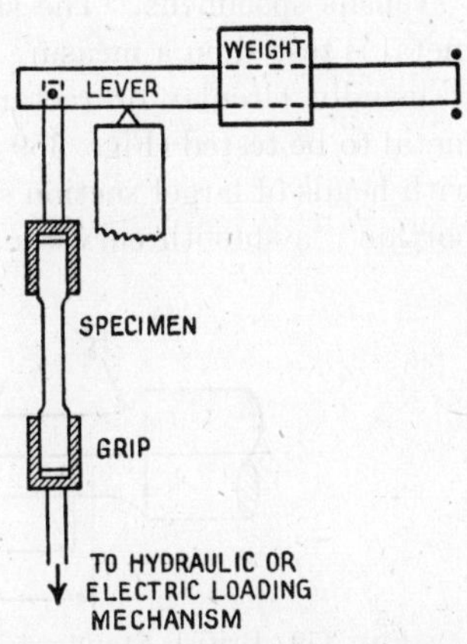

FIG. 358. Principle of single-lever tensile testing machine. From *Metals*, Vol. I, by (Sir) H. Carpenter and J. M. Robertson, Oxford Univ. Press.

The simplest type of tensile testing machine is the single-lever machine (Fig. 358), in which the load is applied by hydraulic means, or by a screw mechanism driven by an electric motor (or by hand). The load is balanced and weighed by a weight sliding on a single lever, which is pivoted on a fulcrum. Hand-operated screw mechanisms are convenient for certain purposes, such as proof-stress determinations. Multi-lever lachines are more compact and have other advantages over single-lever machines; they work on the same principle, except that a number of connected levers are used instead of one large one. In motor-driven machines a gear box is usually provided so that several speeds of straining are possible. With hydraulic machines the speed is varied by means of the valve controlling the flow of oil to the cylinder. Various self-indicating hydraulic or screw machines are available also. Common load capacities for tensile machines are up to 100 tons, which is sufficient for ordinary testing. For special purposes larger capacities are obtainable. In the standard machines, the load is usually applied in a vertical direction. Tensile machines can usually be easily adapted for other tests such as bending and compression. Machines are calibrated or checked by hanging known weights directly on them or applying weights via levers. Alternatively, the results for elastic modulus on a standard specimen may be compared with those obtained on a standard machine.

The Hounsfield Tensometer is a small, hand-operated, screw machine in which tiny specimens of the order of $\frac{1}{8}$ in. diameter may be tested. The load is measured via a spring and column of mercury. This machine is useful especially when only a small piece of metal is available.

Tensile specimens. The shape of the specimens is such that the metal is tested on a measured length of uniform cross-section, which is usually circular or rectangular, depending on the form of the metal to be tested (Figs. 359 and 360). The specimens are machined with heads of larger section so that fracture will occur in the desired portion ; a smooth curve or fillet connects the two sections. Good

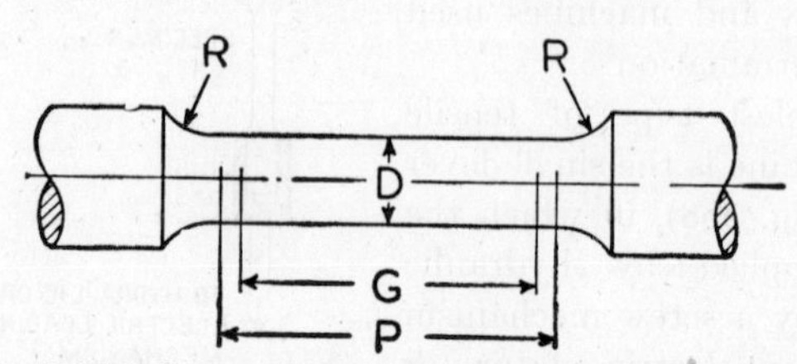

FIG. 359. British Standard Machined Round Tensile Test Piece for general purposes.

Gauge length, $G = 2$ in. ; parallel length, P, to be not less than $2\frac{1}{4}$ in. ; diameter, $D = 0{\cdot}564$ in. ; cross-sectional area, $A = \frac{1}{4}$ sq. in. ; radius at shoulder, $R = \frac{1}{2}$ in. minimum for wrought metals and cast steel, $= 2\frac{1}{2}$ in. for other cast metals.

Smaller but comparable machined round test pieces (Subsidiary Standards) may be used down to 0·125 in. diameter, provided :

$G = 4\sqrt{A}$, $P = \frac{9}{8}G$ (min.), $R = \frac{G}{4}$ (min.) for wrought metals and cast steel, and $R = \frac{5G}{4}$ (min.) for other cast metals. Note : Separate standards are given for cast iron.

Reproduced by permission from *Tensile Testing of Metals.* British Standard 18 : 1950.

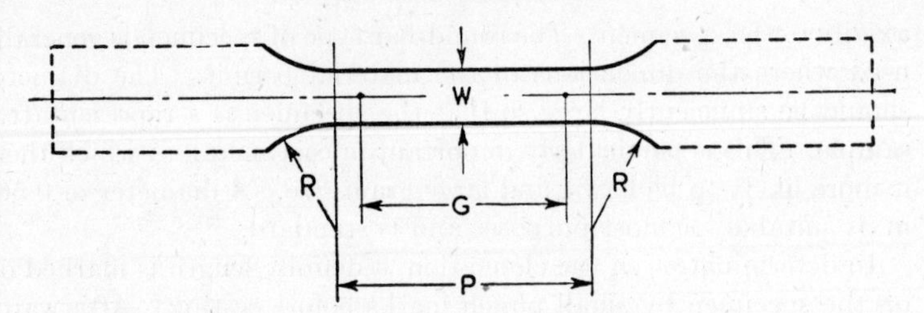

Fig. 360. British Standard Flat Tensile Test Piece, chiefly for sheets, plates, strips, flat bars and sections.

Dimensions

Nominal thickness of test piece	Width, *W*	Gauge length, *G*	Parallel length (minimum) *P*	Radius at shoulder (minimum) *R*	Approximate total length
	in.	in.	in.	in.	in.
Up to but not including $\frac{3}{8}$ in.	$\frac{1}{2}$	2	$2\frac{1}{2}$	1	8
	1	4	$4\frac{1}{2}$	1	12
All thicknesses	$1\frac{1}{2}$ (max.)	8	9	1	18

When the width of the material to be tested is insufficient to permit of the preparation of the standard tensile test piece, a piece of the full width of the material may be used.

Note 1. For some materials it is convenient to use straight parallel test pieces.

Note 2. It is sometimes convenient to use the standard test piece that has a width of $\frac{1}{2}$ in. and a gauge length of 2 in. for thicknesses $\frac{3}{8}$ in. and greater.

Reproduced by permission from *Tensile Testing of Metals.* British Standard 18 : 1950.

surface finish of the specimens is essential. The heads of round specimens may be threaded to screw into the grips, or they may be held by serrated grips. Another method is to machine the specimens with shoulders (Fig. 361). Flat specimens may also be held by serrated grips, or by round pins passing through holes drilled in the heads. The grips should be designed so that the load is applied

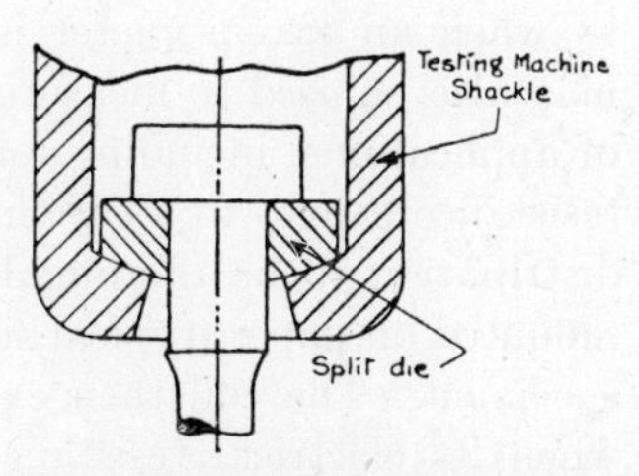

Fig. 361. Arrangement of tensile specimen supported by shoulders. Figs. 361 and 366 are from *Mechanical Testing*, Vol. I, by R. G. Batson and J. H. Hyde. Chapman and Hall.

axially to the specimen. The round-bar type of specimen is generally used where the dimensions of the material permit. The diameter should be sufficiently large so that the specimen is a representative sample. This is particularly important in cast metal, in which there is more likely to be flaws, and large grain size. A diameter of 0·564 in. is suitable for most purposes and is standard.

In determination of the elongation, a definite length is marked off on the specimen by small punch marks before testing. Afterwards the fractured specimen is pieced together, and the distance apart of the marks remeasured; the fracture must occur in the middle section of the gauge-length. The difference expressed as a percentage of the original length gives the elongation figure. For comparable results with round specimens of different sizes the original gauge-length is made to bear a constant relation to the cross-sectional area of the specimen. In Great Britain the gauge-length is made equal to $4\sqrt{A}$, A being the cross-sectional area; in the case of 0·564 in. diameter round specimens, this means a gauge-length of 2 in. Different ratios are used in other countries. In testing flat material, for convenience only a few gauge-lengths and widths are used for a whole range of thicknesses (Fig. 360) and strict comparison is not possible except for the same size of specimen.

Tubes and wires may be tested directly in tensile machines, or in the case of tubes, specimens may be cut out.

Measurement of strain. During test, once appreciable deformation has started, the extension of the specimen at various loads can be measured by dividers. For accurate measurements during the early part of the test, when the strain is slight, an **extensometer** is used. Most testing machines are equipped with autographic recorders by means of which stress-strain diagrams may be automatically plotted during test. The first part of the curve is not so accurately determined as when an extensometer is employed. Resistance strain-gauges may also be used to measure small amounts of strain in all manner of applications, including tensile tests. By attaching a number of resistance gauges to a specimen or structure, they enable the strain distribution to be thoroughly analysed. A small coil of fine wire mounted on paper (typical size mounted 1 in. $\times \frac{1}{2}$ in.) is glued to the specimen. The coil then extends or contracts with the specimen, when its electrical resistance increases or decreases, respectively. The relationship between strain and resistance of the gauge is almost linear over a wide range. The resistance changes can be measured by a Wheatstone Bridge circuit.

Rate of straining. Usually during standard testing, straining is continuous until the specimen breaks, and strain-rates of the order of $\frac{1}{16}$–$\frac{1}{8}$ in. per minute or greater are used. A typical compound-lever machine has the following possible speeds : 0·015 in., 0·024 in., 0·104 in., 0·25 in. and 0·75 in. per minute. Continuous straining may be used in determining stress-strain curves autographically, and in ordinary tests for yield point, ultimate tensile stress (U.T.S.), elongation, and reduction in area. In more accurate determinations of the whole or part of the stress-strain curve the load is applied in stages, and the extension for each load value is measured after waiting a short time for the specimen to settle down.

Some aspects of the effect of time in the straining of metals have been discussed in Chapter 5. Creep and the various phenomena following deformation may play important parts if the time of straining is sufficient. On the other hand, it appears that loads applied extremely rapidly have less effect than those applied at a more moderate rate.

In certain cases the test results are noticeably affected by the rate of straining, although marked effects are not generally obtained with the common engineering materials if the rate is of the order given above. The particular rates recommended in a specification should always be followed. An extreme case is pure lead, in which pronounced creep occurs at room temperature ; results of tensile tests on lead have no real significance unless rate of straining is stated.

Uses of the tensile test. Complete stress-strain curves are not generally determined ; certain characteristics only are required. The value of the tensile test is covered by the discussion in Chapter 5 (p. 120) ; it is most widely used in commercial acceptance testing, together with hardness and notched-bar impact tests. The ultimate tensile stress, the elongation (sometimes the reduction in area), and yield point or proof stress are usually specified for acceptance purposes, although in some cases ultimate stress and elongation only may be called for. The tensile test may be used directly ; for example, couplings, links and chains may be tested to ensure that they will withstand a certain minimum tensile stress. The distribution of strain in a model or full-scale structure may also be studied. For general and commercial testing, stresses are calculated on the original cross-sectional area of the specimen.

(*a*) *Ultimate tensile stress, or maximum stress.* This is the maximum stress sustained by the specimen, when it is tested to fracture. It is easily noted during test without plotting a stress-strain curve. The breaking stress is not usually reported, although in some metals it may coincide with the ultimate stress.

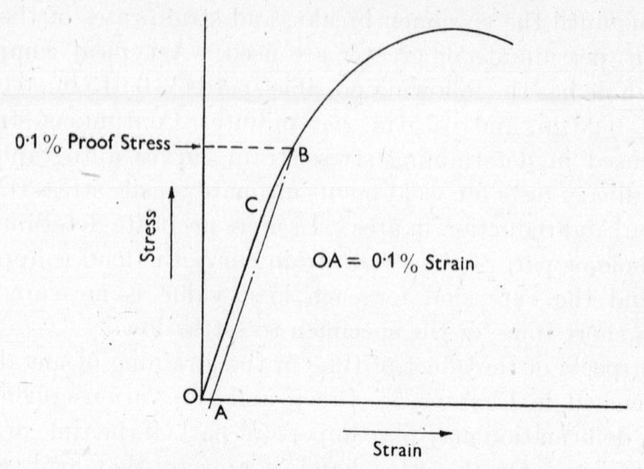

FIG. 362. Determination of proof stress.

(*b*) *Yield point and proof stress.* In mild steel, medium-carbon steel and wrought iron, at a certain stress, prior to which permanent deformation is slight, there is sudden yielding without increase in load (Fig. 102, page 119). This yield point is also clearly apparent without plotting a stress-strain curve.

To obtain a comparable result for metals which do not display a definite yield point, the stress necessary to cause, under load, a prescribed small amount of non-proportional elongation, such as 0·1 or 0·2 per cent is determined. This stress is known as the *proof stress* (or yield strength), and is prefixed by the amount of non-proportional strain it causes, as 0·1 per cent proof-stress. The proof-stress may be determined from the stress-strain curve (Fig. 362); *OC* and *AB* are parallel, thus eliminating the elastic or proportional strain; various other methods are used. To confirm that metal is up to specification, the actual value not being required, it is satisfactory if the proof stress is withstood for 15 seconds and after unloading the extension is not greater than the specified percentage of the gauge-length.

(*c*) *Elastic limit and limit of proportionality.* Confusion sometimes arises over these points. The *limit of proportionality* is the value of the stress at which the stress-strain curve ceases to be a straight line. It is determined by plotting the stress-strain curve using an extensometer. A rough value may be obtained from a diagram recorded autographically. The limit of proportionality is not an easy point to determine on the curve, especially where permanent deformation commences at an early stage during stressing, and hence in general testing the yield point or proof-stress is reported instead. A straight-line relation between stress and strain is the condition for elasticity, and thus the limit of proportionality is the elastic limit.

The *elastic limit* for testing is also defined as the stress up to which no permanent extension remains on unstressing. On this basis the value is determined by loading and unloading in small increments until the first permanent set or extension is indicated on an extensometer. The value of the elastic limit defined and determined in this way does not coincide necessarily with the end of the straight-line relation on the stress-strain curve determined while the stress is acting. Hence typical stress-strain curves are sometimes drawn showing the limit of proportionality and elastic limit as separate points. In the second method of determining the elastic limit, it is difficult to find the stress at which permanent deformation begins, so measurements may be continued into the permanent range, and a graph plotted (Fig. 363), from which the limit is more easily obtained, The values obtained for elastic limit depend on the sensitivity of the extensometer.

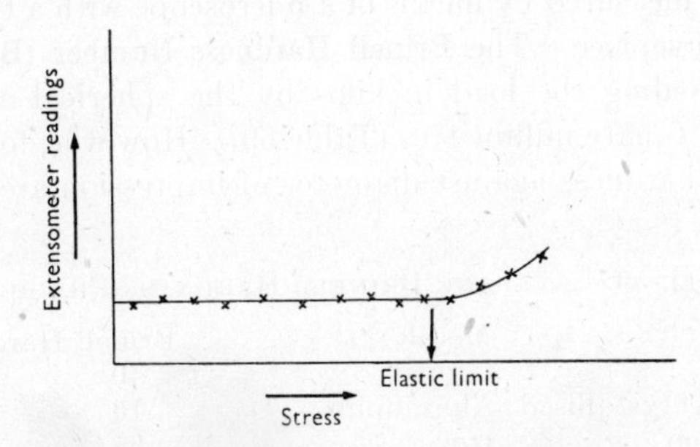

FIG. 363. Determination of elastic limit.

(*d*) *Modulus of elasticity*, *Young's modulus*. This is the slope of the straight-line portion of the stress-strain curve (Table 9, p. 117); extensometers or resistance strain-gauges should be used in its determination. For materials, such as cast iron, which have no real elastic range, a figure for the modulus may be given such as the tangent modulus, which is the slope of a tangent to the curve at the origin or a particular stress (small), or the secant modulus, in which an early stress value is divided by the corresponding strain.

(*e*) *Percentage elongation*. *See* pp. 452, 93 and 118.

(*f*) *Percentage reduction in area* (of round specimens) is the difference in cross-sectional area between that of the specimen originally, and that at the point of fracture, expressed as a percentage of the original (*see also* pp. 93 and 118).

Typical values of tensile characteristics are given in Table 61 (p. 459), Table 10 (p. 118) and Table 11 (p. 122).

Hardness testing. Hardness is a common acceptance test as well as being a useful investigation "tool"; the usual method of gauging it is by indentation methods. In many cases hardness testing need not be destructive.

In the **Brinell test,** a hardened steel ball of 10 mm. diameter is pressed into the surface of the metal for 15 sec. under a definite load of 500, 1000, or 3000 kgm., depending on the hardness of the metal under test. The conditions should be arranged so that the diameter of the impression is between a quarter and a half of that of the ball. For accurate testing, the centre of the impression should not be less than two and a half times the diameter of the impression from the edge of the specimen, the thickness of which normally should not be less than ten times the depth of the impression (although sometimes a thinner specimen may be permitted). Smaller ball diameters with comparably reduced loads may also be used. The diameter of the impression is measured by means of a microscope with a transparent scale in the eyepiece. The **Brinell Hardness Number (B.H.)** is obtained by dividing the load in kilos by the spherical area of the impression in square millimetres (Table 59). However, for standard use tables of hardness against diameter of impression are available.

TABLE 59. AVERAGE BRINELL HARDNESS FIGURES

	Metal	Brinell Hardness No.
High-purity recrystallised condition	Copper	40
	Aluminium	16
	Iron	65
	Nickel	70
"Cementite", iron carbide, Fe_3C		800
Steel of eutectoid composition (pearlitic structure)		200–450 depending on fineness of structure
Same steel, water quenched from γ-region		700
Brass, 60 Cu/40 Zn, cast.		70
"Duralumin"; for example, Al – Cu 4%; Mg, Fe, Si 0·5% each, cast		60
fully hardened		100

The **Vickers hardness testing machine** employs a diamond pyramid for indentation; smaller impressions are obtained than with the **Brinell**. Because of the size of the impressions in the Vickers' test, the test is useful for hardness explorations, for example, across a welded zone, but the Brinell is better for giving an average result. The surface of the metal must be better prepared than for the Brinell test, moderate emerying being suitable in the latter case. The Vickers hardness figure (**Vickers Pyramid Number, V.P.N.**) is computed in the same way as the Brinell. A range of loads is possible also in the Vickers. The Brinell and Vickers Scales are comparable up to about 200. The **Rockwell** is a direct-reading indentation machine which is valuable for fast routine work (Table 60).

TABLE 60. HARDNESS INDENTERS

Indenter	Brinell	Rockwell		Vickers
Material	Hardened steel or Tungsten carbide	Diamond	Hardened steel	Diamond
Shape	Sphere	Cone	Sphere	Square pyramid
Dimensions	10 mm. diameter standard	120°	Diameter $\frac{1}{16}$ in. $\frac{1}{8}$ in. $\frac{1}{4}$ in. $\frac{1}{2}$ in.	Angle between opposite faces =136°

Other means of testing to assess hardness are employed, although indentation methods are most general. In the Shore Scleroscope, hardness is indexed by the height of rebound of a small hammer dropped in a glass cylinder from a definite height above the surface of the metal. It is useful for large objects, when it is not possible to cut out samples, and thus is standard for roll surfaces.

The machines described above determine what may be called the *macro-hardness*. A number of micro-hardness testing instruments have been introduced ; they commonly employ indentation methods with a diamond. **Micro-hardness testers** make it possible to obtain comparative hardness figures for the different constituents of alloys, for example, and may aid in the identification of constituents and inclusions.

Notched-bar impact testing. In this test a notched specimen is struck by a fast-moving hammer, and the energy absorbed in breaking the specimen is measured (although very plastic metals may not break). The great advantage is that it reveals tendency to brittleness, which may not be revealed by other tests such as tensile or hardness. It is used for acceptance and investigation testing (Table 61). The **Izod test** (Figs. 364 and 365) is standard in Great Britain,

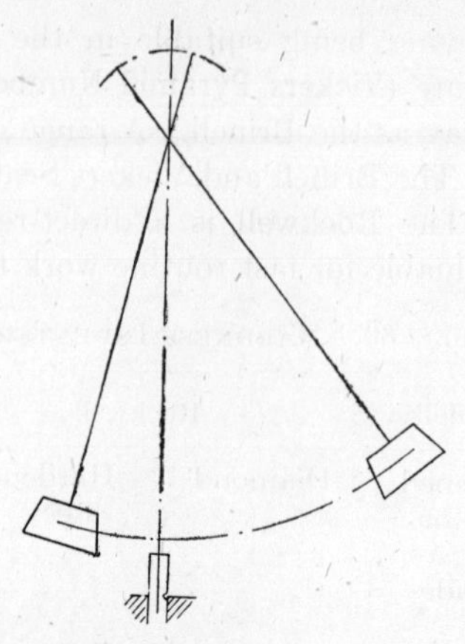

FIG. 364. Principle of Izod test. The striking energy is 120 ft. lb. and the amount absorbed in breaking the specimen is indicated by the pointer at the top.

but the **Charpy test** is being increasingly used especially for sub-zero testing (p. 121). A beam-type specimen is employed in the latter which can be inserted in the machine more quickly than can the cantilever specimen in the Izod test.

A particularly good example of the use of notched-bar testing in connection with brittleness is the case of temper brittleness in certain steels. For example, alloy steels containing about 0·3 per cent carbon and additions of chromium and nickel of the order of one and several per cent respectively, may be heat-treated by quenching in oil from about 850° C. followed by tempering (reheating) in the range

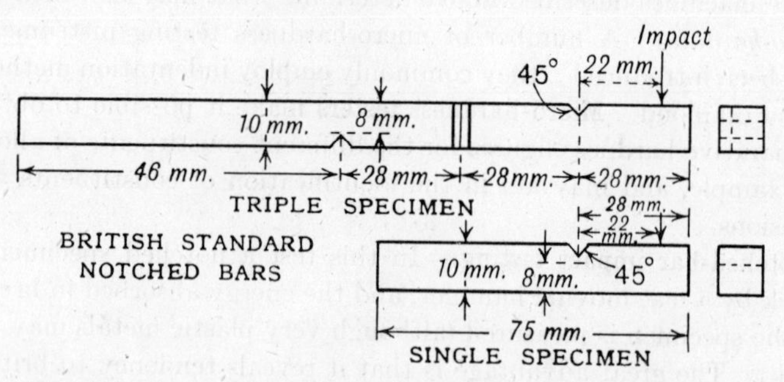

FIG. 365. Izod specimens. A number of other specimens are used including a round one, 0·45 in. dia. For grey cast iron an unnotched 0·798 in. dia. specimen is employed with modified grips. From *Engineering Science*, by H. B. Brown and A. J. Bryant. Macmillan.

TABLE 61. TYPICAL IZOD VALUES

Metal	Izod (ft. lb.)	U.T.S. tons/in.²	Elong. (%)
Commercial nickel (recrystallised)	110	31	47
Pure iron (recrystallised)	80	17	48
Pure copper (recrystallised)	45	14	54
Hot-rolled Monel metal (approx. 70 Ni/30 Cu	115	38	40
Steels, normalised (air cooled from γ-region			
C Mn Si Ni Cr Cu			
0·2 0·36	73	28	33
0·33 0·94 1·1	43	44	29
0·35 0·79 — 1·9	35	39	30
0·31 0·46 0·96	40	39	31
0·31 0·89 0·54	49	39	32
0·31 0·46 — 0·88 1·17	55	41	31
Aluminium bronze 88% Cu, 9% Al, 3%Fe. Forged	35	38	42

See also Table 11 page 122.

250°–650° C. Especially if the cooling is slow after tempering, a brittleness is developed in the steels, which is indicated by low notched-bar test results. The brittleness is not indicated in the tensile or hardness results, nor generally by microscopic examination. The brittleness may be overcome by the addition of about a half per cent of molybdenum to the steel, although the phenomenon is not properly understood.

Other mechanical tests. Simple *bend tests* may be performed on wire, tube, and sheet to indicate the ductility. For example, the test may take the form of determining the number of reverse bends required for fracture. On the other hand, a single bend may be applied and with cast metal this will often cause cracking.

A *transverse test* is fairly commonly applied to cast iron. A standard-sized specimen is supported at its ends and loaded in the middle until it breaks ; the breaking load and maximum deflection sustained are measured. The results for breaking load may be reported as $\frac{W.L}{0{\cdot}4d^3}$ (where W is breaking load, L supported length, and d the diameter of specimen), which is known as the transverse rupture stress or modulus of rupture.

Considerable information as to the *workability* of metals may be obtained from the foregoing mechanical tests at appropriate temperatures. In addition, special tests have been designed to assess workability under different conditions. Thus the *Erichsen cupping test* is used to indicate suitability of sheet for cold pressing and deep drawing. A round-headed steel punch is forced into the sheet (Fig. 366). The depth of impression formed before cracking gives the index of behaviour. The appearance of the deformed surface is important; roughness due to the orange-peel effect may be detected.

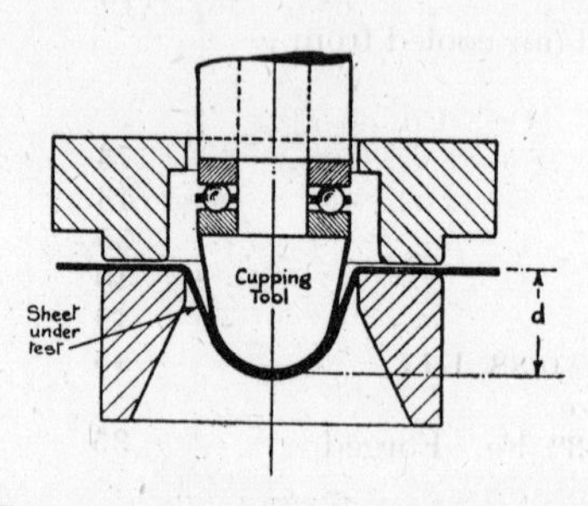

FIG. 366. Erichsen cupping test. From Batson and Hyde.

TESTS FOR DEFECTS AND FLAWS

This group of tests includes examination for flaws such as holes, cracks, and inclusions of foreign matter, or unsatisfactory structure. Low results in mechanical testing indicate that the metal is defective in some way, although generally not the nature and location of the defect. Mechanical testing is the standard method for checking that heat-treatment has been satisfactory.

The tests to be described determine the location and form of the defects. The results, correlated with experience and investigation, enable the origin of the defects to be ascertained in many cases.

Visual examination. This comprises examination of external, fractured, and prepared sectional surfaces by eye alone, or aided by low- and high-power microscopes.

Information as to the presence of surface folds or laps, cracks, and the general condition of the surface is given by external examination by eye or with low-power lenses. Cracks are often better revealed if the metal is etched. If cracks are likely to have absorbed oil, during machining say (or for that matter the parts can be dipped in oil and the surplus wiped off), they may be shown up by the oil oozing out, especially if the surface is white-washed; knocking the metal helps the oil to come out.

An elegant method applying similar principles is the "**Glo-crack**" or **fluorescent method** for crack detection. The technique is useful especially for castings and forgings in non-ferrous metals, for ferrous metals can be tested also by magnetic means. It depends on the fact that if the cracks can be made to take up some fluorescent material, and there is none elsewhere on the surface, when the objects are viewed under ultra-violet radiation in a dim light, the cracks will be revealed by the glowing of the fluorescent material. A light oil to which has been added a fluorescent agent to increase its fluorescing characteristics is used. It is applied by spraying, painting or immersion, when it penetrates the cracks. The excess may be removed from the surface with high-pressure water sprays. The surface is dried, sufficient heating for this being given by dipping into boiling water. Alternatively, the parts may be immersed in a solvent of the fluorescing agent, and then dried in sawdust. Before examination in ultra-violet light, fine powder may be applied to the surface to draw out the oil from the cracks, although it would eventually seep out. In addition to cracks, any surface defects, such as laps or folds, which will absorb and hold the oil, may be shown up. The fluorescent technique is relatively new, and in its full development requires correlation with other forms of crack detection, and with actual sectioning.

Magnetic methods can be applied to crack detection in magnetic materials. In one method the part is placed in a magnetic field ; if there is a crack (which may not be visible) at the surface, the sides acquire opposite magnetic poles. When a suspension of iron powder in paraffin is poured over the surface, the particles cling at the crack, forming a dark revealing line. In some cases it may be advantageous to whitewash the surface previously. Folds and non-magnetic inclusions may also be shown up.

There are also various **electrical** methods in which a current is passed through the metal and flaws are revealed by disturbance of the current.

The foregoing methods of crack detection are non-destructive, but in the main only detect flaws which reach the surface of the specimen, although the magnetic and electrical methods may detect flaws a short distance below the surface.

Examination of fractures. To the experienced eye much information may be obtained from examination of fractures. For example, the depth of the case in carburised steel specimens may be estimated, general grain size of metals may be assessed, and the extrusion defect may be detected. Fracture examination is particularly valuable with cast iron. The study of fractures under the microscope is being developed, and the technique may have some value as a test.

Macro- and micro-examination of prepared sections. Macro- and micro-methods can be employed to reveal cracks, porosity, piping and inclusions, as well as unsatisfactory structure. Composition can be checked approximately in a number of instances, and segregation of alloying constituents or impurities may be detected. Structure examination is also very useful in determining cause of failure. Much depends on careful and knowledgeable choice of the sections for examination. For full value both in testing and investigation of incidence of faults, other tests such as mechanical and radiographic ones should be used in co-operation, together with a chemical analysis.

Micro-examination may be used to confirm that preparation has been correct, as in the hardening of steel, or for checking the success of surface treatments such as case-hardening, galvanising, and anodising. Thickness may be determined microscopically ; adhesion and soundness tests may be carried out by other means. Of value is the examination of the size and evenness of grain in single-phase sheet for cold forming. From experience a satisfactory size-range has been found. Grain size can be measured under the microscope by incorporating a calibrated scale in the eyepiece, by projection on to a screen and comparison with a set of standards, or actually measuring the size of the grains in the image. The sizes are quoted for the plane section as average area or diameter, or as the number of grains per unit area.

External surfaces can also be examined without preparation to assess their degree of smoothness, or to index brightness and reflectivity in some way.

Macro- and micro-examination need not be destructive on finished components, as it is possible to prepare and examine exterior surfaces in a number of cases without causing harm. The taking of plastic replicas is an attractive possibility, especially for large finished objects, such as rolls, which cannot be arranged otherwise for microscopic examination. With stock, no difficulty arises in obtaining samples for examination. In the case of castings and forgings, micro-samples may be taken from unrequired portions. When shaped parts are fairly small, it is not uncommon, if they have high-duty applications, to cut up one every so often and examine it thoroughly by macro- and micro-methods.

Two macro-techniques are worthy of specific mention, namely, the preparation of sulphur prints on iron and steel, and the revealing

Fig. 367. Sulphur print of steel forging (made in closed dies) revealing unsymmetrical flow.

of flow lines in ferrous and non-ferrous forgings and other worked material. **Sulphur prints** neatly reveal the distribution of sulphur (a usual impurity) in ferrous materials and thus any segregation of this impurity, and indirectly the distribution of other impurities which are known to be associated with the sulphides. The metal surface should be flat and fairly smooth from surface grinding or fairly fine emerying. Photographic printing paper is softened by immersion for about two minutes in 2 per cent sulphuric acid; exposure to light does not affect the paper for the present purpose. The paper is drained free of excess acid and placed with the sensitive side in intimate contact with the metal; it is convenient to use a squeegee to make good contact. The sulphuric acid reacts with the sulphides to form hydrogen sulphide which acts on the silver salts in the emulsion giving silver sulphide and darkening of the paper. The dark areas in the print then reveal the location of the sulphur (Fig. 367). Progress of the print can be followed by lifting up one corner of the paper, and when darkened sufficiently the paper is stripped off, rinsed in water, fixed in "hypo", washed and dried. Although the sulphur print is best known, the principles have also been applied for the detection of other elements.

Usually the **etched macrostructure** of worked metal reveals **flow lines,** which indicate the flow of the metal during working (Fig. 368).

FIG. 368. Flow lines in steel forging, made in closed dies, half full size. This illustration has been made from an inked impression (" nature print ") of the etched surface. By courtesy of The English Steel Corporation Ltd.

The plane of the section should include an axis of the specimen. For preparation generally, the surface needs only to be surface ground or moderately ground with emery. A suitable etch for many steels is immersion in hot 50 per cent hydrochloric acid for times up to thirty minutes. A strong mixture of hydrofluoric and nitric acids rapidly reveals the structure of aluminium alloys, and a short time in acid ferric chloride is useful for copper and its alloys.

Flow lines arise from a number of effects produced during deformation, which cause certain areas on the section to be attacked by the etching reagent more than others. Among the effects are changes introduced in the crystal structure by the directional working, and the stringing out of micro-constituents, such as alloy phases and insoluble impurities. The grains may be partly elongated, especially if working is cold, or at relatively low temperatures in hot working. Varying amounts of cold working in different areas will cause differential etching. Similarly, uneven hot working will produce uneven grain size, and elongated membranes of inclusions in worked metal may inhibit grain growth and produce " runs " of fine grains. In the case of a single-phase material, which solidifies with a cored structure due to the segregation of metallic components or soluble impurities, working will elongate the cast grains, and recrystallisation will obliterate them. However, unless the core effect is removed by diffusion, the segregated zones will be elongated and run through a number of recrystallised grains, and thus on etching show differential attack. It should be noted that generally the tendency for flow lines to be etched up is not removed by heating, although some of the contributing effects may be removed.

The mechanical properties parallel to the direction of flow in worked metal are often different from those at right angles; the tensile properties are best parallel to the flow, and bending or shear resistance normal to the flow. In shaped articles such as forgings—and it is to these that the study of flow lines is mainly applied—it is the usual practice to regulate deformation so that service stresses are applied as much as possible in the directions in which the metal is most resistant; in many cases this is obtained by making the flow lines parallel to the outside contours. The flow lines should also be as symmetrical as possible. However, the shearing of blanks for forgings is likely to disturb the symmetry somewhat. A structure having directional differences in properties, and revealing flow lines as above, is sometimes referred to as a *fibre structure*, although this may have restricted use in indicating the presence of preferred orientation; undoubtedly preferred orientation is an important factor in the general case above, but it is not the only one.

Examination of flow lines by sectioning and fairly deep etching is a common test for forgings. It indicates whether the working has been carried out satisfactorily; and, in closed die forging, also that the metal blank has been placed in the right position between the dies. The presence of cracks is also revealed; the deep etching may cause emphasis and opening up of cracks which would otherwise escape notice. The test is not, however, a standard acceptance test, but rather an investigation check. Since the test is destructive, only one object every so often can be examined. There are no hard and fast rules as to what flow lines will pass and what will not.

X-ray testing. *Diffraction techniques* (page 166) may be used to estimate grain size, and to determine whether there is preferred orientation in the metal. The latter is most undesirable, for example, in sheet for deep drawing and pressing, as it gives rise to uneven flowing during deformation.

Radiography. In the radiographic technique (Fig. 369) a beam of X-rays probes through the metal to show up as a shadow picture (*a*) on photographic material, or (*b*) on a fluorescent screen. If the metal is uniform and free from flaws, the rays will be evenly absorbed, and a featureless picture will be obtained. This is because in the section of metal examined the thickness is usually so great relative to the fine microstructure that the macro-absorption is uniform. If exceedingly thin sections are used and the X-ray picture magnified, the internal

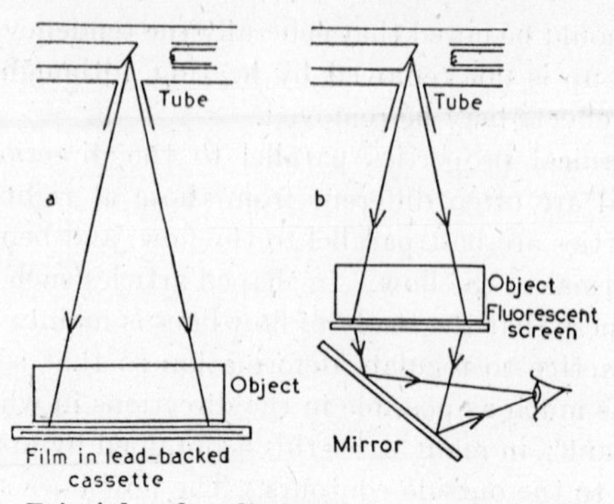

FIG. 369. Principle of radiography. (*a*) Photograpic method. (*b*) Observation of fluorescent screen. Fluorescent materials are zinc blende, calcium tungstate and barium platinocyanide. From *An Introduction to X-ray Metallography*, by A. Taylor. Chapman and Hall.

grain arrangement may be usefully revealed, as in the micro-radiographic technique (p. 167), which may also be used similarly to microscopy for detecting fine cracks and porosity. In the ordinary macro-technique, if the regularity of the metal is disturbed by foreign inclusions, serious segregation of constituents, holes or cracks, there will be different amounts of absorption of X-rays at these places, and consequently they will be represented in the resultant picture as lighter or darker areas according to their nature (Fig. 370). The best sensitivity that can be obtained is such as to distinguish a cavity of dimension (in the direction of the rays) 0·5 per cent of the thickness of the section ; 2 per cent sensitivity is relatively easy to obtain.

In particular, radiography is used for the inspection of castings and welded work. It may be used for one hundred per cent inspection, as it is non-destructive. Visual examination of the image on a fluorescent screen can only be used for the less absorbing metals such as aluminium and magnesium alloys if the objects are of considerable thickness. For the denser metals, such as steel, in any reasonable thickness, unless very high voltage equipment is available, it is usually necessary to use the cumulative method of photography, which is also more sensitive as well as giving a permanent record.

General radiation (*see* page 163) is used in radiography, commonly from a sealed-off tube with a hot tungsten cathode, and air- or water-cooled tungsten target. The applied voltages are much higher than those used in diffraction work, namely up to 1000 kilovolts, and in some cases recently even higher. The rays become shorter in wave-

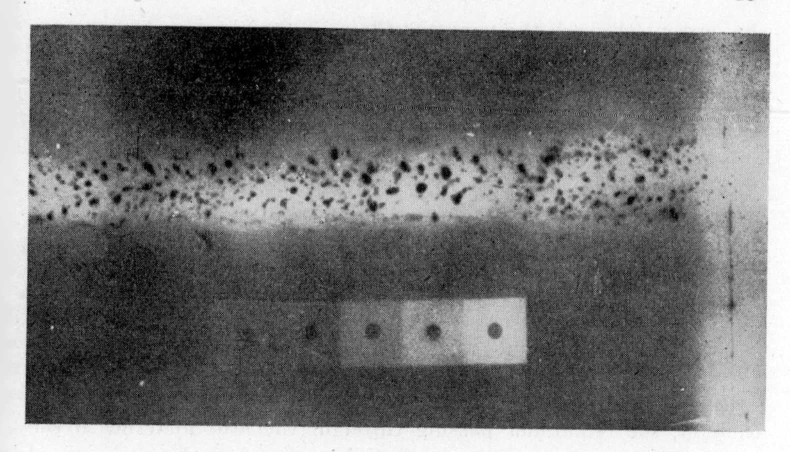

FIG. 370. Radiograph (two-thirds original size) of electric arc butt weld in $\frac{1}{2}''$ mild steel plate, revealing general gas porosity and slag inclusions. There is lack of root penetration in the cross-over weld on the right. The series of squares represents a sensitivity test and 1 per cent is indicated. By courtesy of Kodak Ltd.

length the higher the voltage, and thus more penetrating ; voltages up to 200 kV. will deal with practically all light alloy work, and up to 400 kV. with steel in thickness to about 4–5 in. ; 1000 kV. with a tungsten target will penetrate usefully about 7 in. of steel. This figure may be exceeded by higher voltage sets, but generally radiation from radium sources has been used for penetration greater than about 4–5 in. Radium and its salts give off very short wave-length rays, usually referred to as gamma-rays. In practice, radium sulphate is generally used ; small amounts are packed into small metal containers, which when not in use are stored in very thick lead containers. Radon gas is also used, and recently radioactive isotopes of cobalt, tantalum and iridium have been employed. Photography must be used with gamma-rays, but even so exposure-times may be very considerable.

The voltages required in radiographic work depend on the thickness of the object, and the material of which it is made ; the greater the atomic number the greater the absorption. The time of exposure in photography and the voltage should be so regulated so as to give maximum contrast. It is futile to drench say a small aluminium alloy casting for excessive periods in very short wave-length radiation, as this would produce general uniform fogging, any normal absorption differences being completely masked. The brightness of the X-rays is increased (and exposure-time reduced) by increasing the current through the tungsten filament, which gives an increase in the tube current flowing across the electrodes. The filament current is several amperes at 10–12 volts, whereas the tube current is of the order of milli-amperes. The effect of variation in tube/film distance on exposure-time is the same as with ordinary light, the intensity varying inversely as the square of the distance. To obtain a sharp picture the active target area should be as small, and the target-film distance as great, as practicable.

During the passage of X-rays through the object there is some scattering which causes general fogging on the photograph. To overcome this, special filters are sometimes used between the object and the film ; this makes increased exposure-times necessary. Only about 1 per cent of the energy of the X-rays reaching the film register thereon, the remainder passing through (the lead underneath the film in Fig. 369*a* is to prevent any of these rays from being scattered upwards on to the film from the supporting table). In order to reduce exposure-times, intensifying screens may be used in contact with the film ; the screens contain fluorescent material and the visible blue-violet light emitted adds to the effect of the X-rays. Lead intensifying screens are also used.

Considerable experience is necessary for satisfactory interpretation of radiographs, apart from outstanding flaws. It is best to build up a fund of experience at first by using the technique in conjunction with sectioning and macro-examination. A set of standard examples is useful. By special techniques the location of faults can be established.

X-rays received in an unregulated manner may be extremely harmful to the human body. Thus the operator should never become exposed to the main beam, and should avoid prolonged exposure to scattered radiation. Whenever possible lead sheet of suitable thickness should screen the operator (lead is very opaque to X-rays). The effects of X-rays are cumulative, and thus where the set is used regularly, it is advisable for the operator to have regular blood checks, which will reveal harmful effects. A special set of safety rules has been formulated for the protection of radiographers *and it is most important that they should be followed at all times.* Similar remarks, of course, apply to γ-rays and radiation from radioactive isotopes.

Soundness tests. Determination of the density of cast metal and comparison with that of sound metal is very revealing with regard to porosity. Density may be determined in most cases by weighing in air and water. For use under pressure, castings and forgings are subjected to actual hydraulic pressure tests, which may reveal unsoundness not detected by other methods.

The sonic method. This method of testing has been used for a long time ; the part is struck and caused to emit a note, and it is possible to detect the presence of flaws by the tone, especially when checked against a standard sound specimen. Flaws such as cracks will cause marked damping of the vibrations in the metal and thus of the note. However, this method does not indicate the nature, size or location of the defect.

Supersonic testing. This is based on the same principles as the sonic method, but inaudible sound waves of very short wave-length are used. The waves are sent through the metal and are reflected back or altered by defects so that a " shadow " is cast at the other end. Supersonic testing is being developed into a very refined technique ; the position of the defects can be estimated and finer cracks can be detected than by radiography. The size and nature of flaws are difficult to establish ; it is recommended that the technique is standardised by complementary radiographic examination and sectioning. It is not possible to enter into a description of the means by which the sound waves are produced and studied. However, by employing different methods, very thin material may be tested as well as thicknesses up to a number of feet (especially for steel), and thus affording valuable extension beyond the limits of radiography, which for steel, even with apparatus working on 1–2 million volts, is about 10–12 in. ; γ-rays have about the same limit. The thicknesses that can be tested by supersonics vary very considerably for different materials. Whereas any section may be radiographed, for supersonic testing uniform cross-sections with the ends parallel and smooth are desirable, although application to certain other shapes is possible. Supersonic testing has been applied to aluminium alloy billets and extrusions, steel axles and welds.

Damping capacity tests. The damping capacity of a metal is profoundly affected by the actual metallurgical condition, and the presence of flaws. Damping capacity measurement techniques have been studied as methods of non-destructive testing and applications have been made. They also provide a way of following the behaviour of metals under conditions of fatigue.

TESTS FOR SUSCEPTIBILITY TO SPECIAL WEAKNESS

Under certain conditions of stress, or a combination of stress and environment, some metals display pronounced weakness. The weakness may be peculiar to certain metallurgical conditions. In some cases it has been necessary to discontinue use of that particular metal under the prevailing conditions, although if it has desirable properties in other ways every effort is made to find a remedy. In other cases the phenomena have been investigated in detail, and remedies found and proved by experience. In the latter instances it is necessary to have acceptance tests correlated with experience, which will reveal susceptibility ; the tests should be fairly rapid. One example is *temper brittleness*, which is a weakness encountered in certain steels in the hardened and tempered condition ; it is detected by the notched-bar impact test (page 457).

Another example is the *season-cracking* of alpha-brass (page 132). The standard test for susceptibility to season-cracking is to immerse the brass after suitable degreasing in 1 per cent mercurous nitrate (plus 1 per cent nitric acid) solution for half an hour. If cracks do not develop in this period or in the subsequent 24 hours, the brass has low susceptibility. On immersion in the mercurous nitrate, mercury is deposited on the brass, and the conditions of test are those of contact with molten metal, which are not directly those of season-cracking. Contact with moist ammonia forms a stringent test, although it is not the standard one.

ADDITIONAL READING

1. *Mechanical Testing*, Vol. I., by R. G. Batson and J. H. Hyde. (Chapman and Hall, Second Ed., 1931).

2. *The Mechanical Testing of Metals and Alloys*, by P. Field Foster. (Pitman, Fourth Ed., 1948).

3. *Metals*, by (Sir) H. Carpenter, and J. M. Robertson. (Oxford Univ. Press, 1939).

4. (*a*) *Tensile Testing of Metals*. British Standard 18 : 1950.

(*b*) *Notched Bar Test Pieces*. British Standard 131 : 1933 (Add. Dec. 1942).

(*c*) *Methods and Tables for Brinell Hardness*. British Standard 240—Part I : 1937.

(*d*) *Impact Test for Cast Iron*. British Standard 1349 : 1947.

(*e*) *Mechanical Tests for Metals*. British Standards Handbook No. 13 : 1951. British Standards Institution.

5. *The Hardness of Metals*, by D. Tabor. (Oxford Univ. Press, 1951).

6. *The Hardness of Metals and its Measurement*, by Hugh O'Neill. Chapman and Hall, 1934).

7. *Handbook of Industrial Radiology.* J. A. Crowther (Edit.). (2nd Ed., Arnold, 1949).

8. *Metals Handbook.* 1948 Ed. (American Society for Metals).

9. *The Physical Examination of Metals.* Vol. I, by B. Chalmers (1939). Vol. II, by B. Chalmers and A. G. Quarrell (1941). (Arnold).

10. *Magnetic and Electrical Methods of Non-Destructive Testing,* by D. M. Lewis. (George Allen and Unwin, 1951).

11. *The Non-Destructive Testing of Metals,* by R. F. Hanstock. Monograph and Report Series No. 10. (Inst. of Metals, 1951).

CHAPTER 14

TEMPERATURE MEASUREMENTS IN METALLURGY

THE need for precise temperature measurement and control both in process metallurgy and metallurgical science is apparent. The foundations of present-day pyrometry were laid towards the end of last century. Prior to this, there was little metallurgical science, and in process work dependence was placed on the operator's experience and judgment.

With new processes, today pyrometric control is normally installed, for the processes are developed on a specific temperature basis. In the case of established processes, pyrometric control is being developed ; hindered partly by tradition, and partly by the practical difficulties that exist, as for example, the severe conditions encountered in steel-making. Even when installed, considerable time and study are necessary to correlate experience with the pyrometric measurements made. In industrial applications it is not always possible to determine the specific temperature ; yet apparent readings, provided they are consistent, give valuable guidance.

There is no clearly defined distinction between " thermometry " and " pyrometry ", although the latter in general implies high-temperature measurements. The important instruments used to measure temperature in metallurgy for laboratory or industrial purposes are of three types, namely (1) electrical resistance, (2) thermo-electric, and (3) radiation pyrometers, of which (2) and (3) are by far the most widely used. In addition, mercury-in-steel thermometers, bimetallic elements, fusible cones and crayons, and colour-changing powders have some application.

Resistance pyrometry utilises the progressive change in electrical resistance of a conductor with temperature. The basis of **thermo-electric pyrometers** is that if two dissimilar conductors known as a thermo-couple are joined to form a closed circuit via a current- or E.M.F.-measuring instrument and one junction is heated while the other is kept at a constant temperature, an E.M.F. which is a function of the difference in temperature between the junctions will flow in the circuit. In both resistance and thermo-electric pyrometry the temperature of the "element" is raised to that of the hot body, or very close to it, by suitable contact, such as immersion in molten metal. For continuous measurement it is not advisable to use resistance pyrometers beyond about 600° C., and thermo-couples beyond about 1200° C.–1300° C. Considerably higher temperatures can be measured in each case with intermittent use.

In **radiation pyrometry**, contact is not made with the hot body, and thus the technique is especially useful for high temperatures above the range of thermo-couples. The method depends on the fact that the brightness of the radiation emitted by hot material is related to its temperature. There is a number of different instruments employing part or all of the radiation in various ways. Thus in the *total radiation type* in practice for temperatures above 500° C., a heat-absorbing body in the form of a resistance, thermo-electric, or bimetallic element is placed in the path of the radiation. In a short time the element reaches a steady temperature, producing a change of resistance, E.M.F. or deflection, which is related to the temperature of the hot body. The *disappearing-filament pyrometer* is an optical type of radiation instrument. The brightness of the hot body, which must be at least at 700° C., is matched visually (through a red filter) against a lamp filament. The brightness of the lamp is varied by adjusting the current passing through it until it has the same brightness as the hot body. The current is related to the brightness, which increases with temperature. Brightness measurement is also the basis of *photo-electric cell pyrometers*, at present also limited to visible hotness. The cells are sensitive to several colours, and when illuminated with radiant energy yield a current which increases with temperature.

Although pyrometers are based on sound physical principles, they are calibrated experimentally. Calibration is carried out by comparison with standard instruments, or by direct measurements on the accurately established melting and boiling points of pure substances. Extrapolation must be used for the high-temperature range of radiation pyrometers. A calibration curve is obtained in which the actual temperature is plotted against the units measured on the pyrometers. In use, recourse may be made to the curve for each reading, or the instrument scale may be calibrated in temperature units.

The essential factor for accurate use of resistance and thermo-electric pyrometers is that the element should reach the temperature of the object. In many cases this is closely achieved. In radiation pyrometry the position is unfortunately more complicated. This is due to the fact that emission characteristics vary for different materials and are affected by other factors. Further, the atmosphere separating the hot body and the pyrometer, such as that of a furnace, may affect the results, or heat may be reflected by the body. The accuracies of the various instruments are compared in Table 62.

TABLE 62. RANGE AND ACCURACY OF PYROMETERS

Pyrometer	Accuracy (percentage of scale-range)	Limits of application
Resistance -	±0·75	– 240° to 600° or 1000° C.
Thermo-couples	±1·0	– 200° to 1650° C.
Total radiation	±2·0 under black body conditions of use	>500° C.
Disappearing-filament -	±1·5 (±10° C.)	>700° C.
Photo-electric	—	>700° C.

Thermo-electric, resistance, total radiation, and photo-electric pyrometers may be arranged to make continuous recordings automatically, and also to control furnace temperatures to within certain limits.

RESISTANCE PYROMETERS

Resistance pyrometers utilise the progressive increase in resistance of an electrical conductor with rise in temperature. For moderate temperatures nickel has been used, and in some applications a semi-conductor, in which the resistance decreases with rise in temperature; but generally platinum is the material employed. Platinum is preferred for its good resistance to oxidation and corrosion, because it can be obtained in a pure and reproducible form, and there is a relatively simple temperature/resistance relationship.

The platinum is commonly used as a thin wire, for example, 0·1 mm. in diameter. Generally a length of about 2 metres is wound in a coil around a mica former. The resistance of the coil for the dimensions given above will be about 25 ohms at 0° C., and will increase by 0·1 ohm for every degree rise in temperature. In use, the coil is contained in a sheath of glass, fused silica, porcelain, or some metal, depending on the application. It is best if the coil can be surrounded by clean dry air and sealed off in the sheath. The sheath should be as thin as practicable in order to reduce the time-lag in recording temperature due to the time taken for the coil to reach the temperature to be measured.

The resistance is measured by potentiometric or Wheatstone Bridge methods. Some form of compensating leads has to be provided to balance out the effect of the connecting leads to the actual coil. Consideration must also be given to the heating effects of the current itself (supplied by a battery), the effects introduced by change in temperature of the balancing coils, and to the elimination of thermo-electric effects at the contacts.

The resistance pyrometer is an extremely precise instrument for measurements up to 600° C. It is not considered quite so reliable beyond this figure, although it can be used satisfactorily up to, and even beyond, 1000° C.; but this is not advisable for continuous use. The pyrometer is particularly valuable for laboratory work, and for standardising other instruments; it has some industrial applications, although they are few in comparison with the thermo-electric and radiation instruments.

THERMO-ELECTRIC PYROMETERS

Thermo-electric combinations (Table 63, Fig. 371). In a good thermo-electric combination, the relationship between E.M.F. and temperature should give a smooth curve of sufficient slope for easy measurement and good sensitivity. The materials should be strong, with good resistance to temperature and service environment. They should be easy to obtain in a pure and reproducible form. It is advantageous before calibration to heat or "age" the materials at the maximum temperature of use. Apart from the brittleness of the graphite/silicon-carbide couple, the main troubles with couples arise from contamination in service, which may cause embrittlement and alteration of the thermo-electric characteristics. Thus the calibration should be regularly checked.

The couple-metals are usually employed in the form of wires, which are twisted together and welded or soldered to make the hot junction (Fig. 372*a*). Good contact is essential; it is not generally satisfactory to complete the circuit with the hot metal, as complicating effects are introduced. The wires are insulated by porcelain, silica or fireclay beads or tubing; in addition thermal insulation may be applied. Base metal wires are commonly used up to $\frac{1}{8}$ in. diameter although sometimes greater. Precious metal wires, being more expensive, are used in thinner sizes, the usual diameter being 0·02 in. Thick wires are stronger mechanically and have longer life than thin ones, but are not so sensitive. Thick wires conduct more heat away

TABLE 63. COMMON THERMO-ELECTRIC COMBINATIONS

Couple	General range of use	Approx. max. temperature for continuous recording	Max. temperature for intermittent use	Notes
Copper-constantan (Constantan is essentially a copper-nickel alloy containing 40–65% copper)	– 200° to 350° C.	300° C.	600° C.	Rapidly oxidised. Deteriorates in alternate oxidising and reducing conditions.
Iron-constantan	– 200° to 750° C.	700° C.	900° C.	Gives better service in oxidising than reducing atmospheres.
Chromel-alumel (chromel is 90Ni/10 Cr; alumel is 95Ni + 5% of Al, Si and Mn)	– 200° to 1200° C.	1100° C.	1300° C.	Better service in oxidising than reducing atmosphere. Susceptible to atmospheres containing active compounds of C and S and cyanide fumes. (Ni alloys in general are allergic to sulphur.)
Platinum-platinum containing 13% rhodium	300° to 1400° C. not suitable below 0° C., because E.M.F. produced is slight.	1200° C.	1650° C.	Good reproducibility. Sensitivity not so high a base metals (Fig. 371). Rhodium may volatilise and penetrate the pure platinum. Easily liable to contamination from metal vapours and certain gases, resulting in fall in E.M.F. and mechanical weakness.*
Graphite-silicon carbide	high temperatures, as with molten steel and iron.	1300° C.	1700° C.	Weak mechanically.

* Recently, it has been shown that the presence of small amounts of carbon and sulphur (as might arise from traces of oil) cause embrittlement in the presence of a siliceous sheath. Hydrocarbon gases, carbon or sulphur on their own do not have this effect. Resulting precaution is that steel protection tubes should be thoroughly baked before use to remove any oil. Similar precaution applies to chromel-alumel.

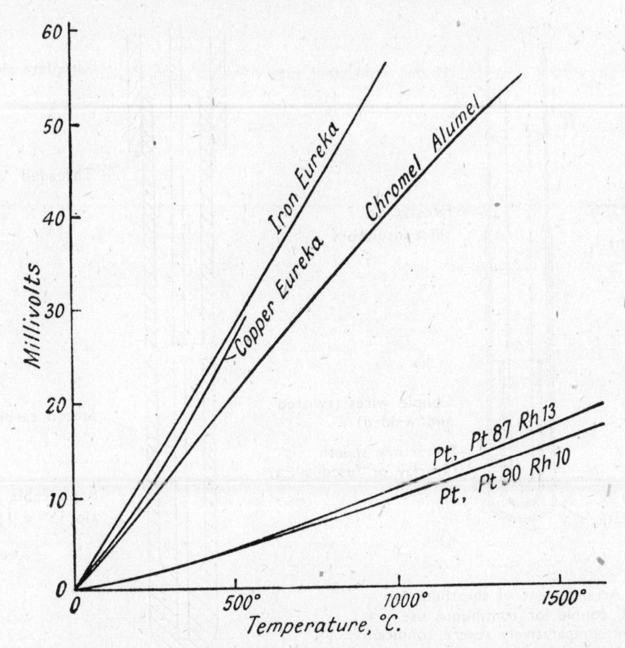

FIG. 371. Relationship between E.M.F. and temperature for various thermo-couples (eureka is the same material as constantan). From *The Physical Examination of Metals*, Vol. II, by B. Chalmers and A. G. Quarrell. Arnold.

from the junction and thus greater depths of immersion are necessary to ensure that the correct temperature is reached.

The hot junction may be used bare, especially at low temperatures; but often it is best protected from gases, slag and metal by a tubular sheath sealed at the working end (Fig. 372*a*). A variety of materials are used for sheaths, such as porcelain, " Pyrex " glass, fireclay, fused silica, graphite and metal, depending on the application (Table 64). Although sheathed couples have longer life, they are less sensitive than bare ones and have to be immersed to greater depths to compensate for conduction losses.

The graphite/silicon carbide couple consists of a graphite tube with a silicon carbide rod inside (Fig. 327*b*); no sheath is necessary. An iron tube with a constantan wire or rod welded in at the closed end may be used in the same way.

Thermo-couple circuits. The E.M.F. is measured either by a galvanometer or a potentiometer (both may be made recording instruments), although potentiometers are used for all accurate

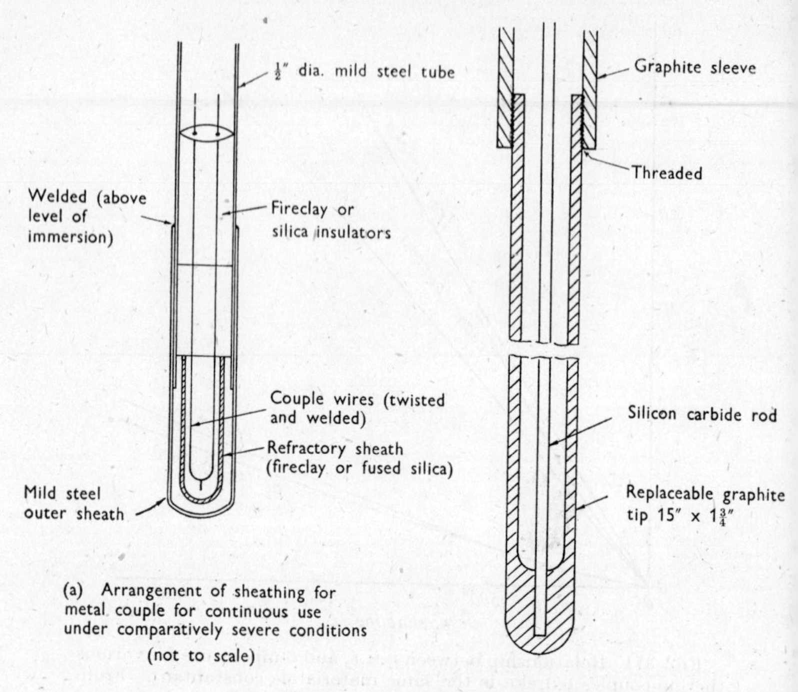

FIG. 372. Thermo-couple construction.

laboratory work. The galvanometers are of the suspended-coil type, calibrated in millivolts and known generally as "millivoltmeters", although current is actually measured. The resistance of the circuit should therefore be kept constant. A large resistance is incorporated in the instrument to minimise the effect of small changes in the resistance of the circuit, or the couple can be calibrated with the meter. With the true null potentiometric technique, no current flows in the thermo-couple circuit at balance.

It is often convenient to have the E.M.F. measuring instrument connected into the thermo-couple circuit by flexible copper leads (Fig. 373). Thermo-couples are generally calibrated with the cold junction at 0° C., and if not used at this temperature, correction must be applied. If the E.M.F./temperature difference curve is approximately linear over the range concerned, the temperature of the cold junction can be added to the apparent temperature, or an instrument calibrated for the couple in degrees of temperature can be set at

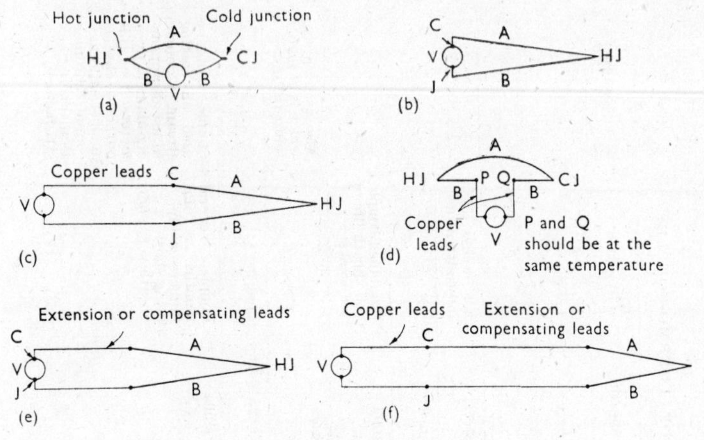

FIG. 373. Thermo-couple circuits.

the cold junction temperature, on open circuit. When the temperature/E.M.F. curve is not a straight line, as with precious metal couples, the millivolt equivalent of the cold junction temperature must be added to the actual millivolts recorded before conversion to temperature. This ensures that the recorded millivolts are converted strictly to the specific temperature interval which generated them ; however, an approximate figure can be obtained by adding half the cold junction temperature to the apparent temperature.

To remove the cold junction from the vicinity of the hot body, it is convenient to use flexible braided extension leads instead of the single-strand couple wires (Fig. 373*e* and *f*). With precious metal couples which are expensive, compensating leads of base metals are used. These should have the same E.M.F./temperature relationship as the precious metals up to about 100° C., in order to avoid the introduction of extraneous effects. Thus a copper-nickel alloy is used against platinum, and copper against the platinum-13 per cent rhodium alloy. For tungsten and graphite, which are difficult to manipulate, mild steel and higher carbon steel may be used as tube and wire, respectively. No compensating materials are known for the graphite-silicon carbide combination, and in this case the cold junction is in the head of the instrument and is water-cooled.

For laboratory use the cold junction is often fixed in melting ice contained in a "Thermos" flask. In industrial applications the cold junction is not usually maintained at 0° C. Its temperature may be measured and appropriate correction applied each time ; or the

TABLE 64. EXAMPLES OF INDUSTRIAL APPLICATIONS OF THERMO-COUPLES

Application	Temperature range	Couple	Method of measurement	Sheath	Life	Notes
Aluminium and alloys. Heat treatment in electrically heated furnace with circulated air	Around 500° C.	Chromel-alumel or iron-constantan $\frac{1}{16}$″–$\frac{1}{8}$″ dia. twisted and welded	Permanently installed	Used bare	Long	
Aluminium alloys. When molten in crucible	Around 700° C.	Iron-constantan wires 0·080″ dia.	Intermittent immersion	Mild steel	3–5 weeks of intermittent use	
Silver; before casting from melting furnace	Around 1100° C.	Chromel-alumel wires	Check immersion	Mild steel		
Tin; tinning pots for steel, containing molten tin	235–325° C.	Iron-constantan wires, 0·064″ dia.	Continuous immersion	Mild steel	Combined couple and sheath life of 4–6 weeks	
Lead from blast furnace	Around 850° C.	Chromel-alumel 0·16″ dia.	Intermittent; check by immersion	Mild steel		Also used on slag, which is at higher temperature
Lead; waste gases leaving top of blast furnace	Around 180° C.	Iron-constantan wires	Continuous	Cast Fe–28% Cr	Long	
Copper; in reverberatory refining furnace	Above 1100° C.	Platinum-platinum 13% rhodium	Quick immersion, 1 minute or more needed	Fused silica	Couple, several months. Total immersion life being short. Sheath very short	Couple can be used on casting stream. Common to use disappearing-filament pyrometers for this purpose—checked against thermo-couple (chromel-alumel being satisfactory)

Copper alloys ; checking pouring temperature after melting and alloying	About 1000°–1200° C.	Chromel-alumel e.g. 0·064″ dia. wires	Immersion ; intermittent	Fused silica or metal	Good	
Tin ; exit gas stream from tin smelting furnace	350–600° C.	Iron-constantan wires	Continuous measurement thermo-couple projects into flue	Mild steel with outer one of nickel-chromium steel	Very long	
Tin ; roasting furnace for ore	600–700° C.	Iron-constantan wires	Fixed just above the ore	Mild steel with outer one of nickel-chromium steel	Extremely long	
Magnesium ; electrolytic cell	Around 750° C.	Both iron-constantan and chromel-alumel are used with mild steel sheaths and give good life	Immersion in top (metal is on top). Intermittent or or continuous			
Steel ; molten lead bath for heat-treatment of steel	Around 875° C.	Chromel-alumel wires	Continuous immersion	Cast Ni–Cr alloy	Outfit gives 4000 hours continuous service	
Steel. Molten in open-hearth and arc furnaces, in converters and in ladles	Up to about 1700° C.	Platinum-platinum 13% rhodium	Quick immersion, reading in 10–15 sec.	Fused silica	Sheath renewed each time. Couple used for 10–15 immersions, then few inches cut off and ends joined again	General in British steel practice*
Steel. Molten in open-hearth and arc furnaces, in converters and in ladles	Up to about 1700° C.	Graphite/silicon carbide		Graphite acts as sheath but generally given a thin coating by means of a refractory wash	Claimed that at least 60 immersions possible before renewal of graphite necessary	Developed in American steel practice*

* These couples can be used for molten pig iron and cast iron.

2 H

couple may be connected directly to the meter terminals, which become the cold junction, some means of compensating for temperature variations being provided in the instrument (this should always be at a uniform temperature). On the other hand, the cold junction may be maintained at a constant temperature by immersing in a container of oil, deep in the ground, or using a thermostatically regulated junction-box.

Applications of thermo-couples (Table 64). The easiest and most accurate application of thermo-couples is to molten metal or molten baths used for heat treatment, provided the conditions are not too severe and the depth of immersion is sufficient to overcome conduction losses.

The surface temperature of solid metal can be measured by contact methods, although it will be appreciated that the temperature will vary through the mass. As regards metal in the open, the problem is to make good contact and to counteract the loss of heat by conduction along the couple wires, without unduly interfering with the cooling of the metal in the vicinity of the point of measurement. The hot junction should be flattened or made from narrow strip and pressed firmly against the hot metal. Such an arrangement will not markedly affect radiant heat losses of the metal. The wires or strip should run along the surface for a distance to minimise conduction losses ; this corresponds to deep immersion. In one form of instrument a small heater is arranged to compensate for conduction losses.

If the hot junction is fitted tightly into a hole drilled in the surface or welded in, the temperature of the bottom of the hole can be accurately measured. The temperature gradient can be determined by using three couples in holes of different depths ; the surface temperature can then be obtained by extrapolation. It is clear that this technique is not generally practicable, but is useful for investigation and for calibrating contact thermo-couples.

Thermo-couples are used in flues for estimating the temperature of hot gases. It is very difficult to measure the true temperature, but when co-ordinated with experience, apparent readings, provided they are consistent, are useful, for example, as a guide to the firing of a furnace. In practice, therefore, a sheathed couple may be arranged projecting into the gas stream. In a similar manner thermo-couples are used in heat-treatment furnaces, projecting inwards a short distance from roof and walls, although the procedure is a compromise.

A bare or sheathed hot junction inserted in a current of hot gas in a flue will pick up heat from the gas ; but, depending on whether the flue walls are hotter or cooler than the gas, the junction will also gain heat from or lose heat to the walls. To approach as close as possible to the true temperature of the gas, it is necessary to surround the junction with a refractory tube open at both ends, and to draw the gas quickly over the junction by an aspirating system.

RADIATION PYROMETERS

Hot bodies emit radiation in a continous band of wave-lengths with a short wave-length limit (Fig. 374). Ideal conditions, in which the intensity is the greatest, are represented by a " black body ". A black body may be defined as one which absorbs all the energy incident upon it, none being reflected ; conversely, it is the best radiator when hot. The intensity, or the rate of emission, of the total energy radiated by a black body is proportional to the fourth power of the absolute temperature (Stefan-Boltzmann Law, $W = KT^4$). The intensity for any particular wave-length can be calculated from Wien's distribution law ;

$$W_\lambda = C_1 \lambda^{-5} \exp(-C_2/\lambda T),$$

where W_λ is the intensity of radiation of wave-length λ ; C_1 and C_2 are constants (C_1 depends on variables involved in measurement ; $C_2 = 14{,}380$, when λ is expressed in microns) ; T is the absolute temperature. Actually, the experimental facts, in general, are more closely represented by a complex law due to Planck, and this was substituted for Wien's law in the new International Temperature Scale adopted in 1948. However, for the wave-length of $0{\cdot}65\mu$ used in the disappearing-filament pyrometer, the two laws differ only slightly, and Wien's law is used.

Approximate black body conditions can be obtained in practical pyrometry, for example, by sighting on a small opening in a furnace, or down a tube with a closed end projecting into the furnace. Similarly, with molten metal, a closed or open-ended tube can be immersed in the metal and the pyrometer focused down it on to the end.

In practice, however, unless examination can be made under black body conditions, the emission of energy at a particular temperature varies from one material to another, and depends on the condition of the surface as well as the actual temperature. For accurate pyrometry it is necessary to know the emissivity of the surface in question. The *emissivity*, E_t is the ratio of the intensity of the total energy emitted to that emitted by a black body at the same temperature, and is always less than unity. The *spectral*

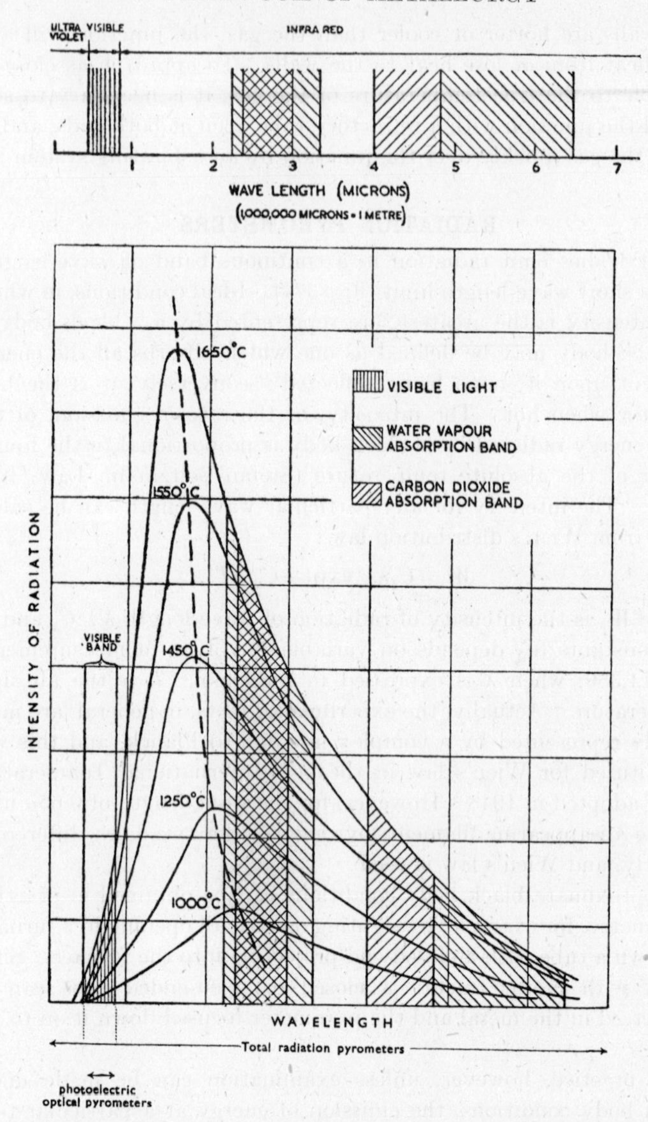

Fig. 374. Radiation spectra of black body at various temperatures The absorption bands represent the ranges of wave-lengths absorbed or radiated by water vapour or carbon dioxide. Thus if these gases are between a total radiation pyrometer and the hot body, the temperature reading will be high or low depending on whether the temperature of the gases is higher or lower, respectively, than that of the hot body. Figs. 374, 375, 376 and 380 are from *The Instrumentation of Open-Hearth Furnaces*. Brit. Iron and Steel Assoc. George Allen & Unwin.

emissivity, E_λ, compares the intensity for any particular wavelength in the same way. The spectral emissivity in the visible range is greater than the total emissivity (Table 65). Generally, a metal

TABLE 65. EMISSIVITIES OF UNOXIDISED AND OXIDISED IRON

Temperature	Iron unoxidised		Oxide	
	E_λ $\lambda=0{\cdot}65\mu$	E_t	E_λ $\lambda=0{\cdot}65\mu$	E_t
900° C.	0·38	0·08 at 1000° C.	0·97	0·87
1200° C.	0·38	0·11	0·92	0·89

oxide has a higher emissivity than the metal itself (in practice, for a solid metal, for example, the effective radiator is the oxide skin); the emissivity is higher for a rough than for a smooth surface. Emissivity values are determined from experimental measurements and more work in this direction is needed; the values at present available are very approximate in most cases.

Usually, radiation pyrometers are calibrated for (approximate) black body conditions. In use, the same conditions are aimed at, as described above. Alternatively, emissivity corrections have to be applied, although as pointed out already, apparent readings, provided they are consistent, may be sufficient. Actually the error involved may not be considerable; thus with steel in the open, a typical error is 15° C. at 1000° C. Sometimes radiation pyrometers are calibrated against thermo-couples for the actual conditions of use.

The reflection of incident energy by a non-black body increases as the emissivity decreases. Thus entirely erroneous readings may be obtained if a radiation pyrometer is sighted on cold metal being heated in a furnace (Table 66).

The readings of radiation pyrometers may also be affected by intervening atmospheres, such as that of the furnace, which may absorb some of the radiation or increase it (Fig. 374). Flames may also cause false readings. Further, it is necessary with molten metal to ensure that the instrument is not sighted on slag.

Total radiation pyrometers. One or more thermo-couples in series are generally used for the thermo-element, which is arranged in a container. The junctions are attached to a small blackened disc on which the radiation falls, or the radially connected junctions may form the receiver. The energy is focused on the element by a

Table 66. Effect of Emissivity on Total-Radiation and Optical Pyrometers Sighted on a Steel Surface surrounded by walls at 1470° C. (Compiled by Hedgcock and Mayorcas from data by Cory and Reid).

True surface temperature ° C.	Apparent Temperatures, ° C.					
	Total-radiation pyrometer			Optical pyrometer $\lambda = 0{\cdot}65\mu$		
	$E_t = 0{\cdot}5$	$E_t = 0{\cdot}95$	$E_t = 0{\cdot}99$	$E\lambda = 0{\cdot}5$	$E\lambda = 0{\cdot}95$	$E\lambda = 0{\cdot}99$
38	1205	560	295	1390	1140	1010
540	1220	641	577	1390	1140	1010
815	1254	888	830	1391	1141	1013
1090	1320	1130	1100	1393	1160	1120
1370	—	—	—	1435	1380	1372
1430	1464	1432	1431	1455	1433	1431

mirror or lens of glass or fused silica (Fig. 375). Sometimes it is necessary to protect, by a lens, the inside of the mirror type from dust or splashing. The instrument may be of fixed or variable focus. It is essential that the image of the hot body should completely cover the thermo-element; provided this is so, the density of the image is constant, irrespective of the size of the source and the distance from it. This does mean, however, that for a given size of target, there is a maximum permissible working distance.

The time taken to reach equilibrium in the ordinary type of instrument is about 15 sec.; but for measuring the temperature of moving objects, instruments have been developed with response times of the order of 1–2 sec. The E.M.F. developed in the thermopile is measured by millivoltmeter or potentiometer; automatic recording and also control are possible. For high-speed radiation pyrometry, quick-response electrical instruments are obviously required.

For various reasons the response of the total radiation pyrometer does not strictly follow the Stefan-Boltzmann law. Glass and fused silica are opaque to radiation of wave-length longer than $2{\cdot}5\mu$ and $3{\cdot}8\mu$, respectively. Thus the lens type does not utilise all the radiation, although for convenience the term total radiation pyrometer is still applied. This limitation is an advantage with respect to interference by gases between the hot body and instrument (Fig. 374). The response of a pyrometer with a glass lens is stated to be approximately proportional to the sixth power of the absolute temperature. Even with mirrors, the amount of reflection may not be constant at all wave-lengths, and of course, the use of a lens for

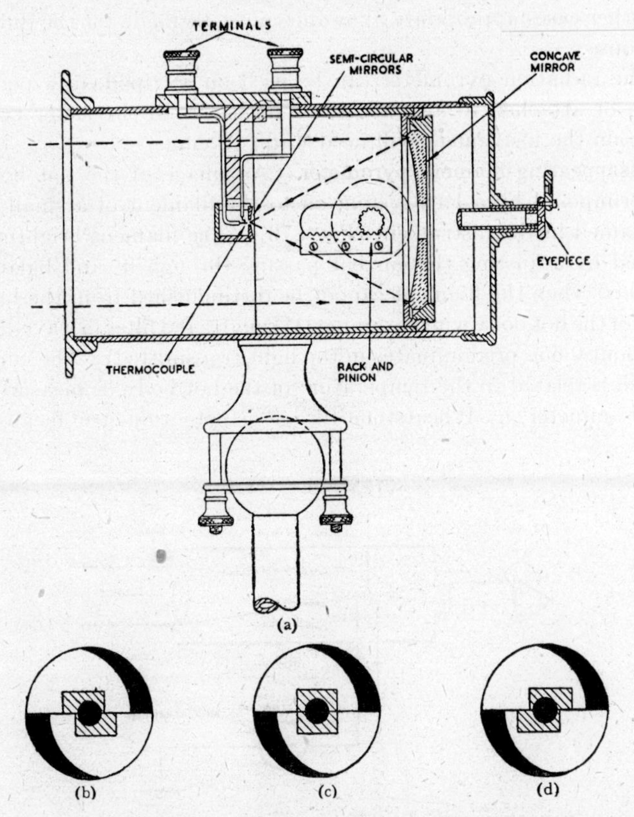

FIG. 375. Focussing, mirror-type, total radiation pyrometer. By means of the semi-circular mirrors and the small telescope, the correct focus is obtained (*c*) ; (*b*) and (*d*) indicate the appearance when out of focus. From *The Instrumentation of Open-Hearth Furnaces.*

protection makes the instrument substantially a lens-type pyrometer.

If the response is approximately proportional to the fourth power of the absolute temperature, as with the mirror type, correction for non-black body conditions may be applied by means of the fourth power law, thus :

$$\text{decreased intensity, } W_1 = KE_t T^4 = KT_\alpha{}^4$$

where E_t is emissivity of surface,

T_α is apparent temperature } absolute.
T is actual temperature }

In other cases appropriate allowance must be made for the different response.

The radiation pyrometer can be used on a tripod, in a portable form or attached to a structure or furnace. In the latter type of position the instrument will need water cooling.

Disappearing-filament pyrometer. An image of the hot body is superimposed by a lens system on to the filament of a small lamp contained in the instrument (Fig. 376). The filament brightness is varied by adjusting the current passing through it, and balance is reached when the filament cannot be distinguished from the brightness of the hot body when examined through a red filter (a wave-length of about $0{\cdot}65\mu$ predominates in the light transmitted). The current, which is related to the temperature of the hot body, is measured by milli-ammeter, by Wheatstone Bridge or potentiometric means.

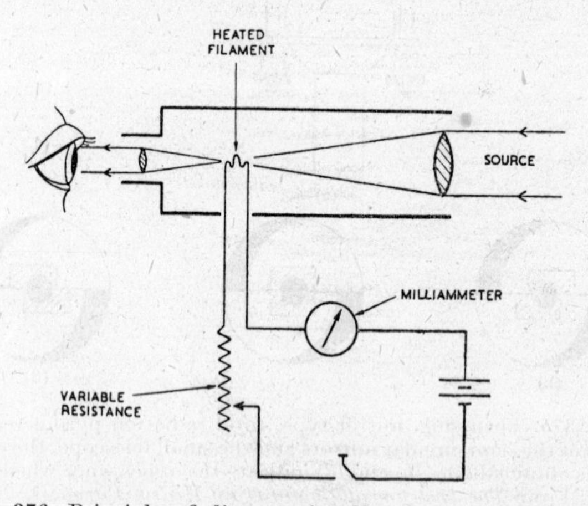

Fig. 376. Principle of disappearing-filament pyrometer. A red filter is incorporated and for high temperatures an absorbing filter is used as well (involving separate calibration). From *The Instrumentation of Open-Hearth Furnaces*.

The lamp filament is important because it has to reach an equilibrium temperature, and from this arises a time lag, which may be considerable in some industrial instruments. Further, the brightness produced by a specific current may be altered by changes in environment temperature. The filament should be as small in diameter as possible so as to reach equilibrium quickly, yet long enough to give sufficient length of the same brightness, for the extreme ends are always duller than the main part of the wire.

The instrument is usually made in a portable form. So long as certain optical conditions are observed, considerable latitude in distance from the object is possible. Readings can be taken quickly, and although they depend on the human element, good agreement can be obtained. The visual aspect of measurement is an advantage in some cases ; for example, partial slag coatings on molten metal can be avoided. Neither automatic recording nor control can be arranged with the usual form of disappearing-filament pyrometer. An automatic instrument has been developed in which brightness is matched by photo-electric cells.

Corrections for emissivity can be made by utilising Wien's law. Thus

$$W_\lambda = E_\lambda C_1 \lambda^{-5} \exp(-C_2/\lambda T) = C_1 \lambda^{-5} \exp(-C_2/\lambda T_\alpha);$$

where E_λ is the spectral emissivity of the surface :
T is the actual temperature (absolute) :
T_α is the apparent temperature (absolute) :
C_1 is not required :
C_2 is 14,380 when λ is expressed in microns (μ) :
λ with a red filter is $0{\cdot}65\mu$.

The expression then becomes :

$$\frac{1}{T} - \frac{1}{T_\alpha} = \frac{\log_{10} E_\lambda}{9608}.$$

Inaccuracies in use are caused by the presence of flames and absorption of radiation by smoke. However, because only one relatively short wave-length is involved, compared with the total radiation instrument, the disappearing-filament pyrometer is little affected by the presence of non-luminous or partly luminous flames, or by the absorption of the long wave-lengths of the radiation by the intervening atmosphere (Fig. 374) (*see also* page 494).

PHOTO-ELECTRIC CELL PYROMETERS

The photo-electric effect. The electrons of the atoms in vapours, liquids, or crystals may be excited to higher energy values by the absorption of the appropriate wave-length of energy from incident radiation. The radiation may be in the form of electron rays, or electromagnetic radiation such as X-rays, light or heat. Provided the necessary wave-lengths are present, electrons may receive sufficient energy to cause them to be ejected from their atoms. Excitation and emission (or ejection) of electrons by electromagnetic radiation constitutes the photo-electric effect ; ejected electrons are known as **photo-electrons**.

Emission effects are most pronounced with solid metals. Excitation without ejection is more noticeable with semi-conductors, for in these cases it increases conductivity, or causes conductivity where previously there was none. This is because the increased energy enables electrons filling the highest energy zone to bridge the energy gap, enter the next band, and become available for conduction (page 29). The photo-electric effects are proportional to the intensity of illumination, and the photo-sensitive materials respond to a range of wave-lengths (Figs. 377 and 379).

Photo-electric cells make use of these effects. Such cells were used initially for photometry, and have since found extensive use in sound films, television and industrial pyrometry. The problem of making a cell consists primarily in finding suitable material sensitive to the wave-lengths of interest. The photo-electric characteristics should be stable and consistent, and the material should be easy to produce and handle, and of reasonable price. As the main interest so far has been in the region of visible light, cells sensitive to these wave-lengths are the principal ones developed. Thus up to the present, pyrometric applications have been at temperatures at which visible radiation is emitted, and mainly in the use of such photo-electric cells with ferrous materials. However, cells incorporating material photo-sensitive to the long wave-lengths of the infra-red have been developed, and their application to pyrometry is being studied ; with these substances, pyrometry should be possible below 500° C., and down at least to 200° C.

There are three main kinds of photo-electric cells, namely, (1) emission, (2) self-generative, and (3) conductivity cells. The first two kinds have had the most applications, and are the ones which have been applied in metallurgy ; the infra-red applications mentioned above are of the third kind.

(1) **Emission cells.** These utilise the electrons emitted from photo-sensitive materials when the latter are illuminated with the appropriate radiation. A cell consists essentially of an evacuated glass vessel in which are arranged two metal electrodes (air would absorb electrons). A potential of about 90–100 volts is applied across the electrodes. The electrode connected to the negative (conventional) side of the supply, the cathode, has a film of the photo-sensitive metal. When the cathode is illuminated, electrons are emitted, and under the applied potential a current passes between the electrodes. There is a linear relationship between current and intensity of illumination. The current produced is very small and requires amplifying for measurement.

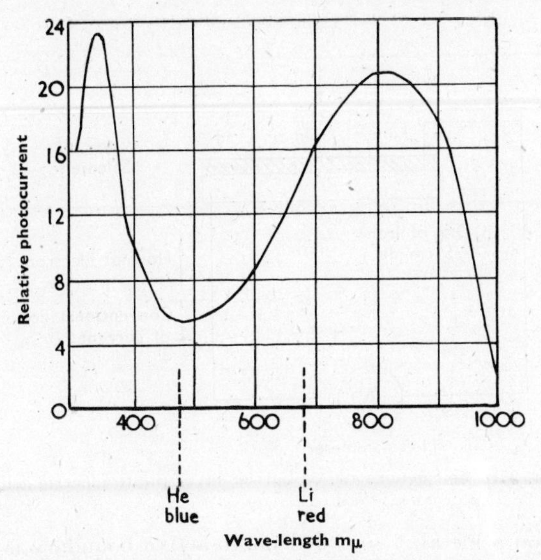

FIG. 377. Sensitivity curve of caesium/caesium oxide/silver photo-electric cell. Figs. 377 and 379 are from M. D. Hedgcock and R. Mayorcas, *J. Iron and Steel Inst.*, 1948, 158, 236.

The alkali metals, such as potassium and sodium, are sensitive to white light, and are used in this type of cell. Most other metals are only sensitive to shorter wave-lengths. Frequently a combination surface is used, which has different sensitivity from the components separately. Thus in the caesium vacuum cell, the cathode is of silver covered with a film of caesium oxide and on which is deposited a film of caesium. The photo-electric effect in this case is due to caesium, oxygen and silver (Fig. 377). This cell has been used in industrial pyrometry.

The sensitivity of emission cells is increased by the introduction of small amounts of various gases. By this means the current due to any specific conditions of illumination is increased through ionisation of the gas by the emitted electrons, and thus a greater number of electrons is produced. However, such gas-filled cells are not quite so accurate as the vacuum cells.

(2) **Self-generative cells.** These are so named because no applied potential is necessary to produce the photo-current. Further, amplification may not be necessary. The cells are also known as blocking-layer, barrier-layer, or rectifier cells. The photo-sensitive material is a semi-conductor. If a thin film of a semi-conductor is

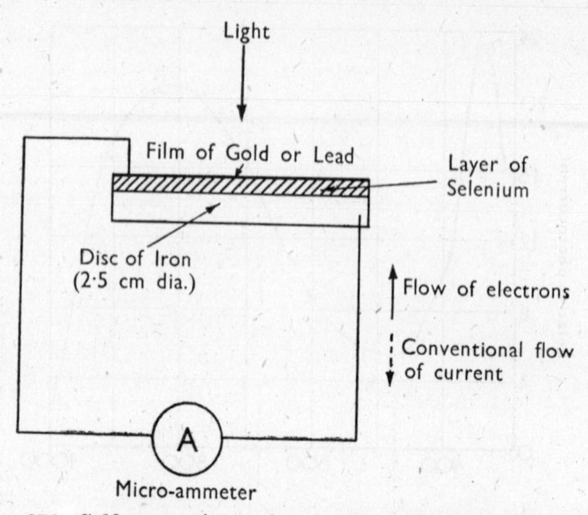

FIG. 378. Self-generative or barrier-layer photo-electric cell.

deposited on a metal, a so-called photo-active boundary is formed. When this is illuminated, a current flows, the electrons moving through it from the semi-conductor to the metal. If connection is made to the two materials, the current can be measured ; it increases with the intensity of illumination, the relation being nearly linear.

A great advantage of this type of cell is that no evacuated glass chamber is required. The cells are simple, sturdy, and cheap. In the type used for pyrometry, selenium is used as the semi-conductor (Figs. 378 and 379). The cell consists essentially of a disc of iron (about 2·5 cm. in diameter) on which is a thin layer of selenium ; on top of the selenium is deposited a thin transparent metallic film, for example, gold or lead. Electrical contacts are made with the metal film and the iron base. The photo-active boundary is between the film of metal and the selenium. Electrons travel in the opposite direction to the light which passes through the film.

(3) **Conductivity cells.** These cells employ a semi-conductor to which a potential is applied, and the increase in conductivity with increase in intensity of illumination is measured. These cells as yet have had no industrial pyrometric application ; but one type using lead sulphide has been shown to be suitable for temperature measurements in the range from 500° to at least 200° C.

Photo-cell arrangements in pyrometry. Although the photo-electric cell is the most recently applied of the radiation pyrometers described, it has been shown to give satisfactory service in a number of applications. The best emission and self-generative cells in use

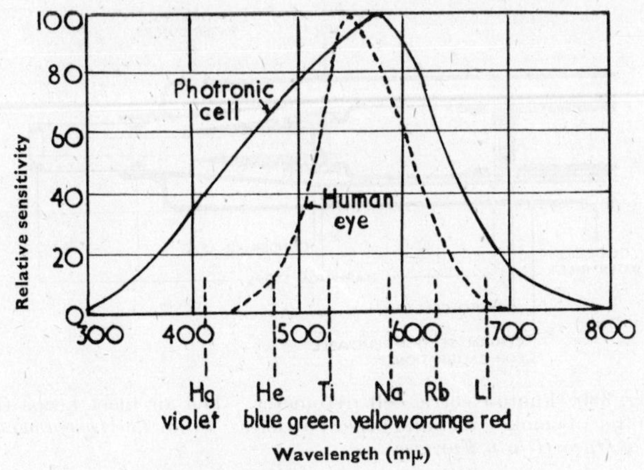

FIG. 379. Sensitivity curve of selenium self-generative cell. From Hodgcock and Mayorcas.

are capable of long and reliable service with virtually no attendance. The speed of response is extremely rapid, being a few thousandths of a second, thus making the cells especially suitable for measurements on moving metal. There need be little or no "after creep" or lag, so a final reading is quickly reached.

The current can be measured by moving-coil micro-ammeters. Amplification is necessary for the emission cells and is recommended for the self-generative cells below about 1000° C. It is possible to arrange the cell in series with a fixed resistance, and measure the current indirectly by potentiometric methods. Continuous recording and control can be arranged. A current-measuring instrument with a high speed of response is necessary to utilise fully the quick response of the cells themselves, when they are being used on fast-moving objects.

The pyrometer is usually mounted and fixed for operation. The photo-cell should be so arranged that its face is illuminated only with radiation from the hot body; no extraneous radiation or daylight should be allowed to fall on it. A typical arrangement is shown in Fig. 380. By means of a lens an image of the hot body is thrown on the diaphragm in front of the cell, giving a field of constant size. The lens also protects the cell from damage, for example, by splashing metal; replacement of the lens is easy. (In some cases a lens is not used). The cell tends to be heated by the rays falling on it, although heating is reduced by the diaphragms and the lens (glass absorbs radiation longer than about $2{\cdot}5\mu$ in wave-length); a filter

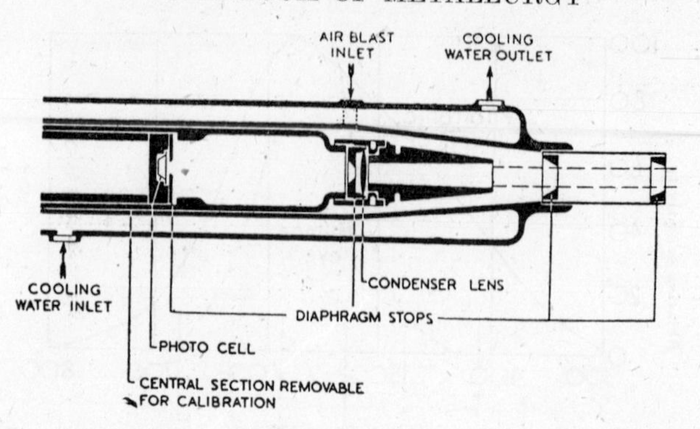

Fig. 380. Photo-electric cell pyrometer. The air blast keeps the tube free of smoke, dust and other particles. From *The Instrumentation of Open-Hearth Furnaces.*

is sometimes also used. The cell characteristics are likely to be altered if the cell temperature rises too much. Water-cooling of the instrument may be necessary if the cell tends to overheat due to the absorbed energy, or if the temperature of the surroundings is high.

Emissivity values are not available for the range of wave-lengths to which photo-electric cells respond (Figs. 377 and 379); but in their absence it has been pointed out the figures used for the disappearing-filament pyrometer should give moderate accuracy, especially for the selenium self-generative cell.

An advantage which the photo-electric cell has, in common with the disappearing-filament pyrometer over the total radiation type, is that the response varies according to a higher power of temperature. Hence absorption by intervening atmosphere has less effect. Moreover, such interference is less likely to occur (Fig. 374).

Applications of radiation pyrometers. The particular field of radiation pyrometry is for high-temperature measurements beyond the range of thermo-couples; it is also for positions not well suited to thermo-couples, provided, of course, the temperature is sufficient for radiation techniques. A notable example of the latter is for solid metal, such as at various stages during hot working. Disappearing-filament pyrometers, especially, are regularly used for checking the temperature of heated steel ingots. Photo-electric and high-speed total radiation pyrometers, in addition, are being applied to moving metal during hot-working. An interesting application of the photo-electric pyrometer is in the electric resistance-heating of steel billets for forging; the cell is sighted on the metal and by means of a relay it causes the current to be switched off when the desired temperature is reached. Radiation pyrometers are generally more suitable than thermo-couples for estimating the temperature of parts such as furnace roofs and regenerator brickwork.

A useful application is for checking the temperature of the metal-pouring stream from a furnace; typical examples are copper from the refining reverberatory, steel from the open-hearth furnace and pig iron from the blast-furnace. Radiation methods may be applied in some cases to a bath of molten metal; a method of obtaining black body conditions by sighting down a tube immersed in the metal has already been mentioned.

For accurate measurement of gas temperature, the radiation pyrometer should be sighted on a tube which is shielded from the flue walls and over which the gas is aspirated, as in the arrangement with a thermo-couple.

ADDITIONAL READING

1. *Pyrometry*, by W. P. Wood and J. M. Cork. (2nd Edit., 1941. McGraw-Hill).

2. *Methods of Measuring Temperatures*, by E. Griffiths. (3rd Edit., Griffin, 1947).

3. *Temperature. Its Measurement and Control in Science and Industry.* American Institute of Physics. (Rheinhold Pub. Corp., 1941).

4. *Heat and Temperature Measurement*, by R. L. Weber. (Prentice-Hall, 1950).

5. *The Pyrometry of Solids and Surfaces*, by R. B. Sosman. (American Society for Metals, 1940).

6. *Temperature Measurement.* British Standard Code 1041 : 1943. (British Standards Institution).

7. *Surface Temperature Measurements*, by M. D. Hedgcock and R. Mayorcas. *J. Iron and Steel Inst.*, **158**, 236, (1948).

8. *Pyrometers for Surface-Temperature*, by M. D. Drury, K. P. Perry and T. Land. *J. Iron and Steel Inst.*, **169**, 245, (1951).

9. *Measurement and Control of Temperatures in Smelting, Refining and Melting Non-Ferrous Metals*, by P. H. Dike and M. J. Bradley. Pp. 1–47 of *Non-Ferrous Melting Practice.* (Institute of Metals Div. Symposium Series. American Institute of Mining and Metallurgical Engineers, 1946).

10. *The Instrumentation of Open-Hearth Furnaces.* British Iron and Steel Research Assoc. (George Allen & Unwin, 1951).

11. *A Photo-Electric Roof Pyrometer for Open-Hearth Furnaces*, by T. Land. *J. Iron and Steel Inst.*, **155**, 568, (1947).

The following deal with the development of the Quick Immersion (Precious Metal) Thermo-couple for Liquid Steel.

12. First Report of Liquid Steel Temperature Sub-Committee (Seventh Report on the Heterogenity of Steel Ingots). Iron and Steel Institute, 1937. Special Report, No. 16, pp. 215–238.

13. Second Report of Liquid Steel Temperature Sub-Committee (Eighth Report on the Heterogenity of Steel Ingots). Iron and Steel Inst., 1939. Special Report, No. 25, pp. 235–264.

14. Third Report of Liquid Steel Temperature Sub-Committee. *J. Iron and Steel Inst.*, **145**, 213*P*, (1942).

15. *Improvement in Design of Immersion Pyrometers for Liquid-Steel Temperatures*, by D. Manterfield and J. K. Thurston, *J. Iron and Steel Inst.*, **154**, 61*P*, (1946).

16. *A Symposium on the Contamination of Platinum Thermocouples*, by the Liquid Steel Temperature Sub-Committee. *J. Iron and Steel Inst.*, **155**, 213, (1947).

17. *Continuous Temperature Measurement of Liquid Steel*, by D. Hardwick and H. Everard, *J. Iron and Steel Inst.*, **166**, 147, (1950).

18. *A Period Immersion Pyrometer*, by R. F. Wright, E. Scorah, T. Land and R. Barber. *J. Iron and Steel Inst.*, **169**, 243, (1951).

19. *The Quick-Immersion Thermocouple for Liquid Steel*, by D. Manterfield, J. D. Cresswell and H. Herne. *J. Iron and Steel Inst.*, **172**, 387, (1952).

20. References to the use of pyrometers in the determination of equilibrium diagrams are given at the end of Chapter 6.

APPENDIX I

ELEMENTS AND THEIR ELECTRON GROUPS

TABLE 67

Element		Electrons						Atomic Number
		Set 1	Set 2	Set 3	Set 4	Set 5	Set 6	
Hydrogen - -	H	1						1
Helium - - -	He	2						2
Lithium - -	Li	2	1					3
Beryllium - -	Be	2	2					4
Boron - - -	B	2	3					5
Carbon - - -	C	2	4					6
Nitrogen - -	N	2	5					7
Oxygen - - -	O	2	6					8
Fluorine - -	F	2	7					9
Neon - - -	Ne	2	8					10
Sodium - - -	Na	2	8	1				11
Magnesium - -	Mg	2	8	2				12
Aluminium - -	Al	2	8	3				13
Silicon - - -	Si	2	8	4				14
Phosphorus - -	P	2	8	5				15
Sulphur - -	S	2	8	6				16
Chlorine - -	Cl	2	8	7				17
Argon - - -	A	2	8	8				18
Potassium - -	K	2	8	8	1			19
Calcium - -	Ca	2	8	8	2			20
Scandium - -	Sc	2	8	9	2			21
Titanium - -	Ti	2	8	10	2			22
Vanadium - -	V	2	8	11	2			23
Chromium - -	Cr	2	8	13	1			24
Manganese - -	Mn	2	8	13	2			25
Iron - - -	Fe	2	8	14	2			26
Cobalt - - -	Co	2	8	15	2			27
Nickel - - -	Ni	2	8	16	2			28
Copper - - -	Cu	2	8	18	1			29
Zinc - - -	Zn	2	8	18	2			30
Gallium - -	Ga	2	8	18	3			31
Germanium - -	Ge	2	8	18	4			32

TABLE 67—*Continued*

Element		Electrons						Atomic Number
		Set 1	Set 2	Set 3	Set 4	Set 5	Set 6	
Arsenic - - -	As	2	8	18	5			33
Selenium - -	Se	2	8	18	6			34
Bromine - -	Br	2	8	18	7			35
Krypton - -	Kr	2	8	18	8			36
Rubidium - -	Rb	2	8	18	8	1		37
Strontium - -	Sr	2	8	18	8	2		38
Yttrium - -	Yt	2	8	18	9	2		39
Zirconium - -	Zr	2	8	18	10	2		40
Niobium - -	Nb	2	8	18	12	1		41
Molybdenum - -	Mo	2	8	18	13	1		42
Masurium - -	Ma	2	8	18	14	1		43
Ruthenium - -	Ru	2	8	18	15	1		44
Rhodium - -	Rh	2	8	18	16	1		45
Palladium - -	Pd	2	8	18	18	—		46
Silver - - -	Ag	2	8	18	18	1		47
Cadmium - -	Cd	2	8	18	18	2		48
Indium - - -	In	2	8	18	18	3		49
Tin - - -	Sn	2	8	18	18	4		50
Antimony - -	Sb	2	8	18	18	5		51
Tellurium - -	Te	2	8	18	18	6		52
Iodine - - -	I	2	8	18	18	7		53
Xenon - - -	Xe	2	8	18	18	8		54
Caesium - -	Cs	2	8	18	18	8	1	55
Barium - - -	Ba	2	8	18	18	8	2	56
Lanthanum - -	La	2	8	18	18	9	2	57
Cerium - - -	Ce	2	8	18	19	9	2	58
Praseodymium -	Pr	2	8	18	20	9	2	59
Neodymium - -	Nd	2	8	18	21	9	2	60
Promethium (Illinium) - -	Il	2	8	18	22	9	2	61
Samarium - -	Sm	2	8	18	23	9	2	62
Europium - -	Eu	2	8	18	24	9	2	63
Gadolinium - -	Gd	2	8	18	25	9	2	64
Terbium - -	Tb	2	8	18	26	9	2	65
Dysprosium - -	Ds	2	8	18	27	9	2	66
Holmium - -	Ho	2	8	18	28	9	2	67
Erbium - - -	Er	2	8	18	29	9	2	68
Thulium - -	Tm	2	8	18	30	9	2	69
Ytterbium - -	Yb	2	8	18	31	9	2	70
Lutetium - -	Lu	2	8	18	32	9	2	71
Hafnium - -	Hf	2	8	18	32	10	2	72
Tantalum - -	Ta	2	8	18	32	11	2	73
Tungsten - -	W	2	8	18	32	12	2	74

TABLE 67—*Continued*

Element		Electrons							At. No.
		Set 1	Set 2	Set 3	Set 4	Set 5	Set 6	Set 7	
Rhenium - -	Re	2	8	18	32	13	2		75
Osmium - -	Os	2	8	18	32	14	2		76
Iridium - - -	Ir	2	8	18	32	15	2		77
Platinum - -	Pt	2	8	18	32	16	2		78
Gold - - -	Au	2	8	18	32	18	1		79
Mercury - -	Hg	2	8	18	32	18	2		80
Thallium - -	Tl	2	8	18	32	18	3		81
Lead - - -	Pb	2	8	18	32	18	4		82
Bismuth - -	Bi	2	8	18	32	18	5		83
Polonium - -	Po	2	8	18	32	18	6		84
Astatine - -		2	8	18	32	18	7		85
Radon or radium emanation - -	Rn	2	8	18	32	18	8		86
Francium - -		2	8	18	32	18	8	1	87
Radium - -	Ra	2	8	18	32	18	8	2	88
Actinium - -	Ac	2	8	18	32	18	9	2	89
Thorium - -	Th	2	8	18	32	18	10	2	90
Protactinium -	Pa	2	8	18	32	18	11	2	91
Uranium - -	U	2	8	18	32	18	12	2	92
Neptunium - -	Np								93
Plutonium - -	Pu								94
Americium - -	Am								95
Curium - - -	Cm								96
Berkelium - -	Bk								97
Californium - -	Cf								98

APPENDIX 2

EQUILIBRIUM DIAGRAMS OF IMPORTANT BINARY ALLOY SYSTEMS

Figs. 381, 383, 385–388, and 390–392 are by courtesy of The Copper Development Association. **Note: composition is plotted as percentage by weight.**

Figs. 382, 389, 393, 394, 396, 399 and 400 are reproduced by permission from *Metals Handbook*, 1948 Edit. Amer. Soc. for Metals.

Figs. 384, 397 and 398 are by courtesy of the Institute of Metals.

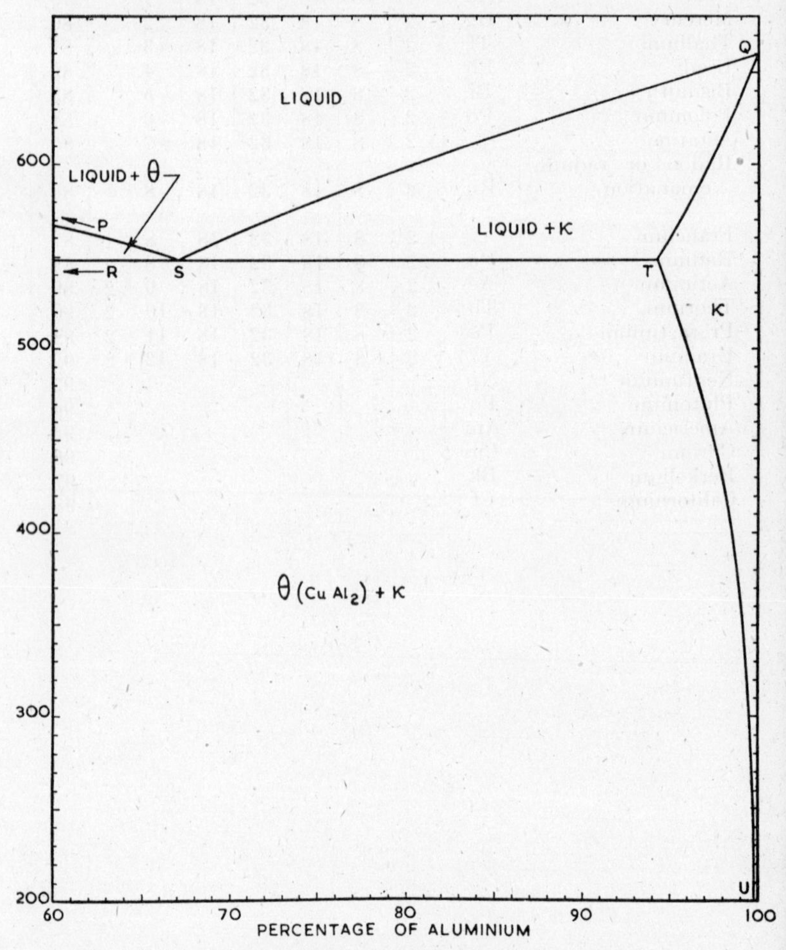

Fig. 381. Aluminium-copper.

One microstructure is shown on p. 79.

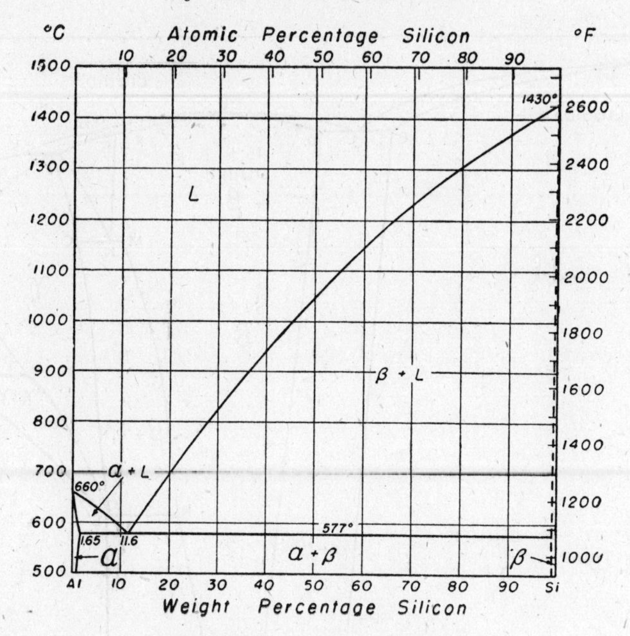

FIG. 382. Aluminium-silicon.

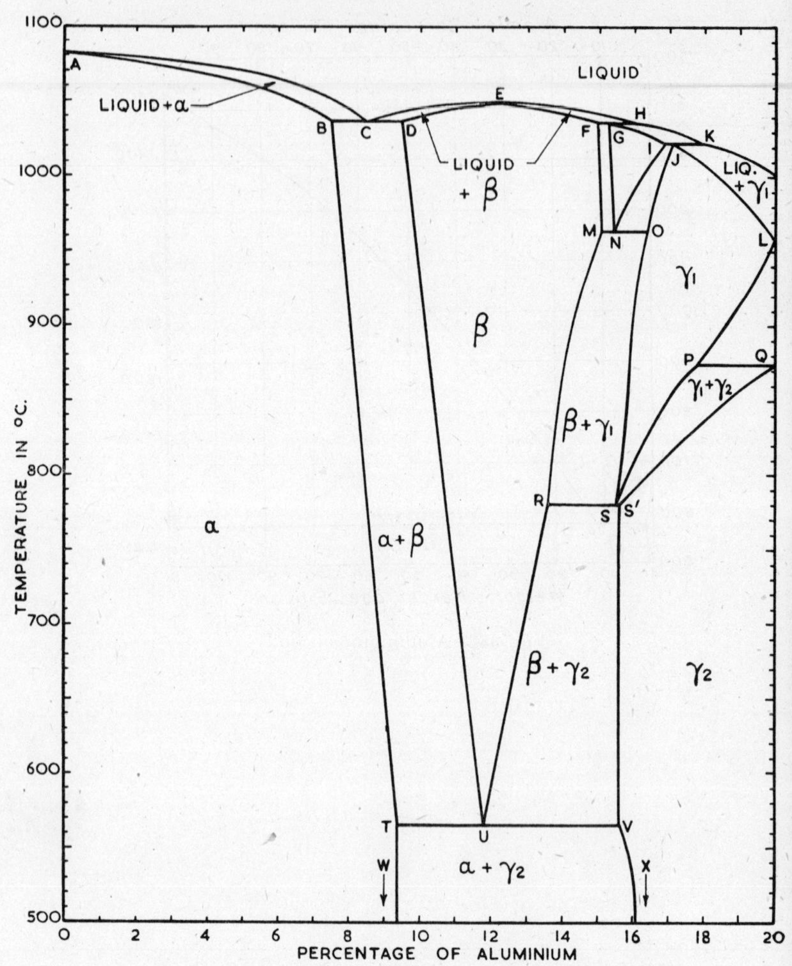

FIG. 383. Copper-aluminium.
Some microstructures are shown on p. 82.

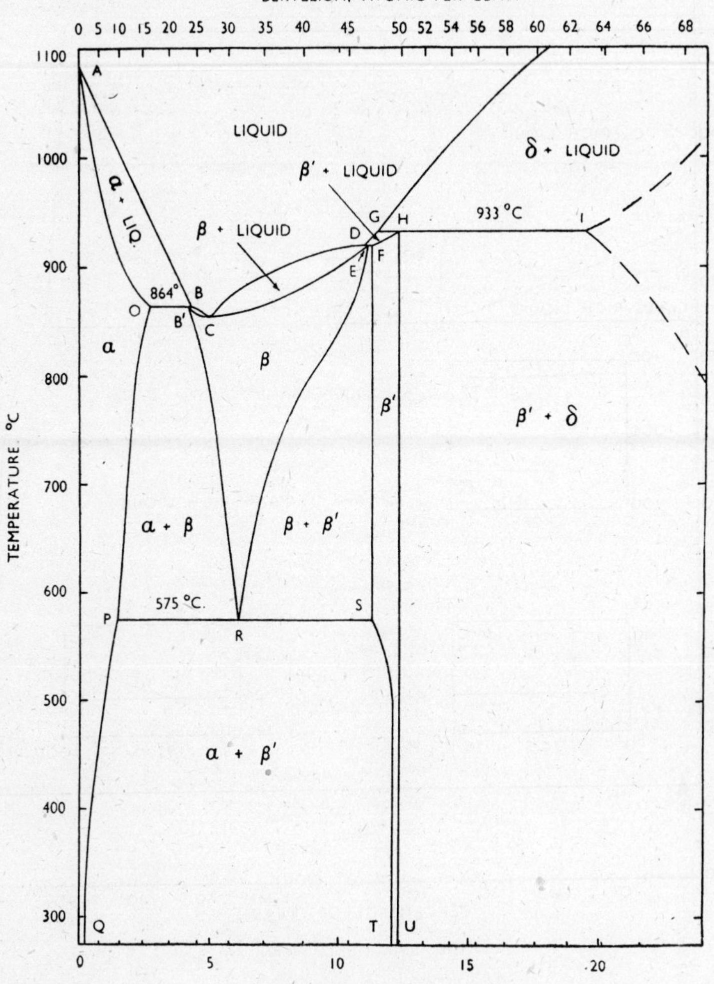

FIG. 384. Copper-beryllium.
One microstructure is shown on p. 78.

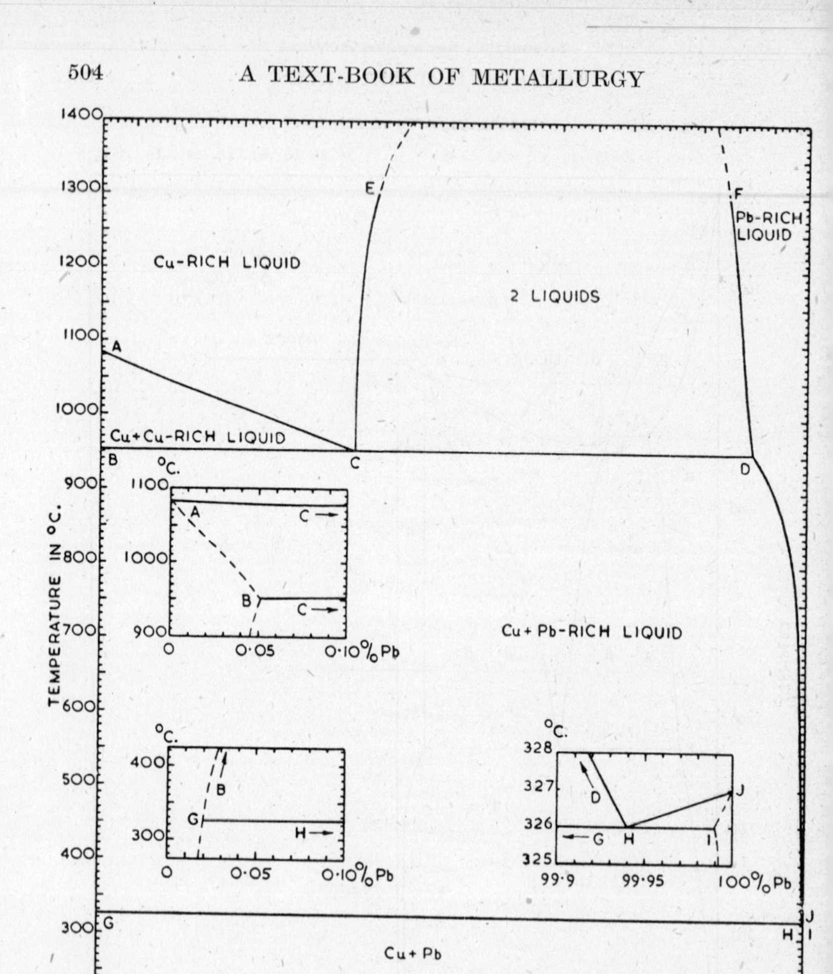

FIG. 385. Copper-lead.

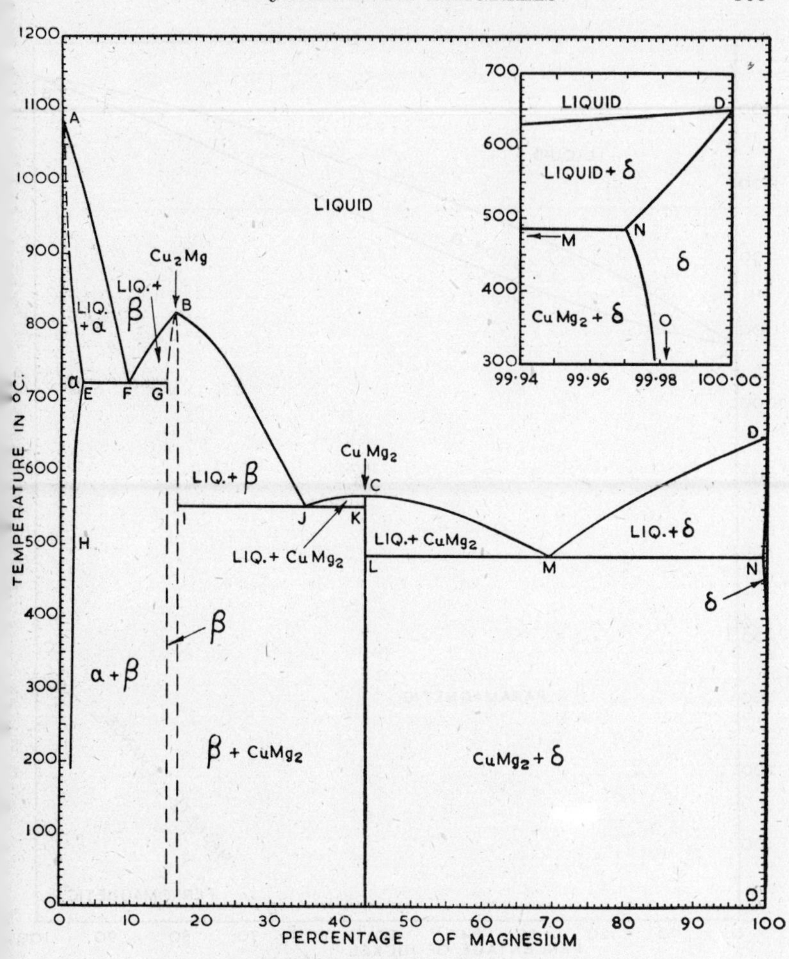

Fig. 386. Copper-magnesium.
One microstructure is shown on p. 71.

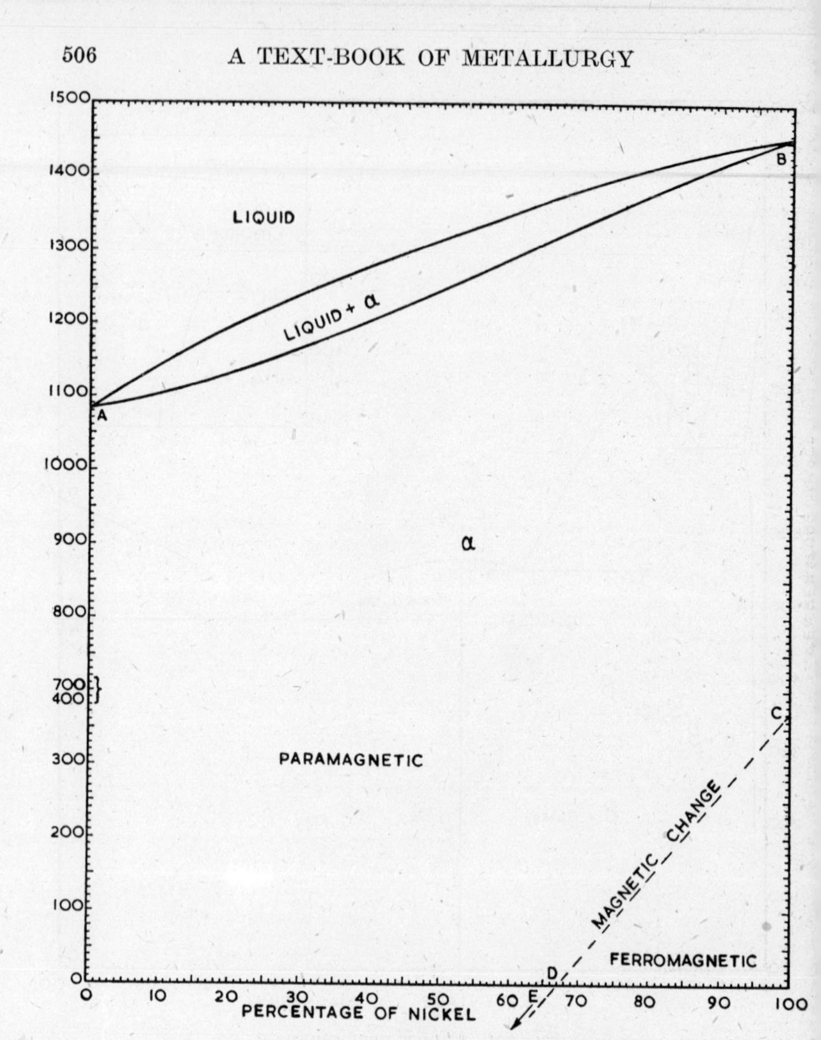

Fig. 387. Copper-nickel.
One microstructure is shown on p. 56,

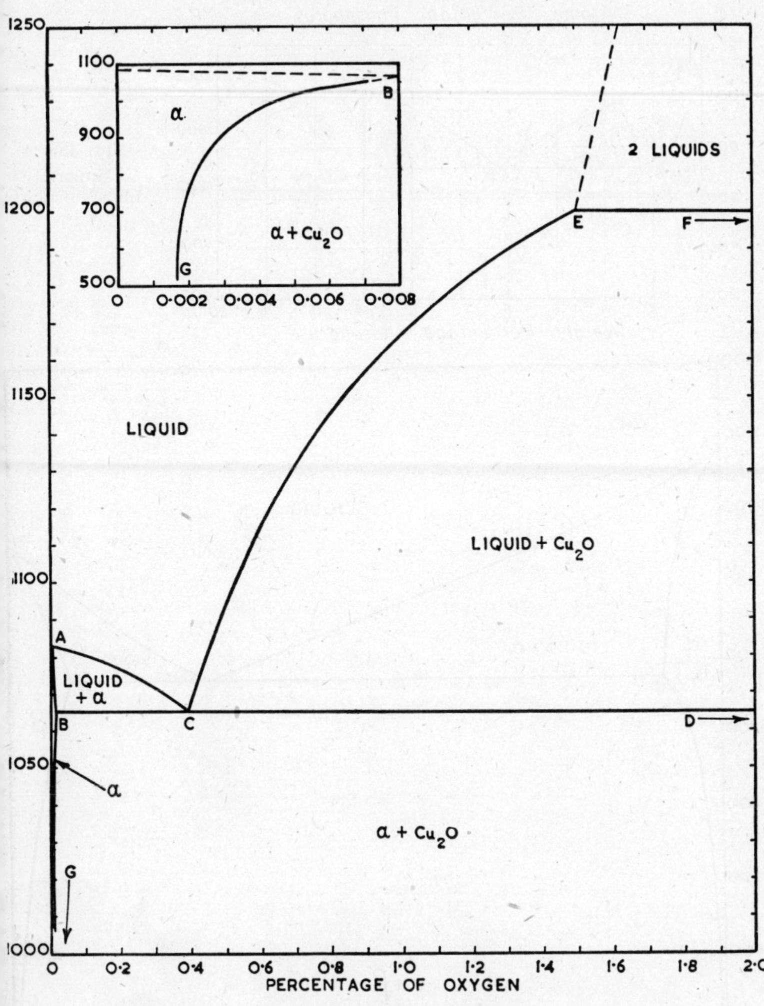

FIG. 388. Copper-oxygen.

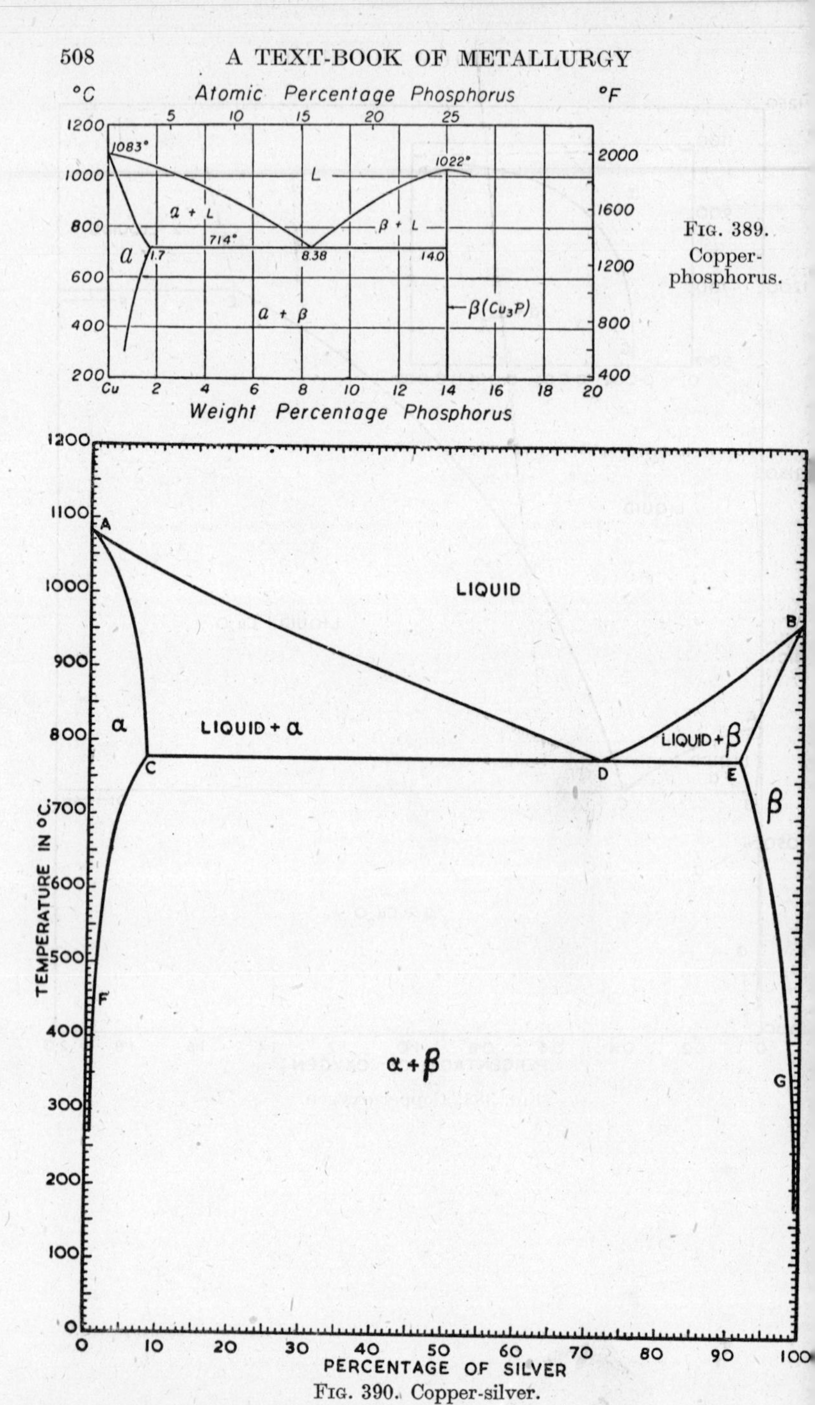

Fig. 389. Copper-phosphorus.

Fig. 390. Copper-silver.

Typical microstructures of copper-silver alloys are shown on p. 60.

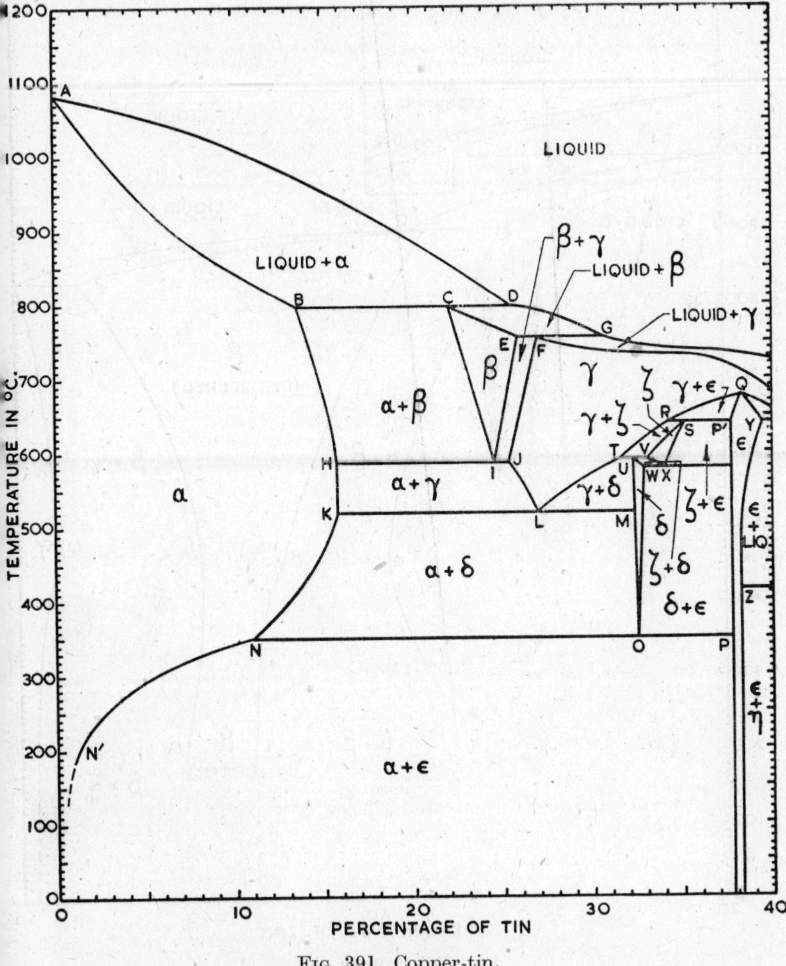

FIG. 391. Copper-tin.

Note: the marked decrease in solid solubility of tin in copper, represented by *KNN′*, is only obtained by long annealing

Typical microstructures of copper-tin alloys are shown on pp. 56, 83, 112 and 386.

For the constitution of tin-rich alloys, see Fig. 190, p. 244.

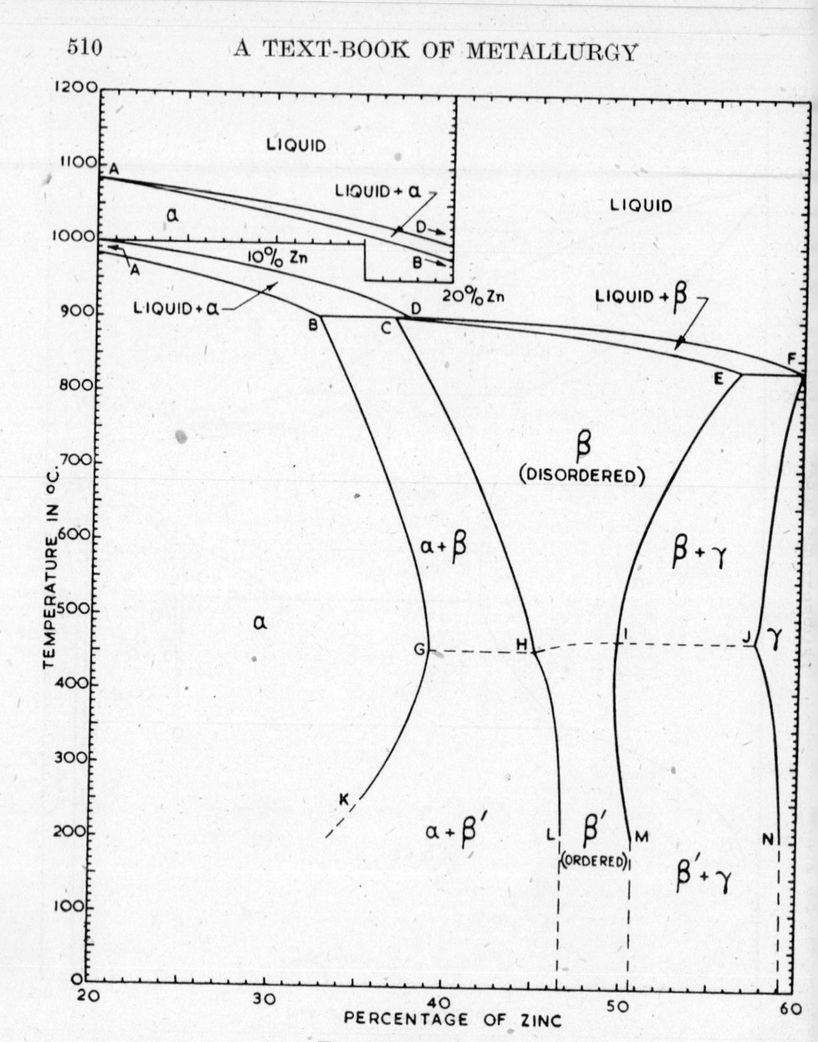

FIG. 392. Copper-zinc.

Typical microstructures are shown on pp. 57, 63, 78, 113 and 114.

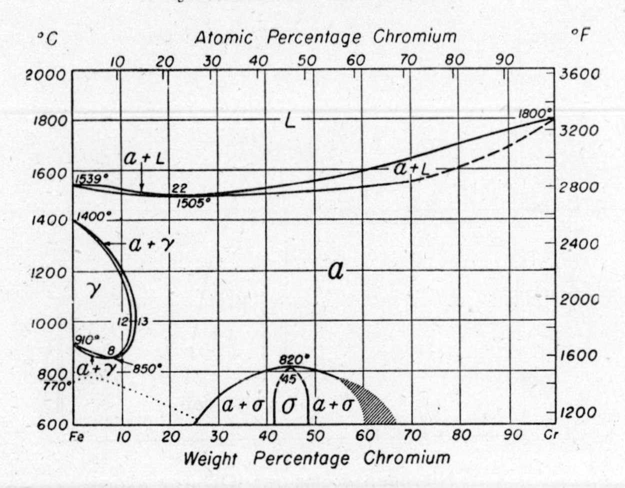

FIG. 393. Iron-chromium.

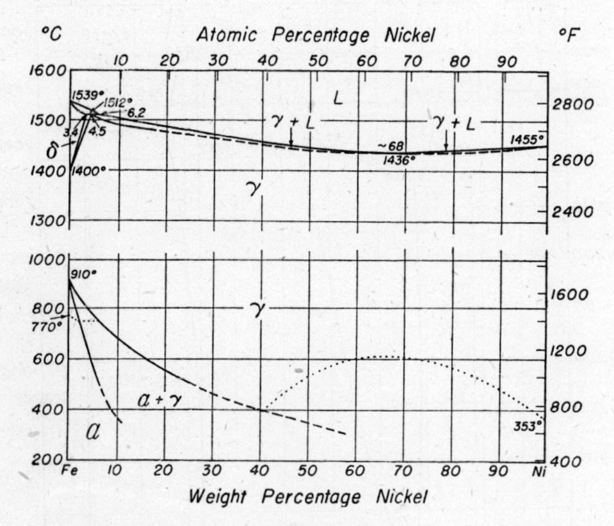

FIG. 394. Iron-nickel.

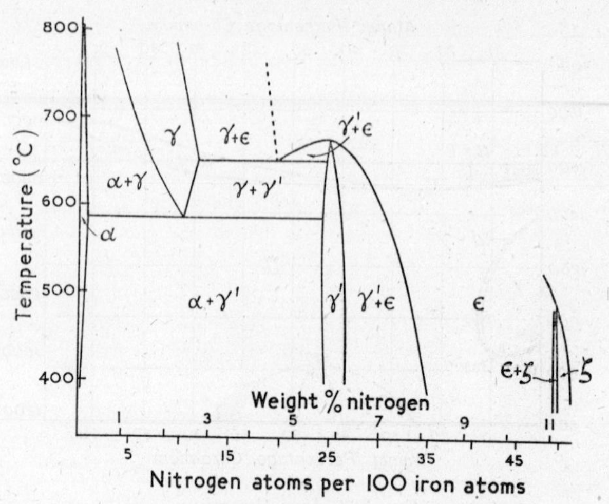

FIG. 395. Iron-nitrogen. (After K. H. Jack.)

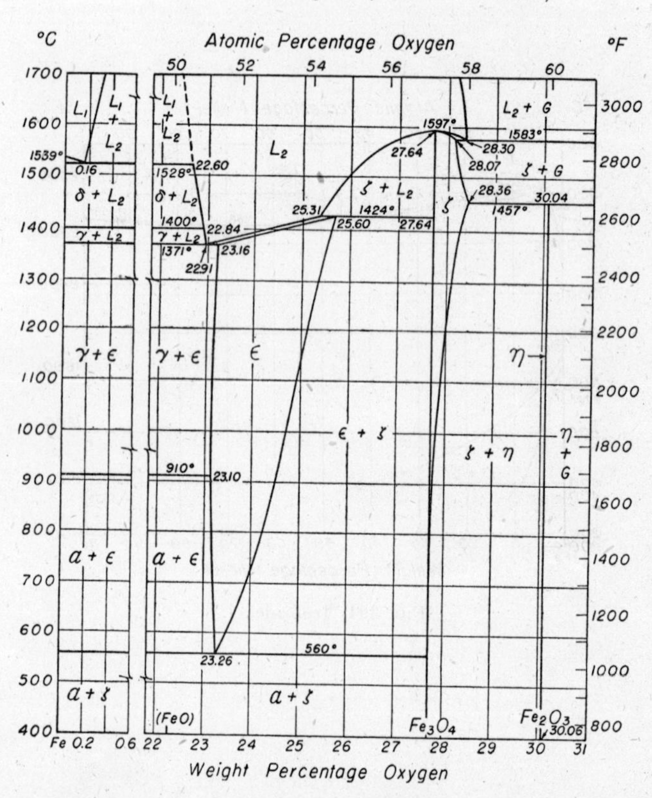

FIG. 396. Iron-oxygen.

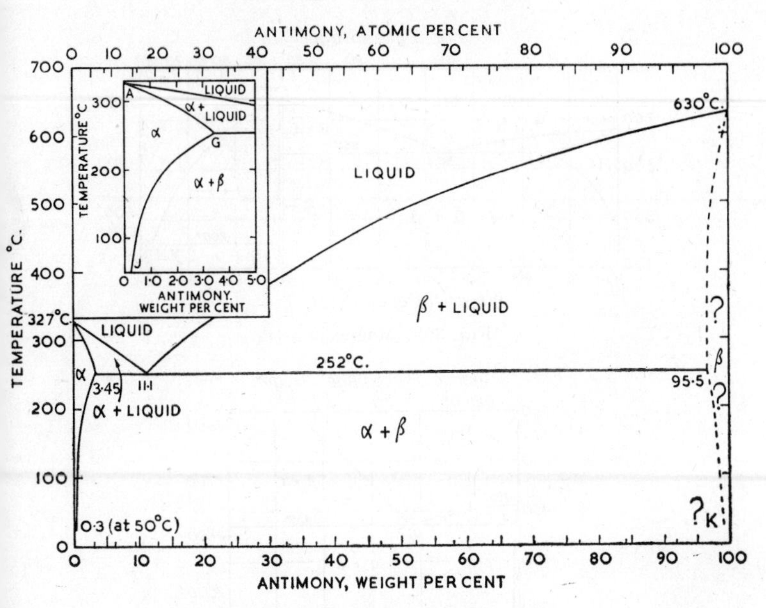

FIG. 397. Lead-antimony.

Typical microstructures are shown on p. 60.

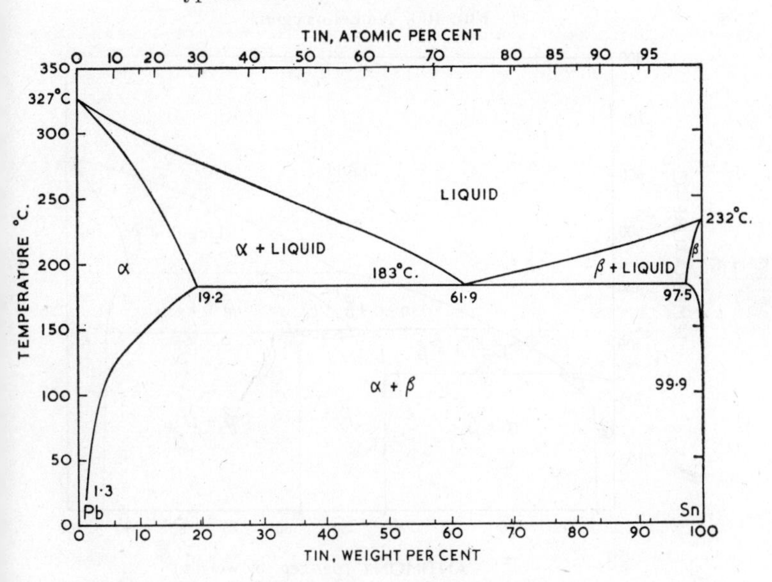

FIG. 398. Lead-tin.

One microstructure is shown on p. 71.

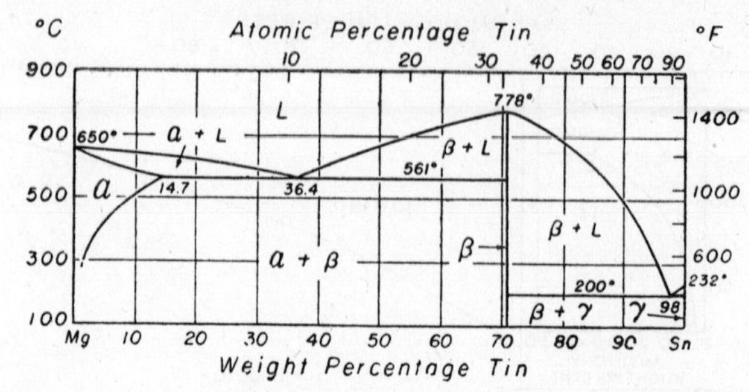

FIG. 399. Magnesium-tin.

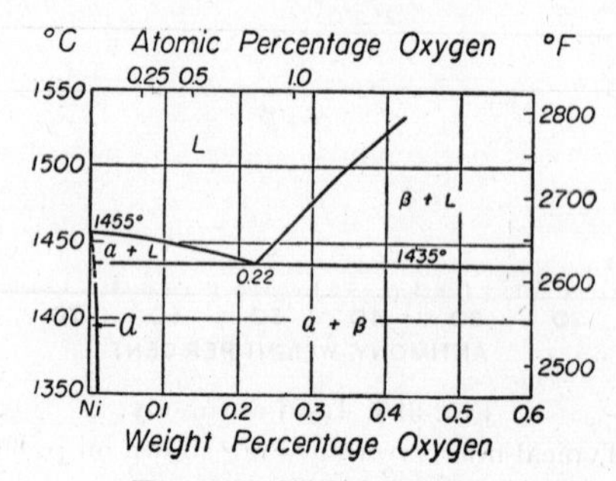

FIG. 400. Nickel-oxygen.

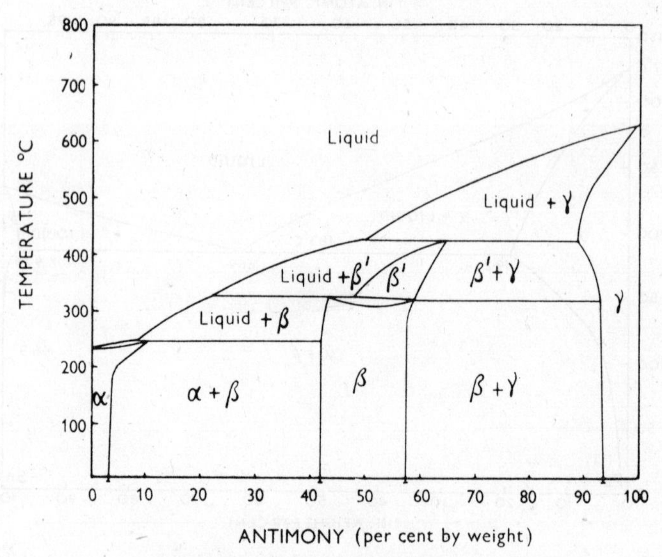

FIG. 401. Tin-antimony.
(By courtesy of The Tin Research Inst.)
Typical microstructures are shown on pp. 58 and 69.

QUESTIONS

The following questions are selected from examination papers by kind permission of the university and other authorities indicated.

The letters R.R. following B.Sc. (Met.) Lond. indicate that the questions have been set in examinations under the present Revised Regulations.

Questions from papers set by other universities are clearly indicated in the abbreviations adopted.

The following abbreviations are also used:

L.I.M.	Licentiateship of the Institution of Metallurgists.
A.I.M.	Associateship of the Institution of Metallurgists.
C. and G. Inter.	City and Guilds of London Institute, Intermediate Examination.
C. and G. Adv.	City and Guilds of London Institute, Advanced Examination.
N.C.	Northern Counties Technical Examinations Council. Metallurgy is in the fourth and final year of the course, and corresponds to ordinary National Certificate level.
E.M.E.U.	East Midland Educational Union. Metallurgy is in the third and final year of the course and corresponds to ordinary National Certificate level.
U.L.C.I.	Union of Lancashire and Cheshire Institutes. Metallurgy is in the third year of the course and corresponds to ordinary National Certificate level.

Unless otherwise stated, the questions are from 3-hour papers in which the candidate is asked to attempt five or six or occasionally four questions.

Chapter 3

1. What are metals and in what respects do they differ from non-metals? [B.Sc. (Met.) Lond. Pt. I]
2. Write a concise essay on " The crystalline nature of solid metallic materials ". [B.Sc. (Met.) Lond. Pt. I]
3. Write an essay on " Metallic Solid Solutions ". [C. and G. Adv.]

4. Discuss the factors which govern the mutual solid solubility of metals. [A.I.M.]
5. Discuss the factors governing the formation of intermediate phases in alloy systems. [L.I.M. and A.I.M.]
6. Write a short essay on intermetallic compounds. [B. Met. (Hons.) Sheffield]
7. Describe the characteristics of intermetallic compounds, explaining how they differ from ordinary chemical compounds. How may the presence of an intermetallic compound modify the properties of an alloy? [Met. for Eng. Terminal Exam. Univ. Birmingham]
8. Write a short essay on " Intermediate Phases in Alloy Systems ". [B.Sc. (Met.) Birmingham Third Exam.]
9. What is meant by the term " electron compound "? Illustrate the answer by reference to the intermediate phases of the copper-zinc and copper-tin alloy systems. [Degree Final Univ. Wales]
10. What are metallic solid solutions? Why are some pairs of metals mutually soluble in the solid state to a much greater extent than others? Why do some pairs of metals form inter-metallic compounds as well as or instead of solid solutions? [B.Sc. (Met.) Lond. Pt. 1]
11. Discuss and compare the following types of solid solutions:
    (*a*) Interstitial;
    (*b*) Substitutional (random);
    (*c*) Substitutional (ordered).

    Why do some pairs of metals form intermediate constituents as well as or instead of primary solid solutions? [B.Sc. (Met.) Lond. Pt. 1.]
12. Discuss the factors which govern the formation of metallic crystals, substitutional solid solutions and intermediate phases in binary alloys. [Hons. Degree, Univ. Wales]
13. Write an essay on " The Crystal Lattice Structures of Metals and Alloys ". [C. and G. Adv.]

Chapter 4

1. Describe the various kinds of microstructures that may be observed in binary alloys containing an eutectic, indicating the effects of the rate of solidification. [B.Sc. (Met.) Lond. Pt. 1.]
2. Describe the mode of solidification of a pure metal melted and allowed to solidify in a crucible without agitation. How would the behaviour of a single phase alloy of the Cu-Ni type differ from that of a pure metal in these circumstances? [B.Sc. (Eng.) Birmingham]

3. Explain what is meant by a "peritectic reaction". Sketch the type of equilibrium diagram involved and describe the mode of solidification of typical alloys. [B.Sc. (Eng.) Birmingham]

4. Explain the mechanism of coreing.
[B.Met. Sheffield Final Exam.]

5. Eutectic structures as observed under the microscope take various forms. Describe these with the aid of sketches and comment upon the different types. [B.Sc. (Met.) Lond. Pt. 1]

6. How are Widmanstätten structures produced? Comment upon their formation and structure.
[B.Sc. (Met.) Lond. Pt. 1]

7. Sketch and describe the main types of eutectic structures appearing in binary alloys. To what extent do the properties of the component metals appear to account for these structures?
[B.Sc. (Met.) Lond. Pt. 1]

8. Define the term eutectic. Given two metals which form a simple binary eutectic system, how could you produce structures containing eutectic? Describe these possible structures and indicate what would be the effect of subsequent heat treatment on them.
[B.Sc. Birmingham Second Met. Exam.]

9. Two metals, A and B, are used to form an alloy containing 75 per cent A, and 25 per cent B. A melts at 600 deg. C. and B at 400 deg. C. When alloyed together these metals form no compounds or solid solutions, but form an eutectic at 40 per cent A, and 60 per cent B. Assume that the liquidus lines are straight. The eutectic solidifies at 250 deg. C. The specific gravity of A is 2·0, and that of B 7·0.
Find :
   (*a*) The temperature at which the alloy will begin to crystallise from the melt and at which the melt will be completely solid.
   (*b*) The percentage of the eutectic in the alloy at room temperature.
   (*c*) The percentage of the solid in the alloy at 300 deg. C.
   (*d*) The specific gravity of the alloy.

   Sketch the typical microstructure of such an alloy. (Squared paper is available.) [B.Sc. (Met.) Lond. Pt. 1]

10. Discuss the effects of rapid cooling from the liquid state on the structure of binary alloys. [L.I.M. and A.I.M.]

11. Describe the possible reactions that may occur in binary equilibrium systems and illustrate your answer by means of diagrams.
[L.I.M. and A.I.M.]

12. Show, by means of drawings and brief comments, that the typical binary metallic systems can be derived from one or two fundamental diagrams. [B.Met. Sheffield Final Exam.

13. Discuss methods of refining the crystal structure of a two-phase alloy. [B.Met. Sheffield Final Exam.]

14. Discuss the uses of the equilibrium diagram in the interpretation of cast structures in binary alloys.
[B.Sc. Birmingham Second Met. Exam.]

15. What are the possible general effects on the constitution of the binary alloy formed when a second metal (*B*) is added to a primary metal (*A*)? How may the quantity of the second metal affect the microstructure and properties of the resulting alloy?
[B.Sc. (Met.) Lond. Pt. 1]

16. Sketch the typical equilibrium diagram of a binary alloy system in which each metal lowers the melting point of the other, and both are mutually soluble to a limited extent in the solid state. Sketch and describe the characteristic microstructure of typical alloys of the series, assuming the samples to have been cut from chill cast bars of about half-an-inch diameter. What relationships would you expect to exist between the chemical composition of the alloys and their physical and mechanical properties?
[B.Sc. (Met.) Lond. Pt. 1]

17. Two metals *A* and *B* are miscible in all proportions in the liquid state, and each is soluble in the other to a limited extent in the solid state, this solubility decreasing as the temperature falls. *B* raises the melting point of *A*, whereas *A* lowers that of *B*. No intermediate constituent is formed.

Sketch the typical equilibrium diagram of such an alloy system.

Describe the changes that occur during the solidification and subsequent cooling of any alloy in the system that solidifies as a single phase but develops a duplex structure while cooling to room temperature, assuming equilibrium conditions. Illustrate your answer with sketches representing the microstructure of the alloy at different temperatures. What effects would chill casting be likely to have on the structure of the alloy?
[B.Sc. (Met.) Lond. Pt. 1]

18. Two metals, *A* and *B*, are miscible in all proportions in the liquid state, and partially soluble in one another in the solid state. The addition of metal *A* to metal *B* lowers the melting point of metal *B*, while the addition of metal *B* to metal *A* raises the melting point of metal *A*. The two metals form a compound, A_xB_y, in which both metals are partially soluble.

Sketch and label a typical equilibrium diagram for such an alloy system.

Show diagrammatically how you would expect (*a*) the hardness, and (*b*) the electrical conductivity of the alloys to be related to their chemical composition.
[B.Sc. (Met.) Lond. Pt. 1]

19. Two metals *A* and *B* are completely miscible in the liquid state and form an unbroken series of solid solutions on solidification. Both metals undergo allotropic transformations, which give rise to an eutectoid reaction.

    Sketch the typical equilibrium diagram of such an alloy system and describe the changes that occur during the solidification and subsequent cooling of an alloy in the system, assuming the cooling to be under (*a*) equilibrium, and (*b*) normal casting conditions. [C. and G. Adv.]

20. Sketch a typical equilibrium diagram of a binary alloy system in which one of the metals undergoes an allotropic transformation. Describe and explain the changes that occur during the solidification and subsequent cooling of any one alloy (belonging to the system) that contains two phases at room temperature when cast and allowed to cool under normal conditions, but consists of a homogeneous solid solution at room temperature under equilibrium conditions.

    [B.Sc. (Met.) Lond. Imp. Coll. Sci. and Tech.]

21. Two metals " A " and " B " are partially soluble in one another in the liquid state. Sketch a typical equilibrium diagram for such a system, and describe the changes that occur during the solidification and subsequent cooling of representative alloys.

    [C. and G. Adv.]

22. Two metals *A* and *B* are miscible in all proportions in the liquid state and form a continuous series of solid solutions on solidification. Between its melting point and room temperature, metal *A* undergoes an allotropic transformation, the temperature of which is lowered by metal *B*, reaching room temperature at a composition of 60% *A* and 40% *B*. At this temperature *B* is soluble to the extent of 25% in the low-temperature modification of *A*.

    Sketch the typical equilibrium diagram of such an alloy system. Describe the changes that occur during the solidification and subsequent cooling of any alloy in the system that has a duplex microstructure, assuming the alloy to cool (*a*) under equilibrium conditions and (*b*) under normal casting conditions.

    [B.Sc. (Met.) Lond. Pt. 1]

23. Some properties of two hypothetical metals, *A* and *B*, are listed below :

	Metal *A*	Metal *B*
Melting point, ° C.	1,000	700
Atomic Diameter (10^{-8} cm.)	2·9	2·6
Space Lattice Type	F.C.C.	B.C.C.
Valency	1	2
Hardness (D.P.N.)	50	15
Percentage Elongation Value	25	45

Sketch a typical equilibrium diagram which in your opinion accords with the information given above. Explain why you think the system might reasonably be assumed to have an equilibrium diagram of this type.

Show, diagrammatically, how you would expect the hardness and ductility of the alloys to be related to their chemical composition. [B.Sc. (Met.) Lond. Pt. 2 R.R.]

24. Some data relating to two hypothetical metals *A* and *B* are listed below :

	Metal A	*Metal B*
Freezing point (F.P.), ° C.	1,000	500
Effect of one metal on F.P. of other	F.P. lowered by *B*	F.P. raised by *A*
Atomic weight	60	70
Atomic diameter (10^{-8} cm.)	2·5	2·7
Space lattice type	F.C.C.	C.P.H.
Valency	1	2
Intermediate constituents	Only one based on compound *AB*	

Sketch a typical equilibrium diagram which, in your opinion accords with the information given above. Explain why you think the system might reasonably be assumed to have an equilibrium diagram of this type.

What type of space lattice do you think the intermediate constituent might have? Give your reasons. Would you expect it to be very hard and brittle?

[B.Sc. (Met.) Lond. Imp. Coll. Sci. and Tech.]

Chapter 5

1. Discuss briefly the relationship between stress and strain in metals and explain the mechanism of deformation.

[L.I.M. and A.I.M.]

2. Define (*a*) hot working, and (*b*) cold working. What are the effects of (i) hot working, and (ii) cold working on the structure and properties of metals? [C. and G. Adv.]

3. What information can be obtained from the tensile stress-strain diagram? Discuss the significance of any discontinuities that may occur. [B.Met. Sheffield Final Exam.]

4. Write a short account of the differences produced by plastic deformation on single crystals and polycrystalline materials.

[B.Sc. (Met.) Lond. Pt. 1]

5. Write an essay on the mechanism of plastic deformation in metals.

[A.I.M.]

6. Sketch and describe the typical microstructure of hard-drawn high-conductivity copper wire. Discuss the effects that would be

produced on the structure and properties of the wire by heating samples of it for various periods of time at various temperatures up to 700° C. [B.Sc. (Met.) Lond. Pt. 1]

7. What are the effects of cold work and subsequent annealing on metals and alloys? [C. and G. Adv.]

8. Discuss the effect of varying degrees of cold work on the microstructure and properties of any pure metal or single phase alloy. What changes take place on subsequent annealing at various temperatures? [B.Sc. (Met.) Lond. Pt. 2]

9. Write a short essay on cold deformation and recrystallisation in metals. [L.I.M. and A.I.M.]

10. Define the terms elasticity and plasticity. How is elasticity affected by plastic deformation in the case of lead and iron at room temperature and of iron at 1000° C.?
    Which metals are incapable of undergoing plastic deformation? [C. and G. Inter.]

11. How are the properties of a cold-worked metal affected by recrystallisation? Describe the recrystallisation process and the factors that influence it. [L.I.M. and A.I.M.]

12. What is understood by the terms " fatigue " and " creep " as applied to metallic materials? How may these properties be measured? [C. and G. Adv.]

13. Explain what is meant by the ultimate tensile strength, fatigue and creep of metals, and discuss their importance in the choice of engineering materials.
    [Met. for Eng. Terminal Exam. Univ. Birmingham]

Chapter 6

1. Describe the procedure employed in preparing metals for micro-examination. What special precautions would you take in preparing samples of lead and aluminium. [N.C.]

2. What precautions are necessary in the shaping, grinding, polishing and etching of metal specimens for metallographic examination? To what extent can the etched surface of a metal or alloy be considered to indicate its true structure.
   [B.Sc. (Met.) Lond. Pt. 1]

3. What precautions would you take in the preparation of specimens for micro-examination in cases in which (i) you wish to make a careful observation of the structure at the extreme edge, (ii) the specimen is known to contain a highly brittle constituent, (iii) the specimen is known to be a mixture of an extremely hard but not brittle constituent, and an extremely soft constituent? How would you prepare a sample of pure lead for micro-examination? [B.Sc. (Met.) Lond. Pt. 1]

4. Describe briefly the preparation of a metallic specimen for microscopical examination.

   Draw the following microstructures: (*a*) any pure metal as cast, (*b*) an elongated grain structure.

   What essential information should be given in relation to any microstructure? [U.L.C.I.]

5. Give an account of any important advance that has been made recently in the methods of preparing or examining metallic micro-sections. Explain why you think it an important advance. [B.Sc. (Met.) Lond. Pt. 1.]

6. Describe a method of electrolytic polishing. What advantages has this method over the normal methods used for polishing a micro-specimen? [B.Sc. (Met.) Lond. Pt. 1]

7. Explain the optical features of a metallurgical microscope with particular reference to its magnifying power and resolving power. [C. and G. Adv.]

8. Describe how a polished metal specimen may be illuminated for microscopical examination. What are the advantages of the various systems described? [B.Met. Sheffield Final Exam.]

9. Give a concise account of the optical features of a metallurgical microscope, explaining clearly what you understand by the following: numerical aperture, spherical aberration, and chromatic aberration. [L.I.M. and A.I.M.

10. Describe, with the aid of sketches, the optics of a metallurgical microscope. In what manner must the optical system be changed when ultra-violet illumination is used? [B.Sc. (Met.) Lond. Pt. 1]

11. It is required to examine visually a fine microstructure at a magnification of about 1,000 diameters. Describe in detail the optical features of a suitable microscope, giving reasons for your choice. [C. and G. Adv.]

12. Enumerate and discuss the factors that may influence resolution in photomicrography. [L.I.M. and A.I.M.]

13. Describe the essential features of an electron microscope and discuss the application of such an instrument to metallurgical problems. [B.Met. Sheffield Final Exam.]

14. Describe how you would determine the approximate diagram showing the relationship between the composition and temperature of a binary series of alloys. [Final Degree, Univ. Wales]

15. What physical determinations other than thermal can be used in the experimental determination of an equilibrium diagram? [B.Sc. (Met.) Lond. Pt. 1]

16. Describe the methods that you would use for determining the equilibrium diagram of an alloy system composed of two metals

which are mutually soluble to a limited extent in the solid state. Solid solubility limits are to be determined as accurately as possible. [C. and G. Adv.]

17. Give an account of the applications and of the limitations of thermal analysis, microscopic examination, X-ray analysis in investigating alloy systems. [A.I.M.]

18. Assume that you are unfamiliar with the aluminium-lithium equilibrium diagram. You are in charge of a well-equipped metallurgical laboratory, with several experienced assistants, and have been asked to determine this diagram with the greatest possible accuracy. Submit a preliminary scheme for the conduct of the investigation, commenting particularly on any special difficulties that you would expect to encounter, and on the steps that you would take to ensure accuracy.
B.Sc. (Met.) Lond. Pt. 1.]

19. What are the chief functions of :
(*a*) thermal analysis,
(*b*) microscopical examination,
and (*c*) X-ray analysis,
in the construction of equilibrium diagrams of alloy systems?
[C. and G. Adv.]

20. Give a concise account of recent developments in optical methods of examining metallic microsections.
[B.Sc. (Met.) Lond. Pt. 2 R.R.]

Chapter 7

1. Write a short essay on the nature and scope of mineral dressing operations. [C. and G. Adv.]

2. For what reasons are mineral dressing operations used as a first step in the extraction of metals from their ores.
[B.Sc. (Met.) Lond. Pt. 1]

3. How would you define an " ore "? Account for the fact that mineral deposits containing $x\%$ of metal " M " may be worked economically in one locality and not in another.
[B.Sc. (Met.) Lond. Pt. 1]

4. Write a short essay on " Comminution, its purpose and control ".
[L.I.M. and A.I.M.]

5. Differentiate between the terms " sizing " and " classification " and explain how these operations are conducted. For what purposes are sized or classified feeds essential?
[B.Sc. (Met.) Lond. Pt. 1]

6. What physical properties of ores may be utilised in the operation of concentration processes? Give examples with brief description of application, showing how the stated properties are used.
[B.Sc. (Met.) Lond. Pt. 1]

7. Under what conditions can a mineral be successfully concentrated by jigging? Describe any one machine which is used for this purpose and explain how the concentration is effected.
[B.Sc. (Met.) Lond. Pt. 1]

8. Sketch and describe a Wilfley table, explaining how its motion is obtained and adjusted, and how this motion effects the concentration. [B.Sc. (Met.) Lond. Pt. 1]

9. Write a description of a flotation process, and illustrate your answer by a suitable sketch. State clearly the objects of the process and give examples of the material treated.
[E.M.E.U.]

10. Give a brief description of the flotation process, and the theories underlying the process. [B.Sc. (Met.) Lond. Pt. 1]

11. Give a brief review of the chemical and physical factors that influence selective flotation. [B.Sc. (Met.) Lond. Pt. 1]

12. What are the principal types of reagents employed in flotation concentration? Explain the purposes for which they are used and the manner in which they operate.
[B.Sc. (Met.) Lond. Pt. 1]

13. Under what conditions are sink and float, jigging and tabling respectively most suitable for mineral concentration. To what extent does flotation supplement or supersede these processes?
[Degree Final Univ. Wales]

14. Draw up a flow-sheet to illustrate a method by which a clean concentrate could be obtained from a coarsely disseminated but low-grade deposit of a non-floatable, heavy mineral in a light gangue. Short explanatory notes may be given, but no detailed description of the machines is required.
[B.Sc. (Met.) Lond. Pt. 1]

15. An ore contains a heavy brittle mineral associated with a light and relatively tough gangue. The mineral occurs in a state of both fine and coarse dissemination. With the aid of a simplified flow-sheet, explain how you would suggest recovering a high-grade concentrate from such an ore. [B.Sc. (Met.) Lond. Pt. 1]

16. A complex ore carries minerals of two metals *A* and *B*. *A* is present as a finely disseminated, heavy, non-floatable mineral. *B* is present as a coarsely disseminated sulphide. With the aid of a flow-sheet, explain how you would suggest recovering a concentrate of each of these minerals.
[B.Sc. (Met.) Lond. Pt. 1.]

17. Draw a diagrammatic flow-sheet to illustrate the use of heavy media separation in conjunction with jigging and flotation. What are the particular advantages of this so-called " sink and float " treatment? [B.Sc. (Met.) Lond. Pt. 2 R.R.]

18. What condition is essential to the satisfactory concentration of a mineral from an ore? How would you test a sample of lump ore to determine how this condition could be satisfied?
[B.Sc. (Met.) Lond. Pt. 1.]

19. Describe briefly the different methods employed in the calcining and roasting of ores. [B.Sc. (Met.) Lond. Pt. 1]

20. Briefly describe *four* methods used in the preparation of ores for smelting, and give reasons for the use of each method. [N.C.]

CHAPTER 8

1. Outline the methods which may be used for the extraction of metals from sulphide ores, illustrating your answer by reference to operations and reactions involved in the extraction of specific metals. [B.Sc. Birmingham Second Met. Exam.]

2. What methods are available to the metallurgist for the recovery of metals from (*a*) an oxide, and (*b*) a sulphide ore? Give examples, without detail, indicating the application of each method in industrial metallurgy. [B.Sc. (Met.) Lond. Pt. 1]

3. A heavy base metal is obtainable as an oxide concentrate, *MO*. What fundamental chemical requirements must be met in order that it may be satisfactorily recovered by:
(*a*) a smelting process, *or*
(*b*) a volatilisation process?
[B.Sc. (Met.) Lond. Pt. 1 R.R.]

4. Why is carbon reduction so frequently employed as a means of reduction for non-ferrous metal oxides? Explain why the method is not of universal applicability and suggest alternative procedures that may be suitable in such cases.
[B.Sc. (Met.) Lond. Pt. 1 R.R.]

5. What conditions are necessary in order that a metal may be satisfactorily extracted by a matte-smelting operation?
[C. and G. Adv.]

6. Describe, in general terms, the chemistry of the process of matte-smelting and Bessemerizing, and explain the conditions under which such a process can be applied to the recovery of a metal from an ore. [C. and G. Adv.]

7. For what reasons and under what conditions would a metal be extracted by a matte-smelting process? How would the metal be recovered from the matte and by what means could this be effected? [L.I.M. and A.I.M.]

8. The heat of formation of a chemical compound plays an important part in the production of metals from their ores. Comment upon this statement, and give evidence of its correctness.
[B.Sc. (Met.) Lond. Pt. 1]

9. Discuss the value of thermodynamical data in extraction metallurgy. [B.Sc. (Met.) Lond. Pt. 1 R.R.]

10. What information regarding the extraction of metals may be obtained from the data shown in the graph?

[A simplified version of Ellingham's free energy graphs for oxides is provided.] [B.Sc. (Met.) Lond. Pt. 1 R.R.]

11. Aluminium or silicon is generally used as a deoxidizer in steel-making.

The principal reactions and the corresponding free energy changes are :

$$Al_2O_3 \text{ (solid)} = 2Al + 3O, \quad \Delta F^\circ = 267{,}400 - 75{\cdot}6T$$
$$SiO_2 \text{ (solid)} = Si + 2O, \quad \Delta F^\circ = 119{,}180 - 43{\cdot}5T,$$

where T is the absolute temperature. From these data show that at 1600° C. aluminium is a much stronger deoxidizing agent. [B.Sc. (Met.) Birmingham Third Exam.]

12. Write a brief essay on the theoretical and practical aspects of thermo-electrolytic methods in extraction metallurgy. [L.I.M. and A.I.M.]

13. What is a refining operation? Tabulate the principal refining treatments, including in your table one example of the application of each method. (No description of these treatments is required.) [C. and G. Adv.]

14. Metals are refined by a number of different types of treatment. Classify these according to the principles upon which they are based, and state the conditions under which each class of process would be applicable. [B.Sc. (Met.) Lond. Pt. 1.]

15. What is "refining" and why should a refining operation be necessary? Enumerate the principal methods employed for this purpose and explain, as briefly as possible, how each attains its results. [B.Sc. (Met.) Lond. Pt. 1 R.R.]

16. Explain, from physico-chemical principles and without reference to specific metals, how any TWO of the recognised refining procedures can be effected and why, and to what extent, their efficiency is limited. [L.I.M. and A.I.M.]

17. What fundamental conditions must be satisfied if a metal is to be refined by one of the following processes : (*a*) liquation, (*b*) drossing, (*c*) fractional distillation? If these three methods are inapplicable, how may the metal be refined? [B.Sc. (Met.) Lond. Pt. 1 R.R.]

18. Describe, briefly and in general terms, how a crude metal may be fire-refined by :

(*a*) Preferential oxidation.
(*b*) Liquation.
(*c*) Drossing.

What are the fundamental principles underlying these operations and to what extent are they effective? Illustrate your answer with examples from current fire-refining practice. [C. and G. Adv.]

19. A metal *A* contains a small percentage of metal *B*. Draw the relevant part, or parts, of an imaginary equilibrium diagram for the *A*-*B* alloy system if *B* can be removed satisfactorily by

    (*a*) drossing,
    (*b*) liquation,
    (*c*) fractional distillation.

    In each case explain, briefly, how the separation could be conducted and why it should be successful.
    [B.Sc. (Met.) Lond. Pt. 1 R.R.]

20. What is "refining"? From the relevant fundamental principles, deduce how any three of the recognized refining operations should be conducted. [L.I.M. and A.I.M.]

21. It is often stated that the best method, technically, for refining a crude metal that contains many impurities is electrolysis. When, however, a metal is to be recovered by electrolysis from a fused bath, a preliminary chemical purification treatment is required. Explain the reasons for this apparent anomaly. [C. and G. Adv.]

22. What are the theoretical principles on which the electrolytic refining of metals is based? Discuss the influence of variations in the following factors on the operation:

    (*a*) Temperature of electrolyte.
    (*b*) Agitation of electrolyte.
    (*c*) Current density.
    (*d*) Purity of electrolyte.
    (*e*) Concentration of the metal ion. [A.I.M.]

23. What factors affect the efficiency of electrolytic refining? Under what conditions is electrolytic refining preferred to pyro-metallurgical methods? [C. and G. Adv.]

24. What are the theoretical principles underlying the electrolytic refining of metals? What influence has the current density, the circulation, temperature and purity of electrolyte on the refining operation? [B.Sc. (Met.) Lond. Pt. 1]

25. Under what conditions may metals be recovered from an aqueous solution by electrolysis? (Detailed description of plant is not required.) [C. and G. Adv.]

26. The following free energies of formation are given in kilogram calories per mole of oxygen:

Temperature °C	0°	500°	1000°	2000°
CO	– 60		– 105	– 150
*X*O	0	12	25	
*Y*O	– 150	– 125	– 100	– 50
*Z*O	– 250	– 225	– 200	– 150

What information can be obtained from these figures regarding the extraction of metals *X*, *Y* and *Z*?
[B.Sc. (Met.) Lond. Pt. 1 R.R.]

Chapter 9

1. How are fuels classified? State, giving reason, what fuels you would use for the following:
   (*a*) blast furnace coke manufacture;
   (*b*) firing an open hearth steel furnace;
   (*c*) generation of producer gas. [N.C.]

2. Compare the composition and metallurgical uses of the following gaseous fuels: (*a*) coke oven gas, (*b*) producer gas, (*c*) blast furnace gas, (*d*) water gas. [C. and G. Inter.]

3. Compare the compositions and properties including calorific values of coal-gas, producer-gas and water-gas. Give a brief account of the production of *either* producer-gas *or* water-gas. [C. and G. Inter.]

4. Give a brief account of the manufacture of producer gas. The reactions involved must be stated. [C. and G. Inter.]

5. Describe briefly and with the aid of sketches, the construction of a modern by-product coke oven. [B.Sc. (Met.) Lond. Pt. 1]

6. Explain the principles on which the dry extraction of copper is based. Outline the modern dry methods of extracting copper from its ores. [B.Sc. Birmingham Second Met. Exam.]

7. Explain, briefly and with the aid of a flow-sheet, how fire-refined copper is produced from a low-grade sulphide ore. [B.Sc. (Met.) Lond. Pt. 2]

8. A sample of sulphide copper ore has been submitted to you for examination and report. Assuming that you have only simple analytical and metallographic apparatus at your disposal, explain, briefly, how you would test this material in order to determine:
   (*a*) Whether gravity or flotation concentration might be feasible,
   (*b*) Whether roasting of the ore or concentrate would be necessary in order to produce a 35 per cent copper matte, and
   (*c*) The method of refining you would recommend for the resulting blister copper.
   [C. and G. Adv.]

9. It has been suggested that unroasted flotation concentrates could be treated direct in a converter for the production of blister copper. Discuss the feasibility of this proposal, and indicate the advantages that would be derived and the difficulties that would be anticipated. [L.I.M. and A.I.M.]

10. Why is " matte smelting " favoured for certain metals? Construct a flowsheet showing how *either* copper *or* nickel is obtained from flotation concentrates as a refined metal. Give a brief statement of the principles underlying each of the operations included in the flowsheet. [L.I.M. and A.I.M.]

11. Give an account of the electrolytic refining of copper by the multiple system. [C. and G. Inter.]

12. Give an account of the various operations involved in producing electrolytic copper wire bars from blister copper. The electrolytic refining of the copper should be described in detail, but only an outline of the other operations is required. Explain briefly why the different operations are carried out.
[B.Sc. (Met.) Lond. Pt. 2]

13. What are the chief impurities liable to be present in blister copper? Explain how, and to what extent, these impurities are removed during refining. [B.Sc. (Met.) Lond. Pt. 2]

14. Compare and contrast the principal methods by which zinc can be recovered from flotation concentrates. [A.I.M.]

15. How is zinc extracted from its ores? Illustrate your answer by sketches of suitable plant. [B. Met. Sheffield. Final Exam.]

16. Describe, briefly, how marketable spelter is recovered from a complex, low-grade sulphur ore. [C. and G. Adv.]

17. What are the fundamental considerations underlying the recovery of zinc by distillation and the refining of this metal by reflux condensation? How are the requisite conditions maintained in practice? [B.Sc. (Met.) Lond. Pt. 2]

18. Compare and contrast the horizontal and vertical retort processes for zinc recovery. What are the principal impurities in commercial spelter and how can they be controlled?
[B.Sc. (Met.) Lond. Pt. 2]

19. The following statement contains a number of errors. Write a corrected copy of this paragraph and, where your corrections are not self-explanatory, state briefly the reasons for your alterations.
"The extraction of a metal by hydrometallurgical means necessitates its conversion into a soluble salt by roasting. Thus the sulphating roasting of zinc blende (ZnS) must convert all the metal into the water-soluble sulphate ($ZnSO_4$). The leached calcine is sent to the tank-house where it is subjected to electrolysis, the metal being 'cemented out' on the cathode. Impurities dissolved from the anode will separate as 'electrolytic slime' which must be collected and treated for the recovery of its precious-metal content. When deposition is complete, the cathodes are washed, 'stripped' from the 'starting sheets', melted and cast into 'finished shapes'."
[B.Sc. (Met.) Lond. Pt. 1 R.R.]

20. Construct a simplified flowsheet showing how refined lead and the more usual by-products are recovered from galena concentrates. Explain, in detail, the fundamental principles underlying the recovery of any *one* of these products. [C. and G. Adv.]

21. A complex sulphide lead ore is subjected to selective flotation. Explain with the aid of a flow-sheet how soft marketable lead could be recovered from the galena product.
[B.Sc. (Met.) Lond. Pt. 2]

22. Draw a flow-sheet showing all essential steps for the separation from a 6″ feed, and by flotation alone, of clean galena and sphalerite concentrates. [L.I.M. and A.I.M.]

23. Give an account of *one* of the following :

(*a*) refining of crude lead bullion,
(*b*) production of magnesium. [L.I.M. and A.I.M.]

24. With the aid of a flow-sheet, indicate a procedure that should be satisfactory for the treatment (ore-dressing) of an ore that carries cassiterite and wolfram, and is relatively free from other heavy base-metal minerals. [B.Sc. (Met.) Lond. Pt. 1]

25. What is Mond nickel? Indicate by means of a flow-sheet how it is produced. How does its purity compare with that of other forms of nickel? [C. and G. Inter.]

26. Outline the alternative processes by which Bessemerized nickel-copper matte can be treated for the production of metallic nickel. What is the relative purity of the products?
[B.Met. Sheffield Final Exam.]

27. In what respects does the procedure for the extraction of nickel from sulphides resemble that for the extraction of copper from sulphides and in what respects does it differ? Briefly describe two methods by which refined nickel is produced from a nickel matte. [L.I.M. and A.I.M.]

28. Give a brief account of one method by which refined nickel is obtained from finely disseminated copper-nickel sulphide ores. In what respects does this nickel differ from the metal obtained by other processes? [C. and G. Adv.]

29. Give an account of the extraction of aluminium, explaining why the procedure is different from that used with the majority of metals extracted from oxide ores.
[B.Sc. Birmingham Second Met. Exam.]

30. Describe the method of obtaining aluminium from bauxite.
[C. and G. Inter.]

31. Give a brief description of the procedure by which alumium is extracted from bauxite. Why is it necessary to subject the bauxite to a preliminary purification treatment?
[C. and G. Adv.]

32. Explain, with the aid of sketches, how refined aluminium is obtained from a good-grade bauxite. [B.Sc. (Met.) Lond. Pt. 2]

33. Compare and contrast the difficulties which attend the reduction of aluminium and of magnesium from their respective oxides. Indicate, in outline, some of the procedures by which the difficulties have been overcome in the case of magnesium. [A.I.M.]

34. What are the principal sources of magnesium? Give a brief account of the means by which metallic magnesium can be obtained from each of these substances. [C. and G. Adv.]

35. Describe a process for producing magnesium on a large scale from sea water. [B.Sc. (Met.) Lond. Pt. 2]

36. Describe, with the aid of sketches, a plant suitable for the roasting and sintering of finely divided sulphide ores and concentrates. Differentiate carefully between the treatments applied in such a plant, to the ores of copper, lead and zinc respectively. [B.Met. Sheffield Final Exam.]

37. Write a short essay on the part played by oxidation in the pyrometallurgical refining of non-ferrous metals. [B.Sc. Lond. Pt. 2]

38. What are the limitations of electro-metallurgical extraction methods? When are electro-metallurgical methods used for the extraction of certain metals? [B.Sc. (Met.) Lond. Pt. 1]

39. Show by means of careful sketches the essential features of (*a*) a blast furnace, and (*b*) a reverberatory furnace used in non-ferrous practice. Compare the means by which these two appliances fulfil the essential requirements of a smelting operation. [B.Sc. (Met.) Lond. Pt. 1]

40. Give a brief account of the essential features of the industrial electrolytic refining of *one* metal. Discuss the particular advantages of this method from the viewpoint of operation, by-products and quality of the material. [L.I.M.]

41. Some of the metals that are commonly extracted or refined electrolytically can be obtained in a high degree of purity by other processes. Discuss the factors that determine the more suitable process to use in a particular case. [A.I.M.]

Chapter 10

1. State the chief properties, emphasising the difference between (*a*) plain carbon mild steel, (*b*) wrought iron, (*c*) ordinary grey cast iron.

   Describe suitable tests to distinguish between these three products. [E.M.E.U.]

2. Comment on the properties of the following types of iron-carbon alloys:

   (*a*) Mild steel;
   (*b*) High-carbon steel;
   (*c*) Grey cast-iron;
   (*d*) White cast-iron.

   Explain why these materials differ so greatly from one another in their properties. [B.Sc. (Met.) Lond. Pt. 1]

3. Draw a sectional elevation of a blast furnace used for the smelting of iron ore. Give full details of the materials charged and of the products obtained. [E.M.E.U.]

4. What auxiliary plant is necessarily associated with a blast furnace used for the production of iron? Illustrate your answer by means of sketches. [B.Sc. (Met.) Lond. Pt. 1]

5. Describe the construction of a basic open hearth steel-making furnace and give a brief account of the working of a charge. [N.C.]

6. Enumerate the important differences between the "acid" and "basic" Bessemer processes of steelmaking. Explain what is meant by the "deoxidation of steel" and state how it may be affected. [E.M.E.U.]

7. Describe the standard basic Bessemer process for the manufacture of cheap, low-carbon steel and suggest at least two variations that might be used to lower the nitrogen content of the finished steel. [B.Sc. (Met.) Lond. Pt. 2]

8. Write an essay of about 300 words on the metallurgical factors in the selection of a steel-making process. [B.Sc. (Met.) Birmingham Third Exam.]

9. What are the conditions necessary for the desulphurisation and dephosphorisation of iron and steel? To what extent are these conditions attained in the various processes? [B.Sc. (Met.) Lond. Imp. Coll. Sci. and Tech.]

CHAPTER 11

1. Differentiate between "sand casting", "chill casting", "die casting" and "centrifugal casting".
   Why are alloys cast by these various methods? [B.Sc. (Met.) Lond. Pt. 1]

2. Describe briefly the equipment and procedure necessary in making a simple sand-casting, e.g. a gear wheel. Assume that a supply of the molten metal or alloy is provided. [C. and G. Inter.]

3. What equipment would you require and what procedure would you adopt for the production, from commercially pure materials, of small, simple aluminium alloy castings? [B.Sc. (Met.) Lond. Pt. 2]

4. What are the causes and effect of gas evolution associated with the solidification of metals? Give examples where removal of gases plays an important part in the production of a sound casting, and discuss the means adopted for such removal. [B.Sc. (Met.) Lond. Pt. 1]

5. Write a brief account of the possible causes of blowholes in cast metals and how they may be obviated. [E.M.E.U.]

6. Give an account of the variables which determine the incidence of shrinkage defects in castings. How may these defects be minimised? [Degree Hons. Univ. Wales]

7. What are the common defects which may occur in ingots and castings? How do they arise? What methods are used to minimize such defects? [N.C.]

8. An alloy passes through various stages of shrinkage in cooling from the liquid state to room temperature. Enumerate the various factors affecting these stages and discuss the influence of each. [C. and G. Adv.]

9. Write an account of the principal defects that may occur in cast metals or alloys. How may the occurrence of such defects be avoided? [B.Sc. (Met.) Lond. Pt. 1 R.R.]

10. What particular factors control the size and form of crystal grains in an alloy casting? What influences play a part in the production of metallic heterogenity? [B. Sc. (Met.) Lond. Pt. 1]

11. Write an essay on segregation in alloys. [L.I.M. and A.I.M.]

12. Compare the modes of solidification in sand moulds of (*a*) a pure metal and (*b*) an alloy of wide freezing range. Indicate the structures you would expect to find in such cases, and comment briefly on those aspects of the solidification process and resultant structures that are of special importance in industrial metallurgy. [L.I.M. and A.I.M.]

13. Give an account of the technical factors to be considered in the production of castings. [B.Met. Sheffield Final Exam.]

14. Write an essay of not more than 800 words on the following topic: "Application of metallurgical principles in production of non-ferrous ingots for subsequent working." [B.Sc. Hons. (Indust. Met.) Birmingham]

Chapter 12

1. Give brief descriptions and sketches of *two* hot-working and *two* cold-working processes. [Nat. Sci. Tripos. Pt. 1, Cambridge]

2. Explain the difference between the cold working and hot working of metals. Why are both these processes used in the shaping of metals? [B.Sc. Birmingham Second Met. Exam.]

3. Distinguish between "hot" and "cold" working of metals and alloys. Describe briefly any fabrication process with which you are familiar. [N.C.]

4. How may the properties of a metallic material be altered as a result of mechanical working? What are the principal defects that may result from such operations? [B.Sc. (Met.) Lond. Pt. 1 R.R.]

5. What methods are available for shaping metallic materials? How may such operations affect the properties of the metal or alloy being treated? [B.Sc. (Met.) Lond. Pt. 1 R.R.]

6. Why are the different forms of passes used on grooved rolls? Describe with the aid of *careful* sketches and with the necessary relevant detail, the types used. What passes and reduction would you use to roll a 4 in. by 4 in. billet to a $\frac{3}{4}$ in. round bar? [C. and G. Adv.]

7. Give a brief description of the method employed in extruding (i) lead, (ii) brass. What is the usual composition of the brass used for this purpose? Comment upon the difficulties likely to accrue in these extrusion processes. [B.Sc. (Met.) Lond. Pt. 2]

8. Give an account of the plant necessary for the production by extrusion of small sections of *one* non-ferrous alloy. What precautions must be taken in the process? What are the advantages of the process compared with rolling for the production of sections? [B.Sc. (Met.) Lond. Pt. 2]

9. What are the advantages and limitations of extrusion over other shaping processes such as rolling and drawing? Discuss the characteristics of extruded material and trace them back to conditions in the extrusion process. [B.Sc. (Met.) Birmingham Third Exam.]

10. Explain three of the following terms: rolling, forging, extruding, spinning, drawing. [C. and G. Inter.]

11. Describe a process used for the manufacture of weldless steel tubes? [B.Sc. (Met.) Lond. Pt. 2]

12. Write a short essay on the production of compacts from metallic powders. [An alternative topic was given. B.Sc. Hons. (Indust. Met.) Birmingham]

13. Distinguish between soldering, brazing and welding as applied to non-ferrous metals. Give an example of each of these operations and indicate the composition of the material you would use in each case for making the joint. [C. and G. Adv.]

Chapter 13

1. Distinguish clearly between (*a*) elastic modulus, (*b*) limit of proportionality, (*c*) yield point, (*d*) proof stress. Explain fully how each can be determined and measured. [B.Sc. (Met.) Lond. Imp. Coll. Sci. and Tech.]

2. What mechanical tests are applied to metals? Describe, briefly, one of them. [C. and G. Inter.]

3. Explain why in the mechanical testing of metals and alloys, the tensile test occupies a very high place. [C. and G. Inter.]

4. Draw a stress-strain curve for mild steel. Describe the properties that may be deduced from such a curve. [N.C.]

5. What information may be obtained from the tensile test? How are the properties measured and reported? What is the value of the data obtained? [C. and G. Adv.]

6. What particular tests would you employ to determine (i) ductility, (ii) malleability, (iii) brittleness, of a metallic substance? Describe, very briefly, the means of testing.
[B.Sc. (Met.) Lond. Pt. 1]

7. What do you understand by the terms: malleability, tenacity toughness and hardness?

Describe the principles of the method of determining the tenacity of metals and alloys. What information can be obtained from this test? [L.I.M.]

8. A small brass test-bar (0·40 in. diam.) broke when tested in a tensile testing machine, under a load of 550 lb. Calculate the tensile stress in tons per sq. inch (cross-sectional area = diam.^{2} × 0·7854). Calculate also the appropriate gauge length for this test-piece in order to comply with the specification :

$$\text{Gauge length} = 4 \times \sqrt{\text{cross-sectional area}}.$$

The total increase in such gauge length was 0·35 inch. Calculate the percentage elongation.
[C. and G. Inter.]

9. Draw, to the same scale, typical load-extension curves (assuming the same gauge length in each case) for annealed copper in the form of $\frac{1}{2}$ in. diameter rod and $\frac{1}{16}$ in. diameter wire. Transform the diagrams you have given into conventional stress strain diagrams. Explain the differences in the curves in the two cases, and state how you would arrange an experiment with these two pieces of material, so that the curves become coincident up to the point of fracture.
[Nat. Sci. Tripos, Pt. 1, Cambridge]

10. Outline the procedure for the determination of the tensile properties, including the elastic properties, of a metal.

Calculate the yield point, ultimate tensile strength, elongation percentage on 2 in. and reduction of area percentage from the following data :

Original diameter,	0·437 in.
Final diameter,	0·292 in.
Gauge length,	2·0 in.
Yield load,	3·5 tons
Breaking load,	4·13 tons
Extended length,	2·75 in.

[U.L.C.I.]

11. *Outline* the procedure for the determination of the tensile properties of a metal, which includes its elastic properties.

Calculate the yield point, tensile strength, elongation per cent. and reduction of area per cent., from the following data:

Original diameter	0·437 in.	Yield load	3·5 tons
Final diameter	0·292 in.	Breaking load	4·13 tons
Gauge length	2·0 in.	Extended length	2·75 in.

What would be the effect of cold rolling the metal before testing on the yield point and tensile strength values? [E.M.E.U.]

12. Describe briefly the method you would employ for each of the following: (*a*) detect porosity in light alloy castings; (*b*) detect cracks in steel forgings; (*c*) determine the toughness of a metal. Give reasons for your choice of methods. [N.C.]

13. Write an essay on non-destructive testing. [B.Sc. (Met.) Lond. Pt. 3 R.R.]

14. Describe *briefly* the non-destructive tests that may be applied to non-ferrous metal parts. Comment on the advantages of each test. [C. and G. Adv.]

15. Give a critical account of the methods available for detecting defects occurring (*a*) near the surface and (*b*) at greater depth, in metal components. [B.Sc. (Met.) Lond. Pt. 2]

16. What considerations must be taken into account in selecting a sample for testing, and the kind of test applied to it, in order to establish the suitability of the material for its subsequent use. [B.Met. Sheffield Final Exam.]

17. Explain the phenomenon of season-cracking and how it may be avoided. What test can be applied to detect the liability of material to this defect. [A.I.M.]

Chapter 14

1. Describe three types of thermocouples used for measuring temperatures, commenting upon the special feature and uses of each. [B.Sc. (Met.) Lond. Pt. 1]

2. Describe the relative advantages and disadvantages of (*a*) base-metal thermo-couples, (*b*) precious-metal thermo-couples, and (*c*) optical pyrometers, giving instances of applications for which each type is best suited. Do not describe any of the pyrometers. [C. and G. Adv.]

3. What methods are available for the measurement of high temperature?

Sketch and describe the working of an instrument suitable for measuring temperatures of over 1000° C. in which there is no actual contact between the instrument and the furnace. [E.M.E.U.]

4. Discuss the measurement of temperature by radiation methods.
[Degree Hons. Univ. Wales]

5. Write an account of the " disappearing filament " pyrometer, using the following headings :
   (a) General Principles.
   (b) Meaning and Importance of " Black Body " conditions.
   (c) Emissivity Corrections.
   (d) Description of Instrument (very brief).
   (e) Functions of Filters.
   (f) Accuracy.
   (g) Effect of Smoke and Flame.
   (h) Advantages and Disadvantages compared with Thermocouples.

[B.Sc. (Met.) Lond. Imp. Coll. Sci. and Tech.]

6. Write a short essay on " Radiation Pyrometers ".
[C. and G. Adv.]

7. How can the temperature of molten metals be measured? State the principles of the methods and also the precautions that must be observed to ensure accurate results.
[L.I.M. and A.I.M.]

8. What type of pyrometer would you select for the purpose of determining the temperatures of each of the following : (i) a large bogie furnace used for annealing steel plates, (ii) the bath of steel in a 100-ton Siemens furnace, (iii) the flue gases in a chimney stack at a position where the hot gases enter? Give reasons for your selection. [B.Sc. (Met.) Lond. Pt. 1]

9. Describe the type of pyrometer you would instal to determine :
   (i) the temperature of the metal in a melting furnace, and
   (ii) the roof temperature of a furnace.

   Give reasons for your choice and state any precautions that must be taken to ensure accurate results.
[L.I.M. and A.I.M.]

10. What type of pyrometer would you use for the following :
   (a) For determining the temperature of the metal in a 100-ton open hearth furnace.
   (b) For determining the temperature of molten brass in a large crucible.
   (c) For determining the temperature of the roof brick in a high-temperature furnace.
   (d) For determining the temperature of a billet of duralumin in a heat-treatment furnace.

   Do not give a description of the pyrometers, but give reasons for your choice of instrument and state any special precautions to be taken to ensure obtaining accurate temperature observations. [L.I.M. and A.I.M.]

11. What type of pyrometer would you recommend for the following purposes?

    (*a*) For controlling the casting temperature of brass.
    (*b*) For measuring the temperature of molten steel during casting.
    (*c*) For measuring the temperature of steel during hot-rolling.

    Do not describe the pyrometers, but give your reasons for selecting them, and comment on any special precautions that should be taken in using them for these purposes.
    [B. Sc. (Met.) Lond. Pt. 1]

General Selection

1. Write an essay on phase changes in the solid state, illustrating your answer by reference to non-ferrous alloy systems of practical importance. [A.I.M.]
2. Sketch and describe the microstructure of a 70/30 cupro-nickel in the chill cast state. Explain by reference to the equilibrium diagram of the copper-nickel system why the alloy has this type of structure. What effects would the following treatments have on the microstructure and mechanical properties of the alloy: (*a*) hot working, and (*b*) hot working followed by cold working? [B.Sc. (Met.) Lond. Pt. 1]
3. Write brief notes on the meaning and importance of the following as applied to metals: (*a*) crystalline nature; (*b*) types of fracture; (*c*) mechanical elasticity; (*d*) toughness. [N.C.]
4. What do you consider to be the chief physical properties of a metal? Illustrate your answer by reference to the properties of *two* of the common metals. [N.C.]
5. Sketch and describe any *four* microstructures of metals and alloys which you have examined under the microscope. [N.C.]
6. Discuss the relative advantages and disadvantages of gravity, magnetic and flotation concentration as a first step in metal extraction. Under what conditions would the production of a clean, high-grade concentrate be considered disadvantageous? [C. and G. Adv.]
7. What is the essential difference between the members of each pair in the following groups: (*a*) Mineral and ore, (*b*) roasting and calcining, (*c*) matte and speiss, (*d*) flux and slag? [C. and G. Inter.]
8. Sketch and describe a gas producer. What principles may be introduced into furnace design to increase the efficiency of producer gas used therein as a metallurgical fuel? [C. and G. Inter.]

9. Essay Subjects (two essays required in 3 hours) :
   The value of mineral dressing in extraction metallurgy.
   Physical chemistry in extraction problems.
   Plastic deformation of metals.

[A.I.M.]

10. Give a short account of *one* of the following :
    (*a*) The theoretical considerations underlying the desilverisation of lead.
    (*b*) The refining procedures suitable for low melting-point metals.
    (*c*) The volatilization processes available for the extraction of metals at atmospheric pressure.

[B.Sc. (Met.) Lond. Imp. Coll. Sci. and Tech.]

11. Review, briefly, the more important features in the extraction or refining of any *one* of the commoner base metals, giving reasons for the significance you attach to them.

[B.Sc. (Met.) Lond. Imp. Coll. Sci. and Tech.]

12. What requirements must be fulfilled if a metal is to be satisfactorily recovered by a volatilisation treatment? Explain how they are satisfied in practice, illustrating your answer by reference to *two* metals of markedly different physical and chemical properties.

[B.Sc. (Met.) Lond. Imp. Coll. Sci. and Tech.]

13. What are the advantages and disadvantages of electrometallurgical methods of metal production and refining. Illustrate your answer by reference to one metal in some detail.

[Degree Hons. Univ. Wales]

14. Discuss the principles employed in the following processes used for metal extraction : (*a*) distillation, (*b*) liquation, (*c*) leaching, (*d*) precipitation. Give one example of metal extraction by any two of the above processes. [U.L.C.I.]

15. What should be the characteristics of a leaching solution? Discuss the place and importance of leaching operations in extraction metallurgy. [B.Sc. (Met.) Lond. Pt. 1 R.R.]

16. How would you define the term " roasting "? For what purposes is roasting employed as a preliminary in ore reduction? To what extent are these objects achieved in practice?

[B.Sc. (Met.) Lond. Pt. 1 R.R.]

17. Either electrolytic or other processes could be applied to the extraction of certain metals. Give an account of the considerations that would determine which process would be suitable in a particular case. [B. Sc. (Met.) Lond. Pt. 2.]

18. Distinguish between (*a*) calcination, (*b*) oxidising roasting, (*c*) blast roasting, (*d*) chloridising roasting. Give examples of each process. [B.Sc. (Met.) Lond. Pt. 1]

19. Certain metals are recoverable from their ores or concentrates by volatilisation treatments. From fundamental considerations, explain how you would classify these operations and state what metals are recovered in each of the classes you mention. [A.I.M.]

20. Write a *brief* account of *one* industrial application of each of the following : (*a*) leaching, (*b*) liquation, (*c*) roasting, (*d*) precipitation. [U.L.C.I.]

21. Write short notes on the following :

(*a*) cupellation,
(*b*) precipitation in the extraction of metals,
(*c*) liquation,
(*d*) the Thermite process.

[E.M.E.U.]

22. What do you understand by the term " fining " as applied to ores? Show how the sequence of " fining " and " refining " operations affects the recovery and composition of the final products. Illustrate your answer by reference to the extraction practice of two metals. [B.Sc. (Met.) Lond. Pt. 1]

23. Give a brief description, illustrated by sketches, of one of the following :

(*a*) Iron blast furnace.
(*b*) Dwight-Lloyd Sintering Machine.
(*c*) Reverberatory furnace for the smelting of copper ores and concentrates.

[C. and G. Inter.]

24. Give a brief account of the principles involved in :

(*a*) conversion of copper matte into blister copper,
(*b*) production of steel in the acid open-hearth furnace,
(*c*) roasting of sulphide ores.

[C. and G. Inter.]

25. Compare and contrast ferrous and non-ferrous process metallurgy. [Degree Final Univ. Wales]

26. How is the extraction of a metal affected by its physical and chemical properties? [Degree Final Univ. Wales]

27. Describe briefly *one* of the following :

(*a*) electrolytic refining of blister copper ;
(*b*) manufacture of steel from pig iron ;
(*c*) production of zinc from a sulphide ore.

[N.C.]

28. What fundamental requirements must be satisfied in order that a metal may be recovered by a leaching process? Indicate the extent to which these requirements are satisfied in the case of any *one* base metal. [C. and G. Adv.]

29. What fundamental requirements must be satisfied in order that a metal may be satisfactorily recovered by a distillation process? Illustrate your answer by brief reference to the relevant chemical and physical properties of the metals magnesium, nickel, zinc. [C. and G. Adv.]

30. Give a résumé of the various methods available in present practice for the roasting of ores. Why are these different methods used? [B.Sc. (Met.) Lond. Pt. 1]

31. What are the essential requirements of a smelting operation? Give, in general terms, a brief review of the principal types of smelting processes and indicate how, and to what extent, these requirements are satisfied in each case. [B.Sc. (Met.) Lond. Pt. 2]

32. Compare the Bessemer process as applied to the smelting of pig iron with the Bessemer process for the smelting of copper matte. [B.Sc. (Met.) Lond. Pt. 1]

33. What methods are available to the process metallurgist for the extraction of metals from oxide ores? Give examples, without detail, indicating the application of each method in industrial practice. Why are these particular methods used for the metals mentioned? [L.I.M. and A.I.M.]

34. What general factors affect the economic and technical value of an ore? [B.Sc. (Met.) Lond. Pt. 1.]

35. Sketch and describe the working of a modern plant for the production of metallurgical coke. What are the important properties of such coke? [U.L.C.I.]

36. Give some examples of the phenomena of undercooling in binary metallic systems. In what way can this property be utilized to obtain results of practical importance? [B.Sc. (Met.) Lond. Pt. 1]

37. Define the following terms and give one example of each : smelting, sintering, welding, hardening, flux. [C. and G. Inter.]

38. Briefly describe the production of zinc from roasted concentrates by the electrolytic process. Tabulate the chief commercial methods of applying a protective zinc coating to steel, briefly indicating the principles involved. [C. and G. Inter.]

39. *Either*, (*a*) Give a brief description of a metallurgical furnace with which you are familiar, illustrating your answer by means of sketches,

Or, (*b*) Give a brief description of the manufacture of coke in a by-product coke oven. What are the requirements of a good metallurgical coke? [N.C.]

40. *Either*, (*a*) Discuss the theoretical aspects of " cold " and " hot " deformation of metals.

Or, (*b*) Describe the principles and operation of any fabrication plant with which you are acquainted. [N.C.]

41. Compare the effects of oxygen on iron, copper and silver at temperatures ranging from that of the molten state to room temperature. [C. and G. Inter.]

42. Describe, with the aid of sketches, the chief features of *one* of the following :

    (*a*) an electric steel furnace,
    (*b*) a Bessemer converter,
    (*c*) a gas producer,
    (*d*) a blast furnace,
    (*e*) a cupola.

    [C. and G. Adv.]

43. Give a classification of metallurgical furnaces, based on the method of heat generation. [U.L.C.I.]

44. What methods may be employed to increase the hardness of ferrous and non-ferrous alloys? Discuss the principles underlying any one of the methods. [L.I.M. and A.I.M.]

45. Give a general account of the ways in which a metal may be hardened and explain as far as you can the reasons for such an increase in hardness. [B.Sc. (Met.) Lond. Pt. 1]

46. Sketch, and describe, the main types of electric furnaces used in metallurgical operations. [B.Sc. (Met.) Lond. Pt. 1]

47. Give a description, with the aid of sketches, of electric furnaces of the following types : (i) Arc furnace for the manufacture of steel ; (ii) Resistance furnace for the purpose of heat-treatment ; (iii) Induction furnace as used for melting non-ferrous metals. [B.Sc. (Met.) Lond. Pt. 1]

48. How would you demonstrate experimentally the effects of impurities on metals? [N.C.]

49. Write a short essay on *one* of the following subjects :

    (*a*) Non-destructive testing of metal parts.
    (*b*) The preparation of metals for micro-examination.
    (*c*) Mechanical testing of metals and alloys.

    [N.C.]

50. Discuss *one* of the following subjects :

    (*a*) the tensile testing of metals and alloys ;
    (*b*) the micro-structure of pure metals, solid solutions and eutectics in the " as-cast " and annealed conditions.

    [U.L.C.I.]

51. An engineering component is to be manufactured by casting. What tests might be applied (*a*) to the material and (*b*) to the casting itself to satisfy the manufacturer as to the quality of the component? [B.Sc. (Met.) Lond. Pt. 1 R.R.]

52. How may the suitability of a particular metal or alloy be assessed for a given engineering purpose? [B.Sc. (Met.) Lond. Pt. 1 R.R.]

53. What are the principal types of defects that are liable to occur in metal castings? How do they arise, and how can they best be detected? [B.Sc. (Met.) Lond. Pt. 2]

54. Compare and contrast the type of information revealed by X-ray and by microscopic examination of metallurgical specimens. Illustrate your answer by examples. [L.I.M. and A.I.M.]

55. Discuss mechanical test results in relation to design and acceptance. [L.I.M. and A.I.M.]

56. Write a short essay on the use of the microscope as an aid to metallurgical practice. [B.Sc. (Met.) Lond. Pt. 1]

57. (*a*) The refining of metals.
(*b*) " Chemical composition may be said to determine the potentialities of an alloy, but not its actual properties " (Jeffries and Archer).
[From 3 hr. Essay Paper Nat. Sci. Tripos. Pt. 1, Cambridge]

58. Write drafts for essays on any two of the following subjects :
(*a*) Non-destructive testing of metal parts.
(*b*) Recent advances in metallographic technique.
(*c*) The cause of work hardening in metals.
The drafts should consist of headings with brief comments indicating how each section would be treated.
(Four subjects were given.)
[B.Sc. (Met.) Lond. Imp. Coll. Sci. and Tech.]

59. Write an essay on one of the four subjects listed in Question No. 58. [B.Sc. (Met.) Lond. Imp. Coll. Sci. and Tech.]

60. A small metal component has failed in service and you are called upon to explain the failure. How would you proceed? [B.Sc. (Met.) Lond. Pt. 1 R.R.]

61. Give a brief definition, covering all essential features, of *eight* of the following :

(*a*) ore,	(*e*) sand,	(*i*) crusts,
(*b*) mineral,	(*f*) slime,	(*j*) flapping,
(*c*) middling,	(*g*) slag,	(*k*) poling,
(*d*) sintering,	(*h*) dross,	(*l*) shock-cooling.

[C. and G. Adv.]

INDEX

Page numbers in heavy type indicate principal references

PRINTED IN GREAT BRITAIN BY ROBERT MACLEHOSE AND CO. LTD
THE UNIVERSITY PRESS, GLASGOW